CONCEPTS OF HEALTH AND DISEASE
Interdisciplinary Perspectives

CONCEPTS OF HEALTH AND DISEASE
Interdisciplinary Perspectives

Edited by

Arthur L. Caplan
The Hastings Center
Hastings-on-Hudson, New York
and
Columbia University
New York, New York

H. Tristram Engelhardt, Jr.
Georgetown University
Washington, D.C.

James J. McCartney
Georgetown University Medical Center
Washington, D.C.
and
Biscayne College
Miami, Florida

Foreword by

Denton Cooley
Texas Heart Institute
Houston, Texas

1981

ADDISON-WESLEY PUBLISHING COMPANY
Advanced Book Program/World Science Division
Reading, Massachusetts

London • Amsterdam • Don Mills, Ontario • Sydney • Tokyo

Library of Congress Cataloging in Publication Data
Main entry under title:

Concepts of health and disease.

Includes bibliographical references and index.
1. Medicine—Philosophy—Addresses, essays, lectures. 2. Health—Addresses, essays, lectures. 3. Diseases—Addresses, essays, lectures. I. Caplan, Arthur L. II. Engelhardt, H. Tristram (Hugo Tristram), 1941– . III. McCartney, James J.
R723.C66 610'.1 81-4922
ISBN 0-201-00973-0 AACR2

Manufactured in the United States of America

ABCDEFGHIJ-AL-8987654321

For **Bernard Schoenberg** and **Andre Hellegers**;
physicians who understood the value of
the philosophy of medicine

Contents

Biographical Data

THE EDITORS

ARTHUR CAPLAN, Ph.D., is Associate for the Humanities, The Hastings Center, New York, and Associate for Social Medicine, College of Physicians and Surgeons, Columbia University, New York. He is editor and author of numerous books and articles on medical ethics and health policy.

H. TRISTRAM ENGELHARDT, JR., Ph. D., M.D., is Senior Research Scholar, and the Rosemary Kennedy Professor of the Philosophy of Medicine, Kennedy Institute of Ethics, Georgetown University, Washington, D.C. He is, with Stuart F. Spicker, co-editor of a book series, *Philosophy and Medicine*.

JAMES J. McCARTNEY, M.A., M.S., Ph.D., is Dean of the College, Biscayne College, Miami, Florida. He is author of articles on medical ethics published in *The Hastings Center Report* and *The New Physician*.

THE CONTRIBUTORS

BERTRAM BANDMAN, Ph.D., is Professor of Philosophy, Long Island University, Brooklyn Center, Brooklyn, New York. He is co-editor, with Elsie Bandman, of *Bioethics and Human Rights: A Reader for Health Professionals* (1978).

ELSIE L. BANDMAN, R.N., Ed.D., is Professor of Nursing, Hunter College—Bellevue School of Nursing, Hunter College of the City University of New York. With Bertram Bandman, she is co-editor of *Bioethics and Human Rights: A Reader for Health Professionals* (1978).

MICHAEL D. BAYLES, Ph.D., is Professor of Philosophy and Director, Westminister Institute for Ethics and Human Values, Westminister College, London, Canada. He is author of *Morality and Population Policy* (1980).

CLAUDE BERNARD (1813–1878)
He succeeded to the Magendie chair of Medicine at the College of France in 1855. In 1868, he was elected to the Académie. He is author of *Introduction à l'étude de la médecine expérimentale* (1865).

XAVIER BICHAT (1771–1802) studied surgery under Marc-Antoine Petil in Lyons and Pierre-Joseph Desault in Paris. He was an anatomist by trade and not a medical practitioner. He is author of *Anatomie générale appliquée à la physiologie et à la médecine* (1801).

CHRISTOPHER BOORSE, Ph.D., is Assistant Professor of Philosophy, Department of Philosophy, University of Delaware, Newark, Delaware. He is author of numerous articles on the concept of health and disease including "What a Theory of Mental Health Should Be," *Journal for the Theory of Social Behavior* 6 (1), 1976.

BARUCH BRODY, Ph. D., is Professor of Philosophy and Chairman of the Department of Philosophy, Rice University, Houston, Texas. He is author of *Identity and Essence* (1980) as well as editor of *Mental Illness: Law and Public Policy* (1980).

F.J.V. BROUSSAIS (1772–1838) studied under Bichat and graduated from the Paris School in 1803. He served three years in Napoleon's army acquiring clinical experience as a physician. He is author of *De l'irritation et de la folie* (1828) as well as *Traité de physiologie appliquée à la pathologie* (1822–1823).

WALTER B. CANNON, M.D. (1871–1945) was George Higginson Professor of Physiology, Emeritus, Harvard University Medical School, Cambridge, Massachusetts. He is author of *The Way of an Investigator* (1945).

SAMUEL A. CARTWRIGHT, M.D., was Chairman of the Committee appointed by the Medical Association of Louisiana to report on the Diseases and Physical Peculiarities of the Negro Race (March 1951).

HENRY COHEN, M.D., D.Sc., LL.D., F.R.C.P., (1900–1977) Professor of Medicine, University of Liverpool, England. Author of *Nature, Method and Purpose of Diagnosis* (1943).

GEORGE L. ENGEL, M.D., is Professor of Psychiatry and Medicine, University of Rochester, School of Medicine and Dentistry, Rochester, New York. He is author of numerous articles including "The Clinical Application of the Biopsychosocial Model," *Journal of Medicine and Philosophy* 6 (2), 1981.

ANTONY FLEW, M.A., D.Litt., is Professor, Department of Philosophy, University of Reading, White Knights, Reading, Berkshire, England. He is author of *A Rational Animal and Other Philosophical Essays on the Nature of Man* (1978).

J .M. FORT, M.D., practiced medicine in Paris, Texas, in 1895 and was a member of the North Texas Medical Association.

VICTOR R. FUCHS, M.A., Ph.D., is Professor of Economics, Stanford University, Stanford, California, and member of Senior Research Staff, National Bureau of Economic Research. He is author of *The Economics of Health and Medical Care* (1972).

RICHARD GREEN, M.D., is Professor of Psychiatry, Department of Psychiatry, Health Sciences Center, State University of New York at Stony Brook, Stony Brook, New York. He is author of *Sexual Identity Conflict in Children and Adults* (1975).

HEINZ HARTMANN (1894–1970) was a psychoanalyst and author of *Ego Psychology and the Problem of Adaptation* (1939). He also co-authored "Comments in the Formation of Psychic Structure" in *Psychoanalytic Study of the Child* (1949).

LEON KASS, M.D., Ph.D., is Henry R. Luce Professor of Liberal Arts of Human Biology, University of Chicago, Chicago, Illinois, and a Founding Fellow of the Institute of Society, Ethics and Life Sciences. He is author of numerous articles on topics that concern both medicine and philosophy.

R.E. KENDELL, M.D., is Professor of Psychiatry, University Department of Psychiatry (Royal Edinburgh Hospital), University of Edinburgh, Morningside Park, Edinburgh, U.K. He is author of "Alcoholism: A Medical or a Political Problem?", *British Medical Journal* 1(6160), (1979).

LESTER S. KING, M.D., formerly senior editor, now contributing editor to *Journal of American Medical Association*, is research associate in the History Department of the University of Chicago and author of *The Philosophy of Medicine* (1978).

F. KRÄUPL-TAYLOR is Emeritus Physician of the Bethlehem Royal and Maudsley Hospitals, London, England.

AARON LAZARE, M.D., is Professor, Department of Psychiatry, Harvard Medical School, and the Department of Adult Outpatient Psychiatry, Massachusetts General Hospital, Boston, Massachusetts.

RUTH MACKLIN, Ph.D., is Associate Professor of Community Health, Albert Einstein College of Medicine, Bronx, New York. She is author of numerous articles on ethical issues in medicine, including "On the Ethics of Not Doing Scientific Research," *Hastings Center Report* 7 (6), (1977).

JOSEPH MARGOLIS, M.A., Ph.D., is Professor of Philosophy at Temple University, Philadelphia, Pennsylvania. He is author of *Knowledge and Existence* (1969) and *Persons and Minds* (1978).

ABRAHAM A. MASLOW, Ph.D., (1908–1970), was Professor of Psychology at Brandeis University, Waltham, Massachusetts. He is author, with B. Mittelmann, of *Principles of Abnormal Psychology* (1941) and author of *Toward a Psychology of Being* (1962).

DAVID MECHANIC, M.A., Ph.D., is Professor of Social Work and Sociology, Rutgers University, New Brunswick, New Jersey. He is author of *A Right to Health* (1976) and *Future Problems in Health Care* (1979).

BELA MITTELMANN (1899–1959), Professor, Albert Einstein College of Medicine, New York, New York. Author, with Abraham Maslow, of *Principles of Abnormal Psychology* (1941).

JONATHAN D. MORENO, Ph.D., is Assistant Professor of Philosophy, Department of Philosophy, George Washington University, Washington, D.C. He is co-author of *To Speak of Madness: Translating Models of Mental Illness* (1981).

G.B. MORGAGNI (1692–1771) was Professor of Anatomy at Padua and author of *De sedibus et causis morborum per anatomen indigatis* (1761).

MICHAEL RUSE, Ph.D., is Professor of History and Philosophy, Department of Philosophy, University of Guelph, Guelph, Ontario, Canada. He is author of *The Darwinian Revolution* (1979) and *Sociobiology: Sense or Nonsense* (1979).

PETER SEDGWICK, Ph.D., is Professor, Department of Politics, University of Leeds, England.

MARK SIEGLER, M.D., is Professor of Medicine, Pritzer School of Medicine, University of Chicago, Chicago, Illinois. He is author of "A Right to Health Care: Ambiguity, Professional Responsibility and Patient Liberty," *Journal of Medicine and Philosophy* 4 (2), (1979).

CARROLL SMITH-ROSENBERG, Ph.D., is Assistant Professor of History and Psychiatry at the University of Pennsylvania, Philadelphia, Pennsylvania.

MERVYN W. SUSSER, M.B., B.Ch., is Gertrude H. Serglevsky Professor of Epidemiology, Director of Serglevsky Center, Columbia University, New York, New York. He is author of *Causal Thinking in the Health Sciences* (1972).

TALCOTT PARSONS (1902–1979), Professor of Sociology, Harvard University, Cambridge, Massachusetts. He is author of *The Social System* (1951) and *Social Structure and Personality* (1964).

F.C. REDLICH, M.D., is Professor in the Department of Psychiatry and Behavioral Sciences, School of Medicine, University of California at Los Angeles, and Chief of Staff, Brentwood Veterans Administration Hospital, Los Angeles, California. He is author of *Theory and Practice of Psychiatry*.

CHARLES ROSENBERG, Ph.D., is Professor of History at The University of Pennsylvania, Philadelphia, Pennsylvania. He is author of *No Other Gods: On Science and Social Thought in America* (1976).

THOMAS SYDENHAM, M.D. (1624–1689) was educated at Oxford and Montpellier and practiced medicine in London. He is author of *Observationes medicae circa morborum acutorum historiam et curationem* (1676).

THOMAS S. SZASZ, M.D., D.Sc., is Professor of Psychiatry at the State University of New York, Syracuse, New York. He is author of numerous books including *The Myth of Mental Illness* (1961) and *The Myth of Psychotherapy* (1978).

OWSEI TEMKIN, M.D., is William H. Welch Professor Emeritus of the History of Medicine and former Director of the Institute of the History of Medicine at Johns Hopkins University. He is author of *The Double Face of Janus and Other Essays in the History of Medicine* (1977).

ROBERT M. VEATCH, Ph.D., is Senior Research Scholar, Kennedy Institute of Ethics, Georgetown University, Washington, D.C., and Professor of Philosophy, Georgetown University. He is author of *Case Studies in Medical Ethics* (1977).

ILZA VEITH, M.A., PH.D., M.D., D.M.S., is Professor Emeritus of History and Psychiatry at the University of California at San Francisco, Medical Center, San Francisco, California. He is co-author of *Acupuncture Therapy: Current Chinese Practice* (1973).

RUDOLF VIRCHOW (1821–1902), graduated from Berlin University (1848), founded the Archiv für pathologische Anatomie (1847) and was Professor of Pathological Anatomy at Berlin University (1856). He is author of *Die Cellularpathologie* (1858).

CAROLINE WHITBECK, Ph.D., is Associate Professor of Preventive Medicine and Community Health, Institute for the Medical Humanities, University of Texas Medical Branch, Galveston, Texas. She is author of "What is Diagnosis," *Metamedicine* (1981).

Foreword

> There are men and classes of men that stand above the common herd; the soldier, the sailor and the shepherd not infrequently; the artist rarely; rarelier still, the clergyman; the physician almost as a rule. He is the flower (such as it is) of our civilization.
>
> ROBERT LOUIS STEVENSON
> Underwood's Foreword, 1887

These elegant words, written nearly a century ago, expressed an almost universal public esteem in which the physician was held. Since then, public opinion has shifted radically as members of the medical profession have accepted increasingly complex and demanding roles in society. The layman's discovery of the fallibility of present-day representatives of the noble calling of medicine has led to an inevitable dilution of influence, suspicion, and even distrust. What has caused this change in reverence towards the doctor of medicine and was it inevitable? First, the practice of clinical medicine is not a precise art with exact answers to fundamental questions. When physicians in modern society falter in their diagnosis and treatment, the public automatically considers them incompetent. Second, there are those who expect sophisticated, modern technology to provide precisely correct, computerized solutions to all problems that confront the physician. Finally, the goals and aims of medical practice often remain unclear.

The basic distinction between health and disease is vague. At what level or degree of anatomic and physiologic alteration should one be judged unhealthy? When is a person considered sick? When is he well? The ambiguity is complicated by a further conceptual puzzle—the distinction between life and death.

Recall the circumstances in 1967, when the first human heart transplant was announced by Professor Christiaan Barnard in Capetown. The confusion and furor expressed by the public may now be attributed to a previous lack of need for a definition of life and death. Under what circumstances could a surgeon decide when one person with a beating heart, namely the donor, was indeed dead, and then remove the heart for implantation into another person, the recipient? On the surface, such actions seemed monstrous, and perhaps even criminal, but at the time—and even after several thousand years of increasing human enlightenment—that fundamental question of life versus death had not been seriously considered. Most human thought was motivated by ignorance, myth, and suspicion. Technologic advances in clinical medicine had already proceeded to the level where the viability of various organs could be maintained mechanically or pharmacologically long after prospects for a patient's ultimate recovery had disappeared.

Recall the case of Karen Ann Quinlan, when no one was willing to make the major decision—neither the physicians nor the lawyers, neither the jurists nor the clergy, and certainly not the parents. Under such circumstances, who was to decide? With advancing medical expertise and improved technology in the future, such problems will arise more frequently. Only through the experience and knowledge gained from philosophic deliberations concerning the central concepts of medical science can we hope to arrive at more acceptable conclusions and public policies.

The concept of "brain death" has contributed greatly to the welfare of our society, because it approaches in a scientific manner a decision that in the past was often pondered aimlessly. My personal concept of life is simple—*life* resides in the brain. This is the nerve center, the watershed for all meaningful and purposeful activity and behavior. The anatomic location of certain intangibles, such as the mind, the soul, and the spirit, must be there. The brain, therefore, is the master of the household and of all the organs, including the trunk and appendages that are subservient. Each performs a function which satisfies a need—some of greater importance than others. Simply because the heart provides one of the indispensable functions, it should not be accorded exaggerated respect or be thought more important than say the liver, which is equally indispensable. In clinical situations that require decisions regarding fatal disease and the existence of life, the focus should be almost exclusively on the status of the brain. Whether to discontinue support systems, such as respirators, circulatory assist or replacement devices, or various drugs that maintain organ function, depends on the brain.

As these conceptual questions are brought more into the open, the physician again emerges as the person who must ultimately decide them. However well-equipped or adequate the technological situation, in the end, the physician must decide. Because traditionally the physician has been the person legally responsible for the declaration of death, he must be willing to testify that death has occurred and that life has terminated at a particular instant. This responsibility may be viewed as privilege. As the medical profession comes under closer scrutiny, some people would usurp the physician's prerogatives, assuming that he has no better qualifications than any other professional person for assuming the role of God.

The physician's role in society continues to place him in ever more complex situations. Health planners call on him to appraise the health needs of various groups or an entire nation. Often he or she must think as a utilitarian does and attempt to achieve the most good for the greatest number of people. Yet programs guided by utilitarian considerations tend to deny certain health advantages to small groups of sick or diseased individuals who are perhaps more deserving of health benefits than the masses. These considerations hamper the planners, who seek to provide a realistically acceptable level of health care to an entire nation through a nationally insured system. Often the physicians best qualified to advise are usually those least involved in providing clinical care to individuals or to a small community. A successful nationwide health insurance program, although beneficial on a widespread basis, could eliminate or restrict the sophisticated types of medical treatment now provided in our major medical centers, staffed by highly qualified specialists, and supported by advanced and expensive equipment. Along with various economic and political considerations, difficulties in deciding what counts as a health need account for the delay in implementing a national health insurance program. Should such a system deliver complicated and expensive treatment or be concerned with routine, more fundamental health needs? Here again, if such a program were to be implemented, the public would call on the physician to decide.

As medical educators ponder the increasing demands on doctors of medicine in a modern society, most conclude that members of the profession must be exposed to disciplines other than those that are purely scientific. The doctor should be a broadly educated person who has had some pedagogic experience similar to that of a doctor of philosophy. Therefore, in establishing premedical entrance requirements, medical school admissions committees are, and must continue, placing an increasing emphasis on background in the study of humanities. Graduates with a knowledge of history, philosophy, and ethics will be better qualified to judge such sensitive problems as the definition of illness, experimentation on human subjects, informed consent, euthanasia, cost containment, the practice of defensive medicine in a litigious society, and the myriad other issues that have already appeared and can be anticipated to increase. Physicians of the future must be better equipped than their predecessors to meet the complex needs of society in the progression, and it is hoped that the trust and respect placed in the doctor of medicine since the dawn of civilization will be restored.

In his *Moral Essays*, written during the eighteenth century, Alexander Pope said, "Who shall decide when Doctors disagree?" The doctors to whom he referred in the essay, however, were not medical doctors, but learned men and philosophers. Let us nurture the hope that physicians of the future will maintain their positions, not just as students of science but also as disciples of learning and wisdom. It is to be hoped that the essays presented in this volume will contribute toward this important goal.

DENTON A. COOLEY, M.D.
Surgeon-in-Chief
Texas Heart Institute
Houston, Texas

Preface

Though most public controversies in the philosophy of medicine have been focused on issues in bioethics, these do not exhaust the important issues raised by health care. In fact, many, if not most, of the decisions in health care are made in terms of appeal to nonmoral values concerning what is normal or abnormal, and general conceptual presuppositions concerning the nature of health and disease. As a result, important issues of evaluation, including but going beyond moral judgment, and explanation intertwine in the analyses of concepts of health and disease. In fact, an adequate understanding of the nature of health care institutions and the presuppositions of health care policy cannot be made without a prior exploration of the fundamental issue in epistemology and in value theory that form the underpinnings of these concepts.

We therefore offer this volume to students and scholars alike, as an introduction to the already substantial literature focused on the analysis of concepts of health and disease. We have included selections from, or concerning, the history of medicine in order to indicate the roots of present ideas and of present conflicts. We have included studies by social scientists, along with essays by physicians, philosophers, nurses, and others, in order to provide multiple perspectives on these concepts that constitute the character of our contemporary health care systems. In doing so, we also have included explorations of the ways in which these concepts frame social reality and are used as modes of societal control. Towards these ends, we have selected essays from the social history of medicine, essays from contemporary literature, as well as a number of new essays.

We should like to take this opportunity to thank the many individuals who have assisted us in the development of this volume. These include Lore Henlein of Addison-Wesley and Susan G. M. Engelhardt, who have contributed to this work in various ways. Without their help this collection would never have taken shape. We are deeply indebted to them.

ARTHUR CAPLAN
H. TRISTRAM ENGELHARDT, JR.
JAMES J. MCCARTNEY

I. Introduction

When one speaks of the health care professions, it may only be natural to assume that there is something called health for which they care. Or, when one speaks of heart disease, mental disease, or skin disease, it is inviting to presume that all these must have something in common, namely, being diseases. Finally, since health and disease are the objects of major Western sciences and technologies, it would appear credible that whether one is healthy or not, or whether one has a disease or not, what would count as health and disease are matters of fact, not functions of value judgments, and surely not functions of judgments relative to a particular time and a particular culture. In various ways, the essays in this volume call these assumptions into question and give reasons for holding that health and disease are complex and multivocal terms. This volume is offered as an introduction to the complex conceptual assumptions made by biomedicine regarding its central cluster of concepts: notions of health and disease.

Disease and health function as directions for health care. Health is that which is to be preserved, restored, and augmented. Views of what count as health will, as a consequence, direct programs aimed at preserving health. So, too, will concepts of disease direct programs aimed at the prevention, care, or amelioration of disease states.[1] That disease concepts are value-imbued becomes apparent through examining the fact that, all else being equal, having a disease is seen to be a detriment, and is disvalued as a failure to achieve a minimal acceptable level of physiological or psychological function, of freedom from pain, or of bodily form or grace. Which is to say, people attempt to use disease explanations if certain states of affairs bother them in particular ways. Diseases are forwarded as explanations for complaints that in previous times might have been attributed to the possession of the devil or the wrath of the deities. Complaints about disabilities, incapacities, pains, and deformities are referred to medicine for amelioration when they are seen to be due to underlying physiological or psychologial processes. Moreover, insofar as medicine is to be distinguished from other major societal institutions, such as those of punishment, the complaints cannot be immediately due to willfulness. Disease language is concerned not only with evaluations and explanations that are part of considering certain complaints (e.g., "I am abnormally short of breath due to my heart trouble; I really hate it"), but it also is involved in assigning social roles ("You are too sick to hold a job for a while; we will put you on sick-leave"). Disease language is thus complex in serving multiple purposes.

To understand the claims made in medicine about diseases and states of health, it is necessary to sort out a number of overlapping issues. Such an analysis must, in part, be done through noticing the different services performed by disease and health language. Disease and health language are employed in explanations of certain states of affairs: "the headache, fever, chills, and macular rash, are all due to Rocky Mountain spotted fever, which is caused by Rickettsia rickettsi," or "she is in very good health, she can run the marathon; her resting pulse is very slow, she has excellent respiratory function, and so on." In addition, the reasons for taking account medically of certain states of affairs are that they are poorly or highly esteemed. Disease explanations are sought for deformities, illnesses, sicknesses, and so on. They are sought not simply to provide an explanation or predictions of the outcomes of a process, but in hope that those disvalued states of affairs can be prevented, ameliorated, cured, or, at least, that one can provide care for them in some fashion. Moreover, disease concepts are used to legitimize social roles. The sick role, as Talcott Parsons has shown, relieves one of blame for being in that state (though not from having become ill—though one cannot blame someone for remaining afflicted with bronchogenic carcinoma of the lungs, one can blame him for having smoked excessively), relieves one of certain social responsibilities (for example, obligations to report for work on time), though it imposes duties to seek therapy from the relevant experts.[2] The availability of an authentically medical explanation secures one's claim on the sick role. As Fabrega has argued, medicine assigns a physiological truth value to complaints.[3]

As a consequence, there is an interplay between three dimensions of disease and health interests. One set of concerns involves the ranking of states of affairs as those to be avoided, cured, or cared for, or as states of affairs to be sought after as special conditions of well-being. These constitute the universes of medical complaints and endorsements. The former states of affairs, because they are states of which one complains due to some suffering and which then evoke pathophysiological explanations, are seen to be the proper focus of biomedical attention. Or, in the case of health, states of affairs evoke explanations to account for their being conditions of well-being. In that it is probably difficult to conceive of a global account of well-being, one is rather determining individual well-beings or healths. In the case of illnesses, deformities, or disabilities, one has graded a state of affairs as falling somewhere below a minimal decent state of physiological and psychological function; in the case of health, one is identifying a particular state of affairs as, in some respect, meeting or exceeding such a minimal standard. As Christopher Boorse has indicated, it is probably the case that positive concepts of health are, in part, mutually exclusive.[4] The build required to be a good weight-lifter is not the build conducive to being a good marathon runner. Beyond that, what would count as health in one environment under certain circumstances will not so count in another. Thus, being fair-skinned is not a wholesome condition if one wants to live sparsely clad in the tropic sun. One will have a decisively higher risk of developing carcinoma of the skin than those with more pigmentation. However, if one wants to live in the Arctic, in areas where there is a minimum exogenous supply of vitamin D, being fair-skinned will offer at least some protection against rickets. In any event, what will count as minimal standards of function or as special levels of excellence will depend on value judgment concerning what is important to be able to do as a human being. One singles out certain physiological and psychological accounts as pathophysiological accounts or as psychopathological accounts because they undergird sufferings. Thus, whether or not one holds baldness to be a genetic disease depends on one's judgment of the importance to a proper human form of a full head of hair. Or, if one wishes to identify physiological and psychological substrata of health, one will first have to choose what excellences one will count as health.

One might rejoin that certain states of affairs may simply be discoverable as disease states or states of health without appeal to particular value judgments. However, as Joseph Margolis indicates in this volume, states of affairs are disease states across cultural boundaries, not because they involve a trans-cultural value or are discoverable as diseases without appeal to values, but because such states in nearly all conceivable cultures and nearly all conceivable environments would preclude the achievement of some important human goals, though the goals may vary from culture to culture. In short, after Darwin, it becomes clear that if disease and health are to be identified as successful or unsuccessful adaptations, one must specify the reference environment (since one is adapted to one environment or one set of environments, not all environments), the goals of the adaptation at issue (for example, to maximize reproductive fitness, pleasure in life, and so on), and whether one is regarding the species or the individual. The last is necessary because some individuals who are poorly adapted may, as such, represent the price paid for the successful adaptation of the species. For example, if, as seems to be the case, sickle cell trait developed because it maximized reproductive fitness in an environment with falciparum malaria and without antimalarial drugs, those who developed sickle cell disease and died early are simply paying the price for the group's advantage.[5] In fact, if one is interested in species survival, one will wish to have a number of individuals poorly adapted to their present environment so that the species can draw on them in the future, should the environment change. Thus, health as successful function or adaptation must be specified with respect to the circumstances (that is, environment), the goals sought, and whether the bearer of such functional success is the species or the individual.

These issues indicate the problem involved in specifying which states are pathological, and what circumstances are properly the focus of medical attention. As the preceding suggests, the boundaries are neither sharp nor clear. Various states of affairs termed illnesses, sicknesses, deformities, injuries, disabilities, or distresses of various sorts are the starting points for disease explanations. There appears to be no single unity or essential characteristic to all these circumstances. Rather, circumstances involving disabilities, pains, or deformities are usually the basis of the complaints that are the focus of medical explanations and interventions. Thus, persons complain about their or others' inabilities to perform a particular task or achieve a particular goal (for example, "I can no longer go upstairs without getting short of breath," "I can't hear well anymore," "He can no longer control himself, he's crazy," or "I want a vasectomy (that is, I want to be helped not to cause a pregnancy)," about pains or discomforts (for example, "I have a pain here," "She has a fever," or "It itches here"), or about deformities (for example, "He has a rash there," "This skin is discolored," "My nose is ugly," or "Her breasts are too small"). Medicine and the allied health professions are thus reduced to address a spectrum of complaints ranging from illnesses to dissatisfactions about psychological or physiological functions or about bodily form. These complaints are identified as medical in that they are focused on conditions of an organism that are held to be nonwillful, but rather due to physiological or psychological processes or bodily states of affairs, which physicians and other allied health professionals have expertise in identifying, in predicting their courses, and in authoring those courses in ways that please those who forwarded the complaint.

States of affairs are thus termed diseases when they are due to physiological or psychological processes that typically cause states of disability, pain, or deformity, and are generally held to be below acceptable physiological or psychological norms. It should be noted that such norms cannot simply be determined by discovering what are the usual physiological or psychological norms apart from one's judgment of their consequences, that is, apart from one's giving a value to them. Thus, there are human capacities, the presence or absence of which would not serve to indicate either health or disease because individuals are generally indifferent to such capacities. One might think here, for example, of the genetically determined capacity to roll in the edges of one's tongue, or the ability to taste phenylthiocarbimide. Though 70 percent of individuals can taste phenylthiocarbimide, those who are taste blind do not, therefore, count as ill, diseased, or defective. Though it is statistically abnormal (it is not species typical) to be taste blind, it is not abnormal in the sense of being a defect, for in most circumstances, humans vest no value in the capacity to taste phenylthiocarbimide, nor does taste blindness appear to impede any human goals. Minimally acceptable norms or physiological and psychological function are bound to the achievement of significant human goals and purposes (that is, night blindness may thus count as a defect or a disease). Further, where the norms are not generally enclosed, they may still, when embraced by a signficant group of individuals, come to be recognized as among the complaints that move plastic surgeons to intervention to noses or bustlines. That is, a state of distress can be identified as being of interest to medicine even where a disease is not involved (that is, where a generally accepted norm of physiological or psychological function is not violated). One might think here, for example, of medicine's caring for pains and discomforts associated with childbirth or teething. Thus, there is a spectrum ranging from diseases associated with generally accepted norms of physiological and psychological function to medically treated distresses, which may make no such appeal to norms, beyond what might be taken to be an easily bearable level of pain or discomfort.

If a complaint is grounded in a view of generally accepted minimal levels of physiological and psychological function, its claim on medical resources is likely to be stronger. Moreover, insofar as medicine authenticates complaints as being actually due to underlying physiological or psychological process, typically beyond the complainer's direct and immediate control, the more the complaint is so authenticated, the more the complaint will be established as bona fide. Here also, appeals to species typical capacities probably have their force. If one lacks a capacity that most individuals possess, it is likely to appear more reasonable that one be aided in recovering or gaining that capacity. Of course, in many cases, there may not be clear species typicality because of the existence of a polymorphism, in which individuals bearing different traits contribute in differing ways to the survival of the species. Thus, it may be the case that, if homosexuality is genetically determined, it evolved because of its recondite contribution to the survival of capacity of the species.[6] As a result, interventions aimed primarily at one variety of being a healthy human may not have a broad appeal (for example, sex therapy aimed at maximizing the capacity of homosexuals to function successfully as homosexuals).

Concrete understandings of health and disease are thus the product of the interaction of what one holds to be the bearer of success, the environments to which one is making reference, and the goals one has in mind for proper human function. In addition, the mapping of diseases and distresses is drawn and redrawn in terms of the underlying explanatory model offered by medicine as a science. To somewhat alter Michel Foucault's idiom, the first spatialization of disease, if one means by this the world of patient complaints and complaints about patients, is redrawn in terms of the second spatialization of disease, the theoretical models offered by pathoanatomists, pathophysiologists, and theoreticians of psychopathology.[7] The world of illnesses and distresses, which initially appears as repeatedly encountered syndromes, constellations, or concatenations of symptoms and problems, becomes better understood and redrawn by an appeal to the underlying seats and causes of the symptoms. But even here, pragmatic interests intrude. In that most illnesses or patterns of distress are the product of many necessary, and many unnecessary, and insufficient causes that in particular patterns become sufficient causes, explanatory models often accent one cause as *the* cause because of the usefulness of that emphasis. Thus, tuberculosis is treated as an infectious disease, though there may be large genetic components. It is simply that genetic components are not as useful for current approaches to treatment and prevention.

In addition, medicine authenticates sick roles, authorizes particular excuses, relieves particular duties, and grants individuals particular rights and privileges. Thus, in addition to evaluating and explaining reality, in the process of authenticating illness and disease states, physicians and other allied health professionals create social reality. Saying that person X has a certain sort of illness caused by a particular disease process is not only descriptive, evaluative, and explanatory, but also performative. It renders the person X the holder of a particular social role with its special compensations. It is through this complex nexus of disease and health notions that biomedicine acts on human reality.

It is because of this complexity that we offer this volume as an introduction to these entangled but important issues. The articles offer various mappings of the interplay among the evaluative, explanatory, and performative functions of biomedicine. It is only through exploring the different services performed by different sorts of concepts of health and disease that an adequate portrayal of the nature of biomedicine is possible. As has been indicated, these concepts direct the various health care insititutions. To say that X is an illness (that is, a state of distress) or a disease (that is, a physiological or psychological process that is likely to cause distress), and that one is not seeking treatment or medical attention, is to invite others to seek a justification for one's inaction. Such a report would be tantamount to saying "I am in a condition which I do not like, and yet, I will not ameliorate it." Of course, one may, in the end, find an illness or a disease to be, on balance, a benefit (for example, "If I hadn't gotten ill that day, I would have had to take the exam and I would have failed," or "Luckily, I have a bad back and that exempted me from the draft.") But all else being equal, being ill or having a disease recruits and directs medical intervention: illnesses are held to be circumstances that ought not to occur (they are disvalued) and the institutions of health care are developed to act on those states (that is, to prevent, abolish, or ameliorate them). The geography of illnesses, diseases, and health thus directs the energies of biomedicine in activities of curing, caring, preventing, and promoting certain states of affairs. The geography is complex as the preceding indicates. The first section of this volume analyzes this complexity by exploring, through various professional viewpoints, the significance of concepts of health and disease. These essays introduce the reader in detail to different approaches to, and views of, the nature and discoverability of these concepts, which so dramatically direct health care and draw lines between what counts as the domain of health care versus other social institutions. The viewpoints range from that developed by Leon Kass, who wishes to restrict what would properly count as the domain of medical care (and leave abortion and cosmetic surgery outside of the bounds of medicine proper), to the World Health Organization's definition of health that would embrace most social problems.

The second chapter gives a historical introduction to the ways in which our current concepts of health and disease have developed. In these readings, one finds reflected, in different ways, disputes regarding the discoverability of disease classifications. That is, these essays mirror general debates concerning nominalism and the existence of natural kinds. One sees, as well, the reconceptualization of the clinician's world that took place through nineteenth-century medicine's establishment of the seats and causes of many diseases. Thus, as one comes to Owsei Temkin's analysis of the concepts of specific disease entities and individual sicknesses, one has already read through the development of our two-tiered concepts of disease, which relate the world of the clinician to the pathoanatomist's and pathophysiologist's world of Bichat, Bernard, and Virchow.

The third chapter offers presentations and analyses of the ways in which values and social expectations have framed the world of medicine, as well as of the ways in which medicine has been required to support prevailing social expectations. It offers insights into the history of our attitudes toward sexuality generally, the treatment of women in particular, the treatment of blacks under the peculiar institution of slavery, and of nineteenth-century attitudes to morphine addiction. These, along with Richard Green's analysis of homosexuality, illustrate how activities disapproved of within certain social or moral viewpoints become transformed into diseases by tranforming what is understood as morally or socially improper into what is viewed as physiologically or psychologically abnormal. In the case of the disease of masturbation, it illustrates, as well, how moral suspicions can lead to certain activities being identified as the causes of illness states. These studies provide insight into the subtle ways in which the power of medicine and of sick roles are employed in social control. This is somewhat obvious in the case of the disease of masturbation. It is less so in the case of Cartwright's article concerning diseases of slaves, for it is not clear whether he is providing slaves from the protection of the sick role, should they attempt to escape or fail to be fully productive, or whether he is employing the power of medicine to maintain prevailing social structures and interests.

These problems are encountered again in the examination of concepts of mental health and illness. As the fourth chapter shows, there has been the recurring temptation to ground mental diseases in pathophysiological ocurrences the lineage of this interest being of considerable ancestry. Endeavors such as that of Broussais can be seen as a part of the more general problem of validating the clinician's world of symptoms in terms of theories that would lead to more powerful classifications, more successsful predictions, and more useful therapies, relating the clinician's findings to other independent findings, such as those that the pathoanatomist and pathophysiologist offer clinicians in somatic medicine. Because such conceptual models have not been generally successful in the case of mental illness, mental illness classifications and diagnoses have appeared to be less well established and therefore, more open to societal abuse. It is surely the case that the sick role generally can be used as a means of social control. Physicians can impose societal force on an individual by finding him or her to be suffering from either active pulmonary tuberculosis or a paranoid psychosis. In both cases, an individual's ability to act on certain life plans can, through the force of the state, be dramatically restricted. The difference lies, at least in great part, in the fact that there is greater intersubjective verifiability of the diagnosis of tuberculosis. In addition, though both diagnoses may subject the individual to the police power of the state, the sick role of being mentally ill specially circumscribes the rights of individuals to determine their own futures and own life plans. Further, in that mental illness can allow an individual to escape the criminal role by claiming the sick role, it raises special questions regarding the boundaries between health care and institutions of punishment.

The final chapters contain articles analyzing the conceptual issues that underlie these disputes. They provide explorations of the extent to which disease categories can be seen to be created or discovered, the extent to which they reflect particular cultural or social values, and the ways in which they are enlisted as general social means of control. These analyses provide a critical dissection of the medical model, both as one explanatory model among others (that is, a predominantly somatic construal of causality), and as a pattern of the provider-consumer relationship (that is, as physician/patient, rather than as provider/client).

Through providing various analyses of concepts of health and disease, this volume thus offers to the student and the scholar a set of perspectives on the contemporary institution of medicine and health care. The historical articles are provided in order to indicate the more important roots of present viewpoints and problems. The contemporary analyses display the ongoing controversies concerning the direction and significance of health care. As has been shown, different views of health and disease will authorize different interventions under different circumstances. It is only through better understanding these cardinal concepts that one will be able to judge which interventions by medicine and health care are proper, which excessive, and which fall short of proper societal goals.

NOTES

1. H. Tristram Engelhardt, Jr., and Stuart F. Spicker, eds., *Evaluation and Explanation in the Biomedical Sciences* (Dordrecht: D. Reidel, 1975).
   H. Tristram Engelhardt, Jr., and Stuart F. Spicker, eds., *Clinical Judgement: A Critical Appraisal* (Dordrecht: D. Reidel, 1979).
2. Talcott Parsons, *The Social System* (New York: Free Press, 1951).
   Talcott Parsons, "The Mental Hospital as a Type of Organization," in *The Patient and the Mental Hospital*, ed. M. Greenblatt et al. (Glencoe, Ill.: Free Press, 1957), pp. 108–129.
   Talcott Parsons, "Definitions of Health and Illness in the Light of American Values and Social Structure," in *Patients, Physicians and Illness*, ed. E. G. Jaco (Glencoe, Ill.: Free Press, 1958), pp. 165–187.
   Talcott Parsons, "Illness, Therapy and the Modern Urban American Family," in *Patients, Physicians and Illness*, ed. E. G. Jaco (Glencoe, Ill.: Free Press, 1958), pp. 234–245.
   Miriam Siegler, and Humphry Osmond, "The 'Sick Role' Revisited," *Hastings Center Studies*, vol. 1 (Hastings-on-Hudson, N.Y.: Institute of Society, Ethics, and the Life Sciences, 1973), pp. 41–58.
3. Horacio Fabrega, Jr., "Disease Viewed as a Symbolic Category," in *Mental Health: Philosophical Perspectives*, eds. H. Tristram Engelhardt, Jr., and Stuart F. Spicker (Dordrecht: D. Reidel, 1978), pp. 79–106.
4. Christopher Boorse, "Health as a Theoretical Concept," *Philosophy of Science* 44 (1977):542–573.
5. F. B. Livingston, "The Distribution of the Abnormal Hemoglobin Genes and Their Signficance for Human Evolution," *Evolution* 18 (1964):685–699.
6. Robert Trivers, "Parent-Offspring Conflict," *American Zoologist* 14 (1974)249–264.
   E. O. Wilson, *Sociobiology: The New Synthesis* (Cambridge, Mass.: Harvard University Press, 1975), p. 555.
7. Michel Foucault, *The Birth of a Clinic: An Archaeology of Medical Perception*, trans. A. M. Sheridan Smith (New York: Random House, 1973).

CONCEPTS OF HEALTH AND DISEASE
Interdisciplinary Perspectives

Part 1

Health and Disease: Basic Interdisciplinary Reflections

The selections included in this section raise a number of important conceptual issues about the notions of health and disease. Persons who differ in cultural background or in age often view disease and health in drastically different ways. One person's paradigm of disease can be another person's paradigm of health. What one society considers a disease another society may consider a sin, crime, or sign of poverty. Interpersonal and cross-cultural variations in the referents of health and disease pose serious practical problems for those concerned with ameliorating and preventing disease and promoting and maintaining health.

The range of phenomena denoted by such concepts as health and disease is a subject of great controversy. Many of the authors represented in this section are concerned with establishing definitions or criteria which capture the correct scope or domain of these concepts. Must every state of being in which human beings find themselves be classified as either healthy or diseased? And is it possible to arrive at univocal concepts of health and disease? Variations in custom and convention concerning what is considered disease and the prima facie differences that characterize ascriptions of mental and physical health suggest to some of the authors that no single definition will suffice.

Disagreement also exists as to the role values play in ascribing and explaining health and disease. If the concepts are merely value-laden social constructs, the health professions may require much more strenuous regulation and policing to ensure that everyone's values are given fair consideration and that basic rights and privileges are not abused. If health and disease can be shown to be matters of dysfunction, deviance, or abnormality, it may be possible to provide a more objective foundation for medical expertise and action.

The role of values in understanding health and disease is central to the practice of health care. Should the role of medicine be simply the amelioration of disease, or should it extend to the promotion of optimal states of health? As a number of authors note, this question is, in part, contingent upon the relationship posited between health and disease—is health merely the absence of disease, or is it some positively valued state or condition? In evaluating the utility and efficacy of medicine, one must attend carefully to the nature of the relationship between these concepts.

1.1

Regarding the End of Medicine and the Pursuit of Health

Leon R. Kass

American medicine is not well. Though it remains the most widely respected of professions, though it has never been more competent technically, it is in trouble, both from without and from within.

The alleged causes are many; I will mention a few. Medical care is very costly and not equitably available. The average doctor sees many more patients than he should, yet many fewer than would like to be seen. On the one hand, the physician's powers and prerogatives have grown, as a result of new technologies yielding new modes of diagnosis and treatment, and new ways to alter the workings of the body. His responsibilities have grown as well, partly due to rising patient and societal demands for medical help with behavioral and social problems. All kinds of problems now roll to the doctor's door, from sagging anatomies to suicides, from unwanted childlessness to unwanted pregnancy, from marital difficulties to learning difficulties, from genetic counseling to drug addiction, from laziness to crime. On the other hand, the physician's new powers have brought new dilemmas, concern over which has led to new attempts to regulate and control his practices, including statutes, codes, professional review bodies, ombudsmen, national commissions, and lawsuits brought by public interest law and consumer groups. More and more physicians are being dragged before the bar, and medical malpractice insurance has become both alarmingly scarce and exorbitantly expensive.

Health care has become an important political issue. A right to health has been frequently claimed and embraced by politicians. Recent legislation has put the federal government most directly into the life-saving business, obliging it to pay for kidney machines for anyone in need. And the National Health Insurance on the horizon will surely bring the medical profession even more under governmental control, at the very least by defining what will count as health care through determining what will be paid for.

Last but not least, people both in and out of medicine have begun to wonder out loud whether and to what extent medicine is doing good. No longer simply charmed by the profession's diagnostic and therapeutic wizardry, some people are seriously asking whether the so-called health care delivery system really does—or can—deliver or foster improved health for the American people.

This last question points to a more fundamental cause of medicine's illness: Medicine, as well as the community which supports it, appears to be perplexed regarding its purpose. It is ironic, but not accidental, that medicine's great technical power should arrive in tandem with great confusion about the standards and goals for guiding its use. When its powers were fewer, its purpose was clearer. Indeed, since antiquity, medicine has been regarded as the very model of an art, of a rational activity whose powers were all bent towards a clear and identifiable end. Today, though fully armed and eager to serve, the doctor finds that his target is no longer clear to him or to us. Sometimes, it appears to be anything at which he can take aim; at other times, it appears nowhere to be found. In fact, the very existence of a target is implicitly questioned by those who have begun to change the name of the doctor from "physician" to "member of the helping professions."

At what should the medical art aim? What is the proper end—or the proper ends— of medicine? Continued confusion about this matter could bring about, more directly than any other cause, the demise of the profession, even if there were to remain people with M.D. degrees whom their clients called "Doctor." For without a clear view of its end, medicine is at risk of becoming merely a set of powerful means, and the doctor at risk of becoming merely a technician and engineer of the body, a scalpel for hire, selling his services upon demand. There is a connection between the two meanings of "end" suggested by the title of this article: Since an end-less profession is an ended profession, there will be an end *to* medicine unless there remains an end *for* medicine. It is in part for this reason that I have chosen to inquire regarding the end, or purpose, of medicine, with the hope that we might more seriously regard—that is, look back at, pay attention to, and finally, esteem—the end or purpose of the medical art. Moreover, only by again attaining clarity about the goal of medicine can we hope intelligently to evaluate efforts to reach that goal and wisely to plan for their improvement. Otherwise, for all our good intentions, our health policies will be mere tinkerings in the dark, at great risk of doing more harm than good.

I. THE END OF MEDICINE

I trust it will shock no one if I say that I am rather inclined to the old-fashioned view that health—or if you prefer, the healthy human being—is the end of the physician's art. That health is *a* goal of medicine few would deny. The trouble is, so I am told, that health is not the only possible and reasonable goal of medicine, since there are other prizes for which medical technique can be put in harness. Yet I regard these other goals—even where I accept their goodness as goals—as false goals for medicine, and their pursuit as perversions of the art.

Let us examine some of the false goals that tempt today's physicians. First, there is what is usually called "happiness" in its sadly shrunken meaning, but which might best be called pleasure—that is, gratifying or satisfying patient desires, producing contentment. This temptation arises largely because of the open-ended character of some contemporary notions of mental health, which consider frustration or anxiety or any unsatisfied desires, no matter how questionable, to be marks of ill health, requiring a remedy.

Some examples of gratification may be helpful. A woman gets a surgeon to remove a normal breast because it interfered with her golf swing. An obstetrician is asked to perform amniocentesis, and then abortion, if the former procedure shows the fetus to be of the undesired gender. "Dr. Feelgood" devotes his entire practice to administering amphetamine injections to people seeking elevations of mood. To these real but admittedly extreme examples, one could add, among others, the now generally accepted practices of performing artificial insemination or arranging adoptions, performing vasectomies and abortions[1] for non-medical reasons (i.e., for family planning), dispensing antibiotics or other medicines simply because the patient wants to take something, as well as some activities of psychiatrists and many of cosmetic surgeons (e.g., where the surgery does not aim to correct inborn or acquired abnormality or deformity). I would also add the practice, now being advocated more and more, of directly and painlessly killing a patient who wants to die.

All these practices, the worthy and the unworthy alike, aim *not* at the patient's health but rather at satisfying his, albeit in some cases reasonable, wishes. They are acts not of medicine, but of indulgence or gratification, in that they aim at pleasure or convenience or at the satisfaction of some other desire, and not at health. Now, some indulgence may be necessary in the *service* of healing, as a useful means to the proper end: I see nothing wrong in sweetening bad tasting medicine. But to serve the desires of patients as *consumers* should be the task of agents other than doctors, if and when it should be the task of anyone.

Even in its fuller sense, happiness is a false goal for medicine. By gerrymandering the definition of health to comprise "a state of complete physical, mental, and social well-being," the World Health Organization has in effect maintained that happiness is the doctor's business (even if he needs outside partners in this enterprise). For complete mental well-being—not to speak of the more elusive and ambiguous "social well-being," which will certainly

1. Abortion—nearly all of it non-therapeutic in this sense—is now the third most common surgical procedure in the United States, after circumcision and tonsillectomy.

mean different things to Pope Paul, President Ford, and Chairman Mao—goes well beyond the medical province of sanity, depending as it does on the successful and satisfying exercise of intelligence, awareness, imagination, taste, prudence, good sense, and fellow feeling, for whose cultivation medicine can do little. (That *happiness*, even in its full sense, is different from *health* can be seen in considering whether it would ever make sense to say, "Call no man *healthy* until he is dead.")

BEHAVIOR MODIFICATION

A second false goal for medicine is social adjustment or obedience, or more ambitiously, civic or moral virtue. The prevention of crime, the taming of juvenile delinquents, the relief of poverty and racial discrimination, the reduction of laziness and philandering, the rearing of decent and moral men and women—all worthy goals in my opinion—are none of the doctor's business, except as the doctor is also a human being and a citizen. These are jobs for parents, policemen, legislators, clergymen, teachers, judges, and the community as a whole—not to speak of the individual citizens themselves.[2] It is doubtful that the physician has the authority and competence, as physician, to serve these goals with his skills and techniques.

The difficulty is, of course, that only doctors are able and legally entitled to manipulate the body; hence, the temptation to lend this licensed skill to any social cause. This temptation is bound to increase as we learn more about the biological contributions to behavior. In an increasing number of circumstances, the biological contribution will be seen as most accessible to intervention and most amenable to change. Hence, biological manipulation will often hold out the promise of dramatic and immediate results. Brain surgery and behavior-modifying drugs already have their advocates in the battles against criminal and other so-called anti-social behavior, and, for better or for worse, there is good reason for believing that these techniques may be effective at least in some cases some of the time. But even assuming that we should accept, for example, psychosurgery for some men committing frequent crimes of violence, or the dispensing of drugs in schools for some restless children, or genetic screening to detect genotypes that may in the future be shown to predispose to violent behavior, I doubt that it is the proper business of medicine to conduct these practices—even though, on balance, there may be overriding prudential reasons for not establishing a separate profession of bio-behavioral conditioners.

---

2. Improvements in public order and private virtue may, of course, lead secondarily to better health, e.g., with the reduction of crimes or drunkenness. (This theme will be discussed more fully below.) Conversely, medicine and its attendant institutions, including programs of health insurance, may have secondary consequences for society and morals, e.g., for the redistribution of income or the sense of personal responsibility for one's state of health.

I reject, next, in passing, the claim that the alteration of human nature, or of some human natures, is a proper end for medicine, whether it be a proposal by a psychologist for pills to reduce human "aggressiveness," especially in our political leaders, or the suggestions of some geneticists for eugenic uses of artificial insemination, or the more futuristic and radical visions of man-machine "hybrids," laboratory-grown "optimum babies," and pharmacologically induced "peace of mind." Also to be resisted is that temptation first dangled by Descartes (and repeated in various forms by others many times since), who wrote in praise of the prospects for a new medicine based on his new physics: "For the mind depends so much on the temperament and disposition of the bodily organs that, if it is possible to find a means of rendering men wiser and cleverer than they have hitherto been, I believe that it is in medicine that it must be sought." I doubt whether some of the improvements proposed would indeed be improvements, and also whether these goals could indeed be realized by using the biomedical techniques proposed. But in addition—and, for the present purpose, this is decisive—I would argue that these goals are not proper goals for the healing profession.

I skip over the much discussed question of whether the physician should be also a seeker after scientific truth, and whether and to what extent he may or should conduct research on patients not for their immediate benefit. Insofar as the knowledge sought is pertinent to the art of healing, its pursuit is a necessary means to the end of medicine and cannot be ruled out of bounds on that score, though serious and difficult moral questions remain whenever human beings are used as means, regardless of the end served.[3] There may be good practical reasons to keep clearly delineated the activities of the physician as healer, and the physician as student of health and disease, all the more so where research done by doctors is not clearly and directly in the service of the health of their patients. But as the art depends upon knowledge, so the search for knowledge cannot be excluded from the art.

DEATH PREVENTION

Let me, with some misgivings, suggest one more false goal of medicine: the prolongation of life, or the prevention of death. It is not so clear that this is a false goal, especially as it is so intimately connected with the medical art, and so often acclaimed as the first goal of medicine, or, at least, its most beneficial

---

3. Perhaps these questions can be resolved, at least in principle, along the following lines. By knowingly and freely consenting to serve as an experimental subject, the patient is not serving as a means *merely*, but he becomes, as it were, a co-inquirer, and the obligation to secure his consent explicitly acknowledges that he is not to be regarded merely as a means. Nevertheless, a whole nest of theoretical and practical questions remains, ranging from the meaning and limits of "consent," "informed," and "free" to the design of procedures that would adequately protect the subject against risk and abuse without undermining the freedom to inquire.

product. Yet to be *alive* and to be *healthy* are not the same, though the first is both a condition of the second and, up to a point, a consequence. One might well ask whether we desire to live in order to live healthily and well, or whether we desire to be healthy and virtuous merely in order to stay alive. But no matter how desirable life may be—and clearly to be alive *is* a good, and a condition of all the other human goods—for the moment let us notice that the prolongation of life is ultimately an impossible, or rather an unattainable, goal for medicine. For we are all born with those twin inherited and inescapable "diseases," aging and mortality. To be sure, we can still achieve further reductions in *premature* deaths; but it often seems doubtful from our words and deeds that we ever regard any particular death as other than premature, as a failure of today's medicine, hopefully avoidable by tomorrow's.

If medicine aims at death prevention, rather than at health, then the medical ideal, ever more closely to be approximated, must be bodily immortality. Strange as it may sound, this goal really *is* implied in the way we as a community evaluate medical progress and medical needs. We go after the diseases that are the leading causes of death, rather than the leading causes of ill health. We evaluate medical progress, and compare medicine in different nations, in terms of mortality statistics. We ignore the fact that for the most part we are merely changing one set of fatal illnesses or conditions for another, and not necessarily for milder or more tolerable ones. We rarely stop to consider of what and how we will die, and in what condition of body and mind we shall spend our last years, once we can cure cancer, heart disease, and stroke.

I am not suggesting that we cease investigating the causes of these diseases. On the contrary, medicine *should* be interested in preventing these diseases, or failing that, in restoring their victims to as healthy a condition as possible. But it is primarily because they are causes of *unhealth*, and only secondarily because they are killers, that we should be interested in preventing or combating them. That their prevention and treatment may enable the prospective or actual victims to live longer may be deemed, in many cases, an added good, though we should not expect too much on this score. The complete eradication of heart disease, cancer, and stroke—currently the major mortal diseases—would, according to some calculations, extend the average life expectancy at birth only by approximately six or seven years, and, at age 65, by no more than one-and-a-half to two years.[4] Medicine's contribution to longer life has nearly reached its natural limit.

By challenging prolongation of life as a true goal of medicine, I may be challenging less what is done by practicing clinicians and more how we think

4. During the period between 1900 and 1970, the average life expectancy among white males in the United States, calculated from birth, increased by about 22 years (the biggest contribution being a decline in infant mortality), but the average life expectancy for those who reached age 65 increased only 1.5 years.

and speak about it. Consider a concrete case. An elderly woman, still active in community affairs and family life, has a serious heart attack and suffers congestive heart failure. The doctor orders, among other things, oxygen, morphine, and diuretics, and connects her to a cardiac monitor, with pacemaker and defibrillator handy. What is the doctor's goal in treatment? To be sure, his actions, if successful, will help to keep her alive. But his immediate intention is to restore her circulatory functions as near to their healthy condition as possible; his more distant goal is to return her to her pre-morbid activities. Should the natural compensating and healing processes succeed, with his assistance, and should the cardiac wound heal and the circulation recover, the patient will keep herself alive.

We all are familiar with those sad cases in which a patient's life has been prolonged well beyond the time at which there is reasonable hope of returning him to a reasonably healthy state. Yet even in such cases—say a long-comatose patient or a patient with end-stage respiratory failure—a sensible physician will acknowledge that there is no longer any realizable therapeutic or medical goal, and will not take the mere preservation of life as his objective. Sometimes he may justify further life-prolonging activities in terms of a hope for a new remedy or some dramatic turn of events. But when reasonable hope of recovery is gone, he acts rather to comfort the patient as a friend and not especially or uniquely as a physician.

I do not want to be misunderstood. Mine is not an argument to permit or to condone medical callousness, or euthanasia practiced by physicians. Rather it is a suggestion that doctors keep their eye on their main business, restoring and correcting what can be corrected and restored, always acknowledging that death will and must come, that health is a mortal good, and that as embodied beings we are fragile beings that must snap sooner or later, medicine or no medicine. To keep the strings in tune, not to stretch them out of shape attempting to make them last forever, is the doctor's primary and proper goal.

To sum up: Health is different from pleasure, happiness, civil peace and order, virtue, wisdom, and truth. Health is possible only for mortal beings, and we must seek it knowing and accepting, as much as we are able to know and accept, the transience of health and of the beings who are healthy. To serve health and only health is a worthy profession, no less worthy because it does not serve all other goods as well.

II. WHAT IS "HEALTH"?

There was a time when the argument might have ended here, and we could have proceeded immediately to ask how the goal of health may be attained, and what the character of public policy toward health should be. But since there is nowadays much confusion about the nature and meaning of "health," we may have made but little progress by our identification of health as the proper purpose of medicine.

If the previous section might be viewed as an argument against a creeping medical imperialism expanding under a view of health that is much too broad, there remains a need to confront the implications of a medical isolationism and agnosticism that reduces its province under a view of health that is much too narrow. Indeed, the tendency to expand the notion of health to include happiness and good citizenship is, ironically, a consequence of, or a reaction to, the opposite and more fundamental tendency—namely, to treat health as merely the absence of known disease entities, and more radically to insist that health as such is, in reality, nothing more than a word.[5]

We are thus obliged, before turning to the question of what we can do to become healthier, to examine the question "What is health?"; for what was once self-evident now requires an argument. I begin with some of the important difficulties that confound the search for the meaning of "health."

1. What is the domain of health? Is it body, or body and soul? Can only individuals be healthy, or can we speak univocally, and not analogically, about a healthy marriage, a healthy family, a healthy city, or a healthy society, meaning by these references something more than collections of healthy individuals? I think not. In its strict sense, "health" refers to individual organisms—plants and animals no less than humans—and only analogically or metaphorically to larger groupings. I will set aside the question of whether only bodies or also souls are or can be "healthy," since it appears difficult enough to discover what health is even for the body. While there is disagreement about the existence of a standard of health for the soul—or, if you prefer, about whether there is "psychic health"—no one I think denies that if health exists at all, it exists as a condition at least of bodies. For the sake of simplicity, then, we shall confine our investigation in the present context to somatic or bodily health.[6]

2. Health appears to be a matter of more and less, a matter of degree, and standards of health seem to be relative to persons, and also relative to time of life for each person. Almost everyone's state of health could be better, and most of us—even those of us free of overt disease—can remember being

---

5. Claude Bernard opens his book *An Introduction to the Study of Experimental Medicine*, held by some to be a founding document of our scientific medicine, with the following sentence: "*To conserve health and to cure disease:* medicine is still pursuing a scientific solution of this problem, which has confronted it from the first." Yet he says in Chapter 1 of Part II, "[N]either physiologists nor physicians need imagine it their task to seek the cause of life or the essence of disease. That would be entirely wasting one's time in pursuing a phantom. The words life, death, health, disease, have no objective reality." (Dover edition, H. C. Green translation, pp. 1, 67).

6. In doing so, we are supported by a sensible tradition which held that health, like beauty or strength, was an excellence of the body, whereas moderation, wisdom, and courage were excellences of soul. While excluding these latter goods from the goal of medicine, I do not mean to deny to a more minimal state of psychic health—namely, sanity or "emotional equilibrium"—a possible place among the true ends of medicine.

healthier than we are now. Yet as Aristotle long ago pointed out, "health admits of degrees without being indeterminate." In this respect, health is like pleasure, strength, or justice, and unlike "being pregnant" or "being dead."

3. Is health a positive quality or condition, or merely the absence of some negative quality or condition? Is one necessarily "healthy" if one is not ill or diseased? One might infer from modern medical practice that health is simply the absence of all known diseases. Harrison's textbook, *Principles of Internal Medicine*, is a compendium of diseases, and apart from the remedies for specific diseases it contains no discussion of regimens for gaining and keeping health. Indeed, the term "health" does not even occur in the index.

Clinical medicine's emphasis on disease and its cure is understandable. It is the sick, and not the well, who seek our medical advice. The doctor has long been concerned with restoration and remedy, not with promotion and maintenance, which were originally the responsibilities of gymnastics and dietetics. This orientation has been encouraged by the analytic and reductive approach of modern medical science and by the proliferation of known diseases and treatments—both leading to a highly specialized but highly fragmented medicine. Doctors are too busy fighting disease to be bothered much about health, and, up to a point, this makes sense.

Yet among pediatricians, with their well-baby clinics and their concern for normal growth and development, we can in fact see medicine clearly pointing to an overall good rather than away from particular evils. The same goal also informs the practices of gymnastics (physical fitness programs) and of dietetics. Together, these examples provide a provisional ground for the claim that health is a good in its own right, not merely a privation of one or all evils. Though we may be led to *think* about health and to discover its existence only through discovering and reflecting on *departures* from health, health would seem to be the primary notion. Moreover, as I hope will become clear, disease, as the generic name for the cluster of symptoms and identifiable pathological conditions of the body, is not a notion symmetrical with, or opposite to, health. Health and *unhealth*—i.e., health and falling short of health—are true contraries, not health and disease.

DO DOCTORS KNOW BEST?

4. Who is the best judge of health, the doctor or the patient? On the surface, this looks like, and has increasingly been treated as, a question about power and the locus of authority. This trend is connected with the rise of consumerism and suspicion about all kinds of expertise, and has been fostered by loose talk about health as a commodity, as something money can guarantee, as something determined by felt needs of patients and delivered or served on demand by doctors. But the question has deeper roots and more important implications.

If medicine is an art which aims at health, and if an art implies knowledge of ends and means, then the physician is a knower. As unnatural as it may seem that someone else should know better than I whether or not I am healthy—after all, it is my body and my pain, and not the doctor's—still, the doctor as a knower *should* know what health and healthy functioning are, and how to restore and preserve them. In principle, at least, and to a great extent in practice, doctors *are* experts—i.e., men who know not only how we feel about, and what we wish for, our bodies, but how our bodies work and how they should work. This alone justifies their prescribing bad tasting medicine, or their mutilating a healthy abdominal wall to remove an inflamed appendix or even a non-symptomatic ovarian cyst; this alone justifies, but surely it *does* justify, doctors giving orders and patients obeying them.

Yet the case for health as an objective condition, in principle recognizable by an expert, and independent of patient wishes and opinions, needs to be qualified. Health and unhealth, as well as all diseases, occur only in particular living beings, each experiencing *inward* manifestations of health or its absence. The patient's feelings of illness or well-being must be reckoned with, not only because the patient insists, but because they are pertinent signs in the assessment of health. To be sure, there are people who feel fine but harbor unbeknownst to themselves a fatal illness (e.g., the vigorous athlete whose routine blood count shows early leukemia). Still, when a patient complains of headaches or backaches, funny noises in his ears, fatigue, weakness, palpitations on exertion, pains or cramps in the abdomen, or dizziness, *he is not healthy*—even if he looks and acts healthy and even if the doctor fails "to find anything wrong," i.e., fails to discover a cause for the symptoms. A *negative* report by the patient always, or almost always, counts.

There need be no discordance between the "objective" and "subjective" manifestations of health and unhealth. For the most part, they do correspond. The individual's state of health shows itself both to himself and to the outsider, including the expert.

THE RELATIVIST ARGUMENT

5. Health is said to be relative not only to the age of the person but also to external circumstances, both natural and societal. A person with hay fever can be well in the absence of ragweed pollen or cats, and incapacitated in their presence. The hereditary deficiency of a certain enzyme (glucose-6-phosphate-dehydrogenase) results in serious illness for the individual who eats fava beans or takes certain drugs, but is otherwise without known consequence. Eyeglasses, it is said, make myopia no longer a disability. Paraplegia may be only an inconvenience to a theoretical physicist or a President of the United States, whereas an ingrown toenail could cripple the career of a ballerina. If various

functions and activities are the measure of health, and if functions are affected by and relative to circumstances, then health too, so the argument goes, is relative.

Yet all these points, however valid, do not prove the relativity of health and unhealth. They show, rather, the relativity of the *importance* of health and unhealth. The person without hay fever, enzyme deficiency, myopia, paraplegia, and ingrown toenails, is, other things being equal, *healthier* than those *with* those conditions. To be sure, various absences of health can be ignored, and others overcome by change of circumstance, while still others, even if severe, can be rendered less incapacitating. But none of this affects the fact that they *are* absences of health, or undermines the possibility that health is something in its own right.

The most radical version of the relativist argument challenges the claim that health is a *natural* norm. According to this view, what is healthy is dependent not only on time and circumstance, but even more on custom and convention, on human valuation. To apply the concept or construct "healthy" is to throw our judgment of value onto a factual, value-neutral condition of the body; without human judgment, there is no health and no illness. A recent commentator, Peter Sedgwick, argues that "all sickness is essentially deviancy" and that illness and disease, health and treatment are "social constructions":

> All departments of nature below the level of mankind are exempt both from disease and from treatment. The blight that strikes at corn or at potatoes is a *human invention*, for if man wished to cultivate parasites rather than potatoes (or corn) there would be no "blight" but simply the necessary foddering of the parasite-crop. Animals do not have diseases either, prior to the presence of man in a meaningful relation with them.... Outside the significances that man voluntarily attaches to certain conditions, *there are no illnesses or diseases in nature*.... Out of his anthropocentric self-interest, man has chosen to consider as "illnesses" or "diseases" those natural circumstances which precipitate the death (or the failure to function according to certain values), of a limited number of biological species: man himself, his pets and other cherished livestock, and the plant-varieties he cultivates for gain or pleasure.... Children and cattle may fall ill, have diseases, and seem as sick; but who has ever imagined that spiders or lizards can be sick or diseased?... The medical enterprise is from its inception value-loaded; it is not simply an applied biology, but a biology applied in accordance with the dictates of social interest.[7]

Insofar as one considers only disease, there is something to be said for this position—but not much. Disease-entities may in some cases be constructs, but the departures from health and the symptoms they group together are not. Moreover, health, although certainly a good, is not therefore a good whose

7. Peter Sedgwick, "Illness—mental and otherwise," *Hastings Center Studies*, Vol. 1, No. 3 (1973), pp. 30–31 (italics in original).

goodness exists merely by convention or by human decree. Health, illness, and unhealth all may exist even if not discovered or attributed. That human beings don't *worry* about the health of lizards and spiders implies nothing about whether or not lizards and spiders *are* healthy, and any experienced student of spiders and lizards can discover—and not merely invent—abnormal structures and functionings of these animals. Human indifference is merely that. Deer can be healthy or full of cancer, a partially eaten butterfly escaping from a blue jay is not healthy but defective, and even the corn used to nourish parasites becomes abnormal corn, to the parasite-grower's delight.

Sedgwick must be partly forgiven for his confusion, for he has no doubt been influenced by a medicine that focuses on disease-entities and not on health, by a biology that does not consider wholes except as mere aggregates, and by that conventional wisdom of today's social science which holds that *all* goods are good because they are valued, and *all* values are in turn mere conventions, wholly tied to the culture or the individual that invents them. To be sure, different cultures have different taxonomies of diseases, and differing notions of their cause. But the fact that *some* form of medicine is *everywhere* practiced—whether by medicine men and faith healers or by trained neurosurgeons—is far more significant than the differences in nosology and explanation: It strongly suggests that healers do not fabricate the difference between being healthy and being unhealthy; they only try to learn about it, each in his own way.

THE LANGUAGE OF HEALTH

I turn next away from these difficulties to the constructive part of the search for health. To begin with, I should say that I am not seeking a precise definition of health. I am rather inclined to believe that it is not possible to say definitively what health is, any more than it is possible to say wholly and precisely what "livingness" or "light" or "knowledge" or "human excellence" is. What I hope to show more clearly is what *sort* of a "thing" health is, so that we can be more secure in recognizing and promoting it, even if we are unable to capture it in speech.

First, I note that in ordinary speech we generally use the terms "health" and "healthy" as if we know what we are talking about. When military questionnaires or civil service applications ask about our state of health, we are not at a loss as to what is being inquired about, even if we may not have a simple or ready answer; the twin tendencies to exaggerate or to deny illness in answering such questionnaires prove all the more that we regard the question as meaningful and the answer as important. Even those cases in which someone feels and acts "fit as a fiddle" but harbors a fatal disease give us no difficulty: We say that the appearance of health was deceptive. The possibility of making such an error, far from undermining the existence of a true condition of health, in fact presupposes it; appearances can only be deceptive if there are realities with a view to which we discover deception.

Various idioms and expressions also support our contention that health is recognizable. Have we not heard it said of someone that he is "the picture of health"? In these and other expressions, we point to certain exemplary individuals as standards, suggesting that healthiness shines forth and makes itself known.

Etymological investigations may provide some clues for what we recognize when we recognize health. The English word *health* literally means "wholeness," and *to heal* means "to make whole." (Both words go back to the Old English *hal* and the Old High German *heil*, as does the English word "whole.") To be whole is to be healthy, and to be healthy is to be whole. Ancient Greek has two etymologically distinct words translatable as "health," *hygeia* and *euexia*. *Hygeia*, the source of our word "hygiene," apparently stands for the Indo-European *sugwiges*, which means "living well," or more precisely, a "well way of living." *Euexia* means, literally, "well-habited-ness," and in this context, "good habit of body."

Two observations are worth noting: 1) Both the Greek and the English words for health are totally unrelated to all the words for disease, illness, sickness. (This is also true in German, Latin, and Hebrew.) The Greek words for health, unlike the English, are also completely unrelated to all the verbs of healing: Health is a state or condition unrelated to, and prior to, both illness and physicians. 2) The English emphasis on "wholeness" or "completeness" is comparatively static and structural, and the notion of a whole distinct from all else and complete in itself carries connotations of self-containedness, self-sufficiency, and independence. In contrast, both Greek terms stress the *functioning* and *activity* of the whole, and not only its working, but its working well.[8]

WHOLENESS

Aided by these etymological reflections, we turn now from words to things in search of instances of *wholeness* and of *working-well* in nature. We shall look,

8. The Greek terms suggest that health is connected with the way we live and perhaps imply that health has largely an inner cause. Indeed, it seems reasonable to think of health understood as "living well" or "well-habited" as the cause of itself. Just as courage is the cause of courageous action and hence also of courage—for we become brave by acting bravely—so "living well" *is* health, is the *cause* of health, and is *caused by* health. The activities which in English usage we might be inclined to see as *signs* or *effects* of health, might in the Greek usage appear as the *essence* of health.

Related to this, the Greek seems to imply that to stay healthy requires effort and care, that however much nature makes health possible, human attention and habit are required to maintain and preserve it. Health is neither given nor usually taken away from the outside, nor is it the gratuitously expected state of affairs.

of course, only at part of what is today called nature. We are not tempted to seek health in mountains or rocks or hurricanes, for these are surely not organic wholes. We look only at *animate* nature, at plants, animals, and man—true wholes, if any there be.

But are plants and animals authentic wholes, or are they mere aggregates masquerading as wholes? I have tried elsewhere[9] to show at greater length why living things cannot even be looked at, much less understood, except as wholes—and in this sense at least, as teleological beings—regardless of whether or not the species originally came to be by non-teleological processes. I will here present only some of the evidence.

First, consider the generation of living things. Each organism comes to be not at random, but in an orderly manner, starting from some relatively undifferentiated but nevertheless specific seed or zygote produced by parents of the same species, and developing, unfolding itself from within, in successive stages that tend toward and reach a limit—itself, the fully formed organism. The adult which emerges from the process of self-development and growth is no mere outcome, but a completion, an end, a whole.

Second, a fully formed mature organism is an organic whole, an articulated whole, composed of parts. It is a structure and not a heap. The parts of an organism have specific functions which define their nature as parts: the bone marrow for making red blood cells; the lungs for exchange of oxygen and carbon dioxide; the heart for pumping the blood. Even at a biochemical level, every molecule can be characterized in terms of its function. The parts, both macroscopic and microscopic, contribute to the maintenance and functioning of the other parts, and make possible the maintenance and functioning of the whole.

But perhaps the best evidence that organisms are wholes, and that their wholeness and their healthiness correspond, is the remarkable power of self-healing. In hydra, planaria, and many plants, the power to restore wholeness shows itself in an amazing degree in the form of adult regeneration. A plant-cutting will regrow the missing roots, a hydra regrows amputated tentacles, and each half of a divided planarian will regenerate the missing half. In human beings, various organs and tissues—e.g., skin, the epithelia of the digestive tract, liver, bone marrow, and lymph nodes—have comparable regenerative powers. More generally, nearly all living things heal wounds or breaks and tend to restore wholeness. Foreign bodies are engulfed and extruded by amoebas and by man. This tendency to maintain wholeness by rejecting *additions* to the whole becomes marvelously elaborate in the immune system of higher animals, which sensitively recognizes and combats the entry of alien elements, whether in the form of infectious agents, tumors, or grafted tissue.

The highly complex phenomenon of pain is also a sign that organisms are

9. "Teleology and Darwin's *The Origin of Species:* Beyond Chance and Necessity?", a lecture given at St. John's College, Annapolis, Maryland (October 11, 1974).

wholes. Pain serves as an advance warning, or as an accompanying sign, of a threat to bodily integrity. Yet its presence is as much a sign of wholeness as of a threat to wholeness, for pain, in normal circumstances, attests to a healthy nervous system detecting, and at the same time representing as an insistent sign, the presence of a threat of unhealth. (Here we see again a connection between experienced bodily feeling and actual bodily conditions.)

WELL-WORKING

So far my examination of wholeness has been largely, or at least explicitly, structural and static, in keeping with a view of health as capturable in a picture of health. Yet can one capture healthiness in a photograph? Don't we need at least a movie camera?

One way to examine this claim is to ask, "Is being healthy compatible with being asleep?" In a way, and up to a point, the answer must be "Yes." If we are healthy, we do not cease being healthy when we sleep. Sleep is necessary to stay healthy, and insomnia is sometimes a symptom of illness. Digestion, respiration, circulation, and metabolism continue quite normally while we sleep, but only if and because we do not sleep for long. Even this vegetative activity requires periodic wakefulness, at least enough to bite, chew, and swallow. Moreover, continued sleep would rapidly produce feebleness and atrophy of bones and muscles, as well as more gradual losses of other functions. And even if none of these disasters were to befall us, ours would be a sleepy kind of wholeness; the sleeping Rip Van Winkle might not have been sick, but he was hardly healthy. The wholeness of a man is not the wholeness of a statue of a man, but a wholeness-in-action, a working-well of the work done by the body of a man.

What constitutes *well-working*? The answers will vary from species to species: among other things, web-spinning for a spider, flight for some birds, swimming for others. For a given species, there will be some variations among individuals, increasingly so as functions are dissected into smaller and smaller subfunctions. For certain functions, the norm will be a mean between excess and deficiency: For example, blood pressure can be too high or too low, as can blood sugar or blood calcium; blood can clot too quickly or too slowly; body temperature can be too high or too low. And while there is some arbitrariness in our deciding on the lower and upper limits of the so-called normal range in all these cases, this indistinctness of the margins does not indicate nature's arbitrariness or indifference about the norm. For we note that the body has elaborate mechanisms to keep these properties balanced, often very precisely, between excess and deficiency, to preserve homeostasis.

Yet it is at the whole animal that one should finally look for the measure of well-working, for the well-working of the whole. That there are mechanisms for restoring well-working at this level can be seen by considering the case of a dog missing one hind leg. Such a dog still runs—though certainly not as well as when he had four legs—by positioning his remaining hind leg as close as he can to the midline of his body, to become a more balanced tripod, and he does this without being taught or without previous experience in three-legged running. There appear to be "rules of rightness," as Polanyi calls them, unique to each level of bodily organization, whose rightness is not explicable in terms of the lower levels, even though failure at the lower levels can cause failure at the higher. For example, a broken wing can prevent flight, but two intact wings, good chest muscles, and hollow bones don't add up to flight. Think about trying to give a mechanical account of the rules of rightness for the well-functioning that is riding a bicycle or swimming or speaking.

Thus, it is ultimately to the workings of the whole animal that we must turn to discover its healthiness. What, for example, is a healthy squirrel? Not a picture of a squirrel, not really or fully the sleeping squirrel, not even the aggregate of his normal blood pressure, serum calcium, total body zinc, normal digestion, fertility, and the like. Rather, the healthy squirrel is a bushy-tailed fellow who looks and acts like a squirrel; who leaps through the trees with great daring; who gathers, buries, and covers but later uncovers and recovers his acorns; who perches out on a limb cracking his nuts, sniffing the air for smells of danger, alert, cautious, with his tail beating rhythmically; who chatters and plays and courts and mates, and rears his young in large improbable looking homes at the tops of trees; who fights with vigor and forages with cunning, who shows spiritedness, even anger, and more prudence than many human beings.

To sum up: Health is a natural standard or norm—not a moral norm, not a "value" as opposed to a "fact," not an obligation, but a state of being that reveals itself in activity as a standard of bodily excellence or fitness, relative to each species and to some extent to individuals, recognizable if not definable, and to some extent attainable. If you prefer a more simple formulation, I would say that health is "the well-working of the organism as a whole," or again, "an activity of the living body in accordance with its specific excellences."[10]

III. THE PURSUIT OF HEALTH

The foregoing inquiry into the nature of health, though obviously incomplete and in need of refinement, has, I hope, accomplished two things: first, to

10. Whatever progress we may have made in our search for health, large questions still remain, which I defer to another occasion. These questions include: What activities of the living body should be considered, and are all of them of equal rank? What are the specific excellences or fitnesses of various organisms, and can one hope to discover these standards for a being as complex as man, whose activities are so highly diversified and differentiated? What is a living body, and what a specifically *human* living body? Finally, what is the relation of health of body to psychic health?

make at least plausible the claim that somatic health is a finite and intelligible norm, which is the true goal of medicine; and second, by displaying something of the character of healthiness, to provide a basis for considering how it might be better attained. *Curiously, it will soon become apparent that even if we have found the end of medicine, we may have to go beyond medicine in order to find the best means for attaining it.*

Though health is a natural norm, and though nature provides us with powerful inborn means of preserving and maintaining a well-working wholeness, it is wrong to assume that health is the simply given and spontaneous condition of human beings, and unhealth the result largely of accident or of external invasion. In the case of non-human animals, such a view could perhaps be defended. Other animals instinctively eat the right foods (when available) and act in such a way as to maintain their naturally given state of health and vigor. Other animals do not overeat, undersleep, knowingly ingest toxic substances, or permit their bodies to fall into disuse through sloth, watching television and riding in automobiles, transacting business, or writing articles about health. For us human beings, however, even a healthy nature must be nurtured, and maintained by effort and discipline if it is not to become soft and weak and prone to illness, and certain excesses and stresses must be avoided if this softness is not to spawn overt unhealth and disease. One should not, of course, underestimate the role of germs and other hostile agents working from without; but I strongly suspect that the germ theory of disease has been oversold, and that the state of "host resistance," and in particular of the immunity systems, will become increasingly prominent in our understanding of both health and disease.

Once the distinction is made between health nurture and maintenance, on the one hand, and disease prevention and treatment, on the other, it becomes immediately clear that bodily health does not depend only on the body and its parts. It depends decisively on the psyche with which the body associates and cooperates. A few examples will make this clear, if it is not already obvious. Some disorders of body are caused, at least in part, by disorders of soul (psyche); the range goes from the transitory bodily effects of simple nervousness and tension headaches, through the often severe somatic symptoms of depression (e.g., weight loss, insomnia, constipation, impotence), to ulcers and rheumatoid arthritis. Other diseases are due specifically to some aspect of the patient's way of life: cirrhosis in alcoholics, hepatitis in drug addicts, special lung diseases in coal miners, venereal diseases in prostitutes.

But the dependence goes much farther than these obvious psycho- and socio-somatic interactions. In a most far-reaching way, our health is influenced by our temperament, our character, our habits, our whole way of life. This fact was once better appreciated than it is today.

In a very early discussion of this question, in the Platonic dialogue *Charmides*, Socrates criticizes Greek physicians for foolishly neglecting the whole when attempting to heal a part. He argues that "just as one must not attempt to cure the eyes without the head or the head without the body, so neither the body without the soul." In fact, one must care "first and most" for the soul if one intends the body to be healthy. If the soul is moderate and sensible, it will not be difficult to effect health in the body; if not, health will be difficult to procure. Greek medicine fails, it is charged, because men try to be physicians of health and of moderation separately.

Socrates does not say that excellence of soul and excellence of body are one and the same; indeed, health is clearly distinguished from moderation. Rather, the claim is that health is at least in large part affected by or dependent upon virtue, that being well in body has much to do with living well, with good habits not only of body but of life.

Now Socrates certainly knew, perhaps better than we, that accident and fortune can bring harm and ill health even to well-ordered bodies and souls. He knew about inborn diseases and seasonal maladies and wounds sustained in battle. He knew that health, though demanding care and discipline and requiring a certain control of our bodily desires, was no sure sign of virtue—and that moderation is not all of virtue. He knew too, as we know, human beings whose healthiness was the best thing about them, and he knew also that to be preoccupied with health is either a sign or a cause of a shrunken human life. Yet he also knew what we are today altogether too willing to forget—that *we are in an important way responsible for our own state of health*, that carelessness, gluttony, drunkenness, and sloth take some of their wages in illness. At a deeper level, he knew that there was a connection between the fact that the human soul aspires beyond mere self-preservation, and the fact that men, unlike animals, can make themselves sick and feverish. He knew, therefore, that health in human beings depends not only on natural gifts, but also on taming and moderating the admirable yet dangerous human desire to live better than sows and squirrels.

THE BRESLOW FINDINGS

Today we are beginning again to consider that Socrates was possibly right, that our way of life is a major key to our sickness and our health. I would myself guess that well more than half the visits to American doctors are occasioned by deviations from health for which the patient, or his way of life, is in some important way responsible. Most chronic lung diseases, much cardiovascular disease, most cirrhosis of the liver, many gastrointestinal disorders (from indigestion to ulcers), numerous muscular and skeletal complaints (from low back pain to flat feet), venereal disease, nutritional deficiencies, obesity and its consequences, and certain kinds of renal and skin infections are in large measure self-induced or self-caused—and contributed to by smoking, overeating, excessive drinking, eating the wrong foods, inadequate rest and exercise, and poor hygiene. To these conditions must be added the results of trauma—including automobile accidents—in which drunkenness plays a leading part, and suicide attempts, as well as accidental poisonings, drug abuse, and many burns. I leave out of the reckoning the as yet poorly studied contributions to unhealth of all varieties made by the special stresses of modern urban life.

There are even indications that cancer is in some measure a disease of how we live, even beyond the clear correlations of lung cancer with smoking and of cancer of the cervix with sexual promiscuity and poor sexual hygiene. If the incidence of each kind of cancer could be reduced to the level at which it occurs in the population in which its incidence is lowest, there would be 90 per cent less cancer. Recent studies show that cancers of all sorts—not only cancers clearly correlated with smoking and drinking—occur less frequently among the clean-living Mormons and Seventh-Day Adventists.

The foregoing, it will be noted, speaks largely about disease and unhealth, and about the role of our excesses and deficiencies in bringing them about. Unfortunately, we know less about what contributes to healthiness, as nearly all epidemiological studies have been studies of disease. But in the last few years, there have appeared published reports of a most fascinating and important series of epidemiological studies on *health*, conducted by Dean Lester Breslow and his colleagues at the UCLA School of Public Health. Having first developed a method for quantifying, albeit crudely, one's state of health and well-functioning, they investigated the effect of various health practices on physical health status. They have discovered, empirically, seven independent "rules" for good health, which correlate very well with healthiness, and also with longevity. People who follow all seven rules are healthier and live longer than those who follow six, six more than five, and so on, in perfect order. Let me report two of their more dramatic findings: The physical health status of those over 75 who followed all the "rules" was about the same as those aged 35–44 who followed fewer than three; and a person who follows at least six of the seven rules has an 11-year longer life expectancy at age 45 than someone who has followed less than four. Moreover, these differences in health connected with health practices persisted at all economic levels, and, except at the very lowest incomes, appeared largely independent of income.[11]

The seven "rules" are: 1) Don't smoke cigarettes. 2) Get seven hours of sleep. 3) Eat breakfast. 4) Keep your weight down. 5) Drink moderately. 6) Exercise daily. 7) Don't eat between meals. ("Visit your doctor" is not on the list, though I must confess that I cannot find out if this variable was investigated.) It seems that Socrates, and also Grandmother, may have been on the right track.

11. Nedra B. Belloc and Lester Breslow, "Relationship of Physical Health Status and Health Practices," *Preventive Medicine* 1 (1972), pp. 409–421; and Nedra B. Belloc, "Relationship of Health Practices and Mortality," *Preventive Medicine 2* (1973), pp. 67–81.

One feels, I must admit, a bit foolish, in the latter half of the 20th century, which boasts the cracking of the genetic code, kidney machines, and heart transplants, to be suggesting the quaint formula, "Eat right, exercise and be moderate, for tomorrow you will be healthy." But quaint formulas need not have been proven false to be ignored, and we will look far more foolish if Breslow and his colleagues are onto something which, in our sophistication, we choose to overlook.

IV. IMPLICATIONS FOR POLICY

What might all this point to for medicine and for public policy regarding health? Let me try to sketch in outline the implications of the preceding sections, which, as a point of departure, I would summarize in this way: Health and only health is the doctor's proper business; but health, understood as well-working wholeness, is not the business only of doctors. Health is, in different ways, everyone's business, and it is best pursued if everyone regards and minds his *own* business—each of us his own health, the doctor the health of his patient, public health officials and legislators the health of the citizens.

With respect to the medical profession itself, there is a clear need to articulate and delimit the physician's domain and responsibilities, to protect against both expansion and contraction. The more obvious and perhaps greater danger seems to be expansion, given the growing technological powers that can serve non-therapeutic ends and the rising demands that these powers be used for non-medical ends. The medical profession must take the initiative in establishing and policing the necessary boundaries. The American Medical Association, the state and county medical societies, and the various specialty organizations would do well to examine current practices and to anticipate new technologies with a view to offering guidance to their members amidst these dangers. In some cases, they might well try to discourage or proscribe certain quasi-medical or extra-medical use of medical technique. For example, the American College of Obstetrics and Gynecology should consider regulations barring its members from helping prospective parents determine or select the sex of their child-to-be; or the American Association of Neurological Surgeons could establish strict guidelines for the permissible uses, if any, of destructive brain surgery for the sake of modifying behavior.

It is true that such guidelines can always be violated in the privacy of an examining room or operating theater—but what rule cannot?—and it is also true that the decentralized character of American medicine makes professional self-regulation more difficult than in, say, Britain. Still, the profession has heretofore not concerned itself with this problem, and it would be foolish to declare inefficacious a remedy not even contemplated because the disease itself had yet to be recognized.

Medical licensure provides an alternative device for drawing boundaries. It would be worthwhile to reconsider the criteria for medical licensure, and the privileges and prerogatives that it is meant to confer. The current system of licensing was designed largely to protect the public, and the reputation of the profession, against incompetents and charlatans. Yet this license to practice healing is now *de facto* a license to conduct research on human subjects, as well as a license to employ biomedical techniques in the service of any willing client, private or public, for almost any purpose not forbidden by law. Because these various techniques involve direct physical or chemical intervention into the human body, and because the practice of such interventions has been restricted to those who know about and can protect the human body, a medical license has been regarded as a necessary condition for all these extra-medical activites; but it has also come to be regarded as a *sufficient* condition.

Some have argued that changes in licensing be made to clearly distinguish the healing profession, and to require special (and additional) licensing for those who would engage in clinical research, practice various forms of biomedical indulgence, or serve purposes of social reform and social control. In some cases, people have called for completely separate professions of, say, abortionists, artificial inseminators, mercy killers, surgical beautifiers, mood elevators, and eugenic counsellors. This approach is recommended not only because it keeps the boundaries neat, but because it prevents the poor use of medical expertise and training, since at least some of these procedures and practices—including first-trimester abortion—could be mastered by moderately intelligent and dextrous high school graduates with six months of technical training.

On the other hand, since the demand for these extra-medical services is unlikely to disappear, it might be dangerous to separate them from the practice of medicine. Keeping the various functions and "professions" mixed together under the medical umbrella might cover them all with the long-standing ethical standards of the traditional medical profession, a protection that might not readily be provided, or even sought, by the "younger professions" if they were to be separated or expelled from the healing profession. Those who hold this view are willing to tolerate some confusion of purpose in exchange for what they believe will help produce necessary restraints. But whether the restraint would in fact be forthcoming is an open question.

But the greatest difficulty is how to protect the boundaries of the medical domain against unreasonable *external* demands for expansion. The public's misperception of medicine is ultimately more dangerous than the doctor's misperception of himself. The movement towards consumer control of medicine, the call for doctors to provide "therapy" for social deviants and criminal offenders, and the increasing governmental regulation of medical practice all run the risk of transforming the physician into a mere public servant, into a technician or helper for hire. Granted, the doctor must not be allowed to be a tyrant. But neither must he become a servant. Rather, he must remain a leader and a teacher. The community must respect the fact that medicine is an art and that the doctor is a man of expert knowledge, deserving more than an equal voice in deciding what his business is. Though one may rightly suspect *some* of the motives behind the medical profession's fear of governmental intrusion, one must acknowledge the justice of at least this concern: Once the definition of health care and the standards of medical practice are made by outsiders—and the National Health Insurance schemes all tend in this direction—the physician becomes a mere technician.[12]

THE CASE FOR HEALTH MAINTENANCE

Yet if the medical profession wants to retain the right to set its own limits, it must not only improve its immunity against foreign additions to its domain, but must also work to restore its own wholeness. The profession must again concern itself with health, with wholeness, with well-working, and not only with the cure of disease. The doctor must attend to health maintenance, and not only treatment or even prevention of specific diseases. He should no longer look befuddled when a patient asks him, "Doctor, what regimen do you suggest in order that I may remain healthy?" This implies, of course, changes in medical orientation that in turn imply changes in medical education both difficult to design in detail and not easy to institute in practice. But again, we have not seriously thought about how to do this, because we have not seen that it was something that might need doing. To recognize and identify this defect is to take the first, and thus the biggest, step toward its amelioration.

I am not saying that doctors should cease to be concerned about disease, or that they should keep us in hospitals and clinics until we become fully healthy. I do suggest, however, that physicians should be more interested than they are in finding ways to keep us from their doors. Though medicine must remain in large part restorative and remedial, greater attention to healthy functioning and to regimens for becoming and remaining healthy could be very salutary, even toward the limited goal of reducing the incidence of disease. Little intelligence and imagination have thus far been expended by members of the profession, or by health insurance companies, to devise incentive schemes that would reward such a shift in emphasis (e.g., that would reward financially both

12. A recent lawsuit in Maryland illustrates how consumerism and governmental participation can work together toward this result. A married woman brought suit against two Washington suburban hospitals that refused to permit her to undergo voluntary sterilization procedures in their facilities, despite her physician's agreement to perform the operation. (One hospital had refused permission on moral grounds, the other because the patient and her husband refused to comply with hospital regulations for sterilization procedures that required permission of the spouse.) The suit claimed that the hospitals, because they had received Hill-Burton funding for construction, were obliged to meet the health needs of all members of the community, without discrimination. The plaintiff blithely *assumed* that the community, or rather each member thereof, is the final judge of what constitutes a *health need*. The case has not yet been decided.

patient and physician if the patient stays free of the need for his services). I invite people cleverer than I to make such efforts, especially in conjunction with the likely changes in the financing of medical care.

Moving beyond implications for the relation between doctor and patient to those for medical research, I would emphasize the importance of epidemiological research on *healthiness*. We need to devise better indices of healthiness than mortality and morbidity statistics, which, I have argued, are in fact not indices of *health* at all. The studies like those of Breslow and his collaborators are a step in the right direction and should be encouraged. Only with better measures of healthiness can we really evaluate the results of our various health practices and policies.

We also need large-scale epidemiological research into health maintenance, to learn more about what promotes, and what undermines, health. More sophisticated studies in nutrition, bodily exercise, rest and sleep, relaxation, and responses to stress could be very useful, as could expanded research into personal habits of health and hygiene and their effects on general healthiness, overall resistance to disease, and specific resistance to specific diseases. We need to identify and learn about healthy subgroups in the community, like the Mormons, and to discover what accounts for their success.

All of these things are probably obvious, and most of them have been championed for years by people in the fields of public health and preventive medicine—though they too have placed greater emphasis on disease prevention than on health maintenance. Their long-ignored advice is finally beginning to be heeded, with promising results. For example, a recent study reports a surprising downturn (after a 25-year climb) in the death rate from heart attacks among middle-aged men, attributed in part to changes in smoking and eating habits and to new treatments for high blood pressure. Yet this approach will always seem banal and pedestrian in comparison with the glamorous and dramatic style of high-technology therapeutics, with the doctor locked in combat with overt disease, displaying his marvelous and magical powers. My high regard for these powers cannot stifle the question whether the men who first suggested adding chlorine to drinking water or invented indoor plumbing didn't contribute more to healthiness than the Nobel Prize winners in Medicine and Physiology who discovered the chemical wonders of enzyme structure or of vision. It might be worthwhile to consider by what kinds of incentives and rewards the National Institutes of Health or the AMA might encourage more and better research into health maintenance and disease prevention.

FOSTERING RESPONSIBIILITY

Yet as has been repeatedly emphasized, doctors and public health officials have only limited power to improve our health. Health is not a commodity which can be delivered. Medicine can help only those who help themselves. Discovering what will promote and maintain health is only half the battle; we must also find ways to promote and inculcate good health habits and to increase personal responsibility for health. This is, no doubt, the most fundamental and also the most difficult task. It is but one more instance of that age-old challenge: how to get people to do what is good for them without tyrannizing them. The principles of freedom and of wisdom do not always—shall I say, do not very often?—lead in the same direction.

Since this is not a new difficulty, we do have some experience in how to think about it. Consider the problem of getting people to obey the law. Policemen and judges are clearly needed to handle the major crimes and criminals, but it would be foolish to propose, and dangerous to provide, even that degree of police surveillance and interference required to prevent only the most serious lawbreaking. But though justice is the business of the policeman and the judge, it is not their business alone. Education—at home, in schools, in civic and religious institutions—can "teach" law-abidingness far better than policemen can, and where the former is successful, there is less need of the latter.

Yet even without considering the limitations of this analogy, the limits of the power of teachers—and of policemen as well—to produce law abidingness are all too apparent. And when one considers that fear of immediate, identifiable punishment probably deters lawbreaking more than fear of unhealth deters sloth and gluttony, we see that we face no simple task. The wages of poor health habits during youth are only paid much later, so much later that it is difficult to establish the relation of cause and effect, let alone make it vivid enough to influence people's actions. If it isn't likely to rain for 20 years, few of us are likely to repair our leaky roofs.

This is not a counsel of despair. On the contrary, I am much impressed with the growing interest in health and health education in recent years, including the greater concern for proper nutrition, adequate exercise, dental hygiene, and the hazards of smoking, and the evidence that, at least among some groups, this attention is bearing fruit. Nevertheless, when we consider the numerous impediments to setting in order our lives and our communities, I think we should retain a healthy doubt about just how healthy we Americans are likely, as a community, to become.

The skepticism is rather lacking in most political pronouncements and policies regarding health. Making unwarranted inferences from medicine's past successes against *infectious* disease, being excessively impressed with the technological brilliance of big hospital medicine, mobilizing crusades and crash programs against cancer and heart disease, the health politicians speak as if more money, more targeted research, better distribution of services, more doctors and hospitals, and bigger and better cobalt machines, lasers, and artificial organs will bring the medical millennium to every American citizen. Going along with all this is a lack of attention to health maintenance and patient responsibility. While it would surely be difficult for the federal government to teach responsibility, we should not be pleased when its actions in fact discourage responsibility.

A RIGHT TO HEALTH?

One step in this direction is the growing endorsement of the so-called right to health, beyond the already ambiguous and dubious right to health care. A recent article argued thus:

> The right to *health* is a fundamental right. It expresses the profound truth that a person's autonomy and freedom rest upon his ability to function physically and psychologically. It asserts that no other person can, with moral justification, deprive him of that ability. The right to *health care* or the right to *medical care*, on the other hand, are qualified rights. They flow from the fundamental right, but are implemented in institutions and practices only when such are possible and reasonable and only when other rights are not thereby impeded.[13]

If the right to health means only the right not to have one's health destroyed by another, then it is a reasonable but rather impotent claim in the health care arena; the right to health care or medical care could hardly flow from a right to health, unless the right to health meant also and mainly the right to become and to be kept healthy. But if health is what we say it is, it is an unlikely subject of a right in either sense. Health is a state of being, not something that can be given, and only in indirect ways something that can be taken away or undermined by other human beings. It no more makes sense to claim a right to health than a right to wisdom or courage. These excellences of soul and of body require natural gift, attention, effort, and discipline on the part of each person who desires them. To make my health someone else's duty is not only unfair; it is to impose a duty impossible to fulfill. Though I am not particularly attracted by the language of rights and duties in regard to health, I would lean much more in the direction, once traditional, of saying that health is a *duty*, that one has an obligation to preserve one's own health. The theory of a right to health flies in the face of good sense, serves to undermine personal responsibility, and, in addition, places obligation where it cannot help but be unfulfillable.

---

13. Philip R. Lee and Albert R. Jonsen, editorial: "The Right to Health Care," *American Review of Respiratory Disease*, Vol. 109 (1974), pp. 591–92 (italics in original). Dr. Lee is a former Assistant Secretary for Health at HEW.

THE "KIDNEY-MACHINE" LEGISLATION

Similarly, the amendment to the Medicare legislation which provides payment for "kidney-machine" treatment for all in need, at a cost of from $10,000 to $40,000 per patient, is, for all its good intentions, a questionable step. First of all, it establishes the principle that the federal government is the savior of last resort—or, as is more likely at this price tag, the savior of first resort—for specific persons with specific diseases. In effect, the government has said that it is in the national interest for the government to pay, disease by disease, life by life, for life-saving measures for all its citizens. The justice of providing benefits of this magnitude solely to people with kidney disease has been loudly questioned, and hemophilia organizations are pressing for government financing of equally expensive treatment. Others have called attention to the impossible financial burden that the just extension of this coverage would entail. Finally, this measure gives governmental endorsement, in a most dramatic and visible way, to the high-cost, technological, therapy-oriented approach to health. This approach has been challenged, on the basis of a searching analysis of this kidney-machine legislation, in a report by a panel of the Institute of Medicine of the National Academy of Sciences, which, with admirable self-restraint, comments: "One wonders how many billions of dollars the nation would now be spending on iron lungs if research for the cure of polio had not been done."[14]

This is not to say that, in the special case of the kidney machines under the special circumstances in which the legislation was passed, a persuasive case was not made on the other side. Clearly, it was hoped that perfection of kidney transplantation or future prevention of kidney disease would make this high-cost insurance obsolete before too long. Moreover, no one wishes to appear to be, or indeed to be, callous about the loss of life, especially preventable and premature loss of life. Still, the dangers of the kidney machine legislation must be acknowledged.

One might even go so far as to suggest that prudent and wise legislators and policy makers must in the future resist (in a way that no private doctor should be permitted to resist) the temptation to let compassion for individual calamities and general sentimentality rule in these matters. Pursuing the best health policy for the American people—that is, a policy to encourage and support the best possible health for the American people—may indeed mean not taking certain measures that would prevent known deaths. Only by focusing on health and how one gets it, and by taking a more long-range view, can our health policy measure up in deed to its good intentions.

---

14. *Disease by Disease Toward National Health Insurance?* (Washington, D.C., Institute of Medicine–National Academy of Sciences, 1973).

IS NATIONAL HEALTH INSURANCE GOOD FOR HEALTH?

The proposals for a National Health Insurance seem also to raise difficulties of this sort, and more. Medical care is certainly very expensive, and therefore, for this reason alone, not equally available to all. The economic problems are profound and genuine, and there are few dispassionate observers who are not convinced that something needs to be done. Many technical questions have been debated and discussed, including the range of coverage and the sources of financing, and organized medicine has voiced its usual concern regarding governmental interference, a concern which I have already indicated I share in regard to the delimitation of the doctor's role and the scope of health care. But some of the most serious issues have received all too little attention.

The proposals for National Health Insurance take for granted the wisdom of our current approaches to the pursuit of health, and thereby insure that in the future we will get more of the same. These proposals will simply make available to the non-insured what the privately insured now get: a hospital-centered, highly technological, disease-oriented, therapy-centered medical care. The proposals have entirely ignored the question of whether what we now do in health is what we should be doing. They not only endorse the status quo, but fail to take advantage of the rare opportunity which financial crises provide to re-examine basic questions and directions. The irony is that real economizing in health care is probably possible only by radically re-orienting the pursuit of health.

One cannot help getting the impression that it is economic *equality*, not health, and not even economizing, that is the primary aim of these proposals. At a recent seminar in which I participated, an official of HEW informally expressed irritation at those who are questioning whether the so-called health care delivery system is really making us healthier, and suggested that their main goal was to undermine liberal programs enacted in recent years. Yet this official went on to say that even if the evidence conclusively showed that all the government's health programs in no way actually improved health, the programs ought to be continued for their extra-medical—i.e., social and economic—benefits. For myself, I confess that I would prefer as my public health official the cold-hearted, even mean-spirited fellow who is interested in health and who knows how to promote it.

All the proposals for National Health Insurance embrace, without qualification, the no-fault principle. They therefore choose to ignore, or to treat as irrelevant, the importance of personal responsibility for the state of one's health. As a result, they pass up an opportunity to build both positive and negative inducements into the insurance payment plan, by measures such as refusing or reducing benefits for chronic respiratory disease care to persons who continue to smoke.

There are, of course, complicated questions of justice raised here, and even to suggest that the sick ever be in any way blamed or penalized flies in the face of current custom and ways of thinking. Yet one need not be a Calvinist or a Spartan to see merit in the words of a wise physician, Robert S. Morison, writing on much the same subject:

> In the perspectives of today, cardiovascular illness in middle age not only runs the risk of depriving families of their support, or society of certain kinds of services; it increasingly places on society the obligation to spend thousands of dollars on medical care to rescue an individual from the results of a faulty living pattern. Under these conditions, one wonders how much longer we can go on talking about a right to health without some balancing talk about the individual's responsibility to keep healthy.
>
> I am told that Thorstein Veblen used to deplore the fact that in California they taxed the poor to send the rich to college. One wonders how he would react to a system which taxes the virtuous to send the improvident to hospital.[15]

But even leaving aside questions of justice, and looking only at the pursuit of health, one has reason to fear that the new insurance plan, whichever one it turns out to be, may actually contribute to a worsening rather than an improvement in our nation's health, especially if there is no balancing program to encourage individual responsibility for health maintenance.

One final word. Despite all that I have said, I would also emphasize that health, while a good, cannot be the greatest good, either for an individual or a community. Politically, an excessive preoccupation with health can conflict with the pursuit of other important social and economic goals (e.g., when cancerphobia leads to government regulations that unreasonably restrict industrial activity or personal freedom). But more fundamentally, it is not mere life, nor even a healthy life, but rather a good and worthy life for which we must aim. And while poor health may weaken our efforts, good health alone is an insufficient condition or sign of a worthy human life. Indeed, though there is no such thing as being too healthy, there is such a thing as being too concerned about health. To be preoccupied with the body is to neglect the soul, for which we should indeed care "first and most," and more than we now do. We must strike a proper balance, a balance that can only be furthered if the approach to health also concentrates on our habits of life.

15. R. S. Morison, "Rights and Responsibilities: Redressing the Uneasy Balance," *The Hastings Center Report*, Vol. 4, No. 2 (April 1974), p. 4.

1.2

The Concepts of Health and Disease

H. Tristram Engelhardt, Jr.

Health and disease are cardinal concepts of the biomedical sciences and technologies. Though the models of health and disease may vary, these concepts play a defining role, indicating what should and what should not be the objects of medical concern. The concepts are ambiguous, operating both as explanatory and evaluatory notions. They describe states of affairs, factual conditions, while at the same time judging them to be good or bad. Health and disease are normative as well as descriptive. This dual role is core to their ambiguity and is the focus of this paper. In this paper I shall examine first the concept of health; second, the concept of disease; and third, I will draw some general conclusions concerning the interplay of evaluation and explanation in the concepts of health and disease.

I. HEALTH

Health is a normative concept but not in the sense of a moral virtue. Though health is a good, and though it may be morally praiseworthy to try to be healthy and to advance the health of others, still, all things being equal, it is a misfortune, not a misdeed, to lack health. Health is more an aesthetic than an ethical term; it is more beauty than virtue. Thus, one does not condemn someone for no longer being healthy, though one may sympathize with him over the loss of a good. Further, it is not clear exactly what is lost when one loses health.

The norms of health are difficult to compass within one homogeneous concept, in particular within an independent definition which does not define health negatively, as the absence of disease. The World Health Organization attempted a positive definition, that "health is a state of complete physical, mental and social well-being and not merely the absence of disease or infirmity."[1] But such a definition of health packs the ambiguity of the concept of health into the ambiguity of a concept of well-being. Further, this concept of well-being suggests the notion of a satisfactory lifestyle, including successful adaptation to one's environment. Yet, even here the norms are obscure. What is a good adaptation? Is a good adaptation possible in a complex industrial society for those with I.Q.'s of less than 80? Are such persons ill? Further, if health is a state of complete physical, mental, and social well-being, can anyone ever be healthy? Does health become a regulative ideal, one to which one strives, but which one can never fully achieve? On the other hand, if no one is truly healthy, is everyone ill? Are health and disease exclusive or overlapping concepts?

These quandaries arise primarily out of the evaluatory, not the explanatory, dimension of the concepts of health and disease. Health could, for example, be defined as the ability to perform these functions which allow the organism to maintain itself, all other things being equal, in the range of activity open to most other members of its species (e.g., within two standard deviations from the norm), and which are conducive toward the maintenance of its species. This, though, is to forego mention of why one might be interested in certain types of well-being (except for the commitment to the survival of the species). Also, it is not clear whether, within such a concept, degenerative processes generally distributed in the population, which appear after the reproductive years, could count as diseases. Finally, if health is to encompass issues raised by particular diseases, the concept may lose its unity. The attempt to understand the concept of health thus brings us to the concept of disease, suggesting that the concept of health may have as many nuances as there are diseases, and that it may be derivative from these particular disease concepts.

II. THE CONCEPT OF DISEASE

The concept of disease is used in accounting for physiological and psychological (or behavioral) disorders, offering generalizations concerning patterns of phenomena which we find disturbing and unpleasant. The concept of disease is a general scheme for explaining, predicting, and controlling dimensions of the human condition. It grades into other concepts which are political, social, educational, and moral. The difference between the concept of disease and these other concepts, and the similarity of the various models of disease is complex and problematic. It is not even clear that all the models of disease fall within a single genus. Perhaps the concept of disease indicates a family of conceptually consanguineous notions. That is, the concept of disease may be a basically heterogeneous concept standing for a set of phenomena collected together out of diverse social interests, not on the basis of the recognition of a natural type or a common conceptual structure. Disease would then be whatever physicians in a particular society treat, rendering circular the definitions of disease and medicine.

It is worthwhile distinguishing, somewhat stipulatively, disease and illness. One can be ill, feel bad, feel under the weather without explaining such phenomena in terms of disease models. The concept of disease competes with other concepts, from demonic possession to simple exhaustion. And, on the other hand, one can have a disease without being ill, as in the case of Alvan Feinstein's concept of lanthanic diseases.[2] A person can, for example, have carcinoma of the lung diagnosed before he is ill. To speak of diseases is to make an explanatory move and at the very least to convert an illness into a syndrome, to recognize a cluster of phenomena as a disease pattern.

The concept of disease acts not only to describe and explain, but also to enjoin to action. It indicates a state of affairs as undesirable and to be overcome. It is a normative concept; it says what ought not to be. As such, the concept incorporates criteria of evaluation, designating certain states of affairs as desirable and others as not so. It delineates and establishes social roles such as being sick or being a physician, and it interconnects these roles with a network of expectations structured by rights and duties.[3] The concept is both aesthetic and ethical, suggesting what is beautiful and what is good. By terming something diseased, one indicates that the state of affairs is both naturally ugly as well as one that imposes some obligations and relieves others.

The concept of disease is thus freighted with important ambiguities. These ambiguities are, as well, bound to what has been termed the physiological and ontological concepts of disease, to the levels of abstraction involved in disease models, and to the nature of particular models of disease, such as the medical and psychological. I wish to introduce the physiological and ontological concepts of disease from a primarily typological, not historical, point of view. They represent two general ways of talking about disease. Historically, they developed out of disputes whether disease was the result of the malmixing of humors, or was due to the entrance of a disease entity. The dispute roughly was whether diseases were primarily relational and contextual in character, or in some sense substantial things. These different ways of talking about disease are still apparent.

There is an important ambiguity in the significance of ontological concepts of disease. The *ens*, the being of the disease, can be variously understood as either a thing, or a logical type, or both. Medical ontology in the strong sense refers to views in which disease is conceived of as a thing, a parasite,[4] in contrast with "Platonic" views of disease entities in which diseases are understood as unchanging conceptual structures. In the strong sense a "disease entity" is a disease thing, a material, invading agent of disease.[5] This strong sense of ontology involves a commitment to hypostatization, an attempt to reify disease. For example, Paracelsus, whom Pagel describes as the prototypical ontologist, opposed the humoral pathologists who held that "the sick individual determines the cause and nature of disease." In contrast, Paracelsus taught "the 'ontological' view in which diseases are regarded as entities in themselves distinguishable by specific changes and causes." In this view, it was "the individual disease that conditions the patient and manifests itself in a characteristic picture."[6] This analysis suggested that specific therapies should be sought for specific diseases. Or, more fundamentally, it advanced the notion that diseases had specific characters, and would thus respond to specific therapies. Moreover, his view suggested a distinction between "symptomatic" and "aetiological" therapy, therapy aimed at the results and therapy aimed at the cause of disease. It was this ontological, aetiological concept of disease which indicated the possibility of classifying therapies according to their focus on the specific causes of diseases. Further, specific diseases led to specific local organ changes being sought by van Helmont and others, and thus to the beginning of modern pathology.[7] The identification of disease with particular causes, therapies, and, finally, with localized pathological changes in organs is the focus of this viewpoint.

The ontological concept of disease spans the meaning of disease from Paracelsus' concept of the disease as a parasite, to concepts of contagion as found in Harvey,[8] to modern bacteriological concepts in which illness is variously identified with infectious agents. Bacteriology finally vindicated Sydenham's faith in the possibility of specific remedies for specific diseases. As Knud Faber put it, diseases "came to be viewed from an etiological point of view, and the efforts of clinicians were directed towards... a nosography founded on the morbific causes."[9] The picture emerged of the host, the environment, and the disease agent as the elements of disease with the accent falling heavily on the agent of disease, particularly as an infectious agent. As Rudolf Virchow remarked, this "idea of particular, parasitic disease entities is without doubt ontological in an outspoken manner."[10] This ontological view involves as well a confusion of the cause of illness and the disease itself, as when the disease, tuberculosis, is identified with Mycobacterium tuberculosis. Virchow saw this as beginning with the discovery of microorganisms and presupposing a "hopeless, never-ending confusion, in which the ideas of being (*ens morbi*) and causation (*causa morbi*) have been arbitrarily thrown together."[11] In this, Virchow was undoubtedly correct. He, though, was himself also, by his own admission, "a thoroughgoing ontologist," who identified the pathological findings as the *ens morbi*, the disease entity.[12] Though he eschewed one form of reifying nosology, he embraced another. Disease became specific pathological changes in specific cells.

But the move to reification is only one dimension of the ontological thesis concerning disease. The other dimension is bound to a judgment concerning the nature of the disease pattern, the constellation or cluster of the signs and symptoms which form the character of a disease. In ontological theories, these characteristic disease patterns are interpreted as enduring disease types often without an immediate connection to a particular theory of material disease entities. It is an ontological question (in the philosophical sense) of the reality of disease types, one that asserts that they have a being beyond their particular instantiations. This interpretation of illnesses as portraying natural or essential disease types suggests an almost Platonic construal. In this view, courses of illnesses more or less fully achieve a natural type. Classical cases of a disease are thus perfect instantiations of a disease type and atypical cases imperfect realizations of a disease reality which exists as a natural, logical possibility. "Ontological" in this sense refers to claims of a reality for diseases existing apart from their embodiment in actual illnesses, which illnesses may be "atypical."

It is not clear that anyone held a fully realist view of diseases, but it is a viewpoint presupposed in the ordinary discussions of hospital wards where reference is made to "cases of *X* disease" in a way parallel with phrases such as "instances of *X* idea." To talk of illnesses achieving certain constant and real patterns, best illustrated by classical cases, and obscured by atypical cases, is to talk in a realist mode. To a point, it is illustrated by such classical nosologies as that of Francois Boissier de Sauvages (1706–1767), *Nosologia Methodica*.[13] Even with his empirical dedication, symptom constellations were for Sauvages types of diseases. Pinel's *Nosographie philosophique*[14] distinguished the varying symptoms of diseases from the "essential fevers" and attracted Broussais' classical critique of ontological theories of diseases. "One has filled the nosographical framework with groups of most arbitrarily formed symptoms... which do not represent the affections of different organs, that is, the real diseases. These groups of symptoms are derived from entities or abstract beings, which are most completely artificial **οντοι**; these entities are false, and the resulting treatise is ontological."[15] As Peter Niebyl indicated, Broussais' objection was against abstraction, not against the specificity of disease entities.[16] The moral of the story is that there are strong Platonic, realist tendencies in talk about diseases, and that the tendencies have met opposition from anti-realist quarters bearing a resemblance, if only distant, to the old humoral theories. When viewed in contrast to such anti-realist theories, ontological theories of disease indicate more "the ever-recurring craving of... clinicians for... fixed categories of diseases,"[17] than an attempt to reify disease concepts, which I have called medical ontology in the strong sense. The ontological sense of disease thus spans a range of significance from the concept of a specific logical entity to a specific material entity.

The traditional viewpoint contrasting with that of the ontologist has been the physiological or functional viewpoint. Lord Cohen drew the contrast as between a Platonic, realist, rationalist versus a Hippocratic, nominalistic, empirical view of disease.[18] The argument against ontological concepts was, as Wunderlich realized, an argument against the logical blunder of confusing abstract concepts with things, "presupposing them as actually existing and at once considering and treating them as entities," as well as against "models of diseases which contain no truly essential feature... [and] to which we only by way of exception or by using compulsion, find an example in nature."[19] But it was not a denial that there are patterns of disease processes. Essential disease types are not the same as basic laws of physiology or pathophysiology.

Those arguing for a physiological concept of disease had at least three points to make, which individual nosologists made more or less completely. First, they wished to secure the concept of disease as a general, not a specific notion. That is, they wished to make diseases functions of the general laws of physiology rather than functions of the more particular laws of the pathology of specific diseases. Yet, second, they wished to argue for a greater appreciation of the individuality of illnesses so that every particular disease-state could be understood in terms of its particular departures from general physiological norms. Heinrich Romberg put it this way, "And we do not regard the mere placing of the disease under this or that rubric as the final aim of diagnosis.... The most important thing remains the determination of the degree that the individual human is injured by his malady, and which cause has produced the momentary disorder."[20] Third, they wished to avoid the metaphysical and logical muddles of ontological concepts of disease. Diseases were not things nor were they perduring types of pathology. Rather, for the physiological or functional nosologists, diseases were more contextual than substantial, more the resultant of individual constitutions, the laws of physiology and the peculiarities of environment, than the result of disease entities. The physiological nosologists were closer to the Hippocratic appreciation of the nexus of airs, waters, and places.

The dispute between ontological and physiological theories of disease turns centrally on the ontological and logical status of disease entities. Ontological theorists framed views within which diseases could be appreciated as specific entities. Physiological theorists framed views within which diseases could be appreciated as particular deviations from general regularities. In the first case, the accent of reality fell upon the disease; in the second case the accent fell upon the individual and his circumstances, including the laws of physiology. There is a temptation to see this contrast as between a realist and a nominalist construal of the meaning of disease. There are surely strongly nominalist leitmotifs in physiological and functional theories of disease. There is an emphasis upon the individual, not the disease, as the reality in the illness. But though there is a sympathy with nominalism, there is no commitment; physiological theorists have been willing to speak of diseases and accord them a conceptual reality. For example, Ottomar Rosenbach's term, "ventricular insufficiency," indicated a disease state which has a real universality, though no reality apart from the instances of which it is the common property. It is a similarity between processes but not a thing, nor a disease entity with a unique cause. It is a resemblance common to a family of processes, not just a family of processes collected together out of various resemblances.

In the end it is because of the need for universality that both ontological and physiological disease theorists required more than a nominalism, though less than a full-blown realism. Progress from syndromes to disease entities helped secure the possibility of diagnosis, prognosis, and therapy, or, more generally, medicine's explanation, prediction, and control of reality. More than the mere ability to name similar objects, one needed as well to indicate a common structure in reality, even if that structure was only the physiological norms from which diseases were departures. Mere syndromes are, as the name implies, the running together of symptoms and signs. They are a constellation of phenomena without a nomological structure to bind the signs and symptoms in a fashion to provide a model for explanation. Treatment and prognosis concerning mere syndromes are empiric in the derogatory sense of a maneuver based on correlations but devoid of an account of the relation between the phenomena correlated. Disease entities offered a level of abstraction that could bind together the signs and symptoms in an etiological matrix. In particular, reifying medical ontological theories could treat diseases as the substances which bear the signs and symptoms, the accidents of the underlying essential reality. Thus identification of phthisis with Mycobacterium tuberculosis or with anatomical pathological findings gave a picture in terms of which the phenomena associated with the clinical entity, consumption, could be collected and organized. This organization involved the binding of the phenomena of the syndrome to the etiological matrix of pathophysiological laws. The temptation was, though, as has been illustrated, to reify the matrix as an *ens morbi*—to, as Virchow remarked, treat disease as "a real substance (*ens*)."[21]

Similarly, the realist ontological theories involved a commitment to disease types. But reality was closer to that of the physiological theorists in being etiologically open—disease entities did not prove to have unique etiologies. As Virchow indicated, known pathogens can exist in hosts without pathology.[22] Disease causality is equivocal. Diseases are, as the physiological nosologists stressed, much more complex than the easy simplicity implicit in many ontological nosologies. Diseases are, in fact, not only multifactorial, but multidimensional, involving genetic, physiological, psychological, and sociological components. The presence of these various components does not merely entail a superimposition of modifying variables upon basic disease structures. Rather, it implies that diseases have a basically relational, not a subject- (i.e., substance) predicate- (accident) nature. That is, there is not necessarily a *bearer* for every disease, a substrate for each type of disease.

This view of disease emerges from consideration of the complex of etiological structures involved in modern "disease entities." Diseases such as asthma, cancer, coronary artery disease, etc., are as much psychological as pathophysiological in that the likelihood of such illness is closely bound to experienced stress and the availability of support for the person stressed.[23] They are thus sociological as well. The result is a multidimensional concept of disease with each dimension—genetic, infectious, metabolic, psychological, and social—containing a nexus of causes bounded by their appropriate, usually different, nomological structures. The multiple factors in such well-established diseases as coronary artery disease suggest that the disease could be alternatively construed as a genetic, metabolic, anatomic, psychological, or sociological disease, depending on whether one was a geneticist, an internist, a surgeon, a psychiatrist, or a public health official. The construal would depend upon the particular scientist's appraisal of which etiological variables were most amenable to his manipulations. For example, the public health official may decide that the basic variables in coronary artery disease are elements of a lifestyle which includes little exercise, overeating and cigarette smoking. He may then address these social variables and consider such diseases to be, as Stewart Wolf suggested, ways of life.[24]

The shift in nosology is back to a "Hippocratic" notion of disease in the sense of a "physiological" or contextual concept. The Greeks have been criticized for producing "many separate disease entities, but never [arriving] at the concept of specific etiology."[25] In a sense, the criticism is justified. The Greeks described syndromes, but did not succeed in providing nomological substructures for diseases so that reliable explanation, prediction, and control of reality (i.e., diagnosis, prognosis, and therapy) were possible. The ontological nosologies can somewhat summarily be described as a response to this shortcoming; they were a move to a further level of abstraction allowing the signs and symptoms clustered in a disease to be understood as the appearance of either a disease-thing (an *ens morbi*), or a specific disease pattern. But the actual complexity of diseases suggests that though Hippocratic medicine failed to advance successfully a general account of the syndromes it described, it was properly cautious in not accepting theories of specific etiologies.

Conclusions in this area are at best tentative. But the ever more frequent epidemiological studies of disease, such as the Framingham study of cardiovascular disease, indicate a pattern-pattern analysis within which the pattern of signs and symptoms clustering in a syndrome is bound to a pattern of causal variables.[26] Appearance is bound to a nomological substructure, with both levels having a fairly open-ended character. Moreover, this open-endedness is controlled by pragmatic interests which can bring the disease to a genetic, metabolic, psychological, or social focus, etc., depending on which variables are to be manipulated. Such focusing, though, does not require a reduction of other variables. That is, the genetic variables in heart disease are not reduced to occult sociological variables when one focuses on the elements of lifestyle central to treating heart disease. They are rather treated as mediate variables placed in relation to a model which has sociological variables and correlations as its central structure. One abandons ontological hypostatization of disease and nosological realism, and construes the reality of disease as a conceptual nexus posited for understanding the world of appearance.

Where does this put us with regard to models of disease? The adoption of either a medical or psychological model is a pragmatic choice to focus on a particular cluster of variables and their correlations in order to make certain explanatory, predictive, and controlling maneuvers. But, to isolate these distinguishable dimensions of diseases, is to separate that which is distinguishable but of one fabric. The question of the correct model is either a pragmatic question or a misunderstanding. All diseases can be construed as both medical and psychological; only a confirmed Cartesian would hold that the models are totally separable, while only a monist would hold that they are not distinguishable. To assert that there is not a somatic substrate for psychological events is to assert that psychological life takes place nowhere in this world, that it is the enterprise of an at least partially nonembodied spirit. If human experience and action is to be integrated in and for this world, it must occur somewhere in this world. On the other hand, those psychological generalizations which coordinate mental events in terms of drives and inclinations are distinguishable as such from models free of such intentional predicates and generalizations.[27] If mind and body are not two substances but two distinguishable levels of human significance, concerning which generalizations of different characters can be made, as indeed does appear to be the case, then medical and psychological models of disease should be complementary, not competitive. They should complete what would otherwise be one-sided assertions concerning a particular model.

The concept of disease is an attempt to correlate constellations of signs and symptoms for the purposes of explanation, prediction, and control. Pitfalls exist, such as the temptation to reify diseases or to treat diseases as rigid, specific types with unique etiologies. Diseases involve patterns of causes correlated with clusters of signs and symptoms which constitute the illnesses at hand. Disease models, as nomological patterns, are interpretable in larger patterns in a way not readily apparent if those models modeled disease things or independent disease types. Thus, one can concomitantly have a medical and a psychological account of the etiology of coronary artery disease, which are not incompatible, but mutually completing. That is, the models are not modeling two different things, nor are they two models of the same thing—a disease thing. Rather, they are two modes of correlating variables intrinsic and extrinsic to an ill person. The variables are chosen for the purpose of speaking about and altering that illness. They are relationships structured for particular diagnostic, prognostic, and therapeutic goals, and are based on distinctions between psychological and physical phenomena, between psychological and physical predicates. The issue of the medical versus the psychological model of disease is thus a rehearsal of the mind-body problem. It is bound in part to the claim that diseases are things, with the consequent problem whether a disease thing can have a psychological reality. The identification of objectivity with physical descriptions suggests that if diseases are things, then they have nothing to do with the subjective world of values and social relations often imported into concepts of mental illness. Under such a view, mental illnesses could be diseases only if they described the malfunctioning of a mental thing (e.g., a *res cogitans*).

Criticisms of medical model accounts of mental illness are heterogeneous.[28] The critique given by Szasz turns in part on the notion that problems in living are diseases only if they have a physical basis and that, moreover, true diseases are value-free.[29] Under this view, all diseases are medical diseases. As a consequence, in such a view psychiatry becomes a moral enterprise where blame and praise (i.e., responsibility for one's own actions) are more appropriate than treatment, prognosis, and therapy.[30] The myth of mental illness is the myth that the autonomy of mental life is intrinsically undermined by disease. Disease in this account is identical with a form of reductionism which hides social judgment under claims to scientific objectivity. The assumption is that medicine deals with things and that psychology deals with broader issues such as social development.[31] But if diseases are means for coordinating phenomena for the purposes of prognosis, diagnosis, and therapy, then the issues can be reformulated not only to allow for the coordination of mental phenomena in diseases, but for the intrusion of values into medical models of diseases as well. To talk of diseases, and an intrinsic role for values in medical diseases, is to abandon ontological nosological analyses of disease and replace them with a contextual view closer to the more open-ended physiological nosologies of the past.

Diseases such as cancer, tuberculosis, and schizophrenia thus exist, but as patterns of explanation, not as things in themselves or as eidetic types of phenomena. Owsei Temkin comes close to such an appreciation of the plastic nature of the concept of disease. "The question: does disease exist or are there only sick persons? is an abstract one and, in that form, does not allow a meaningful answer. Disease is not simply either the one or the other. Rather, it must be thought of as the circumstance requires. The circumstances are represented by the patient, the physician, the public health man, the medical scientist, the pharmaceutical industry, society at large, and last but not least, the disease itself."[32] But the disease in itself is in the end the disease as it exists for us who both experience illness and explain it. Disease as an explanatory account is bound to the circumstances of that account. In short, explanatory accounts are not things; things are what explanatory accounts explain and disease is a mode for explaining things—in particular, ill humans.

The portrayal of particular diseases involves pragmatic judgments which ontological nosologies reified or stereotyped. C. S. Peirce argued that "*In order to ascertain the meaning of an intellectual conception one should consider what practical consequences might conceivably result by necessity from the truth of that conception; and the sum of these consequences will constitute the entire meaning of the conception.*"[33] That is, evaluation enters into the enterprise of medical explanation because accounts of disease are immediately focused on controlling and eliminating circumstances judged to be a disvalue. The judgments are in no sense pragmatically neutral. Choosing to call a set of phenomena a disease involves a commitment to medical intervention, the assignment of the sick role, and the enlistment in action of health professionals. To call alcoholism, homosexuality, presbyopia, or minor hookworm infestation diseases, involves judgments closely bound to value judgments. Granted, there is a spectrum from broken limbs to color blindness along which interest in construing a constellation of phenomena as a disease varies. The pain and discomfort of either a broken limb or a schizophrenic break invite immediate medical aid, while issues of color blindness or dissocial behavior lie at the other end of the spectrum. But all along the spectrum, the concept of disease is as much a mode of evaluating as explaining reality.

Commitment to the concept of disease presupposes that there are phenomena physical and mental which can be correlated with events of pain and suffering, so that their patterns can be explained, their courses predicted, and their outcomes influenced favorably. Further, the pain and suffering cannot be the immediate outcome of circumstances which are directly the subject of free choice. They must result from psychological or physiological laws; that is, they must be open to statement in the form of laws, not moral rules. Medicine is the application of scientific, not moral generalizations. Thus, involutional melancholia, duodenal ulcer, and pneumothorax due to gunshot count as diseases, while ignorance, greed, and political violence do not, insofar as the ignorant are capable of learning, the greedy of virtue, and the violent of pacific action. Thus, mental deficiency, kleptomania, and paranoid reactions do count as diseases.

Of course, a broad concept of diseases including both mental and physical models opens one to greater influence by social values. Yet, social judgments are involved in not considering such events as childbirth to be diseases, even though they are associated with considerable morbidity and in fact mortality. Socially desirable goals help draw the lines.[34] The same is true with regard to aging and what then counts as disease and health. The acceptable physical state of an 80-year-old would be disease for a 20-year-old. Yet, will that always be the case as more can be effected through geriatrics? Diseases are, as Lester King has indicated, patterns which we structure according to our expectations.[35]

This is not to argue that confusion between medical and moral issues is not possible or that such confusion is unlikely. Quite the contrary, such confusion is very likely, given the nature of disease. The concept of disease has fuzzy borders with moral concepts. In the 19th century, for example, masturbation was considered to be primarily a physical disease in the same sense that someone may now hold that coronary artery disease is a physical disease though certain forms of stress may be necessary conditions for the disease.[36]

More alarming examples exist, such as diseases developed to modify political behavior, such as drapetomania, the running away of slaves.[37] Szasz interprets such concepts as a reductio of the use of disease models in psychiatry, rather than as a caveat with regard to confusing compulsive and free action.[38] One of Cartwright's contemporary critics was more to the point in his remark that "if a strong desire to do what is wrong be a disease, the violation of any one of the Ten Commandments will furnish us with a new [disease]...."[39] In short, Cartwright's explanation failed because treating runaway slaves as free agents was a better account than treating them as subjects of fugue states.

Of course, one can still use medical force for political ends. Hookworms can be treated to eliminate anemia and thus make citizens more alert, or conceivably, citizens could be drugged into lethargy. The difference is that the first, unlike the second, is focused as well on the autonomy of the individual, his health. The accent of medicine upon liberating individuals from the hindrances of otherwise uncontrollable psychological and physiological forces, is the focus of the concept of health. The concept of health helps define the concept of disease by providing the telos for the medical enterprise. Disease concepts are, as has been argued, pragmatic concepts whose truth is found in action directed to the elimination of illness and toward the establishment of health.

III. HEALTH AND DISEASE

Models and accounts of disease are necessarily varied—they focus on the varied, particular limitations to human life. Health, though, represents a direction common to all the continua from particular diseases to well-being. If health is a state of freedom from the compulsion of psychological and physiological forces, there is a common leitmotif in the treatment of either schizophrenia or congestive heart failure—namely, the focus on securing the autonomy of the individual from a particular class of restrictions.[40] The unity of models of diseases is found more in the concept of health than in the concept of disease. Health is the common way away from the many ways of disease.

Thus, while the concept of disease is both an evaluatory and explanatory concept, health as a positive concept is more a regulative ideal. This may account in part for the difficulties surrounding attempts to define health operationally, though operational definitions of freedom from particular diseases are more available. Finally, to stress the non-moral character of the concept of health, a reminder from Freud is appropriate: treatment "does not set out to make pathological reactions impossible, but to give the patient... freedom to decide one way or the other."[41] Medicine, whether in the case of medical or psychological models of disease, is not an enterprise of applied ethics,[42] though values influence what limitations on human actions will be considered significant, and at times lead to confusing vices with the compulsions of nature.

In conclusion, health and disease are not symmetrical concepts, nor are they things, though important confusions have arisen from conceiving of them as such. Rather, the concept of disease is a mode of analyzing certain phenomena for the purposes of diagnosis, prognosis, and therapy. The concept is in one respect pragmatic, and in many respects influenced by issues of value. Particular diseases border on questions of moral and political significance. And, while there are many diseases, there is in a sense only one health—a regulative ideal of autonomy directing the physician to the patient as person, the sufferer of the illness, and the reason for all the concern and activity.

NOTES

1. Constitution of the World Health Organization (preamble). *The First Ten Years of the World Health Organization* (Geneva: W.H.O., 1958).
2. Alvan R. Feinstein, *Clinical Judgment* (Baltimore: The Williams and Wilkins Company, 1967), pp. 145–148.
3. Miriam Siegler and Humphry Osmond, "The 'Sick Role' Revisited," *The Hastings Center Studies* 1 (1973), 41–58.
4. H. Tristram Engelhardt, Jr., "Explanatory Models in Medicine: Facts, Theories, and Values," *Texas Reports on Biology and Medicine* 32 (Spring 1974), 225–39.
5. Henry E. Sigerist, *Man and Medicine*, trans. by Margaret G. Boise (New York: W.W. Norton & Co., 1932), pp. 105–106.
6. Walter Pagel, *Paracelsus* (Basel, Switzerland: S. Karger, 1958), p. 137.
7. Walter Pagel, *The Religious and Philosophical Aspects of van Helmont's Science and Medicine* (Baltimore: The Johns Hopkins Press, 1944), pp. 39, 41.
8. Walter Pagel and Marianne Winder, "Harvey and the 'Modern' Concept of Disease," *Bulletin of the History of Medicine* 42 (1968), 496–509.
9. Knud Faber, *Nosography in Modern Internal Medicine* (New York: Paul B. Hoeber, 1923), p. 98; see also pp. 108–109.
10. Rudolf Virchow, *Hundert Jahre allgemeiner Pathologie* (Berlin: Verlag von August Hirschwald, 1895), p. 22; English trans. by Lelland J. Rather, *Disease, Life and Man: Selected Essays by Rudolf Virchow* (Stanford: Stanford University Press, 1958), p. 192.
11. *Ibid.*
12. Virchow, *Hundert Jahre allgemeiner Pathologie*, p. 23; *Disease, Life, and Man*, p. 192.
13. Francois Boissier de Sauvages de la Croix, *Nosologia Methodica, Sistens Morborum Classica. Juxta Sydenhami mentem et Botanicorum Ordinem* (Amsterdam: Fratrum de Tournes, 1768).

14. Philippe Pinel, *Nosographie philosophique, ou la méthode de l'analyse appliqué à la médecine* (Paris: Richard, Caille, et Ravier, 1798).
15. F. J. V. Broussais, *Examen des Doctrines Medicales et des Systemes de Nosologie*, Vol. 2 (Paris: Mequignon-Marvis, 1821), p. 646.
16. Peter H. Niebyl, "Sennert, van Helmont, and Medical Ontology," *Bulletin of the History of Medicine* **45** (1971), 118.
17. Faber, *Nosography*, p. 95.
18. Henry Cohen, *Concepts of Medicine*, ed. by Brandon Lush (Oxford: Pergamon Press, 1960), p. 160.
19. Carl A. Wunderlich, "Einleitung," *Archiv für physiologische Heilkunde* **1** (1842), v.n.; ix.
20. Ernst Romberg, *Lehrbuch der Krankheiten des Herzens und der Blutgefässe*, 2nd ed. (Stuttgart: Verlag von Ferdinand Enke, 1909), p. 4.
21. Virchow, *Hundert Jahre allgemeiner Pathologie*, p. 22; *Disease, Life, and Man*, p. 191.
22. *Ibid.*, p. 38.
23. Thomas H. Holmes and Richard H. Rahe, "The Social Readjustment Rating Scale," *Journal of Psychosomatic Research* **11** (1967), 213–218.
24. Stewart Wolf, "Disease As a Way of Life: Neural Integration in Systematic Pathology," *Perspectives in Biology and Medicine* **4** (Spring 1961), 288–305.
25. Robert P. Hudson, "The Concept of Disease," *Annals of Internal Medicine* **65** (September 1966), 598.
26. U.S. National Heart Institute, *The Framingham Study: An Epidemiological Investigation of Cardiovascular Disease*. Section 1, p. 1b–6, U.S. Government Printing Office, Washington, D.C., 1968.
27. H. Tristram Engelhardt, Jr., *Mind-Body: A Categorial Relation* (The Hague: Martinus Nijhoff, 1973), pp. 148–161.
28. Ruth Macklin, "Mental Health and Mental Illness: Some Problems of Definition and Concept Formation," *Philosophy of Science* **39** (September 1972), 341–365, and "The Medical Model in Psychoanalysis and Psychotherapy," *Comprehensive Psychiatry* **14** (January/February 1973), 49–69.
29. Thomas S. Szasz, "The Myth of Mental Illness," *The American Psychologist* **15** (February 1960), 113–118.
30. Thomas S. Szasz, *The Ethics of Psychoanalysis* (New York/London: Basic Books, Inc., Publishers, 1965).
31. George W. Albee, "Emerging Concepts of Mental Illness and Models of Treatment: The Psychological Point of View," *American Journal of Psychiatry* **125** (January 1969), 870–876.
32. Owsei Temkin, "The Scientific Approach to Disease: Specific Entity and Individual Sickness," in *Scientific Change*, ed. by A. C. Crombie (London: Heinemann, 1961), pp. 629–647.
33. C. S. Peirce, *Collected Papers*, ed. by Charles Hartshorne and Paul Weis (Cambridge, Mass.: Belknap Press, 1965), 5.9.
34. Lester S. King, "What Is Disease?," *Philosophy of Science* **21** (July 1954), 197.
35. *Ibid.*
36. H. Tristram Engelhardt, Jr., "The Disease of Masturbation: Values and the Concept of Disease," *Bulletin of the History of Medicine* **48** (Summer 1974), 234–248.

37. Samuel A. Cartwright, "Report on the Diseases and Physical Peculiarities of the Negro Race," *The New Orleans Medical and Surgical Journal* 7 (May 1851), 707–709.
38. Thomas S. Szasz, "The Sane Slave," *American Journal of Psychotherapy* 25 (April 1971), 228–239.
39. James T. Smith, "Review of Dr. Cartwright's Report on the Diseases and Physical Peculiarities of the Negro Race," *The New Orleans Medical and Surgical Journal* 8 (September 1851), 233.
40. Much is packed in and hidden away in the notion of a "particular class of restrictions" which has only been sketched in part above.
41. Sigmund Freud, *The Standard Edition of the Complete Psychological Works of Sigmund Freud*, ed. and trans. by James Strachey (London: Hogarth Press and The Institute of Psycho-Analysis, 1961), Vol. 19, *The Ego and the Id and Other Works*, p. 50, n. 1.
42. H. Tristram Engelhardt, Jr., "Psychotherapy as Meta-ethics," *Psychiatry* 36 (November 1973), 440–445.

1.3

The Meaning of "Healthy" ("Normal") and of "Sick" ("Abnormal")

Abraham Maslow and Bela Mittelmann

Adjustment of a person may be defined as a characteristic way in which he perceives, reacts to, and solves the main problems of life. For the sake of simplicity, we may classify the main problems of life into three categories: 1) problems set by external reality in its biological and physical aspects (we must get food to eat, and we must have shelter); (2) problems set by the culture in which the person lives—its demands and prohibitions, its habits and taboos, its internal conflicts and inconsistencies; (3) the problems set by internal psychological demands; these in turn may be put under three heads: (a) the need for comfort, gratification, and the avoidance of pain; (b) the need for self-esteem, independence, achievement, and adequacy; (c) the need for security, the love of our fellow men, and a feeling of belongingness.

The words "healthy" and "sick," "normal" and "abnormal," have been used in three senses.

1. The pathological approach: We have mentioned that disturbances and conflicts in the manner of satisfying these needs may produce acute symptoms as well as habitual long-range modes of reaction. The latter we call character disturbances. Such problems are stinginess, the need to produce flawless work, and stubbornness. For example, the patient described in the first chapter worked well as a librarian, but she needed self-aggrandizing attitudes to overcome her feeling of inadequacy and helplessness in the situation. In the history of psychopathology, the extension of the investigation of psychological problems to habitual modes of reaction was a very important enlargement, but it also diminished the sharp delineation between health and sickness, between normal and abnormal. In this respect, even those individuals who did not break down in normal situations of stress, in the face of severe threat had reaction patterns similar to those of the people who did break down. In spite of this, the whole emotional life of the individuals who did break down could not be understood and fully appreciated without taking into account their habitual modes of reaction. Conversely, the individuals who did not break down

showed nevertheless a peculiar rigidity and vulnerability as regards some of the habitual modes of reaction mentioned. The recognition of the similarities in some of the dynamics of sick and healthy individuals is of great psychological importance. It implies, however, in some respects, the definition of pathology as representing only quantitative differences. In other words, an individual may be more or less "sick."

2. The statistical approach: Most psychological traits are assumed to fall into a "normal" distribution, with most of the cases in the middle and a few at the extremes. These extremes, which constitute only a small percentage of the total population, are arbitrarily lopped off and labeled "abnormal" or "pathological" or "deviant," and the far larger percentage clustering around the middle is arbitrarily called "normal" (279). This approach is of value if we recognize its limitations. Much of what lies at the extremes—delusions, anxiety attacks—is pathological; genius is not. Further, many children show an unreasonable fear between the ages of four and seven. Slight fear of harmless animals is common in women. These traits which appear in a great number of individuals are minor "sicknesses," the same way as the common cold is. (See also Morlan [685].)

3. The cultural approach: It is impossible, in many respects, to understand "abnormality" without reference to the cultural background. Some societies expect the individual to show no strong ambition, to refrain from becoming emotionally or physically violent, and to coöperate with other members of the group (Zuñi). Other societies put a premium on boasting, on ambition, on accumulation of wealth, on surpassing and vanquishing others, on certain states of violence, and on killing (Kwakiutl). Each of these two societies strongly disapproves of the "deviant" mode of behavior. It has been suggested that all concepts of normal or abnormal should be considered in terms of conformity to the cultural norms. The facts mentioned pose difficult problems which have not yet been adequately solved, but the following general statements can be made: The "dynamics" of a reaction pattern occurring in a group in which it is accepted has only partial identity with the "dynamics" of the same pattern occurring in individuals living in a society where it is not. This applies even to such phenomena as dream states and hallucinations—including hearing supernatural voices. Occurring in harmony with cultural norms, they may imply, although possibly representing conflict solutions, a desire to develop in a certain direction and to advance one's career—e.g., to become a medicine man. In the group which rejects such phenomena they represent a near-catastrophic solution of conflicts, a state of helplessness—in a word, a state of psychic illness.

In addition, we may add that normality is also relative to social status, age, and sex. Behavior that is healthy in an individual ten years of age may be unquestionably unhealthy in an individual of thirty.

MANIFESTATIONS OF PSYCHOLOGICAL HEALTH ("NORMALITY")

1. *Adequate Feelings of Security.* The feeling that one is safe in contact with fellow beings in the occupational, social, and family settings.

2. *Adequate Self-Evaluation.* This includes (a) adequate self-esteem—a feeling of value proportionate to one's individuality and achievements; (b) an adequate feeling of worth-whileness—feeling morally sound, with the feeling of no severe guilt and the ability to recognize some socially and personally unacceptable common human desires which will always be present as long as one lives in a society.

3. *Adequate Spontaneity and Emotionality.* This involves ability to form strong and lasting emotional ties, such as friendships and love relations; the ability to give adequate expression to resentment without losing control; the ability to understand and to share other people's emotions; the ability to enjoy oneself and laugh. Everyone is unhappy at times, but this must have valid reasons.

4. *Efficient Contact with Reality.* This has at least three aspects: the physical, the social, and the internal world. This implies (a) an absence of excessive fantasy; (b) a realistic and broad outlook on the world, with the ability to withstand the ordinary shocks of life, such as illness and reversals; and (c) the ability to change if external circumstances cannot be modified. A good phrase for this is "coöperation with the inevitable."

5. *Adequate Bodily Desires and the Ability to Gratify Them.* This includes (a) a healthy attitude toward bodily functions in terms of accepting them but not being preoccupied with them; (b) ability to derive pleasure from the physical things in life, such as eating and sleeping, and to recover well from fatigue; (c) sexual adequacy—healthy desire and the ability to gratify it without fear and guilt; (d) ability to perform the excretory functions adequately without shame or conflict; (e) ability to work; (f) absence of an excessive need to indulge in any of these activities, and the ability to stand, at least temporarily, a fair amount of deprivation.

6. *Adequate Self-Knowledge.* This includes (a) adequate knowledge of one's own major motives, desires, goals, ambitions, inhibitions, compensations, defenses, inferiority feelings, etc.; (b) realistic appraisal of one's own assets and liabilities. Honest self-appraisal is based on the ability to accept oneself as natural and not to repudiate any important desires or thoughts even if some of them may be socially or personally unacceptable. These will always be present as long as one lives in a society.

7. *Integration and Consistency of Personality.* This means (a) fairly rounded development, versatility, interest in several activities; (b) morals and conscience which are not too inflexible from the group's point of view; (c)

ability to concentrate; (d) no major conflicting trends within the personality, and no dissociation of personality.

8. *Adequate Life Goals*. These involve (a) achievable, realistic, and compatible goals; (b) reasonable persistence of efforts to achieve them; (c) goals which involve some good to society.

9. *Ability to Learn from Experience*. The ability to learn from experience includes not only accumulation of knowledge and acquisition of skills through practice, but also an elasticity and receptiveness and therefore absence of rigidity in the approach to handling occupational tasks. Even more important are the ability to learn spontaneously—in the muscles and bones and without the need of elaborate meditation—one's own strength, the dangers of certain situations, the possibility or certainty of success, and the carrying over of this knowledge, which is a knowledge in feeling, action, and evaluation, into reaction and behavior in the fields of interpersonal relations, the gratification of bodily needs, and pursuit of life goals. Equally important is the resultant avoidance of methods that have failed when the risk is not worth taking or better methods are available.

10. *Ability to Satisfy the Requirements of the Group*. The individual must be (a) not too unlike the other members of his group in ways that the group considers important; (b) adequately informed and essentially accepting of the folkways of his group; (c) willing and able to inhibit the drives and desires tabooed by his group; (d) able to show the fundamental strivings expected by his group: ambition, promptness, friendliness, sense of responsibility, loyalty, etc.; (e) interested in the recreational activities favored by his group.

11. *Adequate Emancipation from the Group or Culture*. This involves (a) at least some originality, individuality, the ability to consider some things good, others bad; (b) some independence of group opinions; (c) the absence of an excessive need for flattery, reassurance, or group approval; (d) some degree of tolerance and appreciation of cultural difference.

Two Examples

Now let us see, first, what a "healthy" or "normal" individual is like in flesh and blood.

The subject is the middle of three siblings, with a sister four years younger than he and a brother three years older. His father is quick-tempered, although he does not go into rages. His mother is calm and somewhat on the submissive side. Both are affectionate and allowed the children much freedom when they were young—for instance, allowing them to take trips by themselves.

At the age of five, the subject had a nightmare in which a large animal was chasing him. He started to bite his nails at about the same time. He still does so under stress.

He was always very athletic, while his brother was more intellectual. They used to fight a lot. At that time the subject was quick-tempered, "like my father," whenever his brother said to him, "That's silly."

He got along well with his sister and treated her better than his brother did, against whom he would defend her.

When he reached a point where he equaled his brother in strength, he became calm, "like my mother." Thus there was mixed identification.

He always did good average work in school, while his brother was above average.

At the age of sixteen, he met a girl whom he courted for five years. They had frequent quarrels because of her jealousy, which, in turn, would arouse his jealousy. They broke up on an average of twice a year. However, they married after he finished college. Now they have three children, to whom he is much attached.

He went into business, in which he was successful. He makes plans covering broad outlines but is impatient with even important details. His wife is systematic, often scolds him, and gets worked up. He laughs it off.

He was a member of one of the political organizations in his community. There was corruption in the organization which he fought against unsuccessfully. Finally he decided to resign from the organization despite the fact that to do so was disadvantageous for his business.

During the war he enlisted in the service and quickly became an officer. He was in the North African campaign. He experienced some anxiety during action, but did not break down.

After the birth of his sister he saw her in the nude and learned about the difference between the sexes. He did some masturbating during puberty. He started having sexual relations at the age of sixteen and a half with friends, but not with his future wife. He now has intercourse about twice a week. While in the army, he stood the sexual frustration well, although he did not like it, and had occasional relations with other women.

He is a good mixer, with lasting friendships.

This man has engaged successfully in all important activities that his culture has a pattern for. He went through school, got married, had children, is on good terms with his family, is interested in community affairs, and even went through harrowing experiences without breakdown. Had he lived in a different place, as among the Chinese or among the Mohammedans in periods of predominant polygamy, his relationship to his parents would have been quite different, and he would have had many wives instead of one; if he had lived among the Marquesans he would have been one husband among several married to the same woman. Thus the outlook and patterns he developed are very intimately connected with the cultural environment. He went through several periods of stress, with which he coped successfully. The first one occurred around the age of five. Apparently the birth of his sister meant to him the coming of another rival, besides his brother, for the love of his parents. It is also likely that his attachment to his mother at that time was particularly intense and that he feared his father's temper. The anxiety was expressed in the nightmare of being chased by an animal and in the nail-biting. He solved this crisis, because of the persistent affection of his parents, by kindness and playfulness toward his sister. He had a continual stress situation with his brother, who very likely considered him (the subject) a rival. This struggle was fairly well resolved about puberty, when the subject came into his own. There was a situation of stress with his wife also, as witnessed by the recurrent breakups before the marriage.

Is this subject "absolutely normal"? Obviously not. Apart from the history of the nightmare, of the quarrels with his brother, the breakups with his future wife, there is also the recurrent nail-biting when he is in situations of stress. One can further ask: Is there a guarantee that this subject will never have more serious disturbance? The answer to that is, no, there is no guarantee. It is not likely that he will, but he may. For instance, if his wife became seriously disturbed (she is obviously more vulnerable than he); if at the same time, let us assume, in a national economic crisis he lost his business and had to work for a high-handed boss who insisted, let us say, on details, this man might very well break down. There is no absolute dividing line between normality and abnormality, or between emotional health and emotional illness, and it depends not only on the individual, but also on the circumstances, whether he stays well or becomes sick.

The difference between "healthy" and "sick" is so gradual that one might be tempted to say that there is no such thing as normal, or an emotionally healthy, individual. Practically, however, the difference is very important, and there are figures available on a national scale about the percentage of the population that has been emotionally healthy up to early or middle adulthood. It was found during Selective Service examinations that approximately 10 percent of the unselected male population was suffering from a severe enough emotional disturbance to make them, in the opinion of the examining psychiatrist, unfit for military service. Fifteen percent of the population was suffering from a moderate emotional disturbance so that the psychiatrist had to weight the individual's assets and liabilities in order to decide whether he was fit for military duty.[1] Seventy-five percent of the male adult population presented no problem worthy of consideration. It may be added here that only a small fraction (1 or 2 percent of the population or less) was incapacitated for civilian work by emotional disturbance.

The breakdown of a person may occur in a situation which in the past he has unwittingly avoided. A brief illustration will show this point.

A man of sixty-six developed attacks of palpitation, together with a sinking sensation in his stomach and loss of appetite. These symptoms were accompanied by fear of death. His present complaints were the first serious emotional disturbance he ever had. He had been married for thirty years, and, although there had never been any children because of his wife's sterility, there was no unhappiness about this.

He had always had counseling jobs in youth organizations. Six months before his

1. This figure is based upon the personal observations of one of the authors.

symptoms appeared, however, he was made head of the central office of another organization. He was required to attend conferences with the members of the board of directors. These conferences always took place during lunch, and it was usually before or during lunch that he developed his symptoms. It thus became clear that his fears represented reactions to meeting these individuals. He had always had an undercurrent of anxiety concerning people who were his equals or his superiors, but he had never been seriously put to the test until, at the age of sixty-six, he received his present appointment.

REACTIONS TO STRESS SITUATIONS

We will now proceed to discuss two kinds of stress situations and enlarge our concept of the relationship between "healthy" and "sick." One of these situations (the reactions of the brain-injured patient) is definitely pathological; the other (reactions to extreme situations of stress) is on the borderland of pathology.

Reactions of the Brain-Injured Patient

"Here is a man with a lesion of the frontal lobe, to whom we present a problem in simple arithmetic. He is unable to solve it.... He looks dazed, changes color, becomes agitated, anxious, starts to fumble, his pulse becomes irregular; a moment before amiable, he is now sullen, evasive, exhibits temper, or even becomes aggressive. It takes some time before it is possible to continue the examination. Because the patient is so disturbed in his whole behavior, we call situations of this kind *catastrophic situations*."[2]

Some patients may react even more severely and lapse into complete unconsciousness. Such patients may try to defend themselves against the onslaught of any task or stimulus with which they cannot cope. As a result, they may shun the company of other people, they may constantly engage in self-chosen activities, and they may develop excessive orderliness so that they will not get confused by the problem of where to find things and how to utilize them.

Other aspects of the reactions of brain-injured patients will be discussed later. (See Chapters III and XXXV.) The following points should be made here. One may describe the mentioned reactions in negative terms by saying that a patient wants to avoid failure, frustration, helplessness, and anxiety; or one may put them in positive terms and say that the patient wants to retain the feeling of mastery and of integration; he wants to preserve himself. This striving for self-preservation is an equally strong dynamic force in both healthy and "sick" individuals.

---

2. K. Goldstein, *Aftereffects of Brain Injuries in War,* Grune & Stratton, New York, 1942, p. 71.

Reactions to Situations of Extreme Stress

A striking presentation of the problem is given in an account of the reactions to the tortures suffered during transportation to a Nazi concentration camp. These tortures included, apart from the physical suffering, the prisoners' being forced to curse their God, to accuse themselves of vile actions and their wives of prostitution.

"The writer recalls his extreme weariness, resulting from a bayonet wound and a heavy blow on the head.... He wondered that man can endure so much without committing suicide or going insane; that the guards tortured prisoners in the way it had been described in books on the concentration camps; that the Gestapo was so simpleminded as to enjoy forcing prisoners to defile themselves. It seems that he gained emotional strength from the following facts: that things happened according to expectation; that, therefore, his future in the camp was at least partly predictable from what he already was experiencing and from what he had read; and that the Gestapo was more stupid than he had expected. He felt pleased that the tortures did not change his ability to think or his general point of view....

"The writer feels that he was able to endure the transportation and what followed, because he convinced himself that these horrible and degrading experiences somehow did not happen to 'him' as a subject, but only to 'him' as an object. The importance of this attitude was corroborated by statements of other prisoners. They couched their feelings usually in such terms as, 'The main problem is to remain alive and unchanged.' What should remain unchanged was individually different and roughly covered the person's general attitudes and values.

"The author's thoughts and emotions during the transportation were extremely detached. It was as if he watched things happening in which he only vaguely participated."[3]

Examining these statements, we find that the writer developed three main reactions to the tortures suffered: (1) detachment, (2) attitudes of superiority, and (3) attitudes of illusory safety (things are predictable). The latter two, under the circumstances, were entirely unrealistic, and the first one is a not uncommon symptom in psychopathology. However, the key to the meaning of these phenomena is revealed in the statement, "The main problem is to remain *alive* and *unchanged*." Both of these aspects are easily detectable in the manifestations. The detachment dulled the acuteness of the pain; the detachment and the superiority enabled the author not to turn on his persecutors, who would have killed him; the assumption of predictability gave him a feeling of security when everything was in danger. The special manner in which he achieved these measures was characteristic of his whole background and personality: engaging in analysis of his reactions and of the behavior of

3. B. Bettelheim, Individual and mass behavior in extreme situations, in T. M. Newcomb, E. L. Hartley, et al., *Readings in Social Psychology*, Henry Holt and Company, New York, 1947, pp. 231–232.

others and accenting predictability. The author is a psychologist. In this manner of reaction he was maintaining his former personality, he was remaining "unchanged." A similar tendency to maintain the general characteristics of the personality has been found in individuals who, after varying periods of discrimination and less extreme persecution, left Germany.

The tendency to maintain a continuity of personality or of "character" in both healthy and sick individuals was early recognized and was termed "life style" (Adler). The phrase implies that everything a person does, feels, and thinks is characteristic of him. Most of his artistic and intellectual products will bear the stamp of his personality, of his way of living, and of his outlook on the world; e.g., anything by Mozart is Mozartian.

These two tendencies, to preserve life and to maintain the existing interests, goals, and values, are universal psychological trends and are presented in this illustration even more dramatically than in the reactions of the brain-injured patient. One could debate whether to call the reactions described by the author healthy and normal or to say they were on the border line of abnormal and sick. If these reactions were to be sustained for a long time after the conditions eliciting them had ceased to exist, they would be considered pathological. Within the situation, however, since they were successfully adaptive, they cannot be so considered.

In the situation described above, the two aims—self-preservation and maintaining the integrity of the personality—coincided in that they both required the same type of adaptive behavior. In some situations, however, this is not so. In attempting to maintain their personality, prisoners at times found themselves risking their lives. The author cited, for example, was taking such a risk in interviewing other prisoners about their reactions. At other times the prisoners might give up the attempt to maintain their personality intact in order to be able to live with increased safety in the camp. This occurred frequently in the cases of prisoners who had been in concentration camps for several years.

Similar though less dramatic conflicts occur in less extreme life situations. Thus the individual may find it necessary to make a choice between a mode of behavior which would benefit him personally but is contrary to his ideals, and a mode of behavior which, though compatible with his ideals, would mean sacrificing personal advantage. The "normal" person described earlier in this chapter was confronted with such a choice when he resigned from the political organization. Further, conflicts may arise between ways of preserving life or ways of escaping greater pain: namely, through avoidance or through attack, through fight or through submission. The tendency to maintain former personality can also lead to a discrepancy between the realistic situation and the individual's ideals—for example, a man who, courting a woman when his funds are limited, wants to pay all the expenses even though she may have more money than he and even though she would be willing to share the expenses. These various conflicts will be discussed in further detail in the chapter (IV) on unconscious motivation and conflict. We would like to emphasize here the following: In psychopathological reactions, excessive threat is perceived to preservation of life with its various derivatives, namely integration, discomfort and pain, and ability to master situations. There is also excessive clinging to previous goals and thus to the maintenance of the personality. The reasons for this and its details will be elaborated in subsequent chapters. Here one might say that, insofar as the individual is psychologically sick, he behaves as if he were in a concentration camp when he is not in it or long after he has left it.

1.4

Definitions of Health and Illness in the Light of American Values and Social Structure

Talcott Parsons

The aim of the present paper is to try to consider the socio-cultural definition of health and illness in the United States in the light, in the first instance, of American values, but also in terms of the ways in which the relevant aspects of the value system have come to be institutionalized in the social structure. I shall give primary attention to mental health, but will also attempt to define its relation to somatic health and illness as carefully as possible. I shall also try to place the American case in comparative perspective.

First, it is important to try to define the respects in which health and illness can be considered to be universal categories applying to all human beings in all societies and to distinguish them from the respects in which they may be treated as socially and culturally relative. It will be possible here to say only a few rather general things, but the development of social science does, I think, permit us to be somewhat more definite than it has been possible to be until rather recently.

There is clearly a set of common human features of health and illness; indeed more broadly there is probably a set of components which apply perhaps to all mammalian species. There is no general reason to believe that these common components are confined to somatic illness; my view would be that there are also such components for mental illness. It does, however, seem to be a tenable view that there is a range, roughly, from the "purely somatic" to the "purely mental"—both of course, being limiting concepts—and that as one progresses along that range the prominence of the factors of relativity as a function of culture and social structure increases. The importance of the "interpenetration" between somatic and mental aspects is so great, however, that it would be a mistake to draw a rigid line, in any empirical term, between them.

One point is relatively clear. This is that the primary criteria for mental illness must be defined with reference to the social *role-performance* of the

Editors' note: footnotes omitted.

individual. Since it is at the level of role-structure that the principal direct interpenetration of social systems and personalities comes to focus, it is as an incapacity to meet the expectations of social roles that mental illness becomes a problem in social relationships and that criteria of its presence or absence should be formulated. This is of course not at all to say that the state which we refer to as mental, as of somatic, illness is not a state of the individual; of course it is. But that state is manifest to and presents problems for both the sick person and others with whom he associates in the context of social relationships, and it is with reference to this problem that I am making the point about role-performance.

At the same time I would not like to treat mental health as involving a state of commitment to the performance of *particular* roles. Such a commitment would involve specific memberships in specific relational systems, i.e., collectivities. Mental health is rather concerned with *capacity* to enter into such relationships and to fulfill the expectations of such memberships. In terms of the organization of the motivational system of the individual, it therefore stands at a more "general level" than do the more specific social commitments.

There is a set of mechanisms in the operation of which social system and personality aspects are interwoven, which make possible the many complex adjustments to changing situations which always occur continually in the course of social processes. It is when the mechanisms involved in these adjustive processes break down ("adjustive" as between personalities involved in social interaction with each other) that mental illness becomes a possibility, that is, it constitutes one way in which the individual can react to the "strains" imposed upon him in the course of social process. This can, of course, occur at any point in his own life cycle from the earliest infancy on. Also, I take for granted that mental illness is only one of several alternative forms which "deviance" can take, again at every stage. Mental illness, then, including its therapies, is a kind of "second line of defense" of the social system vis-à-vis the problems of the "control" of the behavior of its members. It involves a set of mechanisms which take over when the primary ones prove inadequate. In this connection it can also be readily seen that there are two main aspects of the operation of the mechanisms involved. First, the individual who is incapacitated from performing his role-functions would be a disturbing element in the system if he still attempted to perform them. Hence we may say that it is important to have some way of preventing him from attempting to do so, both in his own interest and in that of the system itself. Secondly, however, there is the therapeutic problem, namely of how it is possible to restore him to full capacity and return him to role-performance after an interval.

So far, I have been speaking of mental health with special reference to its place in the articulation between social system and personality. Mental health—and illness—are states of the personality defined in terms of their relevance to the capacity of the personality to perform institutionalized roles. For analytical purposes, however, I have found it necessary to make a distinction, which a good many psychologists do not make, between the personality and the organism. They are, of course, not concretely separable entities, but they are analytically distinguishable systems. There would be various ways of making the distinction, but for present purposes I think it is best to put it that the personality is that part of the mechanisms involved in the control of concrete behavior which genetically goes back to the internalization of social objects and cultural patterns in the course of the process of socialization. The organism, as distinguished from this, consists of that part of the concrete living individual which is attributable to hereditary constitution and to the conditioning processes of the physical environment. Hence, from the point of view of its relation to the personality, it is that aspect of the mechanisms controlling behavior which is not attributable to the experience of socialization in and through processes of social interaction.

It will be noted that I have been careful not to say that the mechanisms through which the personality component of the concrete individual functions are not "physiological." In my opinion, it is not the distinction between physiological and in some sense "mental" processes which is the significant one here. Indeed, I think that *all* processes of behavior on whatever level are mediated through physiological mechanisms. The physiological mechanisms which are most significant in relation to the more complex forms of behavior are, however, mainly of the nature of systems of "communication" where the physiological mechanisms are similar to the physical media and channels of communication. Hence, in both cases the content of "messages" cannot be deduced from the physical properties of the media. In the higher organisms, including man, it seems clear that the focus of these mechanisms rests in the central nervous system, particularly the brain, and that the next level down in the order of systems of control, has to do with the hormones which circulate through the blood stream.

It is important to stress this "interpenetration" of personality and organism, because, without it, the complex phenomena usually referred to as "psychosomatic" are not understandable. Correspondingly, I do not think that the way in which *both* somatic and mental health and illness can fit into a common sociological framework are understandable without both the distinction between personality and organism and the extreme intimacy of their interpenetrating relationship.

Coming back to the relation of both to the social system, I should like to introduce a distinction which has not been consistently made by sociologists either in this or in other connections, but which I think is very important for present purposes. This is the distinction between *role* and *task*. There are many different definitions of the concept role in the sociological literature. For my present purpose, however, I think one very simple one is adequate, namely a role is the organized system of participation of an individual in a social system, with special reference to the organization of that social system as a collectivity. Roles, looked at in this way, constitute the primary focus of the articulation and hence interpenetration between personalities and social systems. Tasks, on the other hand, are both more differentiated and more highly specified than roles; one role is capable of being analyzed into a plurality of different tasks.

Seen in these terms I think it is legitimate to consider the task to define the level at which the action of the individual articulates with the *physical* world, i.e, the level at which the organism in the above analytical sense is involved in interaction with its environment in the usual sense of biological theory. A task, then, may be regarded as that subsystem of a role which is defined by a definite set of *physical* operations which perform some function or functions in relation to a role and/or the personality of the individual performing it. It is very important that processes of communication, the *meanings* of which are by no means adequately defined by the physical processes involved at the task level, are not only included in the concept of task, but constitute at least one of the most important, if not *the* most important, categories of tasks, or of components of them.

Coming back to the problem of health and illness, I should now like to suggest that somatic illness may be defined in terms of incapacity for relevant task-performance in a sense parallel to that in which mental illness was thought of as incapacity for role-performance. In the somatic case the reference is not to any particular task, but rather to categories of tasks, though of course, sudden illness may force abandonment of level rather than any particular task. Put the other way around, *somatic health is, sociologically defined, the state of optimum capacity for the effective performance of valued tasks*.

The relation between somatic and mental health, and correspondingly, illness, seen in this way, bears directly on the problem of levels of organization of the control of behavior. It implies that the "mind" is not a separate "substance" but essentially a level of organization, the components of which are "nonmental," in the same basic sense in which for example, the hypothetical isolated individual is "non-social." It further implies that the mental level "controls" the somatic, or in this sense, physical, aspect of the individual, the "organism." Somatic states are therefore necessary, but in general *not* sufficient conditions of effective mental functioning.

The Problem of "Cultural Relativity" in Health and Illness. Our present concern is with the relation of personality and organism on the one hand, the social system and its culture on the other. It is now possible to say something on the question of the relations between the universal human elements and the socioculturally variable ones in health and illness on both levels. Clearly, by the above definition, *all* human groups have highly organized personalities which must be built up by complex processes of the sort we call socialization and which are subject to various sorts of malfunctioning at the level of social adjustment which has been referred to. All human societies have language, a relatively complex social organization, complex systems of cultural symbols and the like. The individual in such a society, however "primitive," is always involved in a plurality of different roles which are the organizing matrix of the various tasks he performs.

Clearly this personality element of the structure of the individual person is closely interpenetrating and interdependent with the organic-somatic aspect. Hence, there are clearly "problems" of both somatic and mental illness and health for all human groups. Furthermore, all of them are deeply involved with the structures of the social system and the culture.

That there are uniformities in the constitutions of all human groups at the organic level goes without saying, and hence that many of the problems of somatic medicine are independent of social and cultural variability. Thus such things as the consequences and possibilities of control of infection by specific bacterial agents, the consequences of and liability to cancerous growths and many other things are clearly general across the board. This is not, however, to say that the *incidence* and probably degrees of severity of many somatic diseases are not functions of social and cultural conditions, through many different channels. But within considerable ranges, independent of the part played by such factors etiologically, the medical problems presented are essentially the same, though of course, how to implement medical techniques effectively is again partly a socio-cultural problem.

It follows from the conception of personality put forward here, that constancies in the field of mental health are intimately related to uniformities in the character of culture and social structure. Here it is particularly important that, after a period in which a rather undiscriminating version of the doctrine of "cultural relativity" was in the ascendant, much greater attention has recently come to be paid to the universals which are identifiable on these levels. It is not possible here to enter into any sort of detail in this field, but a few highlights may be mentioned.

Most fundamental, I think, is the fact that every known human society possesses a culture which reaches quite high levels of generalization in terms of symbolic systems, including particularly values and cognitive patterns, and that its social structure is sufficiently complex so that it comprises collectivities at several different levels of scope and differentiation. Even though, as is the case with most of the more "primitive" societies known, there is scarcely any important social structure which is not, on a concrete level, a kinship structure, such kinship systems are clearly highly differentiated into a variety of subsystems which are functionally different from each other.

With minimal exceptions, the nuclear family of parents and still dependent children is a constant unit in all kinship systems, though structural emphases within it vary. It is clearly the focal starting point for the process of socialization and the source of the primary bases of human personality organization. But the nuclear family *never* stands alone as a social structure, it is always articulated in complex ways with other structures which are both outside it and stand on a higher level of organization than it does. This involvement of the nuclear family with the wider social structure is, from the structural point of view, the primary basis of the importance of the incest taboo, which, as applying to the nuclear family, is known to be a near universal. Put in psychological terms, this means that the internalization of the object systems and the values of the nuclear family and its subsystems, starting with the mother-child relation, constitutes the *foundation* of personality structure in all human societies. There are, of course, very important variations, but they are all variations on a single set of themes. Because the internalization of the nuclear family is the foundation of personality structure, I suggest that *all mental* pathology roots in disturbances of the relationship structure of the nuclear family as impinging on the child. This is not in the least to say that there are not somatic factors in mental pathology; some children may well be constitutionally impossible to socialize adequately. But the *structure* of pathological syndromes which can legitimately be called mental will always involve responses to family relationships.

It is, however, equally true and important that in no society is the socialization of an adult exhausted by his experience in the nuclear family, and hence is his personality *only* a function of the familial object systems he has internalized. Correspondingly, mental pathology will always involve elements in addition to disturbances of the nuclear family relations, especially perhaps those centering about peer-group relations in the latency period and in adolescence. These other factors involve his relations to social groups other than the nuclear family and to higher levels of cultural generalization and social responsibility than any of those involved in the family.

It is thus, I think, fully justified to think of both mental and somatic pathology as involving common elements for all human groups. But at the same time both of them would be expected to vary as a function of social and cultural conditions, in important ways, and probably the more so as one progresses from the more "vegetative" aspects of organic function and its disturbances to the more behavioral aspects and then from the "deeper" layers of personality structure to the "higher" more "ego-structured" layers. It is also probable that the lower in this range, the more the variation is one of incidence rather than character of pathology, the higher the more it penetrates into the "constitution" of the illness itself.

Health Among the Problems of Social Control. Health and illness, however, are not only "conditions" or "states" of the human individual viewed on both personality and organic levels. They are also states evaluated and institutionally recognized in the culture and social structure of societies. Can anything be said about the ways in which the constancy-variability problem works out at these levels?

Clearly the institutionalization of expectations with respect both to role and to task performance is fundamental in all human societies. There must, therefore, always be standards of "adequacy" of such performance and of the "capacities" underlying it which must be taken into account, and hence, a corresponding set of distinctions between states of individuals which are and are not "satisfactory" from the point of view of these standards. But by no means all types of "conformity" with performance-standards can be called "health" nor all types or modes of deviation from such conformity "illness." Are the categories health and illness, as we conceive them, altogether "culture-bound" or is there something about them which can be generalized on the social role-definition level? To answer this question, it will be necessary to enter a little more fully into the sociological problems presented by these definitions.

Since I am attempting to deal with illness in the context of "social control," I should like to approach the problem in terms of an attempt to classify ways in which individuals can deviate from the expectations for statuses and roles which have been institutionalized in the structure of their societies. In spite of the fact that it will complicate matters, it seems unavoidable to deal with the problem on two different levels.

The first of these two levels concerns the relation of the problem of health and illness to the whole range of categories of deviant behavior. In this connection, I shall attempt to assess the relative importance given to the health complex in different types of society and to show that it is particularly important in the American case. The second level will take up the problem of selectivity and variation *within* the health-illness complex itself. Here, I shall discuss how this relates to selective emphasis on the different components of the role of illness and of the therapeutic process, and will attempt to show that, not only does American society put greater stress on the problem of illness than do other societies, but that its emphases in defining the role and in therapy are also characteristically different.

I shall outline the classification I have in mind on the first level in terms of the way it looks in our own society and then raise the question of how universally it may be assumed that the relevant categories are in fact, differentiated from each other in different societies. The first category is that of the control of the capacities of units in the social structure in the sense in which this conception has been discussed above in connection with the definition of health and illness. Every society must have important concern for the level of these capacities. The present context, however, is that of social control, not socialization, so it is not a question of how these capacities come to be developed in the first place, but rather of how tendencies to their disturbance can be forestalled, or, once having occurred, can be rectified.

Though comparable considerations apply to collectivities as units, in the present context the relevant unit is the human individual, and with reference to him, we must consider both of the two aspects which have been distinguished, namely, somatic and mental health. Capacity, it will be remembered, is thought of as standing on a more "general" level than commitment to any particular role or task obligations. It does, however, include the motivation to accept such obligations given suitable situation and opportunity.

There is a second category of problem of social control in relation to the individual which in another sense also stands on a more general level than any particular action-commitments. This may be called the problem of *morality*. This concerns the state of the individual person, but not with respect to his capacities in the same sense as these are involved in the problem of health, but with respect to his commitment to the *values* of the society. This is the area of social control which has traditionally been most closely associated with religion, especially when the reference is to the person, rather than to any collective unit of the society. When I associate the problem with religion, I do not wish to imply that every attachment to a religion or religious movement automatically implies reinforcement of commitment to the values of a *society*. This is by no means necessarily the case. The point is, rather, that it is in the sphere of religious orientation, or its "functional equivalents" at the level of what Tillich calls "ultimate concern" that the individual must work out the problem of how far he is or is not committed to the values of his society.

There is, of course, a great deal of historical and cross-cultural variation in the ways in which individuals may be treated as standing in religious states which need to be remedied or rectified. It seems, however, to be sound to distinguish two very broad types, namely, those involving "ritual impurity" of some sort, and those involving the problem of "salvation" or "state of grace" in a sense comparable to the meanings of these terms within the Christian tradition. In speaking of religion in this connection, I also do not wish to rule out cases which do not include an explicitly "supernatural" reference in the meaning we would tend to give that term. Thus from a "humanistic" point of view the problem still exists of ensuring commitment to the humanistic values. Perhaps the best single example of this reference is the ritualistic aspect of classical Chinese culture with its "secular" ideal of the "superior man."

Both the above two contexts of the problem of social control of individuals refer to rather generalized states of individuals which may be conceived to "lie behind" their commitments to more differentiated and particularized role-obligations and norms. If both of these latter categories be interpreted in the context of social system involvement, then it is a problem in every society how far different elements in its population maintain operative commitments on both these levels which are compatible with the social interest.

The reference to norms, which I have in mind in the first instance in a society as a whole, focuses on the legal system. Any going society must cultivate a rather generalized "respect for law," and this must be specified in several directions to come down to the level of particular legal obligations.

It is important to note that commitment to law-observance stands on a level more general than that involved in any particular role. Such principles as honesty in the sense of respect for the property rights of others, "responsibility" in the sense of the obligation to fulfill contractual obligations once entered into, or recognition of the general legitimacy of political authority; none of these is specific to any particular role in a particular collectivity. In a highly differentiated society like our own, the practicing legal profession may be said to carry out functions of social control in this field which are in some ways parallel to those of the medical profession in the field of health.[9]

Of course, commitment to norms is by no means confined to the norms which in a modern type of society are given the "force of law." But the law first may serve as a prototype, and second is, in a well-integrated society, necessarily the paramount system of norms with respect to the society as a system, though norms of "morality" may as noted above, take precedence on a religious or purely "ethical" level. "Below" the legal level, however, every collectivity in the society has some set of rules, more or less formalized, to which it is essential to secure some order of commitment on the part of its members.

The last of the four contexts in which the problem of social control in the present sense arises is that of commitment to role-obligations in particular collectivities. This also is a broad category running all the way from the obligations of marriage, to a particular spouse, and of occupational commitment in a particular "job" to the obligations of the citizen of loyalty to his national government. One would expect mechanisms of social control to cluster about this area. In our own society, this is the least differentiated of the four, but certain relatively specialized agencies have begun to emerge. On the "lower" levels, social work is one of the more prominent. "Industrial sociology," so far as it is oriented to the problem of the individual worker as a member of a formal organization, is another. This is the area of which Chester Barnard spoke as that of "efficiency" in the technical meaning he gave to that term.

I have taken the space to review these four different contexts of the problem of social control, because I think it is essential to have such a classification as a basis for placing the treatment of any of these problems in a comparative setting. In a highly differentiated society like our own, these four functions have become relatively clearly differentiated from each other, and the operative processes of social control are, with certain indefinite borderlines, of course, to be found in the hands of different organizational agencies. The last of the four I outlined is by a good deal the least firmly institutionalized as a distinct function and it is probably significant that, in our society, it is most fully worked out, through social work, for the lower status-levels of the society.

The present situation with respect to differentiation cannot, however, be said to be typical of all societies; indeed, I doubt whether any case can be found where a comparably close approach to completeness in this differentiation can be found.

Two major "axes" of differentiation were implicit in the classification I have just presented. Both need to be taken into account in placing the problem of health and illness relative to the others. The first of these may be called the differentiation in terms of orientation, on the one hand, to the exigencies of the *situation* in which the person must act; on the other hand, orientation to or through *normative patterns*. The second axis concerns not this problem, but that of whether the "problem" lies in the state of the person as a whole, at a level deeper than the problem of his acceptance of particular obligations, or whether it lies in the question of his "willingness" to accept certain more specific obligations, to particular norms and classes of norms, and to particular roles in particular collectivities.

The first of these two axes differentiates the types of deviance involved in illness and disturbance of commitments to collectivities on the one hand from those involved in disturbance of commitments to norms and to values on the other. The second axis differentiates the problems of illness and of disturbance of commitment to values on the one hand from the problems of commitment to collectivities and to normative patterns (rules and law) on the other. The following tabular arrangement may be helpful to the reader.

	Disturbance of Total Person	Disturbance of Particular Expectations
"Situational" Focus	Problem of "capacities" for task and role performance Illness as deviance Health as "conformity"	Problem of commitments to collectivities ("Barnard's efficiency") Disloyalty as deviance Loyalty as conformity
"Normative" Focus	Problem of commitments to values, or of "morality" "Sin" and "immorality" as deviance State of grace or "good character" as conformity	Problem of commitments to norms, or of "legality" "Crime" and "illegality" as deviance Law-observance as conformity

It is in terms of the first axis that one fundamental type of differentiation involving health can be made, that which treats health as a "naturalistic" state which is not to be explained by or treated through religio-magical media. It is of course a commonplace that in all nonliterate societies, with relatively minor exceptions such as fractures, this differentiation has not yet taken place, and much the same can be said about the high civilizations of the Orient such as India and China until touched by Western medicine. This of course, is in no way to say that "therapies" which are couched in magico-religious terms are necessarily ineffective. On the contrary, there is much evidence that they have been very effective in certain cases. It would, however, hardly be denied that with the clear differentiation of roles in this area which has taken place in the modern world, much greater effectiveness has been made possible over at least a very large part of the range.

Though differentiation on the first axis discriminates the problem of health from that of the "ritual" state of the individual, or his state of grace or, more generally, commitment to values, it fails to discriminate between the more general level of his state "as a person" and his commitment to the more specific obligations of societal membership and activity. Here a problem which has been very central in the modern world in drawing the line between problems of mental health and of law seems to be a major one. This is the question of whether and how far the "deviance" of the individual from conformity with social expectations can be considered to be "intentional," i.e., the question of how far he may legitimately be held *responsible* for his actions. In one area, at least, this has in fact come to be accepted as a main differentiating criterion and, I think, rightly so.

Let me try to elucidate some of its implications in the present context. It has long been one of the principal criteria of illness that the sick person "couldn't help it." Even though he may have become ill or disabled through some sort of carelessness or negligence, he cannot legitimately be expected to get well simply by deciding to be well, or by "pulling himself together." Some kind of underlying reorganizing process has to take place, biological or "mental," which can be guided or controlled in various ways, but cannot simply be eliminated by an "act of will." In this sense the state of illness is involuntary. On the other hand, both obedience to norms and fulfillment of obligations to collectivities in roles are ordinarily treated as involving "voluntary" decisions; the normal individual can legitimately be "held responsible."

Certainly both in fields such as law and in that of collectivity obligations, there are many cases where failure to live up fully to "formal" obligations is not "blamed on" the individual. But the distinction is, on the whole, clear; if he is not "ill" (or in a state of ritual impurity, or "sin"), or willfully recalcitrant, it must be the fault of somebody else or of "the system." The essential basis of this possibility of "holding responsible" is the particularity of specific norms and role-obligations. A normal person has the capacity to accept or reject particular obligations without involving a reorganization of the major structures of his personality or of his body. It is only when there is a "disturbance" which goes beyond these particularities that we can speak of illness, or of disturbed commitment to values.

This same problem occurs in the relation to the commitment to values as operating through religion and cognate mechanisms. It is very clear that among many nonliterate peoples, states of ritual impurity are treated as outside the control of the individual victim. They are states for which he may not legitimately be held responsible, except, and this is a most important exception which applies to illness as well, for subjecting himself to the proper treatment institutionally prescribed for those in such a state. In general, some ritual performance is called for, which may even sometimes be self-administered, to "rectify" his state.

Without attempting to discuss the situation in other major religions, it is a very important fact that the conception of original sin in the Christian tradition defines the situation in a cognate way. Though retroactively and mythologically Adam is held to have sinned "voluntarily," the burden of original sin on mankind is held not to be the responsibility of the individual, but something which is inherent in the human condition. Conversely, it cannot be escaped from without outside help.

Here it is important to distinguish original sin from the infraction of the norms and role-obligations of a religious collectivity. I think it can fairly be said that that aspect of "sin" which is treated by religious authorities as *within* the responsibility of the individual is strictly analogous to the civil responsibility for law-observance and/or the responsibility for living up to the obligations of a particular role, in this case of church-membership. Christianity thus has institutionalized the differentiation of these two aspects of the problem of social control. Original sin belongs, with respect to *this* axis of differentiation, on the same side as does illness.

With respect to the major categories I have been discussing for the last few pages, societies may be expected to differ in two major respects. The first I have already been stressing, namely with respect to the *degree* to which these major types of deviance are *differentiated from each other* and the functions of social control with respect to them institutionalized in differentiated agencies. In an evolutionary sense (with societal, not organic reference) they may be said all to have originated in religion. Priests and magicians have thus been the "original" agents of social control everywhere. The role of physician, of lawyer, and, if you will, of "administrator" and social worker have only gradually and unevenly differentiated off from the religious roles.

The second range of variation concerns the relative stress put on conformity with social expectations in each of these categories and hence the seriousness with which deviance in each is viewed, and the importance given to building up effective mechanisms of social control in the area in question as distinguished from others. Thus in a society like that of Hindu caste in India, the overwhelming emphasis seems to have been religious, with ritual purity on one level, the problem of control of and emancipation from the Hindu counterpart of Christian original sin on another as the primary preoccupations. The neglect of health as Westerners understand it in India (until very recently) is too well-known to need emphasizing. Soviet society may be said to be a type which puts primary emphasis on effective role-performance in the socialist state and hence to bend its primary efforts to controlling the commitments of the population (above all through "propaganda" and "agitation") to exerting the utmost effort, especially in production. Finally, with differences, of course, it may be suggested that both classical Rome and modern England have laid more stress on law and integration through the legal system than any other of the major features with which this discussion has been concerned.

Seen in this perspective, contemporary American society is, with respect to the institutionalization of mechanisms of social control, probably as highly differentiated as any known, certainly as any outside the modern Western world. But among those which are highly differentiated, it is also one which places a very heavy emphasis on the field and problems of health and illness relative to the others, probably as high as any. It is also clear that our concerr with problems of health has increased greatly since about the turn of the present century, and furthermore, that the emergence of the problem of mental health into a position of salience, on anything like the scale which has actually developed, is a new phenomenon.

A Restatement of the Criteria of Health and Illness. Before attempting to relate this emphasis systematically to American values and social structure, it would be well to attempt to state somewhat more precisely what seem to be the principal general characteristics of health and illness seen in the context of social role structure and social control.

Health may be defined as the state of optimum *capacity* of an individual for the effective performance of the roles and tasks for which he has been socialized. It is thus defined with reference to the individual's participation in the social system. It is also defined as *relative* to his "status" in the society, i.e. to differentiated type of role and corresponding task structure, e.g., by sex or age, and by level of education which he has attained and the like. Naturally, also there are qualitative ranges in the differentiation of capacities, within sex groups and at given levels of education. Finally, let me repeat that I am defining health as concerned with capacity, not with commitment to *particular* roles, tasks, norms, or even values as such. The question of whether a man wants to remain with his wife or likes his particular job or even feels committed to refrain from highway robbery is not *as such* a health problem, though a health problem may underlie and be interwoven with problems of this sort.

Illness, then, is also a socially institutionalized role-type. It is most generally characterized by some imputed generalized disturbance of the capacity of the individual for normally expected task or role-performance, which is not specific to his commitments to any particular task, role, collectivity, norm or value. Under this general heading of the recognition of a state of disturbance of capacity, there are then the following four more specific features of the *role* of the sick person: 1) This incapacity is interpreted as beyond his powers to overcome by the process of decision-making alone; in this sense he cannot be "held responsible" for the incapacity. Some kind of "therapeutic" process, spontaneous or aided, is conceived to be necessary to recovery. 2) Incapacity defined as illness is interpreted as a legitimate basis for the *exemption* of the sick individual, to varying degrees, in varying ways and for varying periods according to the nature of the illness, from his normal role and task obligations. 3) To be ill is thus to be in a partially and conditionally *legitimated* state. The essential condition of its legitimation, however, is the recognition by the sick person that to be ill is inherently *undesirable*, that he therefore has an obligation to try to "get well" and to cooperate with others to this end. 4) So far as spontaneous forces, the *vis medicatrix naturae*, cannot be expected to operate adequately and quickly, the sick person and those with responsibility for his welfare, above all, members of his family, have an obligation to *seek competent help* and to cooperate with competent agencies in their attempts to help get him well; in our society, of course, principally medical agencies. The valuation of health, of course, also implies that it is an obligation to try to *prevent* threatened illness where this is possible.

These criteria seem very nearly obvious on a common sense level in our society, but some aspects of their subtler significance become evident when we consider the way in which, through the channels of mental and psychosomatic illness, the balance of health and illness comes to be bound up with the balance of control of the motivation of individuals in their relation to the society as a system. This is what I had in mind in discussing illness in the context of the problems of deviance and social control in the first place. I shall not take space to go into this set of problems here, since they have been dealt with elsewhere, but will only call attention to them, and draw a few inferences.

The most important inferences for present purposes concern the importance of *two* related but distinct functions for the society of the health-illness role structure. The first of these is the *insulation* of the sick person from certain types of mutual influence with those who are not sick, and from association with each other. The essential reason for this insulation being important in the present context is not the need of the sick person for special "care" so much as it is that, motivationally as well as bacteriologically, illness may well be "contagious." The motives which enter into illness as deviant behavior are partially identical with those entering into other types of deviance, such as crime and the breakdown of commitment to the values of the society, partly they are dynamically interrelated with these so that stimulation of one set of motives may tend to stimulate others as well.

In the light of the motivational problem the important feature of insulation is the deprivation, for the sick person, of any claim to a more general legitimacy for his pattern of deviance. As noted above, the conditional legitimation which he enjoys is brought at a "price," namely, the recognition that illness itself is an undesirable state, to be recovered from as expeditiously as possible. It is at this price that he is permitted to enjoy the often very powerful gratifications of secondary gain. But the importance of the institutionalization of the role of illness is not confined to its bearing on the motivational balance of the sick person. As Durkheim pointed out for the case of crime, the designation of illness as illegitimate is of the greatest importance to the healthy, in that it reinforces their own motivation *not* to fall ill, thus to avoid falling into a pattern of deviant behavior. The stigmatizing of illness as undesirable, and the mobilization of considerable resources of the community to combat illness is a reaffirmation of the valuation of health and a countervailing influence against the temptation for illness, and hence the various components which go into its motivation, to grow and spread. Thus, the sick person is prevented from setting an example which others might be tempted to follow.

The second important implication of institutionalization of the roles is that being categorized as ill puts the individual in the position of being defined as "needing help" and as obligated to accept help and to cooperate actively with the agency which proffers it. The role of illness, that is to say, channels those categorized as belonging in it into contact with therapeutic agencies. It is therefore involved in both negative and positive mechanisms of social control, negative in that the spread of certain types of deviance is inhibited, positive in that remedial processes are facilitated.

An interesting and important intermediate aspect may also be noted. By defining the sick person as in need of help and tending to bring him into relation to therapeutic agencies, the role of illness tends to place him in a position of *dependency on* persons who are *not* sick. The structural alignment, hence, is of each sick person with certain categories of nonsick, not of groups of sick persons with each other.

American Values and the Health Problem. Now let us turn to the question of the way in which American values and social structure may be said to operate selectively with reference both to the place of the health-illness complex among other mechanisms of social control and with respect to emphases within the health-illness complex itself. To start with it will be necessary to sketch the main outline of the American value system in the relevant respects.

I would like to suggest that even so complex and highly differentiated a society as our own can be said to have a relatively well-integrated system of institutionalized common values at the societal level. Ours I shall characterize as a pattern emphasizing "activism" in a certain particular sense, "worldliness" and "instrumentalism." Let me try, briefly, to explain these terms.

In the first place, a societal value system concerns the orientations of members to conceptions of what is desirable for the society itself and as a whole as a system or object of evaluation. Only derivatively, does it provide patterns of evaluation of the individual. When I refer to activism, I mean that in relation to *its* situation or environment, the society should be oriented to mastery over that environment in the name of ideals and goals which are transcendental with reference to it. The relevant environment may be either physical or social, but because of our relative isolation from other societies until the last generation or so, the physical environment has been particularly prominent in our case. The reference point for exerting "leverage" on the environment has been, historically, in the first instance religious. It will not be possible here to go into the question of the sense in which, or degree to which this is still the case; nevertheless, the main orientation clearly is one of maintaining the pattern of mastery, not of "adjustment" to the inevitable. In no field has this been more conspicuous than that of health where illness has presented a challenge to be met by mobilizing the resources of research, science, etc., to the full.

When I speak of the "worldliness" of the American value system, I mean that, in spite of its religious roots, the *field* of primarily valued activity is in practical secular pursuits, not in contemplation or devotions, or aesthetic gratifications. In its societal application this means a conception of an ideal *society*, originally the Kingdom of God *on Earth*, in a secularized version a good society in which such ideals as liberty, justice, welfare, and equality of opportunity prevail.

Finally, when I speak of "instrumentalism," I refer to the fact that, in the first instance for the society as a system, there is no definitive "consummatory" state which is idealized, no definitive societal goal state which is either attained or not—as in the case of "communism." There is rather an indefinite perspective of possible improvement, of "progress" which fulfills by degrees the ideal by moving in the right *direction*.

The absence of a definitive goal for the system as a whole, places the primary active achievement emphasis on the level of the goals of *units* and measures their achievements in appropriate terms. There is a kind of "liberal" pluralism in that any unit in the society, individual or collective, has liberty to pursue goals which to it may seem worthwhile, but more importantly, there are standards of *contribution* to the progress of society. Perhaps the most obvious (though not the only) field of such contribution is that of economic productivity, for it is the productivity of the economy which is the basis of the availability of facilities for attaining *whatever* goals may seem most worthwhile, since income as generalized purchasing power is nonspecific with respect to particular uses. This is the most generalized basis of opportunity to do "good things." But equally important is the provision of the society with units which have the *capacity* for valued achievement.

I may note that collective units and their achievements are of the utmost importance in the American system, for example, the business firm. But their achievements are fundamentally dependent on the capacities and commitments of the human individuals who perform roles and tasks within them. It is in this connection that the relevance of the valuation of health appears. For the individual, the primary focus of evaluation is universalistically judged *achievement*. The possibility of achievements is, of course, a function of opportunity at any given point in his life cycle, which in turn is a function of the economic level of the community, because openings both for self-employment, e.g., in independent business, and for employment by others, are a function of markets and of funds available through whatever channels. But on a "deeper" and in a sense more generalized level, this achievement is dependent on two basic sets of prior conditions which underlie his capacities, namely, on education in the broadest sense, and on health. It is in the first instance as an essential condition of valued achievement that the health of the individual is itself valued.

There is another very central strand in the pattern of our evaluation in both respects. This is the relation of both education and health to the valuation of *equality* of opportunity. For reasons which cannot be gone into here, but which bear above all on the high level of structural differentiation of our society, it is one which shows a great deal of mobility of resources. Ascribed status is relatively minimized. The "pluralism of goals" which has to do with the instrumental emphasis in our value system raises the problem of "justice" with great acuteness. One aspect of this is distributive justice with references to the allocation of rewards. But with the emphasis on active achievement, even more crucial than justice of reward distribution is that of *opportunity* for value achievement. But education and health are clearly more fundamental conditions of achievement than is access to investment funds or to employment, since they condition capacity to exploit opportunity in this narrower sense. Hence, *access* to education and to health services becomes, in a society like our own, a peculiarly central focus of the problem of justice in the society.

On technical grounds I do not classify education as a function of social control in a society. Within the field of problems of social control, as discussed above, the problem of health clearly constitutes the "rock bottom" of the series. There seem, when the problem is seen in this light, to be a number of reasons which I may review briefly, why it has emerged into a position of special prominence in contemporary America.

First, and of course a very important point, the development of medicine and of the health sciences underlying and associated with it, has made possible an entirely new level of control of illness, both preventive and therapeutic, far higher than has ever existed before in history. There is, of course, interdependence. American medicine did not just take over a medical science ready-made, but has developed the European beginnings with an energy and resourcefulness probably matched only in the field of industrial technology. There is, hence, interdependence between the development, on the one hand, of medical science and technology, and on the other, of interest in, and concern for, effective handling of health problems.

Secondly, the order of significance of the problems of social control, starting with commitment to paramount values themselves, running through commitment to norms, then to roles and tasks, is probably, in a very broad sense, of evolutionary significance. This is to say that there is a tendency for a problem area to emerge into salience only when, to a degree, the ones ahead of it in the priority list have in some sense been "solved." This is not to say that any of them are definitively solved, but in a relative sense one can speak of solution.

It is not possible to discuss this question here in detail. But it may be suggested that by the mid-nineteenth century, with the very important exception of the problem of the South, a certain national unity had been achieved in terms of values and norms. It can then be further suggested that in the latter half of the nineteenth century there was concentration on the problems of setting up the new industrial system with the institutionalization of the principal role categories which have to go into that, notably, of course, an occupational role system which was structurally quite different from that of the earlier society of "farmers and mechanics." Not least important in this connection was the institutionalization of the repercussions of these changes on the family, because of the drastic nature of the differentiation of occupational from familial roles. From the point of view of the individual, it may be said that the development of the industrial economy provided, in terms of a structural type congruent with American values, a new level of solution of the problem of opportunity.

From this point of view, one might say that after the turn of the century the stage was set for a new level of concern with the problems of education and health, which have indeed figured very prominently in this period, though not by any means to the exclusion of the others. Their importance is, I think, further accentuated by another feature of the development of the society. This is the fact that, with the development of industrialization, urbanism, high technology, mass communications and many other features of our society, there has been a general *upgrading* to higher levels of responsibility. Life has necessarily become more complex and has made greater demands on the typical individual, though different ones at different levels. The sheer problem of capacity to meet these demands has, therefore, become more urgent. The motivation to retreat into ill-health through mental or psychosomatic channels, has become accentuated and with it the importance of effective mechanisms for coping with those who do so retreat.

Seen in terms of this kind of historic perspective, it makes sense, I think, that *the first major wave of development of the health institutions was in the field of somatic illness and the techniques of dealing with it, and that this has been followed by a wave of interest in problems of mental health.* This is partly, but by no means wholly, because the scientific basis for handling somatic illness has developed earlier and farther. In addition to this, it is well known that the resistances to recognizing the existence of health problems are stronger in the field of mental than of somatic health. Furthermore, a larger component of the phenomena of mental illness presumably operates through motivation and is hence related to the problems and mechanisms of social control. Social changes, however, have not only increased the strain on individuals, thus accentuating the need for mechanisms in this area, but some of the older mechanisms have been destroyed or weakened and a restructuring has been necessary.

For one thing, levels of mental pathology which could be tolerated under pre-industrial conditions, have become intolerable under the more stringent pressures of modern life; this probably includes the pushing of many types of personality over the borderline into overt psychosis, who otherwise would have been able to "get along." Furthermore, the family, for example, has undertaken a greatly increased burden in the socialization and personality-management fields, and new institutional arrangements for dealing with the health problems of its members are required. This seems, for example, to be one major factor in the rapid spread of hospitalization.

I may sum up this aspect of the discussion by saying that both by virtue of its value system, and by virtue of the high level of differentiation of its social structure, American society has been one in which it could be expected that the problem of health, and within this more particularly of mental health, would become particularly salient. Its "liberal" cast which militates against highly stringent integration with reference to a system goal tends to emphasize the problem of getting units to "come along." The human individual is the end of the series of units on which the functioning of the society depends, and is hence the "last resort" in this connection. At the same time, the activistic orientation of the society militates against any orientation which would be inclined to let individuals "rest on their oars," but puts very much of a premium on the protection and development of capacity in the sense in which I have discussed it here.

The same factors, particularly seen in the context of the stage of development of the society, tend to prevent too strong an emphasis on any of the other primary problems and modes of social control. Generally, I think, contrary to much opinion, it can be said that the American society is very firmly attached to its primary values, so much so that they tend to be placed outside the field of serious concern. There is, to be sure, much controversy about what are alleged to be changes in values. But a careful analysis, which cannot be entered into here, will reveal that very much, at least, of this does not lie at this level, but rather at ideological levels.

A very good example of this is the amount of concern displayed over the developing salience of problems of mental health, and the scope given to the permissive and supportive elements in the orientation to the mentally ill. But people who show this concern often forget to emphasize the other side of the coin, namely, the equally prominent concern with therapy, with bringing the mentally ill back into full social participation, which above all, means into full capacity for achievement. Particularly revealing, I think, is the conception that the therapeutic process involves active *work* on the part of the patient, his seriously *trying* to get well. He is conceived of as anything but a passive object of the manipulations of the therapeutic personnel.

American Selectivity within the Patterns of Health and Illness. I have argued above, that among the problems and mechanisms of social control, both the values and the social structure of American society will tend to place emphasis on the problems of health and illness which concern commitment to roles, as compared with those of commitment to collectivities, to normative rules, or to the values themselves. This essentially is to say that it is *capacity* which is the primary focus of the problem of social control for us. With the increasing complexity and "maturity" of the society in turn, the problem of motivation to adequate role-performance and hence, to mental health becomes a salient one.

The problem now arises of what kind of selectivity we may expect, on the basis of the above analysis, *within* the complex of illness, and the corresponding attitudes toward therapy, relative to other ways of treating the problem of illness as such. In order to approach this question, I would like to use the formulation of the main components of the definition of illness, as stated previously herein, as my main point of reference. The first point, namely, a disturbance of capacity, is general, and is the link with the foregoing discussion of selectivity among the problems of social control. This is to say that in the United States we are more likely to interpret a difficulty in an individual's fulfilling social role-expectations as a disturbance in capacity, i.e., as illness, than is true in other types of society with other types of value systems.

The other four criteria, it will be remembered, were exemption from role-obligations, holding the patient not responsible for his state, conditional legitimation of the state, and acceptance of the need for help and of the obligation to cooperate with the source of the help.

My suggestion is that, compared with other societies in which other value systems have been institutionalized, in the American case the heaviest emphasis among these tends to go to the last. Essentially, this derives from the element in the American value system which I have called "activism" above. The implication of that element, in the context of the others to which it relates, is for the personality of the individual, the valuation of *achievement*. This in turn, as was developed above, implies a strong valuation of the capacities which underlie achievement, capacities which are primarily developed through education or socialization and protected and restored through health education or socialization and protected and restored through health services. But in the American case, this does not imply that the primary stress is on the dependency aspect of the "need for help"—I shall return to the question of the role of dependency presently. It is rather, from the point of view of the society, the attitude which asserts the desirability of *mastery* of the problems of health, and from that for the individual sick person, the obligation to cooperate fully with the therapeutic agency, that is to *work* to achieve his own recovery. The rationale of this is plainly that, if he is not motivated to work to attain the conditions of effective achievement, he cannot very well be considered to be motivated to the achievements which require good health as a condition.

It might then be said that the other three components of the role of illness are institutionalized as subsidiary to, and instrumental to, this one. With respect to legitimation, there is a particularly strong emphasis on its *conditional* aspect, that illness is only legitimized so long as it is clearly recognized that it is intrinsically an undesirable state, to be recovered from as expeditiously as possible. Similarly, with the factor of exemption from role-performance and the "admission" that the patient cannot be held responsible in the sense discussed above. In this connection, there is a very important relation to the scientific aspect of our cultural tradition. That the patient "can't help it" is simply one of the facts of life, demonstrated by medical science. Where scientific evidence is not available, the tendency is to give the benefit of the doubt to the possibility that he can help it. Thus, we tend to be relatively suspicious of plans for "free" health care because of the readiness to impute malingering wherever objective possibility for it exists.

I shall wish to suggest very tentatively how this American emphasis on active therapy differs from emphases in other societies, but before taking this up, I would like to try broadly to answer two other sets of questions about the American case. The first of these is how the patterning of illness in our society relates to the problem of the *directions* of deviant behavior, the second to selective emphases among the social components involved in the therapeutic process.

In a previous publication, I attempted to classify the directions which deviant orientations might take in terms of three major dimensions, two of which were very close to, if not identical with, those set forth by Merton. These were first the variation between *alienation* from social expectations and *compulsive conformity* with them, second between *activity* and *passivity*, and third between *object*-primacy and *pattern*-primacy. The first two of these are the ones also, selected by Merton.

In terms of these first two dimensions, illness clearly belongs in the general category of a type of deviance categorized by alienation and by passivity. This general type I have designated as withdrawal whereas Merton calls it "retreatism." This tendency to withdrawal as the most prominent type of deviance is typical of American society generally. But some of the dynamics of it are relevant to the questions of selectivity within the components of the pattern of illness.

Before entering into these, however, it may be noted that with respect to the American pattern of illness, I think it can be said that the primary focus is object-oriented rather than pattern-oriented. This is above all because illness focuses at the level of capacity for role and task performance, not at the level of norms or values and conformity with them. This would also be true of illness generally but for reasons which will be discussed presently. I think it likely that it is more accentuated in the American case than others.

What then, can be said to be some of the main patterns of motivational dynamics relevant to the problem of illness in American society and their relation in turn to these features of the role of illness as an institutionalized role? I may start by suggesting that all patterns of deviant behavior, as distinguished from creative alteration of the cultural or normative tradition, involves the primacy of elements of *regressive* motivational structure in the psychological sense. But for different types of deviance and within the category of illness as a type of deviance there will be selective emphases on different phases of psychological regression.

It is not possible to enter into all the complications here, but I suggest that in the American case, the primary focus lies in the residues of the pre-oedipal mother-child relationship, that phase of which Freud spoke as involving the "first true object-attachment." The basis on which this develops goes back to the very great, and increasing prominence in socialization of the relatively *isolated* nuclear family. The "American dilemma" in this case is that the child is, typically, encouraged to form an extremely intense attachment to the mother at this time, while at the same time he is required later to break more radically with this early dependency because the process of emancipation from the family of orientation is pushed farther and faster than in other systems. Independence training, that is to say, forms a particularly prominent part of our socialization process and the strength of the mother attachment is an essential condition of its successful carrying out.

The alienation involved in the motivation to illness may then be interpreted to involve alienation from a set of expectations which put particular stress on independent achievement. Because of this complex, the importance of the passivity component of the deviance expressed in illness is particularly great, because the ambivalent motivational structure about the dependency-independence problem is particularly prominent. Therapy then focuses on the strengthening of the motivation to independence relative to dependency and on overcoming the alienation, focussing on the expectations of independence and, through it, achievement.

I suggest, then, that the American pattern of illness is focussed on the problem of capacity for achievement for the individual person. Therapeutically, recovery is defined for him as a *job* to be done in cooperation with those who are technically qualified to help him. This focus then operates to polarize the components of the "problem" in such a way that *the primary threat to his achievement capacity which must be overcome is dependency.* The element of exemption from ordinary role-obligations may then be interpreted as permissiveness for temporary relief from the strains of trying hard to achieve. The patient is permitted to indulge his dependency needs under strictly regulated conditions, notably his recognition of the conditional nature of the legitimacy of his state, and exposure to the therapeutic task.

These elements of the situation relate in turn to the components of the therapeutic process. I have elsewhere designated these, in terms of role-pattern, as permissiveness, support, selective rewarding and reinforcement. An essential point is that the dependency component of the deviance of illness is used constructively in the therapeutic pattern, essentially through what is in certain respects a recapitulation of the socializing experience. This is to say that through permissiveness to express dependency, both in exemption from role-obligations and in supportive relations to others, the patient is encouraged to form a dependent attachment to others. The permissive and supportive treatment of the sick person, by giving him what he wants, undercuts the alienative component of the motivational structure of his illness. He finds it much more difficult to feel alienated toward social objects who treat him with kindness and consideration than he would otherwise be disposed to feel—though, of course, there may be a problem, particularly with some types of mental illness of getting him to accept such kindness and consideration, even to accept his need for the exemptions permitted by virtue of illness.

At the same time the element of dependency, through "transference," is the basis of a strong attachment to therapeutic personnel, which can then be used as a basis of leverage to motivate the therapeutic "work" which eventually should result in overcoming the dependency itself, or mitigating it sufficiently so that it no longer interferes so seriously with his capacities. Building on this, then, the active work of therapy, adapting to the fundamental conditions of the biological and psychological states of the patient, can take hold and operate to propel toward recovery.

I should finally like to turn to a brief and very tentative suggestion of the main differences between the orientations to illness in the United States and in two other modern societies, namely Soviet Russia and Great Britain. Let us take the Soviet case first.

Whereas in the American case I suggested that our concern with capacity for role-achievement put the primary emphasis on the restoration of that capacity through therapeutic work, the general orientation of Soviet society is different; it is to the attainment of a collective goal for the society as a whole, the "building of socialism." With reference to the problem of illness this tends to shift the emphasis from the obligation to cooperate in therapy to the problem of responsibility and non-responsibility. This is most conspicuous in the field of mental illness where the Soviet attitude is an extreme antithesis of our own precisely on this point. Once very telling expression of it is the complete prohibition of psychoanalysis, whereas psychoanalysis has had greater success in the United States than in any other country. My interpretation of this would be that psychoanalysis is a threat from the Soviet point of view, because through the theory of the unconscious, it so strongly emphasizes the elements in the personality of the individual which are outside his voluntary control. It would give too plausible excuses for too many for the evasion of responsibility. In the American case, on the other hand, psychoanalysis is defined more as offering *opportunity* for constructive therapeutic work, to the patient as well as the therapist.

The same general strain seems to be conspicuous, from Field's account, in the field of somatic medicine. The attitude seems to be one of reluctant concession to human frailties. Of course, it is part of socialism to have a national medical service, but at the same time party and administrative personnel keep strict watch on the medical people to be sure that they do not connive in malingering which—because of the great severity of labor discipline—they have been under strong pressure to do. To American eyes the Soviet treatment of illness seems to be marked by a certain perfunctoriness, as if it were up to the patient to prove that he is "really" sick rather than it being the physician's role to investigate the possibilities on his own. I suggest that this may be more than a matter of scarcity of personnel and resources; it is probably at least in part an authentic expression of Soviet values.

Reinforcing this conclusion is the probability that illness is not the primary type of deviance for Soviet society in the sense that I have argued it is in the American case. I think it probable that what I have called "compulsive acquiescence in status-expectations" is the most prominent type. This, of course, very generally does not appear overtly as deviance at all and hence is difficult to detect.

There is, however, another side of the Soviet picture, just as there is in the American case of polarity between the emphasis on active mastery and the problem of dependency. This is that in medical care, especially in the hospital, there seems to be a particularly strong supportive emphasis. This is to say that, once the status of being sick is granted, there is not nearly so strong an emphasis on the conditional character of its legitimacy as in the American case, and patients are encouraged to relax and to enjoy being taken care of.[30]

This suggests a permissiveness for regression, but one which is differently structured from the American. It is less the need to express dependency on particular social objects which does not threaten essential acceptance or belongingness. Psychologically it suggests primacy of oral components rather than of the mother-child love-attachment.

Thus, on the one hand, the role of illness is not given nearly so wide a scope in Soviet Russia as in the United States, particularly in the direction of mental illness. At the same time, it is also differently structured in that the primary focus is the problem of the responsibility of the individual rather than his capacity in our sense to achieve and to cooperate in recovery. The permissive element is more for "rest," for relaxation from responsibility, than it is for the direct expression of object-oriented dependency.

The British case does not seem to be quite so clear, but I think it is different in important ways from either the American or the Soviet. By contrast, with the other two, British society has a particularly strong integrative emphasis. From this point of view, illness is not so much a threat to the achievement of the individual or to his responsibility as it is a threat to his *status* as an acceptable member of the society and its various relevant subgroupings. The main emphasis in treatment then would be on reintegration, an element which is always present, but is more strongly stressed in the British case than in others.

One important type of evidence is the particularly strong British feeling that the sick individual has a *right* to care in case of illness. The whole welfare state is related to the integrative emphasis in the society, but the particularly full coverage provided by the National Health Service for the whole population is one very salient aspect of this general orientation. On the part of the nation and its health agencies then, it is strongly declared that illness, far from jeopardizing the individual's status, gives him special claims on the collectivity. The burden of proof is not nearly so much on him that he is "really" sick as in either the American or the Soviet cases. One might speak of a scale of decreasing "tolerance of the possibility of malingering" in the order, British, American, Soviet.

Another interesting point is that, with respect to the scope given to the recognition of mental illness, the British case is intermediate between the American and the Soviet; this includes the position of psychoanalysis. I suggest that this has to do with the very strong British emphasis on the importance of self-control in social relations. Somatic illness is generally clearly beyond the responsibility of the individual, and generally the legitimacy of illness is not made so highly conditional as in the American case. But capacity is not so highly valued and mental disturbance is not to the same extent seen as an opportunity for therapeutic achievement. The deliberately encouraged regression which, with all the differences, is shared by the Soviet and American cases, is substantially less conspicuous in the British.

The above are, as I have emphasized, extremely tentative and sketchy impressions of relatively systematic differences between American, Soviet, and British selectivities in the definition of health and illness, and in the roles of patient and of therapeutic agencies. I have introduced them and carried the analysis as far as I have, only to try to give some empirical substance to the general view of the nature of variability from one society to another in those respects that have been presented herein.

1.5

Constitution of the World Health Organization[1]

The States Parties to this Constitution declare, in conformity with the Charter of the United Nations, that the following principles are basic to the happiness, harmonious relations and security of all peoples:

Health is a state of complete physical, mental and social well-being and not merely the absence of disease or infirmity.
The enjoyment of the highest attainable standard of health is one of the fundamental rights of every human being without distinction of race, religion, political belief, economic or social condition.
The health of all peoples is fundamental to the attainment of peace and security and is dependent upon the fullest co-operation of individuals and States.
The achievement of any State in the promotion and protection of health is of value to all.
Unequal development in different countries in the promotion of health and control of disease, especially communicable disease, is a common danger.
Healthy development of the child is of basic importance; the ability to live harmoniously in a changing total environment is essential to such development.
The extention to all peoples of the benefits of medical, psychological and related knowledge is essential to the fullest attainment of health.
Informed opinion and active co-operation on the part of the public are of the utmost importance in the improvement of the health of the people.
Governments have a responsibility for the health of their peoples which can be fulfilled only by the provision of adequate health and social measures.

ACCEPTING THESE PRINCIPLES, and for the purpose of co-operation among themselves and with others to promote and protect the health of all peoples, the Contracting Parties agree to the present Constitution and hereby establish the World Health Organization as a specialized agency within the terms of Article 57 of the Charter of the United Nations.

---

1. Adopted by the International Health Conference held in New York from 19 June to 22 July 1946, and signed on 22 July 1946 by the representatives of sixty-one states (*Off. Rec. Wld Hlth Org.* 2, 100)

CHAPTER I—OBJECTIVE

Article 1

The objective of the World Health Organization (hereinafter called the Organization) shall be the attainment by all peoples of the highest possible level of health.

1.6

Concepts of Health—an Economist's Perspective

Victor R. Fuchs*

"What is health?" More particularly, "What is health from an economist's perspective?" Until recently, this question was seldom asked—and even more rarely answered. This paper does not propose a definitive reply but, rather, tries to clarify some of the underlying problems. After a brief introduction, I examine several different concepts of health and the relationships among them. The next section considers health as an object of choice, and the final section indicates some applications of health concepts in economic research.

As far as I can determine, there are no *economic* concepts of health. The concepts and measures of health that a few economists have attempted to incorporate into their theoretical models and empirical analyses (see, e.g., Grossman 1972, or Auster, Leveson, and Sarachek 1972) have come from other disciplines such as medicine, epidemiology, and demography. Economics is the study of the allocation of scarce resources among competing wants. Simply stated, economics is an intellectual "middleman" between nature and technology on the *supply* side and the preferences and desires of individuals and society on the *demand* side. Health, in various forms, enters on both sides of the equation. If people want to preserve and enhance their health and are willing to incur costs (monetary, time, psychic) to do so, economics has a role in broadening our understanding of the process by studying the effect of such factors as relative prices and income. If the health of the population affects the size or productivity of the work force or the demand for medical care, economics can play a role in tracing those relationships.

But which of the many concepts of health should the economist use? Should he (or she) adopt the World Health Organization definition, "A state of

*Stanford University and National Bureau of Economic Research. The author wishes to acknowledge helpful comments from Mark Pauly and Jan Platt and financial support from the Robert Wood Johnson Foundation. The manuscript has not undergone the review accorded official National Bureau of Economic Research publications; in particular, it has not been submitted for approval by the Board of Directors.

complete physical and mental and social well-being"? Or should he heed the wisdom of René Dubos (1959, p. 1), who wrote, "Complete freedom from disease and from struggle is almost incompatible with the process of living"? Shall the economist measure health by mortality, or morbidity, or disability, or the absence of pain? What is the economist to do with the statement of epidemiologist J. N. Morris (1964, p. 40) that "morbidity means what it is defined to mean: whether a subjective malaise, measurable evidence of disorder, pathology diagnosed by a doctor, or certified incapacity to work"?

Out of this welter of conflicting views and divergent measures, is there any reasonable rule or strategy to follow in applying economics to health? One approach that may be useful is that of *instrumentalism*, a version of pragmatism, discussed by philosopher Abraham Kaplan. According to Kaplan, instrumentalism identifies the procedures of analyzing concepts by an attempt to get at the use that is made of them. "What is insisted on is that language is an instrument, and that to use language is to perform an action. The analysis of meanings must therefore focus on the particular contexts in which the action is performed and on the purposes which the action as a whole is meant to achieve" (1964, p. 46). Thus, rather than look for some ideal concept of health, an economist should choose that concept which seems most useful for the particular problem under consideration.

A VARIETY OF CONCEPTS

Death rates are frequently used as indexes of health, because they are relatively objective, comparable, and available. There are, however, many different kinds of rates and many possible uses. For instance, the crude death rate can be a useful measure of health for short-run population projections or for prediction of the demand for funerary services, but age-specific rates become important if one wants to make long-run population projections or to predict the demand for schooling. The aggregation of age-specific rates into an age-adjusted mortality rate is useful for comparing populations with different age distributions but may yield ambiguous results, because different methods give different weights to the death rates at various ages. Again, the crucial point is for the investigator to have a clear idea as to what "action" depends upon the concept and measure being obtained. Death rates by cause of death can also provide useful information about the health of a population. For example, a finding that most deaths are attributable to infectious disease will point to different conclusions from one that shows heart disease and cancer as the major killers, even though the overall death rates are the same.

While different kinds of mortality measures can provide useful indications about the state of health of a population, and particularly about the effectiveness of various programs to improve health, they may be less satisfactory if one is interested in anticipating the demand for health care—that is, utilization of hospitals, physicians' services, and the like. In that case, morbidity would be a more useful measure of health, because it gives more weight to acute illnesses and chronic conditions which may consume large amounts of health services even when not life threatening.

The relationship between morbidity and the demand for medical care is itself very complex. As Kerr White has so graphically shown (1973, pp. 23–33), the morbidity which induces demand for ambulatory care (e.g., common colds, bronchitis, arthritis) tends to be very different from the morbidity which leads to hospitalization (e.g., heart disease, fractures and dislocations, mental disorders).

The interest in morbidity may, however, derive from an interest in labor force participation rather than in projecting demands for medical care. If so, different concepts of health become more important. Physiological impairment must be viewed in relation to available remedies and to expected functions. Ffrangcon Roberts reminds us that our standards of health vary according to the demands made on individuals by society. "A man who may be quite unfit to be an air-pilot may live a prosperous and healthy life as a hairdresser, while another may become an eminent political economist though a lifelong sufferer from asthma" (1952, p. 23). Or, to mention another well-known example, severe myopia is a serious health problem in the absence of corrective lenses but is much less so when they are available.

Moreover, the decision to seek work, just like the decision to seek medical care, is frequently influenced by much more than the health status of the individual as determined by objective measurements. There is a large subjective element in health, and the economic perspective alerts us to the possible influence of wage rates, prices, income, insurance, and similar variables on an individual's perception of his health status, or at least the outward expression of that perception.

RELATIONS AMONG CONCEPTS

While there is not perfect correlation among the different concepts and measures of health, it seems to me an error to assume that there is *no* relationship among them. I found a significant correlation across regions of the United States between age-adjusted mortality and various measures of morbidity (1965). Michael Grossman (1975) found a significant correlation across individuals between self-evaluation of health status ("Is your general health excellent, good, fair, or poor?") and weeks lost from work because of illness and an even stronger correlation between self-evaluation and number of symptoms reported.

Recent studies showing that the marginal contribution of medical care to life expectancy in developed countries is very small are sometimes met with the

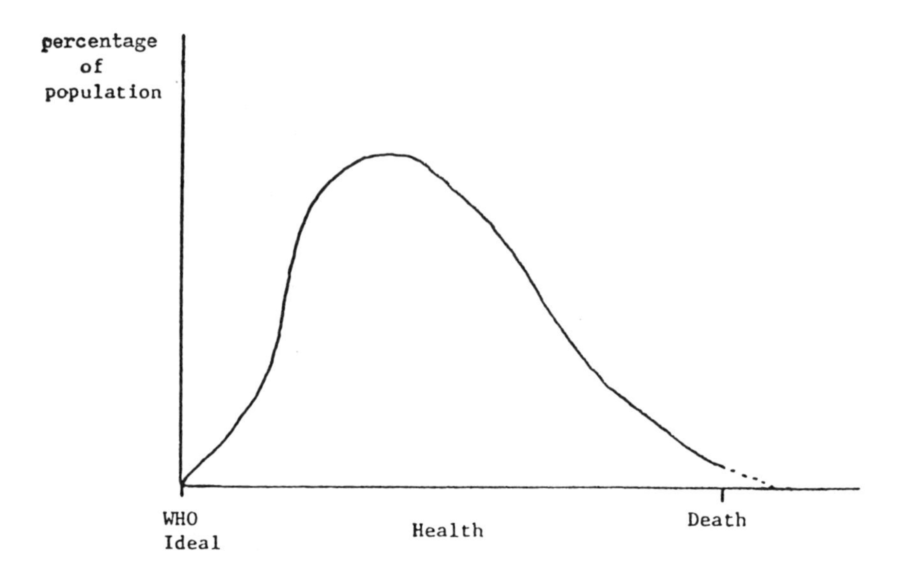

Fig. 1. Hypothetical distribution of population by level of health

assertion that, while care may not reduce mortality, it certainly is contributing to better health (measured in other ways). This may be correct, but the specification and measurement of these other ways and the significance of the marginal contribution of medical care to health (so measured) remains to be established.

It seems to me that death can be viewed as one end of a distribution of health conditions (see fig. 1). I suspect that most factors that reduce mortality also move the entire distribution (adjusted for age) to the left. Thus a finding of no significant relation between mortality and variable *X* would seem to put the burden of proof on those who claim that *X* is related to "health."

What about the distinction between mental health and physical health? In my view, too much is made of this distinction. From the economist's perspective, both are aspects of health: both can affect labor force participation and productivity, and both can be affected by genetics, the socio-economic environment, and personal behavior. Indeed, I will speculate that as we learn more about illness we will discover that even from a purely medical-clinical perspective the distinction has been exaggerated. "The head is connected to the body" is more than an anatomical description. Probably the most important difference is the extent to which it is currently possible to make diagnoses and prognoses; this affects insurability as well as social attitudes toward the two types of ill health.[1]

1. I am indebted to Dr. Herbert Leiderman for this point.

HEALTH AS AN OBJECT OF CHOICE

The economic perspective tends to emphasize that the health of an individual is, in part, under his or her control; it is not merely a "given." Most economists treat health as an object of choice. To be sure, this choice is subject to constraints—genetic endowment, income, information, and the like—but within those constraints the economic perspective focuses on the choices individuals make. In this respect, health does not differ from any other object of choice—all are subject to constraints. The important point is that, in both the getting and spending of income, individuals make choices which affect their health. The economist is particularly interested in how these choices are influenced by relative prices.

But can one put a price on health? Here the economist's reply is much the same as that of the old-timer who was asked if he believed in baptism: "Believe in it?" he said. "I not only believe in it, I've seen it." Not only is it theoretically possible to put a price on health, but, if we observe people's behavior, we can see that they frequently do. Some economists have even attempted to estimate that price. For instance, in an analysis of wage differentials among occupations that have different mortality rates, Richard Thaler and Sherwin Rosen (1975) found that the more hazardous occupations did seem to pay a premium (other things held constant) and that the size of the premium suggests an average valuation of life of about $200,000.

Notice that it is important to distinguish between the price one might place on *certain* death and the price one might place on the probability of death varying by a small amount. For instance, an individual might be unwilling to accept certain death tomorrow, even if offered $10 million, but he/she might be willing to undertake a task with 1/1000 chance of death in return for a payment of $10,000 (Bergstrom, 1974). This is *not* because individuals underestimate the probability of an adverse event when the probability is small. It is, rather, analogous to the case of an individual being willing to give up one unit of commodity X (which he normally consumes in quantity q) for price p, while being unwilling to give up consuming X entirely for pq.

It is readily apparent that individuals do consider trade-offs between health and other goals. (Shall I give up $25 to find out if this is a pimple, a wart, or a tumor? Shall I give up eating steak in order to reduce the probability of having a heart attack?) This suggests another distinctive aspect of the economist's perspective—namely, the determination of the optimal level of health. For the economist, the optimal level is usually much lower than is technically attainable. It is the level at which the marginal value of an additional increment of health (however measured) is equal to the value of what is foregone in order to obtain that increment.

This is not to say, however, that free individual choice always results in a socially optimal level of health. If there are significant *external benefits* from good health—that is, an improvement in your health benefits others, and there is no feasible way of arranging compensation for that benefit—a free-market approach may result in suboptimal levels of health, and collective intervention (through subsidies or other means) may be justified to achieve a more efficient allocation of resources. The benefit to others may arise because their health depends, in part, on your health—as in the case of communicable disease—or your ill health may simply be a source of disutility to them.

USE OF HEALTH IN ECONOMIC RESEARCH

I have tried to indicate some of the conceptual problems faced by economists in studying health. I shall conclude with a few specific examples of the use of health in economic studies. Some treat health as the *dependent* variable; others use health as an *independent* variable.

Most of the attempts to explain variation in health across populations use life expectancy—as inferred from age-specific or age-adjusted mortality rates—as the basic concept of health. The principal explanatory variables are income, education, and inputs of medical care; and the units of observation are typically countries, states, or cities. These studies generally show health to have a very strong positive relation to education, a very slight relation to medical care (measured either by expenditures or physical units such as number of physicians or hospital beds) and no significant relation to per capita income.

The last finding runs contrary to the notion that poverty is a significant cause of premature death, but it can be reconciled in at least two ways. First, the attribution of ill health and death to "poverty" is usually qualified by the statement that "poverty" does not refer only to income levels but to an entire set of cultural and social factors. To the extent that it is these other factors and not income per se that makes the difference, the conventional wisdom is not at odds with the statistical results. Second, it is probably true that, at very low levels of income, there is a significant positive effect of rising income on life expectancy; but, over the range of variation observed in current comparisons across states or developed nations, the marginal effect is insignificant (see fig. 2).

Health as the object of explanation has also been measured by disability days lost from work and self-evaluation of health status. In general, the results of these analyses have been similar to those obtained from studies of mortality. It is indeed striking that variation across individuals in their subjective evaluation of health shows the same relationships as does variation in age-adjusted mortality across states.

Other variables that have been found to be significant in studies that attempt to explain health are marital status and (for male mortality) education of wife. The greater differential by marital status for males than for females (Fuchs 1974) reinforces the economist's view that health is in part "produced" in the

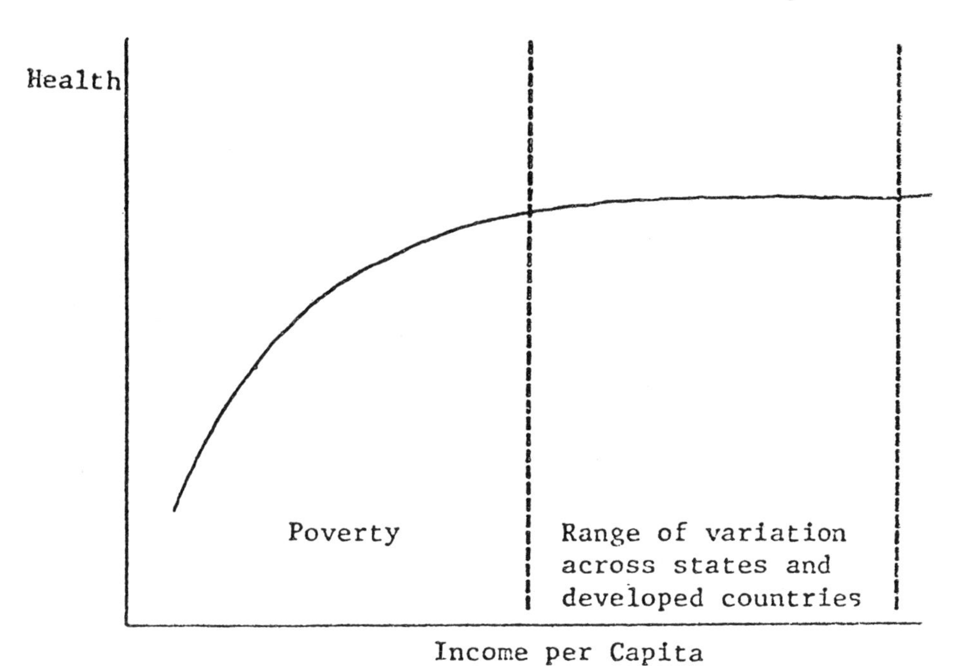

Fig. 2. Relation between health and income per capita

home and that the wife's "input" is probably more significant than the husband's.

Numerous measures of health have been used as "independent" variables in attempts to explain variations in earnings, productivity, school performance, fertility, and the demand for medical care. The particular health concept chosen has depended upon the data available and a priori judgments concerning which aspect of health is likely to be most relevant. Thus some examples are child mortality to explain variations in birthrates (Stettler 1970), number of symptoms and self-evaluation of health status to explain hours of work and wage rates (Grossman and Benham 1974), infant mortality to explain output per agricultural worker (Malenbaum 1970), and symptoms and chronic conditions to explain variations in utilization of medical care (Luft, Hershey, and Gianaris 1974).

Research on health by economists is growing at an exponential rate. Health professionals and policymakers, having ignored economics for many decades, now seem inclined to go to the other extreme. While the economist's perspective does frequently throw new light on health problems and can contribute to better decision making, it is important to be aware of the limits of economics (Fuchs 1975) and of the political, social, and ethical aspects of health.

REFERENCES

Auster, Richard; Leveson, Irving; and Saracheck, Deborah. "The Production of Health, an Exploratory Study." In *Essays in the Economics of Health and Medical Care*, edited by Victor R. Fuchs. New York: National Bureau of Economic Research, Inc., 1972.

Bergstrom, Theodore C. "Preference and Choice in Matters of Life and Death." Unpublished paper, 1974.

Dubos, René. *The Mirage of Health.* New York: Harper & Bros., 1959.

Fuchs, Victor R. "Some Economic Aspects of Mortality in the United States." Mimeographed. New York: National Bureau of Economic Research, Inc., 1965.

Fuchs, Victor R. "Some Economic Aspects of Mortality in Developed Countries." In *The Economics of Health and Medical Care. Proceedings of a Conference Held by the International Economic Association at Tokyo, April 1973*, edited by Mark Perlman. London: Macmillan Press; New York: Halsted Press, 1974.

Fuchs, Victor R. *Who Shall Live? Health, Economics, and Social Choice.* New York: Basic Books, 1975.

Grossman, Michael. *The Demand for Health: A Theoretical and Empirical Investigation.* National Bureau of Economic Research Occasional Paper, no. 119. New York: National Bureau of Economic Research, Inc., 1972.

Grossman, Michael. "The Correlation between Health and Schooling." In *Household Production and Consumption*, edited by Nestor Terleckyj. Income and Wealth Series, no. 40. New York: National Bureau of Economic Research, Inc., 1975.

Grossman, Michael, and Benham, Lee. "Health, Hours and Wages." In *The Economics of Health and Medical Care. Proceedings of a Conference Held by the International Economic Association at Tokyo, April 1973*, edited by Mark Perlman. London: Macmillan Press; New York: Halsted Press, 1974.

Kaplan, Abraham. *The Conduct of Inquiry.* Scranton, Pa.: Chandler Publishing Co., 1964.

Luft, Harold S.; Hershey, John C.; and Gianaris, Joan M. "Factors Affecting the Use of Physicians' Services in a Rural Community." Mimeographed. Stanford, Calif.: Stanford University School of Medicine, December 1974.

Malenbaum, Wilfred. "Health and Productivity in Poor Areas." In *Empirical Studies in Health Economics*, edited by Herbert E. Klarman. Proceedings of the Second Conference on the Economics of Health, Johns Hopkins University, Baltimore, 1968. Baltimore: Johns Hopkins Press, 1970.

Morris, J.N. *Uses of Epidemiology.* 2d ed. Baltimore: Williams & Wilkins Co., 1964.

Roberts, Ffrangcon. *The Cost of Health.* London: Turnstyle Press, 1952.

Stettler, H. Louis, III. "The New England Throat Distemper and Family Size." In *Empirical Studies in Health Economics*, edited by Herbert E. Klarman. Proceedings of the Second Conference on the Economics of Health, Johns Hopkins University, Baltimore, 1968. Baltimore: Johns Hopkins Press, 1970.

Thaler, Richard, and Rosen, Sherwin. "The Value of Saving a Life: Evidence from the Labor Market." In *Household Production and Consumption*, edited by Nestor Terleckyj. Income and Wealth Series, no. 40. New York: National Bureau of Economic Research, Inc., 1975.

White, Kerr L. "Life and Death and Medicine." *Scientific American* 229, no. 3 (September 1973): 16, 22–33, 198.

1.7

Ethical Components in the Definition of Health

Mervyn Susser

In epidemiology, the definition of health sets bounds to the subject. The way health is defined is a necessary antecedent of the way health is measured. The place of ethics is less obvious. Ethics, in one meaning given by the *Oxford English Dictionary*, is a code of conduct. This is the meaning used in the codes of medical associations throughout the western world. These codes often deal with the most particular conduct. The codes appear to legislate courtesies among doctors; they are concerned with who may refer patients to whom, and who may receive patients directly; who may carry out what treatments on which patients; and what advertisement is permissible. In these aspects, the codes can be seen as rules stemming from the monopoly of the profession over the treatment and care of patients; they regulate competitive and monetary relations. For the purpose of this discussion, we must find a broader meaning for ethics than these rules of etiquette.

Another definition of the *Oxford English Dictionary* describes ethics as the "science of morals." Morals rest on values; values provide the criteria by which to evaluate the moral worth or virtue of particular conduct. These values are not, as the Judicial Council of the American Medical Association has held, "uniform in application and universal in their acceptance" (1). The sophists acquired lasting discredit by arguing the uncomfortable truth that morals are relative. Karl Marx and Emil Durkheim among others (uneasy as that pairing may be) taught us further that the relativity of morals and values derives from the structure of societies and the context of social groups.

The incursion of social science into the health field has made familiar the notion that values are determinants of the health behavior of patients, health professionals, communities, and social classes. The notion is not a new one, as shown by an ancient piece of Socratic dialogue from Book III of Plato's *Republic* :

> ...Aesculapius was aware that in all well-regulated communities, each has work assigned to him in the state which he must needs do, and that no one has leisure to spend his life as an invalid in the doctor's hands: a fact which we perceive in the case of the laboring populations, but which with ludicrous inconsistency we fail to detect in the case of those who are rich and happy.
>
> When a carpenter is ill, he expects to receive a draught from his doctor, that will expel the disease by vomiting or purging, or else to get rid of it by cauterizing, or a surgical operation; but if any one were to prescribe for him a long course of diet, and to order bandages for his head, with other treatment to correspond, he would soon tell such a medical advisor that he had no time to be ill, and hint that it was not worth his while to live in this way, devoting his mind to his malady, and neglecting his proper occupation: and then, wishing his physician a good morning, he would enter upon his usual course of life, and either regain his health and live in the performance of his business; or, should his constitution prove unable to bear up, death puts an end to his troubles. Yes, and for a man in that station of life, this is thought the proper use to make of medical assistance....

My concern will be with the health definitions of the physician rather than of the carpenter. I shall argue that any definition of health incorporates values that bear on ethics, and that these definitions vary as values vary. The definition of health depends on who is defining it. I aim to show also that the search for the components of health definitions is not a mere exercise in speculative metaphysics. The values that underlie different health definitions do indeed provide a code, or rationalization, for the conduct of health professionals, and hence for the differing content and quality of health services they provide.

Stated otherwise, the ethical and value content of definitions of health have consequences as well as causes, some intended by the users of the definition and many unintended. What is included in the definition is justified by appeals to an altruism that rises above the self-interest of the group offering the definition. Yet by diligent investigation, one will hardly fail to discover sources of the definition in the social, political, and economic interests of the time. Values have their underlying causes in economic and class interests, in political and social power, and in the culture created by the historical evolution of the social structure and traditions of societies.

Health, we can all agree, is a state of being: health describes the state of individuals in relation to a concept of normality. But the concept of normality is not simple, for at least three concepts are involved. In a first sense of pathology, normality is generally perceived as dichotomous; the disease is either present or absent. Abnormality is all that is disordered, impaired, or diseased; normality (or health) is the absence of disorder, impairment, or disease. In a second statistical sense, normality for a specified condition is defined from its modal distribution in a population. Ill-health is defined by deviations from mode or mean. Mental deficiency, hypertension, and obesity are often defined in this way. In a third social sense, however, normality is defined by values. Ideal norms point to how things ought to be: with regard to health, the idea of positive health belongs in this category. Norms of expectation define what is expected by a given social group. This asks for something less than the ideal of positive health: no more, perhaps, than that an individual should be healthy enough to carry out independently his daily roles. Norms of behavior define the state of things in actuality, in contrast with what is expected. Anyone who has undertaken measurements in populations will know how large the discrepancies can be between expectation and actuality.

All these elements of normality, the pathologic and statistical and not only the social, are bound up with values. Each element enters into the most famous of all definitions of health, that of the World Health Organization in 1948: a state of complete physical, mental, and social well-being and not merely the absence of disease. This definition has been criticized by many, including myself, partly because the definition rests on an aspiration to an ideal and unattainable state, and partly because it has seemed too imprecise for the practical purposes of measurement. On further reflection, I have come to think the criticism ill-advised; there is more danger in encouraging the fallacy that what can only be narrowly measured must also be narrowly conceived, than in aspiring to measure or attain an ideal. Moreover, by imaginative methods, the definition can probably be made operational. To accept less is to support the status quo, a not uncommon position for the health professions despite their avowed altruism and implicit reformism.

I shall consider the components of the definition of health first in the dimension of depth, and then in the dimension of breadth. By the dimension in depth I mean components at successive and increasingly complex levels of organization, each of which can be conceived as subsystems, one encompassing another: thus states of health can be defined in relation to an organic level, to a functional level, and to a social level (2).

At the organic level, we refer to organic and physiologic disorder best described as disease (if in process), or as impairment (if static and persistent). These conditions are confined to the individual organism. At the functional level of health disorder, we refer to a subjective state of psychologic awareness of dysfunction best described as illness (if in process), or as disability (if static and persisting). These conditions too are confined to the individual organism. At the social level, we have learned from Henry Sigerist (3) and Talcott Parsons (4) to refer to a state of social dysfunction, a social role assumed by the individual, best described as sickness (if in process), or as handicap (if static and persisting). Social roles are defined by the expectations of society, and involve the state of relations with others; by definition they extend beyond the individual organism.

No sooner have we described and defined a social state of health, than the place of value systems and social structure in determining the assignment of the roles of sickness and handicap is immediately evident. Values and social structure account for much of the lack of correspondence between the existence of organic disease, of illness, and of the sick role. Millions of Africans and Asians suffer from the organic diseases of malaria or severe malnutrition without assuming the sick role. Likewise, many working-class Englishmen suffer from bronchitis, and many Puerto Ricans in New York suffer from bilharzia, and have not assumed the sick role. Conversely, persons may be assigned the role of sickness or handicap who have no illness or disability and no organic disease or impairment. Institutions for mental sickness and mental deficiency provide perhaps the most notorious examples: about a decade ago, about 10 percent of a sample of inmates of mental deficiency hospitals in England had IQs above a defined functional threshold of mental subnormality, and many were without organic impairment as well.

The intervening factors between definitions of health disorders at one level and the next from which such discrepancies arise go beyond imprecise clinical diagnoses. The great part of the discrepancies arise from the variability in the social component, particularly the component of values and ethics, in the definition of social roles. Any social role has a moral content; it carries obligations and duties. Role also relates to a particular status in the social system. The diagnosis or label by which the sick role is rationalized and legitimized influences the prestige of the assigned status. In the United States, for instance, the element of prestige has been demonstrated by the reluctance of psychiatrists to assign the stigmatized diagnosis of schizophrenia to higher class persons. Moreover, the values that underlie these responses to social stigma change over time. Florence Nightingale was for years confined to her couch by what would now be labeled an anxiety hysteria; she was disabled in a functional sense. No woman so disabled and so labeled in our time, I believe, could wield the influence Florence Nightingale did over national policy. From her couch she developed the major health policies of the War Office, and later the India Office (5). The great epidemiologist William Farr, one might fairly say, was her willing research associate, and Sir Sidney Herbert, brilliant heir of an earl and a major political figure, her project director.

The functions of the health professions relate to each of these levels of organization of health states we have described. In industrial societies, the avowed function of medicine is at the organic level, to cure and prevent disease. It is quite evident also that medicine has a function at the personal level, to reassure and allay anxiety in individuals who seek medical help. The function of medicine at the social level is to rationalize and legitimize the assumption of the sick role. Sickness in this sense is a deviation from the norms for the everyday performance of social roles. All societies have social mechanisms to deal with the strains and conflicts that deviance of any kind creates (4). In simpler societies, the sick may be treated by traditional doctors or priests or lay healers. In industrial societies, the sick are dealt with by a vast and growing system of medical care. This expansion of modern medical care rests on ever-narrowing specialisms based on discrete organ systems or on particular techniques. Paradoxically, there has been a simultaneous extension of the bounds of medical competence, not only technically, but into the field of personal and social problems. These extensions into the personal and social field help to adjust the capacities of individuals to the complicated demands of contemporary society. In such a situation the health professions are not, as some may like to see themselves, neutral or scientifically detached about values: they are a part of the system of social control.

These personal and social extensions of the competencies of health professions bring us to the examination of the definition of health along the second dimension, of components in breadth. Here I shall be concerned with those components of the definition of health that relate to new areas in which the health professions have claimed concern and competence. Extensions of the definition occur when departures from the norms of various forms of behavior are redefined and co-opted as part of health and its disorders; alternatively, departures from norms previously accepted as health disorders can be rejected. Thus the definition of health was narrowed when traditional doctors gave up the function of detecting witches which was theirs in tribal society, and narrowed again when they gave up their medieval function of diagnosing and exorcising devils (which was, indubitably, often depressive illness). More recently, the definition of health was expanded when depressive illnesses, suicide and attempted suicide, and criminality were once more redefined and co-opted into the sphere of medical competence in the guise of genetic and psychiatric disorders.

These changes in the definition of health have implications at the organic level as well as at the functional and social levels. As Raymond Illsley (6) has illustrated, the policies of the specialty of obstetrics and gynecology toward family planning and abortion provide an example of the entry of ethics and values into technical health procedures ostensibly limited to the organic level. In part medicine changes its jurisdiction and its values as an adaptation to social and technical change. In part it does so as a vehicle of society at large: in this larger context, controversial ethical and political issues can be removed from the political arena by reclassification as health issues. We observe both these processes, adaptation to social change and the defusing of issues, in the history of obstetrics and gynecology.

RELATION OF ORGANIZED OBSTETRICS TO FAMILY PLANNING AND ABORTION

As with other major specialties, obstetrics during this century has shifted its practice from the home to the hospital. In the hospital, the social role of sickness or any other socially defined need for medical care is in one clear sense mistreated, in that it is always treated as if it were disease. Thus, obstetric care, like other intramural and specialist care, could become depersonalized. In the obstetric hospital, the technical expertise of an array of specialists has been brought to bear at successive prenatal visits and at delivery. Continuity among the various obstetricians, midwives, dietitians, anesthetists, radiologists, neonatologists, clinical pathologists, and others has rested on a common record system, not on personal contact. A woman with multiple roles in society has been transformed into a patient with all her latent roles suppressed. She has become a case, the object of detached scientific study and decision from which irrelevant nonscientific values are, if not excluded, reduced to a minimum. Technical expertise is freed to do its best, which is to do in the most efficient way possible what has to be done.

Parallel with the technical and organizational changes of obstetrics, the family planning movement developed alongside the movement for women's rights. From this movement the obstetric profession stood aside, although some courageous individuals did not. Obstetricians generally espoused the position that they were practitioners who cultivated a detached scientific judgment, value-free and standing apart from political and ethical controversy. Moreover, the Hippocratic oath forbids abortion. Hence, within the definition of what was a health concern, the function of obstetricians was to promote fertility and to sustain pregnancies to term. As a result, the position of scientific neutrality toward moral concerns was far from a position of ethical neutrality. The professional stance was in fact a support for the status quo in favor of the dominant social and political morality, in favor of the traditional view of marriage, of the family, and of the relations between the sexes, and even responsive to the population policies of the time (7).

Among the questions raised by the family planning and women's rights movements, the demand for legalized abortion posed the most acute and embarrassing challenge for obstetrics. The medical monopoly over this procedure for fertility control, in contrast with contraceptives, meant that safe abortion was denied to any woman who insisted on abortion. Gradually the abstention of obstetricians was eroded by humanist pressures. The discovery of teratogens like rubella and thalidomide helped in the erosion, but most of all the infiltration of issues of mental health undermined the established position. Finally, what had become an acute political and moral issue was depoliticized by making the right to abortion a matter of technical medical judgment. Renée Fox (8) has pointed out how instructive was the judgment of the Supreme Court that accomplished this shift in the United States. The judges provided various legal grounds for abortion, including particularly the health of the mother. At the same time they extended the definition of maternal health to defuse many questions of values. Included under the definition of health effects were such circumstances as "the stigma of unwed motherhood" and "the distress for all concerned associated with the unwanted child."

PSYCHIATRY AND THE LAW

Psychiatry will serve as a second specialty to illustrate the plasticity in breadth of the components of the definition of health. To emphasize the ethical content of psychiatry, one may note by the way that a major therapeutic reform movement of psychiatry—in the first half of the 19th century—was called "moral treatment." However technical and scientifically detached psychiatry may become, concern with behavior and the frequent absence of organic impairment concentrates attention on the personal and social level of health. Nonetheless, the technical model of scientific neutrality is sustained as in other specializations, in this instance by detaching the psyche from the person and converting the person into the case.

The use of psychiatry as an instrument of social control emerges clearly in the shifts in definition that have flowed from its relations with the law. An historic conflict has existed between the medical view that a criminal may be mentally disordered and in need of medical treatment, and the legal view that a criminal is responsible for his antisocial acts and should be punished. In past decades, many male homosexuals were saved from legal penalties by the classification of homosexuality under the diagnostic rubric of psychiatric disorder. Now, under the impetus of the movement for rights for all minority groups including homosexuals, homosexuality has been "laundered" psychiatrically as well as legally, by being removed from the diagnostic list of the American Psychiatric Association and declared healthy.

The inclusion of deviant behavior within the definition of mental health disorders enabled fierce moral issues to be circumvented, and made more humane treatment possible for many criminals. Consequently, the legal system and the system of medical care provide alternative and even competing mechanisms for dealing with the social strains of deviance. The last hundred years have seen the rise of large institutions for custodial care of mental disorder. For patients suffering from severe organic disorder, these institutions provide substitute homes and social and nursing care. For patients classified as psychopaths and sociopaths, high-grade mental retardates, and narcotic addicts, and for some with functional psychosis, these institutions could be said to provide substitute gaols, rather than substitute homes. They have been one means of containing and disciplining individuals whose behavior, while not criminal, deviated from standards acceptable to the values of communities (9).

Some of the more inappropriate claims to extend the competence of psychiatry have not been institutionalized. To seek the causes of war in the causes of individual aggression is a gross instance of the ecologic fallacy; so too is the attempt to explain away radical movements (most recently the student movement of the late 1960s) in terms of Oedipal problems. The ecologic fallacy is committed when events occurring on one level of organization are offered as causal explanations of manifestations occurring at another level. Errors of that kind have led some contemporary social publicists to prefer the due process of the law above the empathy of psychiatry in the adjudication of deviance.

HISTORICAL EVOLUTION OF THE RESPONSIBILITIES OF PUBLIC HEALTH

Public health offers another rich source of illustrative ethical shifts in the definition of health. The public health movement had its origins in a fundamental change in values that accompanied new concepts of the responsibilities of the state that preceded the French Revolution and became institutionalized by it. The rationalizing philosophy of the early public health movement in 19th-century Britain flowed from Jeremy Bentham and the Utilitarians (10). To my naive eye, the Utilitarian philosophy entrenched not only the liberal idea of the maximum good for the maximum number, but the seeds of cost-effectiveness analysis. The Poor Law of 1832 contained the stringent condition of "less eligibility": eleemosynary support should always be less attractive to individuals than support acquired by their labor. The architect of that law was the utilitarian Edwin Chadwick. Chadwick was also the executive architect of the early public health movement.

Thus the justifications for the shifts in values that occurred with the early public health movement were not only altruistic, although public health was of necessity a reformist and sometimes a radical movement. Chadwick's report (11) on the sanitary condition of the laboring population of Great Britain of 1842 pointed to the same set of conditions as Friedrich Engels' report (12) on the condition of the English working class in 1844. Chadwick's solutions were offered in the Public Health Act of 1848; Engels' solutions were offered in the *Communist Manifesto* of the same year. Chadwick offered solutions that would reform and sustain the existing political system; Engels offered solutions that would revolutionize it. The public health movement was a necessity for the survival of the burgeoning cities created by 19th-century industrial capitalism (13).

Public health was nonetheless radical in a real sense. Its originality was to attack disease and poverty in the community at large at their perceived source in the environment. Previously the positive pursuit of health had found a place in the teachings of Galen, and those who followed him, at an individual level only. The pursuit of community health at the population level was something new, and the assumption of state responsibility for maintaining community health was equally so (if one puts aside the acute emergencies of plague and other epidemics). It is no surprise to find that John Simon, a major force in the public health movement and the first medical officer of health of London, and later of England, was a socialist of sorts (14).

Conflict quickly surfaced between the new ethic implicit in a definition of health that included the public health, and the old ethic implicit in the one-to-one responsibilities of physicians for individual patients. It may not be an accident that neither Edwin Chadwick, the major early protagonist of public health in Britain, nor Lemuel Shattuck, the equivalent figure in the United States, was a physician (although both, it is true, were ably supported by physicians). Even Simon and Chadwick were often in conflict (14). Simon was a physician who had the respect of the leading medical establishment. Chadwick's forces campaigned against that establishment, which they saw as sustaining the status quo and its own self-interest. In the United States and elsewhere, this conflict of values persists more than a century after it arose, and the issues remain essentially the same. Individual practitioners resist the incursions of public care into their private ministrations; they see their power, their control over their modes of practice, their relations with patients, and their economic interests threatened thereby. Public administrators seek to extend public health care more broadly; they see the public health, and their own power and prestige, advanced thereby.

Although these conflicts have seemed so unchanging, the definitions of the public health have changed as society changed. At first the concerns of public health were with the physical environment: water, sewage, food, working conditions, and housing. Later, as the miasma theory gave way to the germ theory, concern focused on the biologic environment. Around the turn of the century, attention shifted to mothers and children and the reproductive process (15). This shift in the priorities of public health greatly sharpened the conflict between public health and individual medical practice, because it led to the intrusion of public health into individual care through antenatal and well-baby clinics.

There was nothing inevitable about these developments. The extensions of the definitions of health were each time created by shifts in values occasioned by particular circumstances. By the turn of the century, substantial gains had been made in the matter of adult and child mortality, especially in deaths due to tuberculosis, smallpox, scarlet fever, typhoid, cholera, and other enteric diseases, whereas infant mortality rates had remained unchanged (16). The concern with infant health that then arose remained dominant in public health for the whole of the first half of this century. For instance, in the Dutch famine of 1944–1945, it seemed self-evident to the Dutch administrators in charge of food rations that infants had first claim (17). This is a matter of relative values. By contrast with the Dutch, in the famine of 1967 during the Biafran War of Secession, many Nigerian officials considered that adults of reproductive age should have priority. Familiar with high infant mortality and high fertility rates, they argued that infants were more easily replaceable than adults.

To take another example, the institution of a school health service throughout Britain in 1907 followed from the alarming report of the National Commission on Physical Deterioration. The immediate brief of that Commission had been to study the extremely high rejection rate for the armed forces during recruitment for the Boer War. This civilian institution was in fact a secondary benefit of a military need.

We should note here that the shifts in priorities toward preventive health care for mothers and their children entailed a change in the type of operations that were considered legitimate for public health, and not only a change in the targets of these operations. There had become available an ethical justification for public health action in personal as well as in community health. The road was open for action directed toward health that had as its central concern the personal behavior of individuals; their methods of childbearing and child rearing, their recreations, their use of alcohol and tobacco, their partners in copulation, all became the subject of scientific judgments about the protection of the public health. One does not need a thorough acquaintance with history to know that among these scientific judgments about behavior lurked moral and ethical judgments.

Just as the school health services in Britain could be seen as a response to military needs, the institution of national health insurance by Lloyd George's government in 1911 can be interpreted as a response to industrial needs. That Act provided strictly for workers alone and not for their families. It can be seen as a measure to meet the needs of industry for productivity, while at the same time soothing industrial unrest, rather than as an address to the health problems of the time. The alternative approach, indeed, was put by Sidney and Beatrice Webb in the Minority Report of the Commission that led to the Act of 1911 (18). They argued against private curative services and for integrated services for prevention and care under local public health authorities. Although the Webbs did not prevail, there was bitter resistance to the bill from the medical profession. Medical opposition was directed to the changes that made this legislation significant in the long run for public health in Britain. The protection of the public health had provided the ethical legitimation for state action in dealing first with the physical and social environment, and then with personal prevention successively for infants, mothers, and schoolchildren. The Act signalled the entry of the state into the delivery of medical care, as distinct from preventive services.

Thus shifts in values and consequently in the definition of the content of public health have been constant throughout its history. They have nearly always been justified by altruistic appeals to health needs. The altruism is genuine enough, but has often harnessed forces that are far from altruistic with regard to health. It is well for the lamb to know that it has lain down with the lion.

In the matter of medical care, public health lies down with the lions of politics and ideology. The development of primary medical care through neighborhood health centers provides a case illustration. In this regard, the objectives of the initiators of the Office of Economic Opportunity had as much a political as a health motivation (19). This was probably true also of many who directed such health centers, as Elinson and Herr have reported (20). One can sympathize with the needs that were served in that manner, not least because my own debut as an independent health professional was similar. Four of us, recent medical graduates, constituted what might now be described as a medical collective. To our surprise, we were given charge of a neighborhood health center which served a large black ghetto on the outskirts of Johannesburg. In that community we sought to stimulate demands for health and welfare services. By providing a comprehensive community health service of a high order, we hoped to make people aware of possibilities they could not otherwise imagine (21). In the South African political system such efforts had a short half-life. Similar political realities are illustrated on a national scale by the recent reversal of the health initiatives undertaken by the late Allende government in Chile.

The efforts of the Nixon administration to reverse health policies have been less extreme but more sophisticated. The justifications are often mounted in the language of costs and benefits, and seemingly cut the ground from under public health opposition. In espousing cost-benefit analysis, public health follows a long tradition, one that began with William Petty (15), was revived by Chadwick (11) after a long quiescence, and was further developed by William

Farr (22). John Simon constantly evaluated and monitored his programs. But the dimensions of evaluation have narrowed. People, communities, and patients have been converted into consumers; health services and professionals have been converted into providers. The lion of economics enters as one who "has been involved... because he represents no vested interest group" (23).

The claim of disinterestedness is not defensible. The orthodox economist is concerned primarily with monetary values or monetary equivalents of other values in a given economic system, and in the relatively short term. This range of values tends to be narrow even when broadly interpreted, and places the health economist at special hazard of substituting narrow measures for broad effects and benefits. Thus a few years ago an early effort at cost-benefit analysis (admittedly carried out by an amateur) concluded that the deaths and the morbidity that could be prevented by immunizing the children of Indian reservations against measles did not justify the costs. The analyst omitted to measure some of the broader benefits, say the maintenance of a minority culture or the expiation of historic guilt by a dominant culture.

Yet we owe a debt to more conscious analysts who ask sophisticated questions about comparative benefits (23). Such analysts can force us to recognize that ethical judgments are all the time being made through the choice of priorities consequent on our definitions of health. They can oblige us to consider the equality of treatment accorded to the infant, the child, the adult, and the aged, to the sick and the well, to the white and the black, to the male and the female, to the mentally disordered and the physically disordered, to the individual with a damaged brain and one with a damaged kidney. As Rashi Fein has aptly noted, these questions are not often asked but they are all the time being answered.

REFERENCES

1. Romanell, P. A philosophic preface to morals in medicine. *Bull. N.Y. Acad. Med.* 50: 3–27, 1974.
2. Susser, M. *Causal Thinking in the Health Sciences. Concepts and Strategies in Epidemiology.* Oxford University Press, New York, 1973.
3. Sigerist, H.E. Die Sonderstellung des Kranken. *Kyklos* 2: 11–20. Translated in *The Sociology of Medicine*, edited by M.I. Roemer. McGraw-Hill, New York, 1960.
4. Parsons, T. *The Social System.* The Free Press of Glencoe, Glencoe, Ill., 1951.
5. Smith, C.W. *Florence Nightingale.* Constable, London, 1950.
6. Illsley, R. Developments in the role of medicine in relation to reproduction. Paper presented at the Warsaw Conference on the Sociology of Medicine, Jablonna, August 20–24, 1973.
7. Taylor, H.C. The ethics of the physician in human reproduction. In *Humanistic Perspectives in Medical Ethics*, edited by M.B. Visscher. Prometheus Books, Buffalo, N.Y., 1972.

8. Fox, R. Ethical and existential development in contemporaneous American medicine. Their implications for culture. Paper presented at the Warsaw Conference on the Sociology of Medicine, Jablonna, August 20–24, 1973.
9. Susser, M. *Community Psychiatry. Epidemiologic and Social Themes*. Random House, New York, 1968.
10. Simon, J. *English Sanitary Institutions Reviewed in Their Course of Development and in Some of Their Political and Social Relations*. Cassel, London, 1890.
11. Chadwick, E. *Report on an Inquiry into the Sanitary Conditions of the Labouring Population of Great Britain*, 1842 (reprinted Edinburgh University Press, Edinburgh, 1965).
12. Engels, F. *The Condition of the Working Class in England in 1844*, Ed. 1, 1845 (in German); English translation, J.W. Lovell Company, New York, 1887.
13. Rosen, G. Disease, debility, and death. In *The Victorian City: Images and Realities*, edited by H. J. Dyos, pp. 625–667. Routledge and Kegan Paul, London, 1973.
14. Lambert, R. *Sir John Simon (1816–1904) and English Social Administration*. McGibbon and Kee, London, 1963.
15. Rosen, G. *A History of Public Health*. MD Publications, Inc., New York, 1958.
16. McKeown, T., and Record, R.G. Reasons for the decline of mortality in England and Wales during the nineteenth century. *Population Studies* 16: 94–127, 1962.
17. Stein, Z.A., Susser, M.W., Saenger, G., and Marolla, F. *Famine and Human Development: The Dutch Hungerwinter of 1944/45*. Oxford University Press, New York, 1974.
18. *Report of the Commission on the Poor Laws and the Relief of Distress*, Vol. 3. His Majesty's Stationery Office, London, 1909.
19. Moynihan, D. *Maximum Feasible Misunderstanding*. The Free Press, New York, 1969.
20. Elinson, J., and Herr, C.E.A. A sociomedical view of neighborhood health centers. *Med. Care* 8(2): 97–103, 1970.
21. Susser, M., Stein, Z., Cormack, M., and Hathorn, M. Medical care in a South African township. *Lancet* 1: 912–915, 1955.
22. Farr, W. *Vital Statistics: A Memorial Volume of Selections from the Reports and Writings of William Farr*, edited by N. Humphries. Sanitary Institute, London, 1885.
23. Fein, R. Definition and Scope of the Problem: Economic Aspects, pp. 44–53. Report of the Fifty-sixth Ross Conference on Pediatric Research, 1967.

1.8

What is Disease?

Lester S. King

I

Biological science does not try to distinguish between health and disease. Biology is concerned with the interaction between living organisms and their environment. What we call health or disease is quite irrelevant.

These reactions between the individual and his environment are complex. The individual and his surroundings form an integrated system which we can arbitrarily divide into two parts. There is an "external" component, by which we mean such factors as light, heat, percentage of oxygen in the air, quantity of minerals or vitamins in food, micro-organisms in food or air, and so on. These can induce changes in what we arbitrarily call the "internal" component. Here we include such crude factors as anatomical structures, or finer details like composition of intercellular fluid, or secretions of glands, or changes of electrical potential in nerve or muscle.

Medical science studies the reactions of the internal component and its relations with the external component. A separation is artificial, but none the less necessary for convenience and practicality. In any investigation science exerts its prerogative to break down the total complex event into simple parts. The scientist focuses his attention on limited sequences, and partial aspects. If he tries to preserve the unity entire, he would remain hopelessly bogged down. For example, if we ask, what happens to the food that we eat?, we are asking a question too complex for an intelligible answer. To make any reply meaningful, we must analyze the problem into simpler parts. We must specify what happens *where*. In the mouth? In the stomach? In the small intestines? Or in the liver, the pancreas, or the blood stream? We must specify *what* food. Fats? Carbohydrates? Proteins? And in what quantity? Starvation diets, average amounts, or surfeits? And then of course, *when*? At what points in the time-scale? At what age, at what temporal relation to exercise, or stress? All of these questions reflect our fundamental interest, of trying to isolate the relevant conditions that attend the phenomenon. But there are so many relevant aspects; what is relevant for one person might not be significant for another. If everyone had the same sort of liver or the same sort of pancreas, investigation would be a lot simpler. But they don't. Some individuals, for example, have stones in their gall bladders. Others have very small amounts of thyroid gland secretion. Still others harbor amoebae in their intestinal tract. In reply to our question, what happens to the food that we eat?, our answer will depend, in part, on whether the individual has stones in the gall bladder or amoebae in his colon.

Clearly, this "total environment" of which we speak is not identical for all people. Science tries to isolate as many discrete factors as possible. Some will apply to virtually all humans without exception, others may concern only a minute fraction of the total population. Science, in studying reactions within the total environment, cares not a whit about "health."

Suppose, for example, that we are interested in the skin. As scientists we can learn a great deal about the structure and function of this part of the body. There are many different types of cells and intercellular material. We distinguish the epithelium from the sub-epithelial tissues. We note the various glands, blood-vessels and nerves, the smooth muscle and the lymphatics, the collagen and the elastic tissue. We observe these structures in their growth and in their decay. We follow the circulation of blood, and the exchange of oxygen, carbon-dioxide, and metabolic products. We learn that, with an intact epidermis, the reactions tend to follow a certain pattern. If, now, we sever the skin with a sterile knife, we find that the pattern of reactions undergoes a change. Certain cells, instead of vegetating quietly, become very active. Blood vessels dilate, the flow of blood increases, leucocytes immigrate, cells proliferate, the metabolism alters, and we have a series of reactions which we designate as sterile or aseptic inflammation and repair. If some staphylococci are introduced into the skin, along with the knife edge, there is a different series of reactions; if some tubercle bacilli, then a still different set of reactions. These latter we call infection, indicating a regular pattern clearly distinguishable from other patterns.

We call these examples of disease. But as Sir Clifford Allbutt clearly stated "disease is a state of a living organism . . . the disease itself contains no elements essentially different from those of health, but elements presented in a different and less useful order."[1] One combination, configuration, or pattern is succeeded by another. One is more "useful" than another. One we call health, another "disease." The word "useful" in Allbutt's expression, is a judgment of value. This is something more than the sequences and laws which science studies. "Health" or "Disease" are value judgments based on something more than the study of reactions.

1. *A System of Medicine*, ed. by Thomas Clifford Allbutt, New York, MacMillan and Co., 1896, Volume 1, Introduction, p. xxxii.

When we attend to the "elements" or sequences within the total environment, the distinction between health and disease fades away to nothing. This is readily seen in current research, which disregards boundaries between the "normal" and "abnormal." Physiology, supposedly, deals with the "normal" functioning of the body, while pathology studies the "abnormal" function. This is sheer nonsense, since physiology makes its great advance by studying highly "abnormal" conditions, like animals without a liver, or without a large portion of brain, or lacking a thyroid; while pathology is intelligible only by reference to the "normal." We have books on that remarkable subject, "Pathological Physiology." All medical science studies facets of behavior under a wide variation in conditions. Many of these variations we call disease. But the grounds for calling them disease are not any essential part of the studies. Disease is an arbitrary designation.

As illustrating the confusion surrounding the notion of disease, I recall a very precise young physician who asked me what our laboratory considered the normal hemoglobin level of the blood (with the particular technique we used). When I answered, "Twelve to sixteen grams, more or less," he was very puzzled. Most laboratories, he pointed out, called 15 grams normal, or perhaps 14.5. He wanted to know how, if my norm was so broad and vague, he could possibly tell whether a patient suffered from anemia, or how much anemia. I agreed that he had quite a problem on his hands, and that it is a very difficult thing to tell. So difficult, in fact, that trying to be too precise is actually misleading, inaccurate, stultifying to thought, and philosophically very unsound.

He wanted to know why I didn't take one hundred or so normal individuals, determine their hemoglobin by our method, and use the resulting figure as the normal value for our method. This, I agreed, was a splendid idea. But how were we to pick out the normals? The obvious answer is, just take one or two hundred healthy people, free of disease.... But that is exactly the difficulty. We think health as freedom from disease, and disease as an aberration from health. This is travelling in circles, getting us nowhere.

Now, when we speak of health or disease, we use certain implicit values. Health is something good and desirable, while disease, whatever else it means, implies something bad. These values of "good" and "bad" indicate attraction towards or repulsion from something. There is a very definite sphere of relevance, within which the values apply. The sphere of disease is the realm of pain, disability and death, for its major groupings, while the minor stages we can call (subject to quibbling) "unpleasant" or "disagreeable", or some such term. Health deals with the opposite, with the conditions which give rise to the subjective report, "I feel fine." This state of awareness is subjectively recognized, although indescribable.

One way of determining health is by this subjective report. The man who says, "I feel just fine," may consider himself entirely sound. Conversely, he who complains of feeling "terrible" may think of himself as seriously ill. These subjective impressions are essential, and highly significant, but they are not entirely reliable. Here we come up against the distinction between what "seems" and what "really is," between "appearance" and "reality." We are all familiar with the man who had periodic routine examinations, who passed all tests, who felt subjectively fine, and who suddenly dropped dead. Or the man with no complaints at all but, cajoled into a routine chest x-ray, found he has a symptomless cancer. In such cases the individual "seemed" healthy, subjectively he felt healthy, but "really" he wasn't.

To understand health or disease we must have some objective measurements in addition to the introspective account. If we can weigh or measure something, then we have a little more confidence, and we feel more firmly grounded in objective reality. And there is no end of different features that we can thus quantitate. With the help of measurements and statistical analysis we can get a very reliable picture of what exists and in what distribution, and, moreover, what we may reasonably expect in the future. But ordinarily statistics alone cannot label any part of the data as "diseased." When we apply statistical methods we already have in mind the idea of health. We exert selection on the cases we study. Thus, to find the "normal" blood sugar level we eliminate known diabetics. And the basal metabolic rate, in health, we determine after omitting known thyroid disease.

In spite of the circularity, the concepts of health and disease belong together. There are certain factors which are important for defining and distinguishing them. One is the subjective report, which is of only moderate reliability. The sense of well-being frequently correlates with what we mean by health, but the correlation is not high. Certainly a sense of well-being does not preclude the presence of disease, while the absence of such subjective feeling does not indicate disease.

Another important factor is the statistical distribution, quite independent of any subjective report. Let us imagine, for example, a statistical study of body temperature, on completely random samples. We would find an overwhelming majority of individuals within a narrow band, between 98° and 99° F. However, a very small percentage will show much higher figures, such as 102°, 104°, or 105°, or more. These individuals who depart from the norm, are by definition ab-normal. This deviation, by *itself*, does not make them diseased. Thus, persons with an intelligence quotient of 180, or with the ability to run 100 yards in 9 2/5 seconds, are also highly ab-normal. However, when a deviation is tied up with malaise, pain, or death, or is intimately associated with conditions which lead to disability or death, then the abnormality forms part of Disease.

Statistical norms, even when correlated with malaise, can furnish only a part of the total picture. For example, statistics can establish the normal body temperature and, by correlation with malaise, pain, or death, the desirable body temperature. But in the matter of, say, dentition, the statistical norm does not define the healthy or the desirable. Very few native Americans possess thirty-two intact, well-aligned teeth. Yet when we speak of sound or healthy dentition we have in mind the ideal of thirty-two intact, well-aligned teeth. In this case it is deviation from the *ideal* which constitutes disease, not deviation from a statistical norm.

These ideals stem from two sources. One is concrete observation. Nothing can serve as a model of health unless it has been an observed characteristic or feature. And second, any such feature must be an object of general desire, possessing value which appeals to the mass of the population. One person might desire to be eight feet tall, yet the majority of people do not. The ideals of height, of weight, of bust measurement, or head size, that is, the range which the majority desires, vary from one nation or tribe to another, and from one generation to another. Changes in diet, for example, can in a few generations change the ideals in regard to stature. But at the present time a height of eight feet is not a matter of general craving.

The ideal need not consciously be present in the minds of the majority, as an object of desire, but it may be clearly and intimately connected with such an object of desire. The more technical knowledge pertaining to ideals of health we justify through such an intimate connection. We cannot expect the mass of population to yearn for a particular pH level of the blood, however important it may be, but a given pH level we can connect up with more obvious states that do possess general or even universal appeal.

Disease lies in the realm of pain, discomfort, or death. There are, however, many examples of pain and discomfort which we cannot so designate. A teething infant or a woman in childbirth are suffering pain. We may try to relieve this pain, but we do not think of teething or childbirth as diseases. We call them normal functions. To be a healthy infant is to go through a period of teething. We conclude that discomfort which constantly attends a normal desirable function and is intimately or essentially bound up with that desirable function, is not in the realm of Disease.

It follows that our concepts of disease are very closely related to our values. Frequently our values may be severely determined by convention. China, for example, did not regard as diseased those upper-class women whose feet were bound, and who thereby suffered pain and diminution in function. Our contemporary culture takes a different view. Which means that our conventions and values of health are different from the Chinese. In most of our western civilization the seeing of visions we consider a sign of a diseased state. But in some epochs of our civilization the seer of visions was a leader in the community, receiving special honor because of his unusual endowment. Certainly the egregious and unusual, the literally ab-normal, represent disease only if judged by indigenous cultural values. Convention plays a very important part in shaping our values. And the quantity of our knowledge plays a very important part in shaping our conventions.

Disease is the aggregate of those conditions which, judged by the prevailing culture, are deemed painful, or disabling, and which, at the same time, deviate from either the statistical norm or from some idealized status. Health, the opposite, is the state of well-being conforming to the ideals of the prevailing culture, or to the statistical norm. The ideal itself is derived in part from the statistical norm, and in part from the ab-normal which seems particularly desirable. Environmental states (both external and internal) which are intimately connected with the ideals and norms, are part of health, even though the general public is unaware of them, while environmental states intimately connected with disease are similar parts of disease.

II

When most people talk of disease, they have in mind some particular condition like diabetes or pneumonia, or peptic ulcer. In this more limited sense, the term refers to a pattern of factors which somehow hang together and recur, more or less the same, in successive individuals. Thus, pain in the right lower quadrant of the abdomen, with nausea, vomiting, a fever, and a high white count, spell out the features of acute appendicitis. With variations this combination tends to recur. Or, severe headache, fever, stiffness of the neck, with abundant white cells in the spinal fluid, spell out another condition that we label meningitis. Or again, a condition of fever, cough, runny nose, sore eyes, and the later appearance of characteristic spots on the skin, we call measles. Each of these diseases, so called, is a congeries of factors, and no single factor, by itself, identifies the disease. It is only the recurrence of a pattern of events, a number of elements combined in a definite relationship, which we can label a disease.

Since there is no strict specificity to individual factors, and one factor may recur in a variety of contexts, diseases that are quite distinct may nevertheless have many features in common. So much so that, as Bartlett says, diseases may "approach and touch each other in so many respects, and at so many points, that it may not be possible, always, in the present state of our knowledge, to fix upon positive means... for distinguishing between them."[2] The various properties occur in clusters. We try to distinguish one cluster from another, try to be sure that it is a recurring pattern. This is a difficult thing to do, but if we satisfy ourselves on that score, then we call that pattern a separate disease.

To discriminate and identify a disease entity, we cannot rely on abstract speculation, but must study concrete particular sick people. In observing any group of sick individuals whatsoever, there are always some points in

2. Bartlett, Elisha: *An Essay on the Philosophy of Medical Science*, Philadelphia, Lea and Blanchard, 1844, p. 129.

common. We can always find areas of resemblance. But when we become increasingly critical, we realize that many resemblances are very superficial. It may be a fever, or a rash, or a sore throat that different individuals exhibit. But everyone who has a fever, or a rash, does not have the same disease. We distinguish still more acutely, and we perceive not merely a rash, but a very special type of rash, not merely a fever, but a fever with a definite course; not merely a sore throat but one with a particular recognizable ulceration and membrane formation. Then with development of new techniques we are able to discriminate still deeper, hidden similarities. We are able to say that certain sick individuals have a uniform type of bacterial invader, or show a specific antibody content of the blood.

Out of a number of sick persons the more points that we can compare and find similar, the greater our assurance that a single common pattern affects the individual patients. If we can find enough similar features which recur as a cluster, we can organize these features into a logical coherent order. The great men in medicine are those who can perceive similarities, patterns, relationships, and a "belonging together" of seemingly quite discrete factors.

Now sometimes we confuse one disease with another. The history of medicine is the history of distinguishing one condition from another. What was thought to be one disease is found, on careful analysis, to be two, and these in turn may prove to be multiple. The various exanthemata were long confused. Distinguishing small-pox from measles, measles from German measles, scarlet fever from measles, measles from the "fourth disease," these, over the centuries, were made possible by acute observation. Or, the progressive differentiation of what the Bible called "leprosy", illustrates the confusion that has been growing steadily less.

When there has been a failure of discrimination, and we confuse two diseases, then, as Bartlett points out, we have paid attention only to "certain particular and limited portions"[3] of the diseases. We have not attended to the "most essential affinities."

The implications are clear and significant. Whenever we regard sick people, we see a confusion of phenomena and relationships. Some of these are superficial, inconsequential, others are "essential". According to Bartlett, when we note the "essential" features, we are observing the "real" disease. If we concern ourselves only with the superficial, then we miss the "real" disease. Someone else, more acute than we, may succeed in penetrating to the essential aspects which we have missed.

It is an interesting commentary on human pride, that we are all too ready to assume our own penetration into the real nature of things. Thus Bartlett, in the year 1844, said, "It is only within a few years that we have been furnished with a means of distinguishing, with clearness and certainty, between pleurisy and

3. Ibid: p. 261.

pneumonia; *but these two diseases have always been as distinct from each other as they now are.*"[4]

This point of view is important and influential,—that diseases have an independent reality. They are not created by the act of thinking about them. They are quite distinct, apart from the knowledge and recognition of the inquiring physician. Thus, he states in unequivocal terms, "... classes, or groups, or families, cannot be created, arbitrarily, and at will, by our own skill and ingenuity.... We must take... individual diseases... as they exist in nature."[5]

In view of this forceful assertion, we smile, in our sophistication, as we reflect how Bartlett himself confused pleurisy and pneumonia. To call these separate "diseases" and to maintain that they have been eternally separate even though we did not know it, is rather silly. Nevertheless Bartlett points at a metaphysical issue which very few physicians care to tackle. His blundering dogmatism is only a mask for the important problem, What is Reality?

Let us illustrate this by a little conundrum. Let us ask, "What was the smallest continent before the discovery of Australia?" The majority of persons would answer "Europe," with a few perhaps, claiming North America or South America. But not Bartlett. If he were called on to give an answer he would say, "The smallest continent before the discovery of Australia was... Australia."

Clearly we are beset by the interpretation of the verb "to be," the problem that has afforded 2500 years of philosophical dispute. The little conundrum states, that a thing *is*, whether we know it or not. Now, most people would readily agree that with material tangible things like rocks and trees and rivers and continents, such an answer would seem correct. When we close our eyes, the familiar objects in the room do not cease to exist. The first explorer who came upon a waterfall did not create it by his act of discovery. It was "there" all the time, but neither he nor anyone else had known about it.

But it is a little different to ask, is this also the case with diseases? Diseases are not *things* in the same sense as rocks, or trees, or rivers. Diseases represent patterns or relationships, which are not material. The problem then becomes, how real is a pattern, what is the ontological status of a relationship?

Within the realm of sounds, for example, there exists a certain pattern of musical tones which we call, say, Beethoven's Ninth Symphony. Will we claim that the Ninth Symphony was *there* all the time waiting for someone to discover it? Or will we declare, along with common sense, that the "skill and ingenuity" of Beethoven created it; that before Beethoven, it had no existence?

We are faced with the problem whether certain relational patterns, like diseases, "exist in nature," while other patterns, like a melody or a poem, we

4. Ibid: p. 140, (Italics not in original text).
5. Ibid: p. 272.

can create arbitrarily by our own skill and ingenuity. The question becomes, does a disease, whatever it is, have real existence, somehow, in its own right, in the same way as the continent of Australia? Such real existence would be independent of its discovery by explorer or investigator. A disease exists whether we know it or not. The contrasting point of view would hold, that a disease is created by the inquiring intellect, carved out by the very process of classification, in the same way that a statue is carved out of a block of marble by the chisel strokes of the sculptor.

When we try to discuss the problem, What is a disease?, we are thus led into metaphysical difficulties. Some persons, who may, perhaps, be the most sensible among us, prefer to ignore the difficulty. But it never does any harm at least to stare a difficulty boldly in the face. We can always hurry along and ignore it later.

We will not even try to give a rigorous definition of the Real, for this has baffled far keener minds, and, regardless of how subjectively adequate, no definition could gain general approval. But in a relatively artless fashion we think of the Real as the permanent, something that cannot be tampered with, that to which we must conform. In the history of philosophy there have been two opposing concepts. One equates the real with *things*, which may be coarse and gross or immeasurably fine and subtle, but which nevertheless are things. The classical atomism of Democritus is a good example. Indivisible ultimate particles which do not alter—these were the Real. The particles re-arranged themselves endlessly, into constantly changing patterns and organizations which were evanescent. Such patterns had at best only a derivative or incomplete reality, and were not the Really Real. Atomism is thus one form of doctrine which distinguishes between ultimately real (in this case, the atoms), and the derivatively real relations (i.e., the patterns) into which the atoms enter.

We are not at present concerned with atomism as such, which we offer only as a crude example. We are more concerned with the general principle which gives the primacy to individual *things*, be they separate atoms, or clusters of atoms, packets of energy, or concrete individuals regardless of ultimate physical components.

Attention to the individual as a concrete thing, makes up the doctrine of Nominalism. According to this view, relations, patterns, and qualities are only derivative. We call them abstractions. Thus, green grass and green leaves are objects that we see. The grass and the leaves are real, green is only an abstraction. Or in the field of medicine, Mr. Smith may have diabetes and Mr. Jones hypertension. Then Smith and Jones are real, while diabetes and hypertension as abstractions, are not real in the same sense. This view is summed up in the familiar expression, 'In "reality" there are no diseases, there are only sick patients.'

There is a contrasting viewpoint in the Platonic tradition which the medieval philosophers called Realism. In the Platonic doctrine the search for the Real or the Permanent took a different tack. When we hunt for stability amidst the ceaseless change, we note certain equalities and relationships that persist. Grass and leaves are green, while a ball is round, yet grass will wither and leaves will fall and a ball will disintegrate. Nevertheless, "green" will not fall or wither, and "round" does not change. They remain, permanent, eternal, as Platonic Universals. Each is a Form or Idea. And similarly, according to some thinkers, with properties like beauty or honesty or goodness. What we call particular *things* may be regarded as collections of universals. The reality of a thing would consist, not in its concrete individuality, but in the Forms or Universals which it exhibits. Particulars come into being and pass away, but the Universal qualities or Forms persist.

According to this doctrine, diabetes and pneumonia would be Real, while any particular diabetic, like Mr. Smith, merely manifests the disease, just as a leaf manifests the color green. Of course, Mr. Smith presents other characteristics besides diabetes, in the same way that a leaf has other qualities besides green. But diabetes, according to this view, is a real entity. And whatever we comprehend by that term Real (and we must grant it some meaning), then a disease possesses Reality in the fullest degree.

Bartlett is apparently a Platonist. He would very stoutly deny the *bon mot*, that in nature there are only sick patients, but no diseases. Yet granting Bartlett's point, that disease has reality in the fullest sense, we can wonder, how do we make sure that we have grasped that reality? His assertion that pleurisy and pneumonia are separate diseases, and have always been separate, is grotesquely absurd. Today we regard pleurisy not as a disease but only as a symptom. We must have some sort of distinguishing feature, according to which we say, that pleurisy, or fever, or jaundice, or headache, are not diseases, but only symptoms. In times past, in our ignorance, we may have accorded them full status as disease entities, as did Bartlett, but this we do no longer.

We resolve the difficulty only by admitting that we carve out whatever disease patterns we wish, in whatever way we desire. In accordance with our previous discussion of Classification, a disease pattern is a class, or niche in a framework. This framework is a means of approaching and organizing crude experience, that is, for dealing with everyday events in the most satisfactory way. These classes will vary in their utility in the handling of experience. What we call a fever is a very broad and inclusive class. There is only one reason why we should not regard fever as a disease entity and that is, such an entity is so broad and inclusive, so general and nondiscriminating, that it lacks utility. "Usefulness" means not only the practical taking-care of patients, but also the intellectual facility with which we can assimilate new discoveries and observation. We can continue to call fever a disease, if at the same time we blithely ignore all the various discriminations that keen observers have made over the centuries. If, however, we wish to use these observations either theoretically or practically, then we find it more useful to discard the concept of fever as a disease, and consider it merely a part found in a number of more complex patterns. The term fever then ceases to be a major category for analyzing experience.

A "symptom" is a class or term, which does not serve as a useful major organizing principle, but instead is only an element of the pattern characterizing some other more useful category or class. A disease, on the other hand, is a complex pattern (or class) which does usefully organize experience. That pattern which we call a disease is subject to modification, recombination and subdivision of its elements, as our knowledge increases. What one epoch calls a disease is, to a later period, only a symptom. A pattern has reasonable stability only when its criteria are sharp, its elements cohere, and its utility in clarifying experience remains high. Let these factors become blurred, and the erstwhile disease, as a well-defined and useful class, will melt away.

Medical science concerns itself with tracing out patterns, carving them out according to the insight of the investigator. But we do not carve out or create patterns capriciously. Science does not act in an arbitrary or despotic fashion. There is an ultimate arbiter which we call Experience.

Experience is not a matter of wishful thinking. As William James said, "sensations are forced upon us, coming we know not whence. Over their nature, order, and quantity we have as good as no control. *They* are neither true nor false; they simply *are*."[6] There is Something which forces itself upon our consciousness and determines our experiences, even as the ocean forced itself upon King Canute over his express objections.

This Something which underlies experience and determines its order, can never appear directly in sense experience. It is the Really Real which we can never know in sensation but whose nature we infer. It is, so to speak, a substrate. We have a fundamental assumption that the substrate, directly unknowable, exhibits pattern, order, arrangement, and organization. Moreover, it is remarkably patient of multiple interpretations, each of which may grasp a small fragment of its arrangement. When we create a schema of classification and hold it up to nature, we believe that our schema reproduces the conditions of the substrate. It is faintly analogous to a blind man drawing a picture of an object which he cannot see but whose nature he infers from the other sense modalities. With any pattern, hypothesis, or classification that we create, we say, in effect, we believe the substrate giving rise to our experience has a type of organization, and this particular pattern that we offer is, we believe, an approximation of that organization which obtains in the Unknowable.

Whatever Reality may be, organization and arrangement are part of its

6. James, William: *Pragmatism*, New York and London, Longman, Green and Co., 1925, p. 244.

essence. It is quite absurd to make any separation between Things and their Arrangement. Things are real, but are unthinkable except in some pattern. Patterns and relations are real, but are unthinkable apart from something which is related. As we, in our own experience, create one pattern after another, we wonder whether these match the patterns of Reality. Sometimes we feel that we have constructed a reasonable approximation. Then we can only wait and see how our proffered blueprint of organization enables us to deal with future experience. Our difficulties arise only when we are arrogant in our assurance.

1.9

Illness—Mental and Otherwise

Peter Sedgwick

I am going to develop some thoughts which have arisen out of a study I am at present conducting into the work of the distinguished anti-psychiatrist (or ex-anti-psychiatrist), R.D. Laing. I do not propose to take up the specific questions raised by the work of Laing and the school of thought around him (which is in any case very desultory and unsystematic). Instead I am going to face squarely the central issue raised by all the sociological or quasi-sociological "revisionists" of the idea of mental illness. It appears to me that none of them have begun by asking the question: What is *illness*? Only in the light of an answer to *this* question could we determine our answer to the question: Is mental illness really illness in the "medical" sense? . . .

WHAT IS 'ILLNESS'?

What, then, is "illness"? It will be recalled that critical theory in psychiatry has tended to postulate a fundamental separation between mental illnesses and the general run of human ailments: the former are the expression of social norms, the latter proceed from ascertainable bodily states which have an "objective" existence within the individual. One critic of psychopathological concepts, Barbara Wootton, has suggested that the expurgation of normative references from psychiatry is at least a theoretical ideal, though one immensely difficult of achievement:

> . . . anti-social behavior is the precipitating factor that leads to mental treatment. But at the same time the fact of the illness is itself inferred from the behavior . . . . But any disease, the morbidity of which is established only by the social failure it involves, must rank as fundamentally different from those of which the symptoms are independent of the social norms . . . long indeed is the road to be travelled before we can hope to reach a definition of mental-cum-physical health which is objective, scientific, and wholly free of social value judgments, and before we shall be able, consistently and without qualification, to treat mental and physical disorders on exactly the same footing.[1]

1. Barbara Wootton, *Social Science and Social Pathology* (London, 1959), p. 225.

Wootton's view has stimulated at least one attempt to begin the task of purging all cultural norms—with their inconvenient variability from one society to another—from the diagnosis of mental illness: Dr. Joseph Zubin has reported some work on "culture-free" assessments of schizophrenia which involve the analysis of reaction-times, responses to electrical stimulation, and the like among schizophrenic patients.[2] It would be fair to say that research in the refinement of psychiatric categories has been mounted with a similar perspective in mind, straining towards the physical-medicine ideal of a set of symptom-descriptions "independent of the social norms." Value-judgments and cultural stereotypes are seen as one form of "error" coming between the investigator and his desired data, and the ultimate standard sought in the description of illness is to be taken to be a socially inert, culturally sterile specification of facts and processes which are grounded in the bacteriology, bio-chemistry, physiology or perhaps some variety of cybernetic systems-theory.

But this enterprise, tending constantly towards the microscopic and molecular analysis of the "objective" substrate of behavior, forms only one of the ways in which we might begin to place mental and physical illnesses "on exactly the same footing." If we examine the logical structure of our judgments of illness (whether "physical" or "mental"), it may prove possible to reduce the distance between psychiatry and other streams of medicine by working in the reverse direction to Wootton: not by annexing psychopathology to the technical instrumentation of the natural sciences but by revealing the character of illness and disease, health and treatment, as social constructions. For social constructions they most certainly are. All departments of nature below the level of mankind are exempt both from disease and from treatment—until man intervenes with his own human classifications of disease and treatment. The blight that strikes at corn or at potatoes is a *human invention*, for if man wished to cultivate parasites (rather than potatoes or corn) there would be no "blight," but simply the necessary foddering of the parasite-crop. Animals do not have diseases either, prior to the presence of man in a meaningful relation with them. A tiger may experience pain or feebleness from a variety of causes (we do not intend to build our case on the supposition that animals, especially higher animals, cannot have experiences of feelings). It may be infected by a germ, trodden by an elephant, scratched by another tiger, or subjected to the aging processes of its own cells. It does not present itself as being *ill* (though it may present itself as being highly distressed or uncomfortable) except in the eyes of a human observer who can discriminate illness from other sources of pain or enfeeblement. Outside the significances that man voluntarily attaches

2. J. Zubin, "A Cross-Cultural Approach to Psychopathology and Its Implications for Diagnostic Classifications," in *The Classification of Behavior Disorders*, ed. by L.D. Eron (Chicago, 1966), pp. 43–82.

to certain conditions, *there are no illnesses or diseases in nature*. We are nowadays so heavily doctrinated with deriving from the technical medical discoveries of the last century-and-a-half that we are tempted to think that nature does contain diseases. Just as the sophisticated New Yorker classes the excrement of dogs and cats as one more form of "pollution" ruining the pre-established harmony of pavements and gardens, so does modern technologized man perceive nature to be mined and infested with all kinds of specifically morbid entities and agencies. What, he will protest, are there no diseases in nature? Are there not infectious and contagious bacilli? Are there not definite and objective lesions in the cellular structures of the human body? Are there not fractures of bones, the fatal ruptures of tissues, the malignant multiplications of tumorous growths? Are not these, surely, events of nature? Yet these, as natural events, do not—prior to the human social meanings we attach to them—constitute illnesses, sicknesses, or diseases. The fracture of a septuagenarian's femur has, within the world of nature, no more significance than the snapping of an autumn leaf from its twig: and the invasion of a human organism by cholera-germs carries with it no more the stamp of "illness" than does the souring of milk by other forms of bacteria.[3] Human beings, like all other naturally occurring structures are characterized by a variety of inbuilt limitations or liabilities, any of which may (given the presence of further stressful circumstances) lead to the weaking or the collapse of the organism. Mountains as well as moles, stars as well as shrubs, protozoa no less than persons have their dates of expiry set in advance, over a time-span which varies greatly over different classes of structure but which is usually at least roughly predictable. Out of his anthropocentric self-interest, man has chosen to consider as "illnesses" or "diseases" those natural circumstances which precipitate the death (or the failure to function according to certain values) of a limited number of biological species; man himself, his pets and other cherished livestock, and the plant-varieties he cultivates for gain or pleasure. Around these select areas of structural failure man creates, in proportion to the progress of his technology, specialized combat-institutions for the control and cure of "disease": the different branches of the medical and nursing profession, veterinary doctors, and the botanical specialists in plant-disease. Despite their common use of experimental natural science, these institutions operate according to very different criteria and codes; the use of euthanasia by vets, and of ruthless eugenic policies by plant-pathologists, departs from most current medical practice with human patients. All the same, the fact that these specialisms share the categories of disease and illness indicates the selective quality of our perceptions in this field. Children and cattle may fall ill, have diseases, and seem as sick; but who has ever imagined that spiders or lizards can be sick or diseased? Plant-diseases may strike at tulips, turnips, or such prized features of

3. The above discussion is heavily indebted to René Dubos' masterly *The Mirage of Health* (New York: Harper & Row, 1971), especially pp. 30–128.

the natural landscape as elm trees: but if some plant-species in which man had no interest (a desert grass, let us say) were to be attacked by a fungus or parasite, we should speak not of a disease, but merely of the competition between two species. The medical enterprise is from its inception value-loaded; it is not simply an applied biology, but a biology applied in accordance with the dictates of social interest.

It could be argued that the discussion of animal and plant pathology deals in cases that are too marginal to our central concepts of health and illness to form a satisfactory basis for analysis. Such marginal instances are of course frequently used by logicians in the analysis of concepts since their peripheral character often usefully tests the limits within which our ideas can be seen to be applicable or inapplicable. However, a careful examination of the concept of illness in man himself will reveal the same value-impregnation, the same dependency of apparently descriptive, natural-scientific notions upon our norms of what is desirable. To complain of illness, or to ascribe illness to another person, is not to make a descriptive statement about physiology or anatomy. Concepts of illness were in use among men for centuries before the advent of any reliable knowledge of the human body, and are still employed today within societies which favor a non-physiological (magical or religious) account of the nature of human maladies. Our own classification and explanation of specific illnesses or diseases is of course tremendously different from the categories that are current in earlier ages or in contemporary tribal societies, but it is implausible to suppose that the state of illness itself has no common logical features over different types of society. Homer's sick warriors were tended by magical incantations as well as by herbs and other primitive technical remedies, but the avowal and ascription of illness in Homer does not set up a distance between his characters and ourselves but rather (like his descriptions of bereavement or of sexual attraction) a powerful resonance across the ages.[4] Similarly, the meaning of illness among primitive peoples is usually sufficiently close to our own to enable them to take advantage of modern medical facilities when these are made accessible within their territories: tribesmen and peasants do not have to be indoctrinated into Western physiological concepts before they can accept help from physicians and nurses trained in advanced societies. Sickness and disease may be conceptualized, in different cultures, as originating within bodily states, or within perturbations of the spirit, or as a mixture of both. Yet there appear to be common features in the declaration or attribution of the sick state, regardless of the causal explanation that is invoked.

---

4. See the excellent account of Homeric medicine in P. Lain Entralgo, *The Therapy of the World in Classical Antiquity* (New Haven: Yale Univ. Press, 1970).

VALUATION & EXPLANATION

All sickness is essentially deviancy. That is to say, no attribution of sickness to any being can be made without the expectation of some alternative state of affairs which is considered more desirable. In the absence of this normative alternative, the presence of a particular bodily or subjective state will not in itself lead to an attribution of illness. Thus, where an entire community is by Western standards "ill," because it has been infected for generations by parasites which diminish energy, illness will not be recognized in any individuals except by outsiders.[5] The Rockefeller Sanitary Commission on Hookworm found in 1911 that this disease was regarded as part of normal health in some areas of North Africa.[6] And in one South American Indian tribe the disease of dyschromic spirochetosis, which is marked by the appearance of colored spots on the skin, was so "normal" that those who did not have them were regarded as pathological and excluded from marriage.[7] Even with modern urbanized nations we cannot assume that aches, pains and other discomforts are uniformly categorized as signs of illness among all sections of the community. Although little work has been done on social-class variations in the construction of what constitutes "health" and "sickness,"[8] the example of tooth–decay is suggestive: among millions of British working-class families, it is taken for granted that children will lose their teeth and require artificial dentures. The process of tooth-loss is not seen as a disease, but as something like an act of fate. Among dentists, on the other hand, and in those more-educated sections of the community who are socialized into dental ideology, the loss of teeth arises through a definite disease-process known as caries, whose aetiology is established.[9] Social and cultural norms also plainly govern the varying perception, either as essentially "normal," or as essentially "pathological," of such characteristics as baldness, obesity, infestation by lice, venereal infection, and the presence of tonsils and foreskins among children.

Once again it can be argued that these cultural variations apply only to marginal cases of sickness and health, that there are some physical or psychological conditions which are *ipso facto* symptomatic of illness, whether among Bushmen or Brobdignagians, duchesses or dockworkers. But there is

---

5. I have taken this observation from Dr. L. Robbins' discussion in Eron (ed.), *The Classification of Behavior Disorders*.

6. Cited by A. L. Knutson, *The Individual, Society and Health Behavior* (New York: Russell Sage, 1965), p. 49.

7. Cited by Mechanic, *Medical Sociology*, p. 16

8. Knutson, *The Individual, Society and Health Behavior*, p. 48, quotes one New York study showing lower-class indifference to the need for medical attention for such conditions as ankle-swelling and backache. But these should still have been regarded as illnesses by the respondents, who could have had their own reasons (such as lack of cash) for refusing to consider medical treatment.

9. There is now some doubt among dental experts as to whether "caries" is a genuine disease-entity or an artifact of diagnostic labeling.

no reason to believe that the "standardized" varieties of human pathology operate according to a different logic from the "culturally dependent" varieties. The existence of common or even universal illnesses testifies, not to the absence of a normative framework for judging pathology, but to the presence of very wide-spread norms. To be ill, after all, is not the same thing as to feel pain, or to experience weakness, or to fail to manifest this or that kind of behavior. Rather it is to experience discomfort (or to manifest behavioral failure) in a context of a particular kind. Consider the imaginary conversations between physician and client:

(a) *Client*: Doctor, I want you to examine me, I keep feeling terrible pains in my right shoulder.

Doctor: Really? What are they like?

Client: Stabbing and intense.

Doctor: How often do they happen?

Client: Every evening after I get home from work.

Doctor: Always in the same spot?

Client: Yes, just in the place where my wife hits me with the rolling-pin.

(b) *Client*: (Telephoning Doctor). Doctor, I haven't consulted you before but things are getting desperate. I'm feeling so weak, I can't lift anything heavy.

Doctor: Goodness, when does this come on you?

Client: Every time I try to lift something or make an effort. I have to walk quite slowly up the stairs and last night when I was packing the big suitcase I found I couldn't lift it off the bed.

Doctor: Well, let's have some details about you before you come in. Name?

Client: John Smith.

Doctor: Age?

Client: Ninety-two last February.

In the first example, the "patient's" pain is not an illness because we expect pain as a normal response to being hit in tender places; indeed, if he did *not* feel pain when he was hit or prodded he would be taken to be suffering from some disease involving nerve-degeneration. In the second example, the patient's infirmity would usually be ascribed not to the category of "illness" but to that of "aging." (If he had given his age as "twenty-two" the case would be different.) In our culture we expect old people to find difficulty in lifting heavy weights, although it is easy to conceive of a culture in which mass rejuvenation among the aged had been perfected (perhaps by the injection of hormones, vitamins or other pep-pills into the water-supply) and where, in consequence, a dialogue of the type recounted would lead to a perfectly ordinary referral for medical treatment. The attribution of illness always proceeds from the computation of a gap between presented behavior (or feeling) and some social norm. In practice of course we take the norm for granted, so that the broken arm or the elevated temperature is seen alone as the illness. But the broken arm would be no more of an illness than a broken fingernail unless it stopped us from achieving certain socially constructed goals; just as, if we could all function according to approved social requirements within any range of body temperature, thermometers would disappear from the household medical kit.

This is not to say that illness amounts to any deviancy whatsoever from social expectations about how men should function. Such deviancies are regarded as instances not of sickness but of criminality, wickedness, poor upbringing or bad manners (though not all cultures do in fact draw a firm line between illness and these other deviations, e.g., primitive societies for whom illness is also a moral flaw and modern liberal circles for whom drug-addiction is categorized in medical as well as moral terms). Looking over the very wide range of folk-concepts and technical ideas about illness which exist in the history of human societies, one finds it difficult to discern a common structural element which distinguishes the notion of illness from other attributions of social failure. Provisionally, it is possible to suggest that illness is set apart from other deviancies insofar as the description (or, at a deeper level, the explanation) of the sick state is located within a relatively restricted set of causal factors operating within the boundaries of the individual human being. One may become ill as the result of being infected by germs, or through being entered by evil demons, or visited by a curse from the Almighty. Each culturally specific account of illness must involve a theory of the person, of the boundaries between the person and the world "outside" him, and of the ways in which adverse influences can trespass over these limits and besiege or grip him. If the current theory of the person is positivistic and physical, the agencies of illness will be seen as arising from factors within (or at the boundaries of) his body; in cultures with an animistic tradition, the invasion will be one of the spirit or soul. But, however variously the nature of illness is specified from culture to culture, the attribution of illness appears to include a *quest for explanation*, or at least the descriptive delimiting of certain types of causal factor, as well as the normative component outlined above. It is indeed likely that the concept of illness has arisen in close parallel with the social practice of therapy, i.e., with the development of techniques to control those human afflictions which can be controlled at the boundaries of the individual person. It is hard to see how the category of illness, as a distinct construction separate from other kinds of misfortune, could have arisen without the discovery that some varieties of pain and affliction could be succored through individual specialized attention to the afflicted person. In traditional societies, of course, the institution of medicine is not crystallized out as an applied branch of natural science: "Therapy" for the Greeks was simply the word used for looking after or tending somebody, and in Greece as well as elsewhere, a great deal of therapy goes on either in the patient's household or in conjunction with religious and magical specialisms. A specifically "medical" framework of treatment is not necessary to provide the link between illness and practical action.

Practice and concept continue their mutual modification over the ages. In a society where the treatment of the sick is still conducted through religious ritual, the notion of illness will not be entirely distinct from the notion of sinfulness or pollution. Correspondingly, with the growth of progressively more technical and more autonomous specialisms of therapy, the concepts of disease and illness themselves become more technical, and thereby more alienated from their implicit normative background. Thus we reach the position of the present day where any characterization of an "illness" which is not amenable to a diagnosis drawn from physiology or to a therapy based on chemical, electrical, or surgical technique becomes suspect as not constituting, perhaps, an illness at all. Such has been the fate of mental illness in our own epoch. It has been much easier for societies with an animistic theory of the person (and of his boundaries and susceptibilities to influence) to view mental disturbances on a par with bodily ailments. Ceremonies of ritual purgation and demon-expulsion, along with primitive "medical" methods of a herbal or surgical type, are used indifferently by traditional healers on patients with a mental or with a bodily dysfunction. Fever and madness, the broken limb or the broken spirit are situated within the same normative frame, within the same explanatory and therapeutic system. Even the development of a technical-physiological specialism of medicine, such as emerged with the Hippocratic tradition which runs in fits and starts from antiquity to modern times, does not impair the possibility of a unitary perspective on physical and mental illness, *so long as a common structure of valuation and explanation applies over the whole range of disorders of the person*. The medicine of the seventeenth and eighteenth centuries in Western Europe, for instance, was able to interpret our present-day "mental" disorders as a group of illnesses inhabiting the embodied person on much the same plane as other sorts of malady: the insane or the emotionally disturbed patient was suffering from a fault of "the vapors," "the nerves," "the fluids," "the animal spirits," "the spleen," "the humors," "the head," or the forces and qualities of the body.[10] This unitary integration of human illnesses was of course only achieved at the cost of a stupendously inaccurate and speculative physiology. But an integrated theory of illness, whether achieved within a unitary-animistic or a unitary-physicalistic doctrine of the person, has one singular advantage over a more fragmentary perspective: it is not beset by the kind of crisis we now have in psychopathology and psychiatry, whose conceptual and moral foundation has been exploded

10. See Foucault, *Madness and Civilization*, pp. 119, 121, 123, 129, and 151 ff. Entralgo, in *The Therapy of the Word in Classical Antiquity*, has similar explanations collected from ancient Hippocratic medicine.

now that "illness" has acquired a technical-physical definition excluding disorders of the whole person from its purview. Animistic and unitary-physicalistic accounts of illness both dealt in the whole embodied individual, but the medical technology of the nineteenth century and onwards has succeeded in classifying illnesses as particular states of the body only. Psychiatry is left with two seeming alternatives: either to say that personal, psychological, and emotional disorders are really states of the body, objective features of the brain-tissue, the organism-under-stress, the genes or what have you; or else to deny that such disorders are illnesses at all. If the latter, then the way is open to treat mental illnesses as the expression of social value-judgments about the patient, and psychiatry's role will not belong to the disciplines of objective, body-state medicine. Instead, it will be analogous to the value-laden and non-medical disciplines of moral education, police interrogation, criminal punishment or religion (depending on how low or how lofty a view one takes of the values inherent in psychiatric practice).

This dilemma will perhaps seem somewhat to dissolve if we recapitulate what was previously said about the nature of illness as a social construction. *All* illness, whether conceived in localized bodily terms or within a larger view of human functioning, expresses both a social value-judgment (contrasting a person's condition with certain understood and accepted norms) and an attempt at explanation (with a view to controlling the disvalued condition). The physicalistic psychiatrists are wrong in their belief that they can find objective disease-entities representing the psychopathologic analogues to diabetes, tuberculosis, and post-syphilitic paresis. Quite correctly, the anti-psychiatrists have pointed out that psychopathological categories refer to value-judgments and that mental illness is deviancy. On the other hand, the anti-psychiatric critics themselves are wrong when they imagine physical medicine to be essentially different in its logic from psychiatry. A diagnosis of diabetes, or paresis, includes the recognition of norms or values. Anti-psychiatry can only operate by positing a mechanical and inaccurate model of physical illness and its medical diagnosis.

In my own judgment, then, mental illness can be conceptualized just as easily within the disease framework as physical maladies such as lumbago or TB.

THE FUTURE OF ILLNESS

There are several misunderstandings that might arise, or indeed have arisen, from my declaration of this position: let me try to remove these misapprehensions at once. In the first place, it does not follow from my statement that the existing "official" diagnostic categories of mental illness are the most useful or truthful ones that we can reach. I believe, for example, that "psychopathy" represents no more than an attempt at social labelling, for control purposes, by psychiatrists working in tandem with the judicial authorities. It is likely, also, that "schizophrenia" is a pretty useless dust-bin category for a variety of psychic ills which have little logically or biologically in common with one another. Equally, though, I have no doubt that many current diagnostic categories in physical medicine will disappear in the next century or so, and be replaced by others apparently (and provisionally) more adequate. I can see that, for example, by the year 2072 nobody will be classed as having diabetes or asthma, though they will undergo feelings of discomfort similar to those experienced by present-day diabetics and asthmatics. In the future development of our species, we can anticipate *either* that some conditions now classified as illnesses will be re-allocated to a different framework of deviancy (or, more drastically, become regarded as essentially normal and non-deviant), *or* that, on the contrary, conditions which are nowadays viewed in a non-illness category of deviancy (as sins, perhaps, or as consequences of aging or excessive effort) will be re-grouped into the range of the illnesses or diseases. The latter prospect—the progressive annexation of not-illness into illness—seems at the moment much more likely to happen than the former, especially since the stupendous achievements of medical technology make it more and more difficult for doctors to sign death certificates under the rubric "died of natural causes." The natural causes of death are becoming, more and more, causes that we can control: so that the terminally ill, and their relatives, will be putting strong pressures on the medical profession to redefine the natural (and inevitable) causes of fatality, rendering them into medical (and hence controllable) pathologies which require the services of a doctor rather than of a mortician. *The future belongs to illness:* we just are going to get more and more diseases, since our expectations of health are going to become more expansive and sophisticated. Maybe one day there will be a backlash, perhaps at the point when everybody has become so luxuriantly ill, physically or mentally, that there will be poster-parades of protest outside medical conventions with slogans like ILLNESS IS NOT SO BAD, YOU KNOW? or DISEASE IS THE HIGHEST FORM OF HEALTH. But for the moment, it seems that illness is going to be "in," a rising tide of really chronic sickness. Even despite the Canutes of deviancy-sociology.

Secondly and much more importantly, nothing in my argument confirms the technologizing of illness, the specialized medical model of illness is not the only possible one, as I have already indicated. As Dubos points out in his fundamental work *The Mirage of Health* (to which this paper is merely more or less a vulgarized addendum), the greatest advances in the control of disease have often come about through non-medical measures, and in particular through social and political change. The insertion of windows into working-class houses (with the consequent beneficial influx of sunlight), or the provision of a pure water-supply and an efficient sewage-disposal, did more to clear up the plagues of modern epidemic infection than did the identification of particular microbes or the synthesis of "medical discoveries" like the various antibiotics and antitoxins. There are some authorities, notably Siegler and Osmond,[11] who argue that, since the category of illness is infinitely preferable from the standpoint of the mentally deranged, to any other variety of deviancy, we have to concentrate entirely on a narrow medical model for explaining diseases and curing them; in their view, social explanations for the onset of illnesses like schizophrenia and drug-addiction are incompatible with any illness-model, and so should be ruthlessly jettisoned. But we do not need to technologize illness beyond the point at which we decide that it is helpful to do so; even with a physical illness, the concept of a "social disease" is indispensable in the understanding and treatment of, for example, tuberculosis. Preventive medicine and public medicine are bound to invoke social explanations and social measures, to occupy a space which occurs, in short, at the intersection of medicine and politics. My case points, not to the technologizing of illness, to the medicalization of moral values (so obvious in the practice of psychiatry that it needs no fresh rehearsal); but, on the contrary, to the politicization of medical goals. I am arguing that, without the concept of illness—including that of mental illness since to exclude it would constitute the crudest dualism—we shall be unable to *make demands* on the health-service facilities of the society that we live in. . . .

11. Miriam Siegler and Humphry Osmond, "Models of Madness," *British Journal of Psychiatry* 112 (1966), 1193–1203; "Models of Drug Addiction," *International Journal of the Addictions* 3 (1968), 3–

1.10

The Scientific Usefulness of the Idea of Illness

Horacio Fabrega, Jr.

An idea of disease is a common feature of cultures and is probably a universal. In a practical sense the idea is useful, since it has served to focus attention on certain types of problems and facilitated ways of understanding and controlling them. Although of value when applied to humans and for practical and social ends, its usefulness in general biology is unclear. In this paper I review how the idea of disease is used to describe happenings which take place in human and in animal groups and point out differences as well as inconsistencies in its meaning. Analysis of this problem area leads me to propose that we really need two ideas, namely, disease and illness. I then illustrate some of the implications of my proposed conventions.

DEFINITIONAL ISSUES

We use the term "disease" frequently and mean by it an impairment in health and well-being [1]. All peoples have ideas of disease roughly analogous in meaning to ours [2, 3]. However, because my purposes have been to explore the theoretical and scientific implications of this idea, I have adopted rigorous definitional criteria: "Disease" refers to a negative (i.e., unwanted) discontinuity or deviation in the condition of a person (4–8). The condition of a person is assessed on the basis of his verbal reports (e.g., pain, body functioning, etc.), the observations of others, and/or by means of various procedures applied to the person. The process of assessment (i.e., diagnosis) involves determining whether a person's condition deviates, and two types of norms seem to be used to establish that this deviation is present: norms set by the person across time (i.e., personal norms) and norms set by a relevant group to which the person belongs during the present time period (i.e., group norms). I have indicated elsewhere that from a social standpoint this stipulation constitutes a necessary condition for claiming that someone is diseased. The class of diseased persons of a society is a subset of those classed as deviant [9]. Cultural conventions about well-being and health are used to measure deviations. When preliterate people use the idea of disease, they usually have in mind changes in the (sick) person's behavior and functioning. In modern nations, behavior and functioning are important, but more and more abstract attributes of the person (e.g., physicochemical, anatomical, physiological, etc.) are implied. When the latter attributes are salient, I say that the idea or concept of disease is biomedical.

THE CONCEPT OF DISEASE IN GENERAL BIOLOGY

Since man is a member of the class of living animals, one would think that the idea of disease would have scientific utility in general biology. However, though the idea is used, its meaning is ambiguous and its explanatory power can be questioned. For example, in the mathematical study of populations, disease and its effects are constantly being considered. Here the idea is used to mean factors, often genetic, which are harmful to the population [10]. The condition of deviations which is central to the use of the concept in human communities seems far removed. Moreover, one can envision states of a population which an evolutionary biologist might describe as involving disease, but which would not meet the condition involving deviations. Thus, members of a previously stable population whose size is now decreasing because they are showing evidence of poor adjustment (e.g., because of genetic defects, acquired metabolic or physiologic disturbances) could not easily be diagnosed as diseased. Many "successful" populations have probably gone through such phases, but developments during them could not have been explained by means of the idea of disease if the condition about deviations posited earlier had been required. In other words, one would be forced to say that the minority of the population did not have the disease which proved lethal to the majority, a claim which thoroughly discredits the condition of deviation from group norms which seemed needed to articulate and apply the idea in the first place. Many genetic diseases pose similar logical problems if the condition of deviation from past personal norms of the individual is required, since organisms may fail to adapt and reproduce, yet biologic measures which account for this may show no changes (i.e., deviations) from earlier values.

The idea of disease is often used to point to one of the selective influences of the environment. An ecologically differentiated environment, as an example, is said to pose more hazards involving parasitic diseases than one which is not as differentiated. When used in this way, the idea appears to refer to potentially harmful attributes of the physical environment itself (e.g., along with others such as altitude, availability of foodstuffs, etc.). At other times, the idea of disease is used to qualify acquired characteristics of the organisms which limit or militate against its capacity to reproduce and/or survive. As an example, the effects of crowding and inadequate diet or water supply are said to pose health hazards and to interfere (through disease) with the survival of a group. Implicit in these uses of the idea is the view that the behavior and adaptation of the organism are compromised by physiological and/or structural changes. However, it is the cumulated effects on reproduction and survival which are critical, not the social-behavioral changes of the organisms.

Many observations of biologists deal with organisms with acquired defects and diseases. It is generally assumed that diseased members are shunned if they are unable to keep up with the group since they can attract predators [11, 12]. However, Berkson has indicated that in some instances physically compromised members are protected and dealt with in special ways, and this was, of course, noted by Darwin [13, 14]. One can thus see behaviors which are an outgrowth of "disease" which, moreover, comembers "notice" and "do something about," in the process seeming to suspend the selfish pursuits expected on the basis of evolutionary theory. Berkson has suggested that the ecology of these defects and diseases can be used as clues of what the environment is currently selecting for. In other words, if (as an example) visually handicapped organisms are found in a particular group, then the environment of the group is said not to be selecting for visual acuity. Here then, it is acknowledged that disease is linked to a maladaptation of the organism, but its survival is explained as a socially constructive group effort made possible by the balance of other selective factors. Social-behavioral changes in the diseased or defective members and in comembers have been explained in terms of ideas of social bonding, social support, dependence, and, ultimately, parent-offspring interactions [15]. These types of behaviors are integral to the idea of disease when we use it to qualify happenings in human groups, but similar behaviors in animal groups seem not to warrant the idea since concepts and principles linked to the sciences of social biology and ethology suffice.

The material reviewed in this section leads me to conclude that when the idea of disease is used in general biology, it can mean a number of different sorts of things, some of which are not usually implied when the idea is used in a human practical framework. Moreover, states of disease in animals can be linked to changed social behaviors, some of which can elicit support; however, these behaviors are not included in the meaning of the idea of disease when it is applied to animals. It should be emphasized that the synthetic theory of evolution has available many ideas whose meanings embrace much of what one has in mind when using the idea of disease. Ideas such as organism, development, genetic variation, fitness, natural selection, and environment seem sufficient to explain many of the phenomena linked to disease. The explanatory power of these ideas and the seemingly motivated and expressive aspects of behaviors linked to disease in humans are thus factors that create tensions when the idea of disease is used in a general frame of reference.

THE SEPARATE MEANINGS OF DISEASE

The discussion thus far suggests to me that a general definition which provides one with conditions for using the idea of disease in a human-practical as well as in a general biological frame of reference may not be possible. One needs to make explicit specific kinds of phenomena which require explanation and develop guidelines for using ideas with reference to them. I propose that we give the general idea of disease alternative meanings. In some circumstances these meanings would be separated and in others fused.

The idea of disease as "illness" may be used to signify purely behavioral changes. In a general anthropological sense, it is a set of behaviors, judged as undesirable and unwanted in a culture, which is considered as having medical relevance. It is changes in the behavioral sphere in the form of symptoms which initially concern members of a social group and lead them to seek help. Relief from these unwanted behaviors is very often the end point of treatment. Disease as illness, then, may serve as a suitable idea for explaining certain changes which are of special significance to human groups. Because it refers to properties of an individual and is used in a present-oriented time frame, the condition of deviations from past personal norms and prevailing social norms (of behavior) can be stipulated and met.

An idea or concept is also needed in general biology to describe an emergent set of changes in the structures and internal processes of living forms which underlie and account for their failure to adapt. The biomedical meaning of disease seems useful here. Because this idea of disease also refers to properties of an individual and requires diagnosis, the condition of deviations, this time involving abstract attributes of the individual (and not behaviors), still seems relevant. However, if a stipulation about reproduction and survival is included, disease as deviation from personal and group norms is difficult to sustain, since in this instance the future of the organism is implied. I also indicated earlier that in an unbounded time frame, the condition of deviation from current group norms was problematic; the criteria for establishing group deviations would not hold up when clear-cut interferences in functioning existed among the majority of a population. I also indicated that genetic diseases made the condition of deviation from personal norms problematic. Moreover, in a strict evolutionary sense, the meaning of disease as a "harmful" interference in internal structures and processes which subserve living and reproduction of an organism really does require consideration of genetic material as well as future course. In addition to the difficulty of specifying future states of affairs, it is hard to see how one could equate harm between altogether differing levels of phenomena (e.g., between whole structures and genes) [16]. I note, in summary, that application of strict logical criteria about deviations is problematic in the case of our biomedical disease.

In referring to abstract (e.g., chemical, molecular) structures and internal processes which underlie and account for failures in adaptation and reproduction, the biomedical idea of disease can be used to describe organisms of any type. Because of its special meanings and the fact that it is used with reference to all types of living forms, the idea of a biomedical disease has a restricted utility in a human social and valuational frame of reference. The biomedical "disease" may be especially relevant for explanations about biologic evolution, whereas the social-medical "illness" seems relevant for explanations about the complementary process of social evolution (see following).

CAN THE CONCEPT OF ILLNESS BE APPLIED TO NONHUMAN ORGANISMS?

I have suggested that the idea of illness applies principally to human groups and operates in a social-practical framework. Nonetheless, it seems useful to search for analogues among nonhumans. Since through illness an individual communicates disability and dysfunction and group members "respond" by offering help and support, it presupposes highly socialized groups and also motivated actions. This points me in the direction of our closest relatives, the nonhuman primates. For heuristic reasons I will stipulate that states of (biomedical) disease can give rise to illness behaviors and these to reciprocated ("altruistic") responses by other group members. Illness behaviors will be judged as communicative and functional, a product of natural selection. What kinds of questions and problems are raised by this stipulation?

The first set of issues involves a consideration of the conditions under which so-called illness behaviors and reciprocated actions of others occur. It is intuitively compelling that a weak and diseased animal who emits distress signals poses a hazard to its group, for predators can also be drawn by the signals. In addition, should others heed this call, they themselves are rendered less mobile and able to forage for food, which in turn can blunt their competitiveness. Both of these consequences of heeding a diseased member's calls are disadvantageous and suggest that group members will avoid responding and in fact will shun sick members. On the other hand, it is very clear that behaviors which attract and link members together are prominent among nonhuman primates. Maternal-offspring attachments and, later, kinship bonds are powerful socializing influences which consolidate a group and facilitate coping and adaptation. Behaviors which promote such bonds could be activated during episodes of disease. It is well known that primates send and receive messages by means of facial displays which inform about the valuational quality of situations, and thus communications linked to (unpleasant, undesirable) states of disease are realistic possibilities [17]. On the basis of these considerations I will posit that states of disease bring into play conflicting tendencies and behaviors, and it may well be that ecological factors influence which of the tendencies will predominate. It is obvious that this whole problem needs further research.

Another set of issues which needs to be considered has to do with whether "illness behaviors" are merely similar or actually equivalent to those linked to helplessness, dependence, and parent-offspring interaction. Evolution is by definition a conservative process, and common sense leads me to believe that natural selection did not forge a special class of illness behaviors (which reflected internal biomedical disease processes) if behaviors already in the repertoire of a species could serve similar ends. Yet the cost of hastily concluding that illness behaviors are merely those of social support and analogues of parent-offspring interactions is high indeed, since one would miss exploring a facet of adaptation which may contain useful insights.

Until this question is resolved by empirical research, I will assume, as have others, that the behaviors generated when organisms have a defect, or biomedical disease ("illness behaviors"), are in essence those of helplessness, dependence, care giving and seeking, and parent-offspring situations. This assumption raises two sets of questions. The first is why the evolutionary process allows neurobiological routines which subserve these behaviors to persist beyond the time when they are most critical for survival. In other words, parent-offspring-related care seeking and care giving seem "natural to" and critical during a specified development period. Once this period of time is passed and the special survival pressures are mastered, one would think that the evolutionary process might reuse elements of the neural routines for other purposes more critical to the organism, in the process modifying the integrity of the routines. Instead, it seems that the potential for such dependence and helplessness behaviors remains "in" the organism, the neural routines subserving them being reasonably coherent but dormant. To explain these behaviors in adults, it seems necessary to reexamine the role which disease plays in the social behaviors of an infraprimate group.

The second set of questions raised by the assumption that illness behaviors are those natural to helplessness, dependence, and care seeking and giving involves the mechanism of how they are elicited or released. One must assume that dormant neurological substrates are somehow activated, but the question here is how this is accomplished. A biomedical disease process can involve the dysfunction of neuroendocrine systems directly or through the mediation of toxins or inflammatory products, all of which may alter brain-cell thresholds and neural circuits subserving potential illness behaviors. In the case of permanent defects, the mechanism is less clear, although the dehydration and/or undernutrition of the organism which is a consequence of the defect may be a factor. Those who posit a degree of "self-awareness" and motivated actions in animals might develop interesting clues about the mechanisms which trigger illness behaviors and reciprocated responses in a group [18].

The preceding discussion leads me to suggest that, at least in nonhuman groups, the existence of a biomedical disease could be a necessary condition for a (behavioral) state of illness (it can "trigger" this state). But since I am also dealing with the (reciprocated) responses of other group members, I am forced to inquire as to the mechanisms and conditions which account for such responses. An obvious necessary condition for the responses of other group members to occur is the presence of illness behaviors in the first place. In addition, others in the group must somehow be provided with a target to which to respond and also somehow decide whether, in light of selective pressures, it is prudent to engage in (altruistic) responses vis-à-vis the sick member. At this point the requirement for the definition of illness comes to mind, namely, that of a deviation from past personal and prevailing social norms. Let me elaborate on its possible significance.

The behaviors which realize a state of illness are different in kind from those ordinarily descriptive of an organisms's identity. In other words, organisms are individuated, among other things, on the basis of their social rank, age, sex, and—important to my theme—style of behavior. It is to this "whole" that comembers are "locked in" during group activities. In order for an individual to show illness and have it be "recognized" by others, his behavior must deviate from the accustomed norm or behavior set by him in the past. Speaking anthropomorphically, the organism has to signal that he is changed. The stipulation that illness involves a deviation from an individual's past personal behavior norms may be viewed as also providing a condition for having illness behavior recognized by others. This is of course a hypothesis which could be tested under field conditions.

I have indicated that a state of illness also appears to require that the behavior of the individual in question deviate from the prevailing (social) norms set by a relevant group or subgroup to which the individual belongs presently. I will suggest that the condition of social-norm violations is also a factor which plays a role in eliciting reciprocated responses, specifically, in the evaluation by others in the group of whether it is prudent to engage in reciprocal (altruistic) responses toward the sick individual [19]. In other words, when behaviors which can potentially elicit reciprocated (altruistic) responses are infrequent in the group (they constitute a deviation from group norms), members in the group are provided with a distinguishable target toward which it may be safe to behave altruistically. This point can be stated differently. If a disease process affects the majority of the members of a group, then it may very well not be in the interest of the nondiseased group members (who now constitute a minority) to respond altruistically. The fact that under such conditions the behaviors of the diseased members may not in fact constitute a deviation from group norms (i.e., not on social grounds constitute an illness) is a factor which may mar their visibility and effectiveness as signals for altruistic responses. In summary, deviations from observable social norms, an apparent feature of illness behaviors, may constitute a condition for the occurrence of reciprocated responses from comembers. Observations in the field would clarify whether (or under what conditions) this, in fact, takes place.

THE IDEA OF ILLNESS IN A COMPARATIVE HUMAN FRAMEWORK

A review of the literature in anthropology reveals that people of different cultures make a basic distinction when judging the behavior and functioning of comembers. This distinction is between normative-desirable conditions and deviant-undersirable ones. The latter class is usually broken down into two basic types, illness and nonillness, and people differ in their ways of explaining and dealing with each of these. Ways of explaining illness vary across cultures, and because of this behaviors associated with illness will vary and so will reactions of comembers toward the ill. An assumption which I make is that in any human group the boundary between illness and nonillness is fluid and changes across time: Behavioral changes which in a particular group are viewed as illness at one point may at a later time be viewed as nonillness, and vice versa.

The accumulated experiences which groups have with illness and with its treatment yield what we can call a system for understanding and explaining illness, and in this sense it can be viewed as a theory. The group's theory of illness constitutes a culturally adaptive trait and is an outgrowth of the process of social evolution [20]. It is used by the medical practitioners and serves as their basis for action embodying nomenclatural systems, principles of diagnosis, and methods for treatment; the latter include procedures, medicines, and regimens which are deemed efficacious for dealing with the illnesses of the group. The behaviors of medical practitioners and of their clients are partially patterned and regulated by directives which devolve from the group's theory of illness.

Groups also show what I term a folk system of understanding about illness. Folk understandings also constitute cultural traits of the group and serve as the lay (i.e., nonprofessional) basis of orientation and action toward illness. They include names of illness, lay beliefs about causation, standard remedies and routines for home treatment, and a body of rules and expectations which serves to pattern the behaviors of lay persons who are ill and of those who come into contact with them. I assume that in many societies there is a feedback relationship between the (formal) theory of illness and the (informal) folk system. By this I mean that formal understandings, with time, may spread and become standard and traditional (i.e., "informal") in the lay populace. Conversely, some of the informal, lay accumulated wisdom about illness which some group members derive contains insights and clues about diagnosis and treatment which the medical professionals use and test out. When this knowledge is "proven" useful, it then becomes systematized and comes to be used by the medical professionals. In this sense, folk knowledge has entered the formal theory of illness and the body of knowledge which derives from it.

The formal theory of illness of a group, together with folk understandings, gives a distinctive ideological cast to what can be termed the group's medical care system (MCS). The MCS constitutes what can be viewed as the group's social approach to illness. It embraces the knowledge, tradition, guidelines, and values that groups have vis-à-vis illness. In the process of its operations, a group's MCS achieves a given level of control over illness. Groups differ in terms of the frequency and duration of illness conditions—that is, in terms of how well their medical theory and system of care function. Moreover, a group's theory of illness and its MCS obviously change across time. The processes of variation, selection, and retention which are judged as integral to evolution can, when applied to social evolution, be seen as involving medical-cultural traits of a society [21, 22]. Social scientists and historians are the individuals principally concerned with the analysis and comparison of how societies orient to and handle illness.

The special human capacity for the elaborate use of symbols appears necessary for the idea of illness, vulnerability, finitude, and death to arise. These ideas, and the experiences which they realize, together with other human social accomplishments, give rise to ideas of religion, sanctity, and ethics all of which, when institutionalized, may play a role in blunting strict natural selection as posited in biologic evolution. The sum of this, human culture and experience, allows for the persistence of illness in human groups as opposed to nonhumans. In other words, illness-related behaviors and medical care activities are to some extent (see earlier discussion) emergent phenomena in humanoid and human groups. Implicit in this reasoning is the drawing of a clear distinction between the processes of biological as opposed to cultural or social evolution. In the former, the concept of disease has currency since at stake is the selection for basic biologic traits which are realized in genes, chemistries, and/or physiologies. On the other hand, in the complementary process of social evolution, one is dealing with the selective retention of key ideas and correlated social institutions which prove advantageous to the individual (and by extension, the group) and in this context, the concept of illness may play an appropriate role.

This discussion makes clear that social policies in the group regulate and certify criteria and standards of illness. Because medical theories and MCS are socially sanctioned, they are subject to political, economic, and historical influences as well. Moreover, because the social-medical practices of a people are situated in an evaluative scheme, one is allowed to make moral judgments about whether the criteria of a particular illness are sound, good, proper, practical, and useful...

TOWARD A SCIENTIFIC THEORY OF ILLNESS

A theory can be viewed as a set of beliefs by means of which one explains a particular class of problems. A scientific theory consists of a set of interrelated beliefs whose meaning and logical structure incorporate the guidelines of the scientific method. Problems which are explained by scientific theories are said to be formulated in an impersonal and technical language. Although social concerns and human needs may point to problems or "puzzles" which need to be resolved, when such problems are formulated scientifically, they are said to be abstracted out of social circumstances.

A scientific theory about illness may be defined as a set of interrelated beliefs whose meaning and logical structure are "scientific" and whose function is to provide an understanding about illnesses and the problems which surround them. In this paper I have dealt with aspects bearing on a scientific theory of illness. Such a theory should explain the causes, manifestations, and consequences of illness so as to promote a high and prudent level of control through prevention and treatment. At the same time, such a scientific theory of illness should ideally allow comparing and analyzing the theories of illness of different people so as to promote an understanding of their own system of medicine. Ultimately, use of a scientific theory of illness may lead to the development of a better understanding of relations between illness, medical care, and social systems.

My assumption is that the domain of a scientific theory of illness embraces a reasonably complex set of changes, namely, particular kinds of disvalued conditions of individuals, and that because of this such a theory cannot easily be separated from social factors as can other scientific theories. A basic point is that illness becomes an object of concern to people by the observable effects which it produces on behavior and adaptation. The cultural meaning of these behaviors, which is to say the sense which is made of them in the system of medicine of the group, also requires explanation, and a scientific theory of illness should facilitate this.

There is a related factor which makes the domain of illness different and renders theory building very much a social enterprise. Given the character of social change and evolution, the application of scientific knowledge is not likely in the foreseeable future to eventuate in the eradication and "full" control of illness. For many illnesses there does not, at present, exist a suitable level of understanding about causation, and given the holistic character of human adaptation and functioning, many illnesses may never be amenable to full control even if such understanding existed. Illnesses are in many respects a natural outcome of the processes of individual coping and adaptation and are to be expected in any society as a matter of course [4–8]. Moreover, an increasingly bureaucratic and technological society is likely to "produce" illness by altering physical and social environmental factors which impinge on human adaptation, just as the application of biomedical knowledge of illness can be expected to lead to the inadvertent outbreak of new (iatrogenic) illnesses. And as social values and the level of technology change, ways of defining illness (i.e., vs. nonillness) will also change. All of this means that illnesses are likely to persist as human problems. This persistence, the need for continuous control, and the finite amount of resources with which to handle related problems indicate that the generation and application of knowledge about illness will require a rational and prudent scheme of cost-benefit accounting. Such a scheme necessarily must be developed in the light of how other problems of a society are handled by institutions and service professions. In sum, given the character of human illness, persons seeking to explain how these develop, what their consequences are, and how best to control them are faced with social questions and practical matters not often encountered in other scientific disciplines.

REFERENCES

1. G. L. Engel. Science, 196:129, 1977.
2. C. C. Hughes, *In*: I. Gladstone (ed.). Man's image in medicine and anthropology. New York: International Univ. Press, 1963.
3. A. Young. Am. Anthropol., 78:5, 1976.
4. H. Fabrega, Jr. Disease and social behavior. Cambridge, Mass.: M.I.T. Press, 1974.
5. H. Fabrega, Jr. J. Nerv. Ment. Dis. 162:199, 1976.
6. H. Fabrega, Jr. Perspect. Biol. Med. 20:108, 1976.
7. H. Fabrega, Jr. J. Theor. Biol. 63:191, 1976.
8. H. Fabrega, Jr. *In:* J. Englegardt (ed.). Disease viewed as a symbolic category. New York: Raven, 1978.
9. T. Parsons. The social system. New York: Free Press, 1951.
10. T. Dobzhansky. *In:* G. Hook and A. Boyce (eds.). The structure of human populations, p. 213. Oxford: Clarendon, 1972.
11. C. Bramblett. Am. J. Phys. Anthropol. 26:331, 1967.
12. H. Harlow and M. Harlow.*In:* A. Schrier, H. Harlow, and F. Stollnitz (eds.). New York: Academic Press, 1965.
13. G. Berkson. *In:* M. Lewis and I. Rosenblum (eds.). Origins of behavior. New York: Wiley, 1974.
14. C. Darwin. The descent of man. New York: Random House, Modern Library, 1914.
15. R. Hinde. Biological bases of human social behavior. New York: McGraw-Hill, 1974.
16. R. Lewontin. Genetic basis of evolutionary change. New York: Columbia Univ. Press, 1974.
17. R. E. Miller. *In:* L. A. Rosenblum (ed.). Primate behavior: developments in field and laboratory research, p. 139. New York: Academic Press, 1971.
18. D. R. Griffin. The question of animal awareness. New York: Rockefeller Univ. Press, 1976.
19. R. Trivers. Q. Rev. Biol. 46:35, 1971.
20. C. Wilcocks. Medical advance, public health and social evolution. Oxford: Pergamon, 1963.
21. W. Durham. Hum. Ecol. 4:89, 1976.
22. D. Campbell. Am. Psychol., p. 1103, 1975.
23. A. R. Feinstein. Clinical judgment. Baltimore: Williams & Wilkins, 1967.

Part 2

Historical Development of Disease Concepts

Two different sorts of articles are represented in this section. The first part of the section consists of original source material drawn from what might be termed the "modern" view of disease. The selections by Sydenham, Morgagni, Bichat, Bernard, Virchow, and Cannon represent key advances in the philosophy of medicine concerning disease. This is not to say that the modern concept of disease admits of a univocal explication, or that it represents a revolutionary break with earlier approaches to understanding the concept. As the selections by Cohen, Veith, King, and Temkin make abundantly evident, the various approaches to understanding disease are often extensions of particular philosophical approaches to disease with roots dating back to ancient times. Rather, the modern flavor of these selections resides in their commitment to the pursuit of explanations for, and a causal understanding of, disease. Prior to Sydenham, the practice of medicine focused, with few exceptions, on curing disease. The writings of physicians such as Sydenham and Bernard reveal their belief that therapeutics could not remain the sole and exclusive goal of medicine. They held that the pursuit of knowledge regarding diease was a central, if instrumental, goal for medicine. While no unanimity of opinion is to be found in their beliefs about the nature of disease, all the physicians included here are bound by a common commitment to analyze and explain disease.

These selections reveal two important conceptual legacies, which still reverberate through contemporary disputes about the nature of the disease concept. First, the issue of whether disease is best understood as a peculiar ontological entity, as a set of internal physical changes, or as a set of externally manifested physical, mental, and social states still divides contemporary thought about disease. Second, current disagreements about the role of normative evaluation in assessing and treating disease can be traced, in part, to efforts to articulate a criterion or a set of criteria that pinpoints a unifying property common to the notion of disease. Much of the contemporary discussion of the concept of disease presented later in this volume represents efforts to defend or criticize this brand of philosophical essentialism.

2.1

Preface to the Third Edition, *Observationes Medicae*

Thomas Sydenham
trans. by R. G. Latham

1. Inasmuch as the structure of the human frame has been so set together by Nature, that it is unable, from the continuous flux of particles, to remain unchanged; whilst, from the action of external causes, it is subjected to influences beyond its own: and since, for these reasons, a numerous train of diseases has pressed upon the earth since the beginning of time;[1] so without doubt the necessity of investigations into the Art of Healing has exercised the wit of mankind for many ages before the birth, not only of the Greek but of the Egyptian Esculapius, the latter being earlier by a thousand years than the former.

2. And, indeed, as no man can say who it was that first invented the use of clothes and houses against the inclemency of the weather, so also can no investigator point out the origin of Medicine—mysterious as the sources of the Nile. There has never been a time when it was not. Like other arts, however, it has been zealously or remissly cultivated, according to the difference of time and place.

3. How much the ancients, and pre-eminently amongst these Hippocrates, performed is known to all. It is to these, and to the compilers from their writings, that we owe the greater part of our skill in therapeutics.

Besides these, however, in the succeeding ages, others have been conspicuous for their industry: men who, by attending to anatomy, to pharmacy, to the *methodus medendi*, have done their best towards enlarging the boundaries of medicine. Nor have there been wanting those who, in our own time, and in

1. "Satis scimus haberi Historiam Naturalem, mole amplam, varietate gratam, diligentia saepius curiosam; attamen si quis ex ea fabulas, et authorum citationes, et inanes controversias, philogiam denique et ornamenta eximat (quae ad convivales sermones hominumque doctorum noctes potius quam ad insituendam Philosophiam sunt accommodata) ad nil magni res recidet. Longe profecto abest ab ea historia quam animo metimur."—Descript. Glob. Intellect., e. iii, vol. xi, p. 8.

our own island, have done good work in each kind of science that advances medicine. The praises of these I leave to better pens than my own.

4. Nevertheless, how great soever the efforts of others may have been, I, for my own part, have always considered that the breath of life would have been to me a vain gift, unless I, working in the same mine with them, contributed my mite to the treasury of physic. Wherefore, after long meditation, and the diligent and faithful observations of many years, I at length determined—firstly, to state my opinion as to the means by which the science of medicine was to be advanced; secondly, to publish a sample of my endeavours in that department.

5. I conceive that the advancement of medicine lies in the following conditions:

There must be, in the first place, a history of the disease; in other words, a description that shall be at once graphic and natural.

There must be, in the second place, a *Praxis*, or *Methodus*, respecting the same, and this must be regular and exact.

To draw a disease in gross is an easy matter. To describe it in its history, so as to escape the censure of the great Bacon, is far more difficult. Against some pretenders in this way, he launches the following censure—"*We are well aware that there existeth such a thing as a Natural History; full in bulk, pleasant from its variety, often curious from its diligence. Notwithstanding, whoever would take away the same, the citations of authors, the empty discussions, and, finally, the book-learning and ornaments which are fitter for the convivial meetings of learned men than for the establishment of a Philosophy, would find that it dwindled into nothing. Such a natural history is far distant from the one we contemplate.*"[1]

In like manner, it is exceedingly easy to propound some common-place cure for a complaint. It is far harder, however, to translate your words into actions, and to square your results with your promises. This is well known to those who have learned that there occur in practical writers numerous diseases, which neither the authors themselves, nor any persons else besides, have been able to cure.

6. In respect to the histories of a disease, any one who looks at the case carefully, will see at once that an author must direct his attention to many more points than are usually thought of. A few of these are all that need be noticed at present.

7. In the first place, it is necessary that all diseases be reduced to definite and certain *species*, and that, with the same care which we see exhibited by botanists in their phytologies; since it happens, at present, that many diseases, although included in the same genus, mentioned with a common nomenclature, and resembling one another in several symptoms, are, notwithstanding, different in their natures, and require a different medical treatment.

---

1. ..."nova Febrium
Terris incubuit cohors." (Hor. 1.)

We all know that the term *thistle* is applied to a variety of plants; nevertheless, he would be a careless botanist, indeed, who contented himself with the general description of a *thistle*; who only exhibited the marks by which the class was identified; who neglected the proper and peculiar signs of the species, and who overlooked the characters by which they were distinguished from each other. On the same principle, it is not enough for a writer to merely note down the common phenomena of some multiform disease; for, although it may be true that all complaints are not liable to the same amount of variety, there are still many which authors treat alike, under the same heads, and without the shadows of a distinction, whilst they are in their nature as dissimilar as possible. This I hope to prove in the forthcoming pages.

8. More than this—it generally happens that even where we find a *specific* distribution, it has been done in subservience to some favorite hypothesis which lies at the bottom of the true phenomena; so that the distinction has been adapted not to the nature of the complaint, but to the views of the author and the character of his philosophy. Many instances prove the extent to which medicine has been injured by a want of accuracy upon this point. We should have known the cures of many diseases before this time if physicians, whilst with all due good-will they communicated their experiments and observations, had not deceived in their disease, and had not mistaken one species for another. And this, I think, is one reason why the Materia Medica has grown so much and produced so little.

9. In writing the history of a disease, every philosophical hypothesis whatsoever, that has previously occupied the mind of the author, should lie in abeyance. This being done, the clear and natural phenomena of the disease should be noted—these, and these only. They should be noted accurately, and in all their minuteness; in imitation of the exquisite industry of those painters who represent in their portraits the smallest moles and the faintest spots. No man can state the errors that have been occasioned by these physiological hypotheses. Writers, whose minds have taken a false colour under their influence, have saddled diseases with phenomena which existed in their own brains only; but which would have been clear and visible to the whole world had the assumed hypothesis been true. Add to this, that if by chance some symptom really coincide accurately with their hypothesis, and occur in the disease whereof they would describe the character, they magnify it beyond all measure and moderation; they make it all and in all; the molehill becomes a mountain; whilst, if it fail to tally with the said hypothesis, they pass it over either in perfect silence or with only an incidental mention, unless, by means of some philosophical subtlety, they can enlist it in their service, or else, by fair means or foul, accommodate it in some way or other to their doctrines.

10. Thirdly, it is necessary, in describing any disease, to enumerate the peculiar and constant phenomena apart from the accidental and adventitious ones: these last-named being those that arise from the age or temperament of the patient, and from the different forms of medical treatment. It often

happens that the character of the complaint varies with the nature of the remedies, and that symptoms may be referred less to the disease than to the doctor. Hence two patients with the same ailment, but under different treatment, may suffer from different symptoms. Without caution, therefore, our judgment concerning the symptoms of disease is, of necessity, vague and uncertain. Outlying forms of disease, and cases of exceeding rarity, I take no notice of. They do not properly belong to the histories of disease. No botanist takes the bites of a caterpillar as a characteristic of a leaf of sage.

11. Finally, the particular seasons of the year which favour particular complaints are carefully to be observed. I am ready to grant that many diseases are good for all seasons. On the other hand, there is an equal number that, through some mysterious instinct of Nature, follow the seasons as truly as plants and birds of passage. I have often wondered that this disposition on the part of several diseases, obvious as it is, has been so little observed; the more so, as there is no lack of curious observations upon the planets under which plants grow and beasts propagate. But whatever may be the cause of this supineness, I lay it down as a confirmed rule, that the knowledge of the seasons wherein diseases occur is of equal value to the physician in determining their species and in effecting their extirpation; and that both these results are less satisfactory when this observation is neglected.

12. These, although not the only, are the main points to be attended to in drawing up the history of a disease. The practical value of such a history is above all calculation. By the side thereof, the subtle discussions, and the minute refinements wherewith the books of our new school are stuffed full, even *ad nauseam*, are of no account. What short way—what way at all—is there towards either the detection of the morbific cause that we must fight against, or towards the indications of treatment which we must discover, except the sure and distinct perception of peculiar symptoms? Upon each of these points the slightest and most unimportant circumstances have their proper bearings. Something in the way of variety we may refer to the particular temperament of individuals; something also to the difference of treatment. Notwithstanding this, Nature, in the production of disease, is uniform and consistent; so much so, that for the same disease in different persons the symptoms are for the most part the same; and the selfsame phenomena that you would observe in the sickness of a Socrates you would observe in the sickness of a simpleton. Just so the universal characters of a plant are extended to every individual of the species; and whoever (I speak in the way of illustration) should accurately describe the colour, the taste, the smell, the figure, &c., of one single violet, would find that his description held good, there or thereabouts, for all the violets of that particular species upon the face of the earth.

13. For my own part, I think that we have lived thus long without an accurate history of diseases, for this especial reason; viz. that the generality have considered that disease is but a confused and disordered effort of Nature

thrown down from her proper state, and defending herself in vain; so that they have classed the attempts at a just description with the attempts to wash blackamoors white.

14. To return, however, to our business. As truly as the physician may collect points of diagnosis from the minutest circumstances of the disease, so truly may he also elicit indications in the way of therapeutics. So much does this statement hold good, that I have often thought, that provided with a thorough insight into the history of any disease whatsoever, I could invariably apply an equivalent remedy; a clear path being thus marked out for me by the different phenomena of the complaint. These phenomena, if carefully collated with each other, lead us, as it were, by the hand to those palpable indications of treatment which are drawn, not from the hallucinations of our fancy, but from the innermost penetralia of Nature.

15. By this ladder, and by this scaffold, did Hippocrates ascend his lofty sphere—the Romulus of medicine, whose heaven was the empyrean of his art. He it is whom we can never duly praise. He it was who then laid the solid and immoveable foundation for the whole superstructure of medicine, when he taught that *our natures are the physicians of our diseases*.[1] By this he ensured a clear record of the phenomena of each disease, pressing into his service no hypothesis, and doing no violence to his description; as may be seen in his books, 'De Morbis,' 'De Affectionibus,' &c. Besides this, he has left us certain rules, founded on the observation of the processes of Nature, both in inducing and removing disease. Of this sort are the 'Coacae Praenotiones,' the 'Aphorisms,' &c. Herein consisted the theory of that divine old man. It exhibited the legitimate operations of Nature, put forth in the diseases of humanity. The vain efforts of a wild fancy, the dreams of a sick man, it did *not* exhibit.

Now, as the said theory was neither more nor less than an exquisite picture of Nature, it was natural that the practice should coincide with it. This aimed at one point only—it strove to help Nature in her struggles as it best could. With this view, it limited the province of medical art to the support of Nature when she was enfeebled, and to the coercion of her when she was outrageous; the attempt on either side being determined by the rate and method whereby she herself attempted the removal and the expulsion of disease. The great sagacity of this man had discovered that Nature by herself *determines diseases, and is of herself sufficient in all things against all of them.*[2] This she is, being aided by the fewest and the simplest forms of medicine. At times she is independent of even these.

16. The other method whereby, in my opinion, the art of medicine may be

---

1. *Νούσων φύσιες ἰητροί*—Epid. vi. 5. 1. t. iii, p. 606 [G].

2. *τάς νούσους κρίνει, καὶ ἐξαρκέει τὰ πάντα πᾶσι.*—De Aliment, t. ii, p. 19. [G]

advanced, turns chiefly upon what follows, viz., that there must be some fixed, definite, and consummate *methodus medendi*, of which the commonweal may have the advantage. By *fixed*, *definite*, and *consummate*, I mean a line of practice which has been based and built upon a sufficient number of experiments, and has in that manner been proved competent to the cure of this or that disease. I by no means am satisfied with the record of a few successful operations, either of the doctor or the drug. I require that they be shown to succeed universally, or at least under such and such circumstances. For I contend that we ought to be equally sure of overcoming such and such diseases by satisfying such and such intentions, as we are of satisfying those same intentions by the application of such and such sorts of remedies; a matter in which we generally (although not, perhaps, always) can succeed. To speak in the way of illustration, we attain our ends when we produce stools by senna, or sleep by opium.

I am far from denying that a physician ought to attend diligently to particular cases in respect to the results both of the method and of the remedies which he employs in the cure of disease. I grant, too, that he may lay up his experiences for use, both in the way of casing his memory and of seizing suggestions. By so doing he may gradually increase in medical skill, so that eventually, by a long continuance and a frequent repetition of his experiments, he may lay down and prescribe for himself a *methodus medendi*, from which, in the cure of this or that disease, he need not deviate a single straw's breadth.

17. Nevertheless, the publication of particular observations is, in my mind, of no great advantage. Where is the particular importance in telling us that once, twice, or even oftener, this disease has yielded to that remedy? We are overwhelmed as it is, with an infinite abundance of vaunted medicaments, and here they add a new one. Now, if I repudiate the rest of my formulae, and restrict myself to this medicine only, I must try its efficacy by innumerable experiments, and I must weigh, in respect to both the patient and the practice, innumerable circumstances, before I can derive any benefit from such a solitary observation.

But if the medicine never fails in the hands of the observer, why does he confine himself to particular cases? He must either distrust himself, or he must desire to impose upon the world in detail, rather than in gross. How easy a matter it is to write thick volumes upon these points is known even to beginners. It is also known that the foundation and erection of a perfect and definite *methodus medendi* is a work of exceeding difficulty. If, in each age of the world, a single person only had properly treated upon one single disease, the province of the physician, or the art of healing, would long ago have reached its height; and would have been as complete and perfect as the lot of humanity admits. It is ruin of our prospects to have departed from our oldest and best guide, Hippocrates, and to have forsaken the original *methodus medendi*. This was built upon the knowledge of immediate and conjunct causes, things of which the evidence is certain. Our modern doctrine is a contrivance of the word-catchers; the art of talking rather than the art of healing.

That I may not seem to speak these things rashly, I must be allowed to make a brief digression; and to prove that those remote and ultimate causes in the determination and exhibition of which the vain speculations of curious and busy men are solely engaged, are altogether incomprehensible and inscrutable; and that the only causes that can be known to us, and the only ones from which we may draw our indications of treatment, are those which are proximate, immediate, and conjunct.

18. We must begin with noticing that humours may be retained in the body longer than is proper; Nature being unable to begin with their concoction, and to end with their expulsion. They may also contract a morbific disposition from the existing atmospheric constitution. Finally, they may act the part of poisons from the influence of some venomous contagion. From any one of these causes, or from any cause akin to them, the said humours become exalted into a *substantial form* or *species*; and these substantial forms or species manifest themselves in disorders coincident with their respective essences. Of these disorders the symptoms, in the eyes of the unwary, originate either in the nature of the part which the humour has attacked, or else in the character of the humour itself anterior to its specific metamorphosis. Nevertheless, in their true nature, they are the disorders that depend upon the essence of the said species recently exalted to the particular degree in question. Hence every specific disease is a disorder that originates from this or that specific exaltation, or (changing the phrase) from the specification of some juice in the living body. Under this head may be comprised the greatest part of those diseases that are reducible to some given form or type, in the production and maturation whereof Nature binds herself to a certain method as stringently as she does with plants and even animals. Each plant and animal has its proper and peculiar disorders. In like manner, each juice has its exaltations as soon as it has broken out into a species. Of this we have a clear, visible, and daily proof in the different species of excrescences, which trees and fruit exhibit in the shape of moss, and mistletoe, and fungi, and the like. Whether arising from a perversion and depravation of the nutritive juice, or from any other cause, these excrescences are, each and all, essences or species wholly distinct and different from the parent stock, whether tree or shrub.

19. Let a person seriously and accurately consider the phenomena which accompany such a fever as a quartan ague. It begins almost always in autumn; it keeps to a regular course of succession; it preserves a definite type; its periodical revolutions, occurring on the fourth day, if undisturbed by external influences, are as regular as those of a watch or any other piece of machinery; it sets in with shivers and a notable feeling of cold, which are succeeded by an

equally decided sensation of heat, and it is terminated by a most profuse perspiration. Whoever is attacked must bear with his complaint till the vernal equinox, there or thereabouts.

Now putting all this carefully together, we find reasons for believing that this disease is a species equally cogent with those that we have for believing a plant to be a species. The plant springs from the earth; the plant blooms; the plant dies: the plant does all this with equal regularity. All its other affections are those of its essence. It cannot easily be comprehended how the disease in question can arise from a combination of either principles or evident qualities, whilst a plant is universally recognised as a substance, and as a distinct species in nature. Nevertheless, I cannot deny that whereas all species, both of plants and animals, with the exception of a very few, subsist by themselves, the species of disease depend upon the humours that engender them.

20. Now, although it appears, from what has been said, that we have shown reason for considering the causes of the majority of diseases as inscrutable and inexplicable, the question as to how they may be cured is, nevertheless, capable of solution.

All that we have just dealt with has been the case of the remote causes. Here it is evident to every one, that curious speculators lose their labour; since the investigation and illustration of primary and ultimate causes is a neglect of our capabilities, and a violation of nature. Hand in hand with this is the contempt for those causes that ought to be, and which can be understood; which lie before our feet; which require no rotten supports; which appeal to the understanding at once; which are revealed by either the testimony of our senses, or by anatomical observations of long standing. Such are the causes which we call conjunct and immediate. As it is clearly impossible that a physician should discover those causes of disease that are not cognisable by the senses, so also it is unnecessary that he should attempt it. It is quite sufficient for him to know whence the mischief *immediately* arises, and for him to be able to distinguish with accuracy between the effects and symptoms of the complaint which he has in hand, and those of some similar one. In a pleurisy, for instance, a man may work much, and work in vain, before he will understand the vicious crasis, and the incoherent texture of blood which is the primary cause of the disease; yet, if he know rightly the cause by which it is *immediately* produced, and if he can rightly discriminate between it and other diseases, he will be as certain to succeed in his attempts at a cure, as if he had attended to idle and unprofitable searches into remote causes. This, however, is a digression.

21. Now if any one ask whether, in addition to the two aforesaid *desiderata* in medical science (viz., the true and genuine history of diseases, and the regular and definite *methodus medendi*), a third may not also be enumerated, viz., the discovery of specific remedies, he will find that I agree with, and that I second his doctrine. For the cure of acute diseases the method seems the best; since,

inasmuch as in these Nature herself establishes some process of evacuation, whatever method promotes such evacuation, and thereby helps Nature, conduces, of necessity, towards the cure of the disease. Nevertheless, by the help of specifics, if such could be found, the patient might find a shorter way to his recovery. And such is desirable. He might also (which is more important still) be placed beyond the pale of those dangers which follow the aberrations of Nature; for into such, during the expulsion of morbific causes, and in spite of the best and most powerful assistance from the physician, she frequently and unwillingly has fallen.

22. In respect to the cure of chronic diseases, although I have no doubt but that a greater progress in it than is expected at the first glance may be hoped for from the method alone, I am still convinced that, in the cure of many of the most important that afflict humanity, our method is unavailing. This happens because in chronic diseases the method of Nature herself for the ejection of the morbific matter is less efficacious than in the acute ones; whilst it is by joining hands with Nature, and by aiming properly at the same mark, that we are enabled to destroy the disease. In overcoming a chronic disease, he has the best and truest claim to the name of physician, who is in possession of the medicine that shall destroy the *species* of the disease, not he who merely substitutes one primary or secondary quality for another. This he can do without extinguishing the species at all; i.e., a gouty patient may be cooled or heated as the case may be, and his gout continue unconquered. This method of merely introducing different qualities can no more effect the direct destruction of specific diseases, than a sword can quench a flame. What can be done by cold, or heat, or wet, or dry, or by any of the secondary qualities that depend upon them, against a disease whose essence consists in none of them?

23. Any one who objects to me that a sufficiency of specific remedies is already known to the world, will, upon a due consideration of the subject, take the same view with myself. I am sure of this, since the only medicine that supports his doctrine is the Peruvian bark. Medicines that *specifically* answer to the indications of treatment, and medicines that *specifically* cure diseases, are as wide as the poles asunder. In the first case, we satisfy the curative indications, and drive away the ailment: in the second, we take no cognisance of the indication or intention at all, whilst we destroy the disease directly and immediately. For instance, mercury and sarsaparilla are commonly called specifics in syphilis. Nevertheless, they are no proper and direct specifics at all; nor will they be considered as such, until it be shown by cogent and irrefragable proofs that the one produces its beneficial effects without salivation, and the other without diaphoresis. In this way many different diseases are cured by their different appropriate evacuations; but it is the evacuation that performs the cure, the medicine being specific to the evacuation. To the disease itself, self-sufficiently and directly, they are no more specific than a lancet is specific to a pleurisy.

24. Specific medicines, in the restricted sense of the word, are by no means of every-day occurrence. They do not fall to every man's lot. Nevertheless, I have no doubt, but that out of that abundant plenitude of provision for the preservation of all things wherewith Nature burgeons and overflows (and that, under the command of the Great and Most Excellent Creator), provision also has been made for the cure of the more serious diseases which afflict humanity, and that near at hand and in every country. It is to be lamented, indeed, that the nature of plants is not more thoroughly understood by us. In my mind, they bear off the palm from all the rest of the *Materia Medica*. They offer also the most reasonable hopes for the discovery of remedies of the sort in question. The parts of animals are too like those of the human body: minerals are too unlike. That minerals, however, are more energetic in satisfying indications than either of the two other classes of remedies, and that the difference in character is the reason for their doing so, I freely confess. Still they are not specific remedies in the sense and manner explained above.

For my own part, I can claim nothing beyond the credit of having undergone the labour and trouble of considering these matters carefully, and that for many years past. Nevertheless, I have not yet been so successful as to venture upon the public with my ideas upon these things at once with prudence and confidence.

25. Although, however, the vegetable world is my favorite source for medicines, I am far from despising those excellent remedies which we procure from the other two kingdoms; and which having been discovered, in either this or any other age, by human labour and human industry, are found to satisfy the intentions of treatment. Amongst these, the place of honour is due to what are called *Dr. Goddard's drops*. They are prepared by Dr. Goodhall, a learned man, and a skilful investigator, both of methods and remedies. I give these a just preference over all other volatile spirits whatsoever for energetically and efficaciously attaining the end for which they are applied.

26. To conclude—having in this introduction promised that I would give a sample of those improvements which I have done my best to effect for medicine, I here attempt to fulfil my promise by publishing 'A History and Cure of the Acute Diseases.' In doing this I am well aware that I shall exhibit for the benefit of the idle and ignorant the labour of the best years of my life, and the results of much toil both of mind and body. I know, too, the bad temper of the age I live in. I shall reap only a harvest of abuse. Better would it have been for my present fame to have continued some vain and useless speculation. Be it so. I wait for my reward elsewhere.

27. Now if any one object that men as conversant with medicine as myself differ from my doctrines, I can only answer that my business has been to support my own observations, not to discuss the opinions of others. In doing this, I beg the reader's patience, not his favour. The facts themselves will shortly speak for themselves; and they alone will show whether on the one side

I act with truth and honesty, or whether, on the other, like a profligate and immoral and wicked man, I am to become a murderer even in the grave. I ask pardon where the history is less careful than I meant it to be, since I wish less to exhaust my subject than to encourage those who have better parts than myself to undertake hereafter what I now attempt imperfectly.

28. One point still remains to be indicated to the reader. I have no intention of swelling out the following pages with an infinite number of particular cases, under the idea of claiming credit for the method that they embody. It would be vain and wearisome to repeat in detail the points which I have reduced to a general expression. I consider it sufficient to append here and there, at the conclusion of the general statement, some particular observation containing the substance of the method preceding; and I do this more especially for the last few years. In the mean time I warrant my general methods. Each has been established and confirmed by reiterated experiments.

29. Whoever expects a great mass of remedies and formulae in the following pages will be disappointed. The physician must apply these according to circumstances and his discretion. I only mention the indications he must satisfy, and that in respect to their order and their time. True medicine consists in the discovery of the real indications rather than in the excogitation of remedies. Those who have neglected this have put arms into the hands of the empiric, and taught him to imitate the physician.

30. One objection against me will be made by the vulgar and unthinking only, viz. that of having renounced the proper pomp of physic, and of having recommended medicines so plain and simple as not to be reducible to the 'Materia Medica.' Wise men know this—*whatever is useful is good*. They know, also, that Hippocrates recommended bellows[1] for the colic, and nothing at all for the cancer.[2] They know, too, that similar treatment is to be discovered in almost every page of his writings; and withal that his merits in medicine are as great as if he had loaded his pages with the most pompous formulae.

31. I also intended to have written a history of Chronic Diseases, or at least one on those that I had most frequently treated. As this, however, is a work of great labour, and as the present lucubrations are experimental, I waive the subject for the present.

1. De Morbis, iii, tom. ii, p. 305. [G.]
2. Aphor, vi, 38; tom. iii, p. 754. [G.]

2.2

The Seats and Causes of Disease: Author's Preface

G. B. Morgagni

There are two sayings of C. Lucilius, as you have it in Cicero (a): I mean, "That he neither wish'd to have his writings fall into the hands of the most unlearned, nor of the most learned readers;" which I should equally make use of on the present occasion, if it were not my desire to be useful to the unlearned, as well as to be assisted by the learned, reader. For I have had two views in publishing these writings; the first, that I might assist the studies of such as are intended for the practice of medicine; the second, and this the principal view, that I might be universally useful, though this cannot happen without the concurrence and assistance of the learned in every quarter. In what manner I have endeavour'd to execute these intentions will appear from this preface.

2. Theophilus Bonetus was a man who deserved the esteem of the faculty of medicine in particular, and of mankind in general, in an equal degree with any other, on account of his publishing those books which are entitled the *Sepulchretum*. For by collecting, in as great a number as possible, and digesting into order, the dissections of bodies, which had been carried off by diseases, he form'd them into one compact body; and thereby caus'd those observations, which, when scatter'd up and down through the writings of almost innumerable authors, were but of little advantage, to become extremely useful, when collected together and methodically dispos'd.

As the publication of this work gave pleasure to everyone, which it was natural to expect, the same was republished in the year 1700, under the inspection and revisal of Jo. Jacobus Mangetus, but at the same time with additions which made up a third part of the work. Of this, therefore, as of a fuller edition, I would always be understood to speak.

3. And first, if there are any persons who think that the intention, and labour, of both these editors are greatly to be commended, I readily concur in opinion with them, and shall always concur. But when I read in the writings of authors, in other respects very excellent, that the Sepulchretum is a work compil'd "with incomparable diligence, by collecting the choicest observations from every author, and reducing them under proper heads," and other

(a) L. 2. de Orat.

assertions of a similar nature, I wish it were in my power to assent to these likewise.

Why I think it is not in my power to agree, I will presently declare: yet I shall always be mindful of what I just now readily granted; and, besides this, shall consider, that two men alone, though never so industrious, could not possibly be equal to an undertaking which was not only new in itself, but almost inconceivably vast and laborious: for, as you have it in the fourth book of the Iliad, if I rightly remember, "The gods have not put everything in the power of men;" and, in the twelfth book, "The work of many is most perfect."

4. All these things, then, I readily advance and acknowledge: yet if a work so useful is to be render'd more useful for the future, it ought not to be conceal'd, that there are observations still remaining, not only in ancient, but even in modern authors, whose works were extant before the second edition of the Sepulchretum, which ought by no means to have been omitted: these observations are far from being few, and do not merely belong to writers whose names are never mention'd in that work, but even to such as are mention'd therein.

On the other hand, it may be observ'd, that such observations as, through negligence, are repeated in one and the same section sometimes even in one and the same page, after having been given before, ought to have been omitted in the second place; and not only these, but such as, being so metamorphos'd by a certain crafty writer, that, if you consider the names of the patients, their conditions, and places of abode, appear to be entirely new; yet, if you consider the things themselves, and the doctrines resulting therefrom, you immediately perceive to be the same as we read above from their true authors.

To these add the observations wherein you have natural appearances propos'd as morbid ones, or those things which relate to some peculiar species of injury, as appearances of a far different nature, when an aneurism, for instance, is represented as an abscess: for such observations, certainly, ought not corrected, may lead readers into the most grievous mistakes, and for doubting being subjoin'd; since any one who is but slightly practis'd in the dissection of sound and morbid bodies, would at once discover their fallacy.

I omit such as are not dispos'd under the heads whereto they properly belong, such as are falsely copied from their authors, such as are taken from you know not what author, or such as you would suppose to be from authors in whose writings they do not exist: and lest I should be too prolix, I willingly omit, besides these, whatever you might rather choose to ascribe to the carelessness, or ignorance, of the printers; notwithstanding these oversights, if not corrected, may leader readers into the most grievous mistakes, and therefore diminish the usefulness of the work. And this usefulness is greatly diminished by two other circumstances, of which I shall immediately speak; but in the mean while I will take upon me to affirm, that whoever shall peruse these books of mine, will be fully satisfied, that none of the assertions which I have now made, were hastily or rashly advanced.

5. As there are very few diseases, especially if of any long continuance, to which some other disorder is not join'd, or to which many different symptoms are not added; for this reason every observation of such a disease, after having been given at large under the head whereto it particularly belongs, ought, without doubt, to be made mention of under other heads to which it likewise relates in some measure: this, however, should be done in a few words only, so as just to refer to the place where the reader, who ought to consider the whole of the observation, and not take it piece-meal, may immediately find it complete.

Nor is it sufficient, as is done in the Sepulchretum, to refer to the section, which frequently contains a great number of observations, as at that observation of Jo. Petrus Lotichius, for instance; to produce one example, at least, from among others almost innumerable; which, besides that it is not made mention of under all the heads it ought to be, is, in four of the sections wherein we find it referr'd to, I mean those *De Dolore Capitis*, obs. 10. *De Insomniis & Incubo*, obs. 2. *De Vertigine*, obs. 7 & *De Convulsione*, obs. 13, always referred to in the section *De Melancholia*.

The reader, therefore, is under a necessity of turning over the whole of this section, or, in other words, the fifty observations of which it consists, in order to find, with difficulty, that which is there mark'd thirty-one. And I say with difficulty, because in all those four places the patient is spoken of as *a young man* only, in the beginning of the observation, but as *the servant of a tradesman* in this.

Yet even when he has read it over, and has found it to be that to which he was referr'd, do you think he then sees the whole of it? Certainly not. For the external cause of the disorder is wanting, I mean the philtre which had been given: and other circumstances are also deficient, where the reader would not so much as suspect it, unless he should happen to stumble on that place in the section *De Dolore Capitis*, or, what would be still more to his purpose, should read it in the work of the author.

But to attend solely to the assertion with which we set out; I mean, that a great deal of time is necessarily consumed in looking for any article to which we are referr'd; you undoubtedly see that the work would have been much more useful, if the whole of the observation, having been fully propos'd, on the most convenient opportunity, and mark'd out by a certain number, were always to be made mention of, wherever it was necessary, as under that number, and not merely by saying in what section it had been given.

6. But two very accurate indexes, added to the work, would, at least, have been of far greater advantage. I remember that when the Sepulchretum, which had been lately printed, was just imported to Bologna, where I then resided, I

was prodigiously pleas'd to find these words in the title-page, *With the necessary indexes*.

But my joy lasted no longer than till, looking for these indexes, I found that there was only one, and that this contain'd nothing more than the titles prefix'd to the observations: and as a great number even of these titles are either undesignedly imperfect, or confessedly so, and without any disguise, and all of them are disposed exactly in the same order as the observations themselves; it is impossible to say, how many symptoms, or how many morbid constitutions of parts in like manner, are described in the observations indeed, but not taken notice of in the index; not to say that each of these symptoms, or morbid appearances, are not exhibited, at one view, together with the others which are similar thereto.

For from this defect the great and primary advantage of the work is totally cut off; as this advantage could only have arisen from having a great number of similar symptoms at hand, so that you might readily compare them with many morbid appearances; which were either similar, or not similar, to each other; and by this means be able at once to conceive, which of those symptoms are most frequently, most rarely, or never, join'd with any particular species of internal morbid constitution.

I remember, likewise, that, as young men are generally presumptuous enough to entertain thoughts of the most difficult and laborious undertakings, I did not even then despair, but if I should have sufficient leisure in future time, I should not only be able to supply the deficiencies that I have pointed out in the Sepulchretum, and others besides these, but also that I should be able to reform the indexes; and I even thought of a plan whereby this might be done, and communicated my plan to that respectable society, which is now call'd the Academy of Sciences.

7. As to the remaining inconsistencies of the Sepulchretum, which I just now hinted at, they chiefly relate to the scholia. And though I did not doubt, but many of these were longer than was needful, I nevertheless found that they seem'd to be so much the longer, by advancing, in the place of useful remarks, either such as were but of little use, or such as could scarcely be admitted; and even sometimes by repeating these things over again.

It would not have been proper, however, to repeat even good things, but only when a remark has once been given, to say in a single word, whenever there was occasion to refer to it, in what place it was to be found: and it would have been proper conveniently to subjoin to some places of observations the doubts of the compiler, and at other places to observe how far they agree with other observations, to show what consequences might be drawn therefrom, in order to illustrate the theory, but particular to illustrate the practice of medicine; and this not by doctrines which are, at present, either quite given up, or call'd into question, by most persons, but by the more probable, easy, and even, as far as could be, the most common modes of explication.

I do not, indeed, deny that some of these cautions are here and there attended to, in the scholia of the Sepulchretum; nor am I ignorant what doctrines were in vogue in the time of Bonetus. But the question is not here of refuting him; but of rendering his work more useful, and more consistent with the superior doctrines of the present times.

8. As, therefore, I had not fail'd to resolve in my mind, more than once afterwards, all these circumstances which I have hinted at in regard to the Sepulchretum; and had even begun to contribute, as much as my poor abilities would allow, in order to increase its utility; I was exceedingly encourag'd in the prosecution of my design by the remarks that I read, from time to time, in new publications of learned men: for instance,

> "That scarcely any-thing was more useful than that work;" nor was there any work which "better deserv'd to have a supplement added to it, and be brought down to the present times:" and, in like manner, that "It is surprising how much it might be increas'd, and with how much a better index it might be furnish'd, in order to make it advantageous to students:" but, to omit other things, "That the work of Bonetus would, however, have deserved greater praise and more esteem, in part, if he had been somewhat more accurate in selecting the observations, and referring them to particular diseases, as to their respective heads; and in part, if he had admonish'd us in the scholia and annotations, what things were here and there uncertain, or altogether false, or what were not properly explain'd by their authors."

Now, then; in an affair wherein everyone is concerned, and not only in the present, but in future ages; in order to judge more easily what may be expected from me alone, and how far it is just to expect it, I must by no means conceal the circumstance which first gave occasion to my writing these books.

9. The anatomical writings of Valsalva being already publish'd, and my epistles upon them, it accidentally happen'd, that, being retir'd from Padua, as in those early years I was wont frequently to do in the summer-time, I fell into company with a young gentleman, of strict morals and an excellent disposition, who was much given to the study of the sciences, and particularly to that of medicine. This young gentleman, having read those writings, and those letters likewise, every-now-and-then engag'd me in a discourse, than which nothing could be more agreeable to me; I mean a discourse in respect to my preceptors, and in particular Valsalva and Albertini, whose methods in the art of healing, even the most trifling, he was desirous to know: and he even sometimes enquir'd after my own observations and thoughts as well as after theirs.

And having among other things, as frequently happens on conversations, open'd my thoughts in regard to the Sepulchretum, he never ceas'd to entreat me, by every kind of solicitation, that I would apply to this subject in particular; and, as I had promis'd in my little Memoir upon the Life of

Valsalva, to endeavor that a great number of his observations, which were made with the same view, should be brought to public light, he begg'd that I would join mine together with them, and would show in both his and mine, by example as it were, what I should think wanting to compleat a new edition of the Sepulchretum, which he, perhaps, if he could engage his friends to assist him, would, at some time or other, undertake. He also desir'd that I would write in as familiar a manner as I would wish; and by this means throw in, at any time, what I had said in conversation, or medical conferences, or any thing of that kind, which, though ever so minute, would always be very grateful to him.

You ask me what was the effect of his entreaties? I suffer'd myself to be prevail'd upon. For you see what he requir'd of me was partly what I had promis'd in that Memoir, and partly what I hop'd would be of use, if it should turn out agreeably to my design; as by being afterwards revis'd and publish'd, it might, some time or other, excite persons, far more capable than myself, to undertake the same kind of labour.

With this view, then, I began, upon returning to Padua, to make a trial of that nature, by sending some letters to my friend. And that he was pleas'd with them appears from two circumstances; the first, that he was continually soliciting me to send him more and more after that, till he drew me on so far as the seventieth; the second, that when I begg'd them of him, in order to revise their contents, he did not return them, till he had made me solemnly promise, that I would not abridge any part thereof.

10. You see then, candid reader, why I said in the beginning that I would not have these writings of mine be read by the most unlearned; and should also have said, nor yet by the most learned, if they had only contained those things which he insisted upon being retain'd; I mean, such as might be useful to students.

But I am not at liberty here to make use of that expression of Lucilius (*b*), *Persium non curo legere haec: Laelium Decimum volo:* "I do not choose Persius should read these things; but would wish Laelius Decimus to read them:" may, I even wish the *Persi*, that is the most learned men, to read them, and, leaving the other parts to the *Decimi Laelii*, that is to youths of learning and genius, to consider only my intention and desire; and if these are not disagreeable to them, to assist by their assent, or, if they think it will answer a better purpose, by their admonitions and examples, in making the Sepulchretum of the most utility it can possibly be. And that they may do either one or the other the more easily, I will tell you what I have done with this intention, in the subsequent letters; and that in as few words as it is possible on a subject which is so complex, and requires to be related so clearly.

(b) Ciceron. 1. cit.

11. The observations, (for I will begin with them in order to preserve nearly the same method which I made use of above) the observations, I say; I mean those which I have observ'd to have been omitted in the Sepulchretum, from the ancient or more modern authors, though they might have been included; and those moreover that have been made public since the second edition of this work; I have pointed out each under their proper heads, in as great a number as occurr'd to me when writing.

And this I say, that every-one may know a great number to be still remaining, which might be added; for out of the books that I have read, I did not call to mind all the contain'd observations, and from those which I had not read, it is certain none could occur to my mind: and there are many which I have never seen, either because they have never been imported hither during the present calamities in which Europe is involv'd, or because I am not very well skill'd in the languages wherein they are written; and I do not choose to put great confidence in any interpreters, especially in affairs of this kind.

In each section of the Sepulchretum also, if you except a few of the former ones, I have not neglected to take notice, as far as it was in my power to observe, what observations are given more than once, either from the effect of carelessness, or in consequence of the impositions of a crafty metamorphoser; nor yet in which of them either natural appearances are described as morbid, one disease is represented as another, or the printers have been so careless as to subvert the very intention of the observers by their preposterous blunders; so that by such strictures, I think I cannot fail being of great assistance to any persons, who shall hereafter undertake to give a new edition of the Sepulchretum: for though some of these animadversions are minute, yet they are by no means of little importance.

I wish I could have been of equal assistance, either when the readers are referr'd to some other place, where they may find this or that observation more fully describ'd, and yet the number of the observation is not expressly pointed out; or when they are overwhelm'd with stupendously-long scholia, and yet such as do not contain the more useful remarks, but at one time superfluous things, at another time repetitions, and sometimes such as are false, or, at least, very doubtful. Of these things, indeed, I have sometimes admonish'd my readers: but always to do it would have been endless.

There is no occasion, however, to tell those who know any thing of the matter, that I had not leisure to compose the indexes which are so necessary, and would require so long and so arduous a labour. I hope it will be thought quite sufficient, by any reasonable persons, that at my time of life, and without anyone to assist me, even a pupil, or an amanuensis, I have at least, not only in these last-mention'd instances, but also in others whereof I have spoken, all of which shall now be recapitulated in their order, shown by my own example, such as it is, in what manner it appears to me, that the Sepulchretum may be much enlarg'd, and at the same time render'd much more useful and correct.

12. I therefore produce observations which have never been publish'd before, a great number of which are Valsalva's, not a few of my friends, but the greater part mine. To the first, on account of the author's merit, and the respect which I owe him, I give the first place under each head. And these, which have been collected with the same care that other things were formerly, as has been said in his life, and where they were written in Italian translated into Latin, and all of them copied over again in the manner that I knew he had been accustom'd to wish, I give with such a scrupulous exactness, that, as I have sometimes doubted whether I rightly conceiv'd of them or not, I have chosen rather to produce his own words, without taking away or adding any thing, except what I had receiv'd from his own mouth: for this happen'd in regard to a few observations which he had given an accurate relation of to me, and had not committed to writing. And the other observations I took from his papers, which were some of them connected together, and some loose.

And although these papers, after having taken out from them, in every respect that was necessary, the observations, experiments, and other things that are given in these letters, I return'd, number'd, and seal'd up, in the same manner as before, to his son-in-law Lewis Montefani, that celebrated man, who is librarian to the Academy of Sciences at Bologna; yet if any-one should choose to compare a particular paper with these my descriptions, and should ask me by what mark he might find it, in so great a number of papers, I shall have no objection to telling him, nor yet to show any letter, whereby my friends have communicated to me their observations which I make use of in these books, as they are all of them men of well-known integrity, skill, and accuracy.

For, finally, in respect to my own observations, I have particularly related in each, the year, month, and place in which they were made, and who assisted me, or were present, at the time, unless I had sufficiently done it before. And I have not only remark'd the age and sex of the patient, but other things also that Peyerus (c) requires, as far as it was in my power to learn, and amongst these such as relate to the method of cure which had been applied: though it may be necessary to admonish my readers, that they are not, by any means, to impute a particular method of treatment to me or to Valsalva, unless we say it was prescribed by us, any more than they would the external causes and the symptoms of the diseases; for we relate these just in the same manner as we do the method of treatment.

And in describing the dissections themselves, I thought it particularly behoov'd me to take care, that I did not admit, what I so greatly disapprov'd, in some certain descriptions of other authors; I mean, that I should not consider as morbid appearances, either those which are agreeable to the usual

(c) Meth. Hist. Anat. Medic. c. 2. & 3.

order of nature, or not far different therefrom, such as some varieties, for instance, are.

I have endeavour'd also that the histories should not be divided, but should be exhibited at one view: or if it did, at any time, happen (though this was but rarely) to seem more advantageous to divide them, or, what happen'd very often, to take notice of them, I have taken care to point out that very place, in which either the remaining part, or the whole, of the history might be found: and I have been equally cautious of repeating even any-thing that might have been formerly treated of fully in some of my writings; inasmuch as it is *odious to me*, in the same manner as it was to the Ulysses of Homer (d), *to relate over again any-thing that has been fully related*. For by these means the histories really become too long; but not when all the circumstances which relate to the foregoing causes of the disease, and to the symptoms, (all of which I wish could be equally and fully known at all times) or to the injuries of parts observ'd in the bodies, are accurately describ'd. And indeed they often give us occasion to observe, as I have done, not only what, in each of these classes, were present, but what were absent likewise.

2.3

Pathological Anatomy: Preliminary Discourse

Xavier Bichat

Medicine has two general objects in view; first, the knowledge of diseases, and second, their cure. Under this last relation there are few diseases submitted to the empire of medicine, and it is only to the former that we refer pathological anatomy.

Diseases may be divided into two classes: those which affect the general system, and those which attack only one organ in particular. The first do not come under the cognizance of pathological anatomy. All the diverse kinds of fevers produce a general derangement, although, oftentimes no organ be particularly injured. The knowledge of general diseases differs essentially from that of organic diseases: for the former, observation is sufficient; in the latter, on the contrary, we have besides observation, *post-mortem examination*.This is the reason why the knowledge of general diseases is only founded on certain signs which attach themselves to nothing. Such is the etiology of fevers and of other similar diseases; all the distinctions, and classifications which have been made according to seasons, humors, &c., are evidently fallacious. Their nosology presents an extreme difficulty.

Not so with local diseases, which may be classified according to the character of the lesion of the affected organ. Their diagnosis is infinitely more easy than the first, since there exists one more means to discriminate them, *post-mortem examination*; and it is only since some interest has been excited in this science, that we may flatter ourselves with having made some progress in the knowledge of these diseases. It is well known into how many errors we have fallen, so long as we had confined ourselves to the simple observation of symptoms. Let us take for example consumption. It has been considered as an *essential malady*, before we had recourse to post-mortem examination; since, it has been shown that marasmus was only a consecutive symptomatic malady of the affection of an organ. Jaundice has been for a long time considered by practitioners as an *essential malady*; post-mortem examination has also proved that this affection, thought primitive, was in reality only consecutive to diverse alterations of the liver, of which it is always the symptom. The same has happened with respect to dropsies, which although for a long time considered as essential affections, have never been other than the result of some organic disease. It is, then, ignorance of organic affections, resulting from a total neglect of post mortem examination, which is the cause that has misled the ancient practitioners on most diseases; thus, *Cullen* and *Sauvages* have erred in their classifications.

It is true that symptoms are also advantageous in the examination of organic diseases; but for a methodical classification we must shun every thing which is only accessory; a nosology founded on the affections of the organs will necessarily be invariable. It is also to the want of post-mortem examination, that we may ascribe the hypothetical reasoning of the ancients on the atrabile, pituita, &c., imaginary substances that they have never seen, but which they fancied. The solids have also been the subject of these erroneous principles: every swelling was called obstruction, and every obstruction (*engorgement*) was a scirrhus. Physicians have never followed the natural course which we indicate, a rapid view of the progress of the science of medicine will convince us of it.

We may distinguish two classes of physicians; those who have only observed, and those who to observation have added post-mortem examination. The former are very numerous; the latter are confined to a very small number, and are only to be met with in the last century. Hippocrates, Celsus, Aretaeus, and all the Greek authors, have been satisfied with observing the symptoms; and consequently most of their diseases are badly described.

Immediately after the Greeks, physicians were divided into two sects: the empirics, who cured according to experience, and the dogmatics, who were guided by symptoms. Not one, among either, has left a post-mortem examination. The same thing happened with the Arabs, who only imitated the Greeks. Five or six centuries elapsed without any improvement in medicine. At its revival, the Greek authors were again commented upon. Afterwards followed the sect of the chymists: *Paracelsus*, and *Van Helmont*, explained every thing by the laws of fermentation. *Sydenham* was satisfied with observing symptoms. Then *Stahl* and *Boerhaave* appeared. Their disciples, and particularly those of *Montpellier*, in these last centuries, very seldom have had recourse to post-mortem examination. It was not until about the middle of the seventeenth century that surgeons made, for the first time, anatomical examinations. Physicians adopted this method. *Bonnet* made a collection of observations, but replete with erroneous theories.

Morgagni appeared after him, and truly created pathological science, and whilst yet in its infancy, he carried it to perfection, and his work on chronic diseases is a *chef-d'oeuvre*. Several tried to write on the same subject, particularly *Lieutaud*, but all are far inferior to *Morgagni*. *Portal* and *Vicq-d'-Azyr* have also shone on this subject, and the article in the *Encyclopé*die does honour to the latter.

This practice, of post-mortem examination, is that which is followed, in our days, all over Europe.

CONSIDERATIONS ON POST-MORTEM EXAMINATION

Before we establish precepts on the manner of examining dead bodies, we must consider first the diverse alterations which different diseases produce. Any one who has had the opportunity to see only few post-mortem examinations, has observed that the condition of the organs, either internal or external, varies according to the affection which has produced death. We may distinguish three kinds of death: sudden death; that which happens in an acute malady; and finally, that which follows a chronic disease.

In sudden death, there is hardly any alteration present, either in the internal or external organs; in the greatest number of cases the disease is concentrated either in the brain, heart, or lungs; such as, asphyxia, syncope, poisoning, &c.

The muscles are red, with a texture as firm as in a natural state; the skin is hard to the touch, the eyes prominent; the mucous surfaces, and often, even the cheeks retain a blush; the expression of the physiognomy remains; in a word, the appearance of all the organs differs essentially from what they are in chronic diseases.

The second kind of death begins to have some influence in altering the aspect of the cadaver. Every acute disease always alters more or less perceptibly the parts; there are even some, the effects of which, on the corpse, are similar to those in the most protracted diseases; all the solids are altered, almost decomposed; as is the case in pestilential fever, &c.

When acute diseases are continued for a long time, then the fat is absorbed, serosity abounds, and the phenomena become, soon after, like those of chronic diseases. Nevertheless, we must observe that the organs most altered, are those in which nutrition is most active in an healthy state; and on the contrary, those which enjoy only an obscure vitality, are the least sensibly injured. Such are the tendons and oponeuroses.

Lastly, the third kind of death, produced by chronic diseases, totally changes the state of the organs in the subject. Their texture is ordinarily found very much altered, especially when death has been protracted; they have a flaccidity foreign to the usual state; the alterations affect also the tendons and oponeuroses, which become yellow.

In general, these are the diverse influences of disease on the body, necessary to be known. We must be on our guard not to take for the effect of the disease, what only belongs to that kind of death. Nevertheless, many have fallen into this error; thus, in inflammatory fevers they were looking for an engorgement in the brain, without reflecting that it was produced by the state of the lungs at the moment of death; if, for example, the patient had had, for some time, a difficulty of breathing, and were they to find an effusion in the brain, they never failed to ascribe the effusion to the disease, although it was entirely foreign to it.

If the patient dies in a syncope, no traces of blood are to be found in the brain.

The same takes place in all the organs: often the condition in which we find them, is only the consequence of the state in which the subject was at the time he died. Sometimes also, the disease may have produced it, but we are ignorant of any such circumstance.

The lividity and flushing of the face may be numbered among these phenomena. We should also be aware of the changes that death produces in the diseased organ: inflammatory tumours, which during life are red and prominent, are resolved entirely after death, which is not observed in chronic tumours; it is probable that in acute inflammation of the internal organs the same thing happens, and we judge so by analogy.

In an inflammation of the intestines, the tension of the abdomen may be partially produced by the gases, and also by the swelling of the neighbouring cellular tissue; and indeed it may disappear almost entirely after death. That which causes the resolution of acute tumours, is, that the irritation which retains the blood in the part, disappears with life. In chronic inflammation, this change does not take place after death, because the blood is then found almost blended with the parts.

In the examination of a corpse we should pay particular attention to the essential phenomena, without stopping to observe accessory circumstances.

It is equally advantageous to seek for the connection of the phenomena which have resulted after death, with those which have taken place before.

The manner to proceed in autopsic examinations, must differ according to the different kinds of diseases we have established; commonly it is prosecuted in an anatomical order, but it is not the best method to give precise ideas on the subject; in general diseases, it is a great deal better to follow the order of the functions: in this manner we arrive at a knowledge of those which are injured.

In local diseases the manner of proceeding must be different: we must first examine the affected organ, then the neighbouring organs which participate in the lesion; and afterwards proceed to examine the functions. The advantage resulting from this method is, that we may narrowly sift the maladies which affect every system. By this means, the diseases of two organs utterly different will not be confounded, although situated in the same cavity. However, there are some affections which do not admit this methodical classification: such are scurvy, syphilis, &c.; but persevering study may enable us hereafter to find for them a fit place.

ORDER TO BE FOLLOWED IN PATHOLOGICAL ANATOMY

We shall divide at first the examination of diseases into two parts. In the first, we shall examine the affection peculiar to each system individually, and the modification which general diseases experience in these same systems. In the second, we shall consider these diseases in the diverse organs which they occupy; and in order to be the more methodical, we shall proceed in the order of the functions.

Every system has an order of functions which is peculiar to itself, whatsoever be its situation. Such is the phlegmon or inflammation of the cellular tissue: whether it be in the extremities,or in the trunk of the body, it is always of the same nature; the pus which it produces is always The same. Whatever may be the place in which the serous membranes are found, their diseases are analogous: they only are susceptible of adhesion. The cutaneous system is the exclusive seat of certain morbid affections, such as tetter, syphilitic eruptions, and inflammatory pustules. This was so obvious in the eyes of practitioners, that they had formed a particular class of cutaneous diseases. To conclude, from all we have said, it is easy to see, that it is all important to examine the diseases of the systems singly.

In considering diseases under the first relation, we shall make a continual abstraction of the systems, which, conjointly with the affected one, concur to the formation of an organ. Hence the inference, that every system may be affected singly. Post-mortem examinations demonstrate it to us, since it shows, that almost all the local diseases have each their seat only in one particular tissue of the affected organ.

Let us take for example the lungs. These organs are composed of the pleura, of the parenchymatous structure of the lungs, and of the internal membrane. In pleurisy, the pleura only is inflamed, the pulmonary tissue and the mucous membrane remain untouched. In peripneumonia, it is, on the contrary, the parenchymatous structure of the lungs, whilst its two membranes are healthy. In the same manner catarrhal cough is exclusively confined to the mucous membrane, whilst the pulmonary tissue and the serous membrane are sound and healthy. We may reason in the same manner in relation to all the other organs. The affections of a serous membrane extend throughout and are common to all its parts: and indeed, the ancients mistook, in relation to chronic interitis, in considering it as entirely located in the external coat of the intestines; it spreads itself always all over the peritoneum. However, at the bed-side of the patient, this manner of considering diseases would seem inconsistent, since, for the supposed affection of a single tissue, the whole organ appears to be affected. Thus in the inflammation of the peritoneum, which covers the stomach, this organ is affected with vomiting. One does not know how to explain so constant a sympathy; but the affection of one single tissue only, is nevertheless true.

When we are familiar with diseases, in order to distinguish them we must bear in mind three kinds of symptoms. The first belongs exclusively to the affected organ, the second depends upon the surrounding organs, and the third is general. Thus in pleurisy, the pain in the side, which belongs to the pleura, must be arranged with the first class; the oppression and the difficulty of breathing which belong to the lungs, are comprised in the second; and lastly the state of the pulse, and that of the secretions, compose the third.

In chronic diseases, the principle that we have just laid down referring to the singleness of the affections of the systems, often is apparently contradicted, since, when these diseases are of so great violence as to cause death, commonly the whole substance of the organ is found *morbid*. But this general malady is always owing to a principal affection which has been developed in one of its tissues, and the state in which the others are found, after death, is only consecutive. Thus in cancer, the disease commences by a small moveable tumour in the cellular tissue of the breast; it is soon engorged and adheres; its progress continues; the muscles ulcerate; finally the surrounding bones grow carious, and the state exhibited by the injured part towards the end is only a consecutive effect of the primitive affection. This example is sufficient to establish the progressive stages at every kind of chronic diseases, either of those which are seen on the exterior surface, or of those, the phenomena of which takes place within. In cancer of the stomach it often happens that the affection extends itself to the whole peritoneum by the medium of the part of this membrane which immediately covers this organ; sometimes the liver also in this case becomes tuberculous. It is an essential difference between acute and chronic diseases, that the symptoms of the former are only produced by the sudden affection of a single organic system, whilst in the latter they are caused by a slow alteration of the whole organ.

All the chronic diseases do not propagate themselves in an equal degree. Cancer is very susceptible of it, whilst the arterial ossification never spreads.

OF THE ALTERATIONS OF THE FLUIDS

All that we have heretofore said, refers particularly to the alterations of the solids; let us treat now of those of the fluids; which are as frequent as the first, but much less known. Every one knows what great importance physicians have ascribed to them. Almost all have made them the seat of diseases; but if we compare what they have said of them, with what examination teaches us, we shall soon see how illusory was their theory. In this respect pathological anatomy has as yet much to do. Their different alterations cannot be observed with the same precision as in the solids. Abandoned to themselves, the fluids soon experience new alterations, the same does not happen in organic affections of the viscera.

In order to facilitate the study of the maladies of the fluids, we will divide them into two classes: those which exist in a normal, and those which are formed in a pathological state. We shall speak, at first, in a general manner of the alterations of the fluids which exist in a natural state. These fluids are of three kinds: the *circulating*, the *secreted*, and the *exhaled*.

The blood undergoes singular and numerous variations in diseases; they can only be known by the examination of the corpse or of the blood after venesection. Indeed the quantity of blood is very variable in different bodies. In general it is very abundant in persons dead of asphyxia, and in every kind of death which terminates life instantaneously, such as apoplexy &c.; in other affections post-mortem examination presents hardly any, such is the case in chronic diseases, which waste the vital forces for a long time, as phthisis and all those which induce marasmus or dropsy; hence the pulse, in such cases, is very small towards the end, and the arteries contract on themselves. Finally, there are other diseases which hold a middle course in this respect.

The colour of the blood differs materially in different diseases. In almost all cadavers it is black, in whatsoever part it is found.

It is particularly in its consistency that blood differs. Certain diseases change it very much; scurvy, putrid fever, and asphyxia render it always very fluid. Other affections concrete it. The polypus is nothing more than a bloody concretion, formed in the large vessels or in the heart. The ancient physicians ascribed much importance to it, and attributed to it many deaths produced by very different causes. Morgagni, Bonnet, Lieutaud, Viq-d'Azyr, relate observations of polypus, in which we perceive that they entirely mistake in ascribing the death to a concretion utterly passive in the malady; they had taken the effect for the cause.

2.4

Introduction to the Study of Experimental Medicine

Claude Bernard

A. Experimental Considerations Peculiar to Living Beings

I. THE PHENOMENA OF LIVING BEINGS MUST BE CONSIDERED AS A HARMONIOUS WHOLE

So far we have been explaining experimental considerations applicable to both living and inorganic bodies; for living bodies the difference consists merely in the greater complexity of phenomena, making experimental analysis and determination of the conditions incomparably harder. But in the behavior of living bodies we must call the reader's attention to their very special interdependence; in the study of vital functions, if we neglected the physiological point of view, even if we experimented skillfully, we should be led to the most false ideas and the most erroneous deductions.

We saw in the last chapter that the object of the experimental method is to reach the determinism of phenomena, no matter of what nature, whether vital or mineral. We know, moreover, that what we call determinism of a phenomenon means nothing else than the determining cause or immediate cause determining the appearance of phenomena. Thus we necessarily obtain the conditions in which the phenomena exist, and on which the experimenter must act to make the phenomena vary. We therefore consider the various expressions above as equivalents; and the word determinism sums them all up.

It is indeed true, as we have said, that life brings absolutely no difference into the scientific experimental method which must be applied to the study of physiological phenomena, and that in this respect physiological science and physico-chemical science rest on exactly the same principles of investigation. But still we must recognize that determinism in the phenomena of life is not only very complex, but that it is at the same time harmoniously graded. Thus complex physiological phenomena are made up of a series of simpler phenomena each determining the other by associating together or combining for a common final object. Now the physiologist's prime object is to determine the elementary conditions of physiological phenomena and to grasp their natural subordination, so as to understand and then to follow the different combinations in the varied mechanism of animal organisms. The ancient emblem representing life as a closed circle, formed by a serpent biting its own tail, gives a fairly accurate picture of things. In complex organisms the organism of life actually forms a closed circle, but a circle which has a head and tail in this sense, that vital phenomena are not all of equal importance, though each in succession completes the vital circle. Thus the muscular and nervous organs sustain the activity of the organs preparing the blood; but the blood in its turn nourishes the organs which produce it. Here is an organic or social interdependence which sustains a sort of perpetual motion, until some disorder or stoppage of a necessary vital unit upsets the equilibrium, or leads to disturbance or stoppage in the play of the animal machine. The problem for experimenting physicians consists, therefore, in finding the simple determinism of an organic disorder; that is to say, in grasping the initial phenomenon which brings all the others in its train through a complex determinism as necessary in character as the initial determinism. This initial determinism is like Ariadne's thread guiding the experimenter in the dark labyrinth of physiological and pathological phenomena, and enabling him to understand how their varied mechanisms are still bound together by absolute determinisms. By examples cited further on, we shall see how a dislocation of the organism or an apparently highly complex disorder may be traced back to an initial simple determinism which later produces more complex determinisms. A case in point is poisoning by carbon monoxide (cf. Part III). I am devoting my whole course at the Collège de France this year to the study of *curare*, not for the sake of the substance itself, but because this study shows us how the simplest single determinism, such as the lesion of a terminal motor nerve, re-echoing successively from all the other vital units, leads to secondary determinisms to which I shall later return, because I consider study of them the true basis of pathology and of scientific therapeutics.

Physiologists and physicians must never forget that a living being is an organism with its own individuality. Since physicists and chemists cannot take their stand outside the universe, they study bodies and phenomena in themselves and separately without necessarily having to connect them with nature as a whole. But physiologists, finding themselves, on the contrary, outside the animal organism which they see as a whole, must take account of the harmony of this whole, even while trying to get inside, so as to understand the mechanism of its every part. The result is that physicists and chemists can reject all idea of final causes for the facts that they observe; while physiologists are inclined to acknowledge an harmonious and pre-established unity in an organized body, all of whose partial actions are interdependent and mutually generative. We really must learn, then, that if we break up a living organism by isolating its different parts, it is only for the sake of ease in experimental analysis, and by no means in order to conceive them separately. Indeed when we wish to ascribe to a physiological quality its value and true significance, we must always refer it to this whole, and draw our final conclusion only in relation to its effects in the whole. It is doubtless because he felt this necessary interdependence among all parts of an organism that Cuvier said that experimentation was not applicable to living beings, since it separated organized parts which should remain united. For the same reason, other physiologists or physicians, called vitalists, have proscribed and still proscribe experimentation in medicine. These views, which have their correct side, are nevertheless false in their general outcome and have greatly hampered the progress of science. It is doubtless correct to say that the constituent parts of an organism are physiologically inseparable one from another, and that they all contribute to a common vital result; but we may not conclude from this that the living machine must not be analyzed as we analyze a crude machine whose parts also have their role to play in a whole. With the help of experimental analysis we must transfer physiological functions as much as possible outside the organism; segregation allows us to see and to grasp hidden conditions of the phenomena, so as to follow them later inside the organism and to interpret their vital role. Thus we establish artificial digestion and fecundation, so as to know natural digestion and fecundation better. Thanks to their organic self-regulation, we can also detach living tissues, and by means of artificial circulation or otherwise, we can place them in conditions where we can better study their characteristics. We occasionally isolate an organ by using anesthetics to destroy the reactions of its general group; we reach the same result by cutting the nerves leading to a part, but preserving the blood vessels. By means of experimental analysis, I have even transformed warm-blooded animals, as it were, into cold-blooded animals, so as to study better the characteristics of their histological units; I have succeeded in poisoning glands separately and in making them work, by means of dissected nerves, quite apart from the organism. In this last case we can have a gland, at will, in a state, first, of absolute rest, then, of exaggerated action; when both extremes of the phenomenon are known we can later easily grasp all the intervening stages, and we then understand how a completely chemical function can be regulated by a nervous system, so as to supply organic fluids in conditions that are always the same. We will not further amplify these suggestions about experimental analysis; we sum up by saying that proscribing experimental analysis of organs means arresting science and denying the experimental method; but, on the other hand, that practising physiological analysis, while losing sight of the harmonious unity of an organism, means misunderstanding the science of life and individuality, and leaving it characterless.

After carrying out an analysis of phenomena, we must therefore always reconstruct our physiological synthesis, so as to see the joint action of all the parts we have isolated. *À propos* of the phrase physiological synthesis, we must further explain our thought. It is generally agreed that synthesis reunites what analysis has divided, and that synthesis therefore verifies analysis, of which it is merely the counterproof or necessary complement. This definition is entirely true for analysis and synthesis of matter. In chemistry, synthesis produces, weight for weight, the same body made up of identical elements combined in the same proportions; but in the case of analyzing and synthesizing the properties of bodies, i.e., synthesizing phenomena, it is much harder. Indeed, the properties of bodies result not merely from the nature and proportions of matter, but also from the arrangement of matter. Moreover, as we know, it happens that properties, which appear and disappear in synthesis and analysis, cannot be considered as simple addition or pure subtraction of properties of the constituent bodies. Thus, for example, the properties of oxygen and hydrogen do not account for the properties of water, which result nevertheless from combining them.

I do not intend to go into these difficult yet fundamental problems about the relative properties of combined or combining bodies; they will find their proper place elsewhere. I shall here only repeat that phenomena merely express the relations of bodies, whence it follows that, by dissociating the parts of a whole, we must make phenomena cease if only because we destroy the relations. It follows also, in physiology, that analysis, which teaches us the properties of isolated elementary parts, can never give us more than a most incomplete ideal synthesis; just as knowing a solitary man would not bring us knowledge of all the institutions which result from man's association, and which can reveal themselves only through social life. In a word, when we unite physiological elements, properties appear which were imperceptible in the separate elements. We must therefore always proceed experimentally in vital synthesis, because quite characteristic phenomena may result from more and more complex union or association of organized elements. All this proves that these elements, though distinct and self-dependent, do not therefore play the part of simple associates; their union expresses more than addition of their separate properties. I am persuaded that the obstacles surrounding the experimental study of psychological phenomena are largely due to difficulties of this kind; for despite their marvellous character and the delicacy of their manifestations, I find it impossible not to include cerebral phenomena, like all other phenomena of living bodies, in the laws of scientific determinism.

Physiologists and physicians must therefore always consider organisms as a whole and in detail at one and the same time, without ever losing sight of the peculiar conditions of all the special phenomena whose resultant is the individual. Yet particular facts are never scientific; only generalization can establish science. But here we must avoid a double stumbling block; for if excess of detail is anti-scientific, excessive generalization creates an ideal science no longer connected with reality. This stumbling block, unimportant to a contemplative naturalist, is large for physicians who must first of all seek objective, practical truths. We must doubtless admire those great horizons dimly seen by the genius of a Goethe, an Oken, a Carus, a Geoffroy Saint-Hilaire, a Darwin, in which a general conception shows us all living beings as the expression of types ceaselessly transformed in the evolution of organisms and species—types in which every living being individually disappears like a reflection of the whole to which it belongs. In medicine we can also rise to the most abstract generalizations, whether we take the naturalist's point of view and conceive diseases as morbid species to be classified nosologically, or whether we start from the physiological point of view and consider that disease does not exist, in the sense that it is only a special case of a general physiological state. Doubtless all these brilliant views do, after a fashion, guide and serve us. But if we gave ourselves up exclusively to hypothetical contemplation, we should soon turn our backs on reality; and in my opinion, we should misunderstand true scientific philosophy, by setting up a sort of opposition or exclusion between practice, which requires knowledge of particulars, and generalizations which tend to mingle all in all.

A physician, in fact, is by no means physician to living beings in general, not even physician to the human race, but rather, physician to a human individual, and still more physician to an individual in certain morbid conditions peculiar to himself and forming what is called his idiosyncrasy. Hence it seems to follow that medicine, in contrast with other sciences, should be established more and more on particulars. This opinion is incorrect and based only on appearances; for in all sciences, generalization leads to the law of phenomena and the true scientific goal. Only we must recognize that all the morphological generalizations to which we alluded above are too superficial and are therefore insufficient for physiologists and physicians. Naturalists, physiologists, and physicians have wholly different problems in view; their investigations advance in far from parallel lines; hence we cannot, for instance, exactly superpose a physiological scale on the geological scale. Physiologists and physicians delve much more deeply than zoologists into the problem of biology; physiologists consider the general conditions necessary to vital phenomena as well as the various changes to which they may be subject. But physicians cannot content themselves with knowing that all vital phenomena occur in identical conditions among all human beings; they must go still further by studying the details of these conditions in each individual considered in given morbid conditions. Only after delving, then, as deeply as possible into the secrets of vital phenomena in the normal and pathological states can physiologists and physicians attain illuminating and fertile generalizations.

The primary essence of life is a developing organic force, the force which constituted the mediating nature of Hippocrates and the *archeus faber* of Van Helmont. But whatever our idea of the nature of this force, it is always exhibited concurrently and parallel with the physico-chemical conditions proper to vital phenomena. Through study, then, of physico-chemical details, physicians will learn to understand individualities as special cases included in a general law, and will discover there, as everywhere, an harmonious generalization of variety in unity. But since physicians deal with variety, they must always seek to define it in their studies and to comprehend it in their generalizations.

If I had to define life in a single phrase, I should clearly express my thought by throwing into relief the one characteristic which, in my opinion, sharply differentiates biological science. I should say: life is creation. In fact, a created organism is a machine which necessarily works by virtue of the physico-chemical properties of its constituent elements. Today we differentiate three kinds of properties exhibited in the phenomena of living beings: physical properties, chemical properties and vital properties. But the term "vital properties" is itself only provisional; because we call properties vital which we have not yet been able to reduce to physico-chemical terms; but in that we shall doubtless succeed some day. So that what distinguishes a living machine is not the nature of its physico-chemical properties, complex as they may be, but rather the creation of the machine which develops under our eyes in conditions proper to itself and according to a definite idea which expresses the living being's nature and the very essence of life.

When a chicken develops in an egg, the formation of the animal body as a grouping of chemical elements is not what essentially distinguishes the vital force. This grouping takes place only according to laws which govern the chemico-physical properties of matter; but the guiding idea of the vital evolution is essentially of the domain of life and belongs neither to chemistry nor to physics nor to anything else. In every living germ is a creative idea which develops and exhibits itself through organization. As long as a living being persists, it remains under the influence of this same creative vital force, and death comes when it can no longer express itself; here as everywhere, everything is derived from the idea which alone creates and guides; physico-chemical means of expression are common to all natural phenomena and remain mingled, pell-mell, like the letters of the alphabet in a box, till a force goes to fetch them, to express the most varied thoughts and mechanisms. This same vital idea preserves beings, by reconstructing the living parts disorganized by exercise or destroyed by accidents or diseases. To the physico-chemical conditions of this primal development, then, we must always refer our explanation of life, whether in the normal or the pathological state. We shall see, indeed, that physiologists and physicians can really act only indirectly through animal physico-chemistry, that is to say, through physics and chemistry worked out in the special field of life, where the necessary conditions of all phenomena of living organisms develop, create, and support each other according to a definite idea and obedient to rigorous determinisms.

B. Investigation and Criticism as Applied to Experimental Medicine

Methods of investigation and of scientific criticism cannot vary from one science to another nor, for that matter, in different parts of the same science. It will therefore be easy to show that the rules for physiological investigation, suggested in the last chapter, are absolutely the same as those which should be followed in pathology and therapeutics. Thus methods of investigation of the phenomena of life should be the same in normal as in pathological conditions. This seems to us fundamental in biological science.

I. PATHOLOGICAL AND THERAPEUTIC INVESTIGATION

As in physiology, so in pathology and in therapeutics, the starting point of scientific investigation is now a casual fact or one occurring by chance, now an hypothesis, i.e., an idea.

I have sometimes heard physicians express the opinion that medicine is not a science, because all our knowledge of practical medicine is empirical and born of chance, while scientific knowledge is deduced with certainty from theories or principles. There is an error here, to which I wish to call attention.

All human knowledge had to begin with casual observations. Man indeed could know things only after seeing them; and the first time, necessarily, he saw them by chance; then he came to conceive ideas about things, to compare old facts and to deduce from them new ones; in a word, after empirical observation, he was no longer led to find other facts by chance, but by induction.

Fundamentally, then, all the sciences began with empiricism, that is to say, observation or chance experience had to form the first period. But empiricism is not a permanent state in any science. In the complex sciences of humanity, empiricism will necessarily govern practices much longer than in simpler sciences. Medical practice today is empirical in most cases; but that does not mean that medicine will never escape from empiricism. The complexity of its phenomena will make it harder to escape; but that should make us redouble our efforts to enter the scientific path as soon as we can. In a word, empiricism is not the negation of science, as certain physicians seem to think; it is only its first stage. We must even add that empiricism never wholly disappears from any science. Sciences, in fact, are not lighted up in every portion at once; they develop only a little at a time. In parts of physics and chemistry, empiricism still persists. This is proved every day by chance discoveries, unforeseen by prevailing theories. I therefore conclude that we make discoveries in the sciences only because are all still partially obscure. In medicine more numerous discoveries are still to be made, because almost everywhere empiricism and obscurity prevail. So this very complicated science is proved further behind the times than others; but that is all.

New medical observations are generally made by chance; if a patient with a hitherto unknown affection is admitted to a hospital where a physician comes for consultation, surely the physician meets the patient by chance. But a botanist in the field happens on an unfamiliar plant in exactly the same way; and by chance also an astronomer catches sight of a planet, whose existence he did not know of, in the sky. In such circumstances, the physician's originality consists in seeing the fact that chance presents to him and in not letting it escape, and his only merit is accurate observation. I cannot here analyze the characteristics of good medical observation. Reporting instances of chance medical observations would be just as dull. Medical work teems with them; everybody knows them. I shall therefore limit myself to saying in general that, to make a good medical observation, it is not necessary to have an observing mind, but also to be a physiologist. We shall the better interpret the various meanings of a morbid phenomenon, we shall assign it the proper value, and we shall certainly not fall into the difficulty, with which Sydenham[1] reproached certain physicians, of putting important phenomena of a disease on the same plane as insignificant and accidental facts, like the botanist who described caterpillar bites among the characteristics of a plant. Besides, we must bring to observation of a pathological phenomenon, i.e., a disease, exactly the same state of mind and the same rigor, as to observation of a physiological phenomenon. We must never go beyond facts and must be, as it were, photographers of nature.

But once made, every medical observation becomes the starting point, as in physiology, for ideas and hypotheses which experimental physicians go on to investigate through fresh observations of patients or by experiments on animals.

We said that, in making physiological investigations, it often happens that a fresh fact arises unsought; that also occurs in pathology. To prove it, I need only cite the recent case of Zenker, who,[2] in pursuing his investigations of certain muscular changes in typhoid fever, found trichinae, which he was not looking for.

Pathological investigation may also take for its starting point a theory, an hypothesis, or a preconceived idea. We might easily give examples to prove

1. Sydenham, *Médecine pratique*. Preface, p. 12.

2. See *Rapport des prix de médecine et de chirurgie pour 1864 (Compt. rendus d l'Acad. des sciences)*.

that absurd ideas, in pathology as in physiology, may sometimes lead to useful discoveries, just as it would not be hard to find arguments to prove that even the best accredited theories should be regarded only as temporary, and not as absolute truths to which facts should be bent.

Therapeutic investigation conforms to exactly the same rules as physiological and pathological investigation. Everyone knows that the first promoter of therapeutic science was chance, and that only by chance were the effects of most medicines first observed. Physicians have also often been guided in their therapeutic attempts by ideas; and it must also be said that they were often the strangest and most absurd theories or ideas. I need only cite the theories of Paracelsus, who deduced the action of drugs from astrological influences, and recall the ideas of Porta, who assigned medicinal uses to plants, deduced from their resemblances to certain diseased organs; thus carrots cured jaundice; lung-wort, phthisis, etc.[3]

Summing up, we cannot establish any valid distinction between methods of investigation that should be applied in physiology, in pathology and in hygiene. The method of observation and experiment is still the same, unchangeable in its principles and offering only a few peculiarities in its application, according to the relative complexity of phenomena. We cannot, indeed, find any radical difference in the nature of physiological, pathological and therapeutic phenomena. Since all these phenomena depend on laws peculiar to living matter, they are identical in essence and vary only with the various conditions in which phenomena appear. We shall see later that physiological laws are repeated in pathological phenomena, whence it follows that the foundations of therapeutics must reside in knowledge of the physiological action of morbid causes, of medicines and of poisons; and that is just the same thing.

II. EXPERIMENTAL CRITICISM IN PATHOLOGY AND THERAPEUTICS

Criticism of facts gives sciences their true individuality. All scientific criticism should explain facts rationally. If criticism is attributed, on the other hand, to personal feeling, science disappears; because such criticism rests on a criterion that can neither be proved nor conveyed as scientific truths should be. I have often heard physicians answer, when asked the reason for a diagnosis, "I do not know how I recognize such and such a case, but it is evident"; or when one asks them why they give certain remedies, they answer that they cannot exactly tell, and besides that they need not explain since they are guided by their medical tact and intuition. It is easy to understand that

3. See Chevreul, *Considérations sur l'histoire de la partie de la médecine qui concerne la prescription des remèdes (Journal des savants, 1865).*

physicians who reason in that way deny science. But we cannot too strongly protest against such ideas, which are bad, not only because they stifle every germ of science, but also because they especially encourage laziness, ignorance and charlatanism. I entirely understand a physician's saying that he cannot always rationally acount for what he is doing, and I accept his conclusion that medical science is still plunged in the shades of empiricism; but if he goes on to proclaim his medical tact or his intuition as a criterion which he then means to impose on others without further proof, that is wholly antiscientific.

As in physiology, the only scientific criticism possible in pathology and in therapeutics is experimental criticism; and whether applied to ourselves or to the work of others, this criticism should always be based on absolute determination of facts. Experimental criticism, as we have seen, should reject statistics as a foundation for experimental therapeutic and pathological science. In pathology and therapeutics, we should repudiate undetermined facts, that is to say, those badly made, and sometimes imaginary, observations which are constantly brought forward as perpetual objections. As in physiology, there are crude facts which can enter into scientific reasoning only on condition that they be determined and exactly defined as to their necessary conditions.

But it is characteristic of criticism in pathology and therapeutics, first and foremost to require comparative observation and experiment. How, indeed, can a physician judge the etiology, if he does not make a comparative experiment to eliminate all the secondary circumstances, that might become sources of error, and make him take more coincidences for relations of cause and effect? Especially in therapeutics, the need of comparative experiment has always struck physicians endowed with the scientific spirit. We cannot judge the influence of a remedy on the course and outcome of a disease if we do not previously know the natural course and outcome of the disease. That is why Pinel said in his clinic: "This year we will observe diseases without treating them, and next year we will treat them." Scientifically, we ought to adopt Pinel's idea without, however, accepting the long-range, comparative experiment which he proposed. Diseases, in fact, may vary in seriousness from one year to another; Sydenham's observations on the undetermined or unknown influence of what he calls the epidemic genius prove it. To be valid, comparative experiments have therefore to be made at the same time and on as comparable patients as possible. In spite of that, such comparisons still bristle with immense difficulties which physicians must strive to lessen; for comparative experiment is the *sine qua non* of scientific experimental medicine; without it, a physician walks at random and becomes the plaything of endless illusions. A physician, who tries a remedy and cures his patients, is inclined to believe that the cure is due to his treatment. Physicians often pride themselves on curing all their patients with a remedy that they use. But the first thing to ask them is whether they have tried doing nothing, i.e., not treating other patients; for how can they otherwise know whether the remedy or nature cured them? Gall wrote a little known book[4] on the question as to what is nature's share and what is the share of medicine in healing disease, and he very naturally concludes that their respective shares are quite hard to assign. We may be subject daily to the greatest illusions about the value of treatment, if we do not have recourse to comparative experiment. I shall recall only one recent example concerning the treatment of pneumonia. Comparative experiment showed, in fact, that treatment of pneumonia by bleeding, which was believed most efficacious, is a mere therapeutic illusion.[5]

From all this, I conclude that comparative observation and experiment are the only solid foundation for experimental medicine, and that physiology, pathology and therapeutics must be subject to this criticism in common.

4. Gall, *Philosophische medicinische Untersuchungen über Kunst und Natur im gesunden und kranken Zustand des Menschen*. Leipzig, 1800.

5. Béclard, *Rapport général sur les prix décernés en 1862 (Mémoires de l'Académie de médecine*, Paris, 1863, Vol. XXVI, p. xxiii).

2.5

Three Selections from Rudolf Virchow

Rudolf Virchow
trans. by Susan G. M. Engelhardt

Natural Scientific Methods and Standpoints in Therapy

We, finally, should call to mind Descartes' view that, if it be in any way possible to improve the human race, the means for this lies only in medicine. In reality, if medicine is the science of both the healthy and the sick person, which is what it should be, what other science could be better qualified to begin legislation in order to validate these laws, given by definition in the nature of man, as the bases of societal order. The physiologist and the general practitioner will be counted among the wise men on whom the public edifice is erected, when medicine is at last established as anthropology, and when the interest of individual personalities will no longer determine public affairs. Medicine is "in its innermost core and being a social science," as Mr. Neumann demonstrated by means of the sharp weapon of iron logic in his work on public health and property,[1] a work smaller in compass but infinitely larger in content than everything that had been written on these matters before. No physiologist and no physician in practice should ever forget that medicine collects within itself all knowledge of the laws capable of determining the body and the spirit. Schlosser's [Friedrich Schlosser 1776-1861] attempt, in his history of the 18th century, to show that only literature (namely, the beautiful and historical) changes its physiognomy during political changes fails; it is also incorrect to believe that the so-called natural sciences could see into the deepest well of knowledge, unlike the sciences of the state and the church, without becoming aware of the desire to use this knowledge. Let us think of the words of Lord Bacon, that knowledge is power, and let us forgive our great and so promising science nothing of what Hippocrates imputed to it: *quae ad sapientiam requiruntur, in medicina insunt omnia.*

1. Salomon Neumann, *Die öffentliche Gesundheitspflege und das Eigenthum*, Berlin: Adolph Riess, 1847.

Concerning Standpoints in Scientific Medicine

When one speaks nowadays of scientific medicine, it is above all necessary to clarify the meaning of these words with one's listeners.

According to our view, the concept of medicine, of the art of healing, involves the concept of healing, although according to the newest development of medicine it could appear to have nothing to do with it. However, only those individuals can be called physicians who consider healing to be the final purpose of their striving.

Ever since we recognized that diseases are neither self-subsistent, self-contained entities, nor autonomous organisms, nor entities that have invaded the body, nor parasites rooted in it, but rather that they represent only the course of corporeal appearances under changed conditions—since this time, healing has had to compass maintaining or restoring the normal conditions of life.

The real accomplishment, or to say it more exactly, the striving for a real accomplishment of this goal, is the aim of general medicine.

Scientific medicine has as its object the discovery of changed conditions, characterizing the sick body or the individual suffering organ. Its object is also the delineation of deviations experienced by the phenomena of life under certain conditions, and finally the determination of means by which these abnormal conditions can be counteracted. This therefore presupposes the knowledge of the normal course of the phenomena of life and of the conditions under which this course is possible. Its foundation is thus physiology. It is composed of two integrated parts: pathology, which transmits or should transmit the knowledge of changed conditions and of changed phenomena of life; and therapy, which determines the means by which to counteract these conditions or to maintain the normal ones.

Medicine in practice is thus actually never scientific medicine itself, even when it is in the hands of the greatest master, but rather only an application of it. In this way the scientific practitioner is differentiated from the routineer, from the medical opportunist; the achievements of scientific medicine are his province, they form the basis of his performance, and he does not engage in idolatry of either routine or chance.

Medicine appears to us in this way when we trace out an ideal picture of it. We should not deceive ourselves about the fact that its realization still lies very far in the future. We recognize, though still in a singularly incomplete way, the conditions under which certain deviant manifestations appear in the living body. However, even when we recognize the conditions, we unfortunately do not often know by what means they can be counteracted. In such cases the practicing physician has the right to subscribe to a certain empiricism, but he at the same time has the duty to vanquish this empiricism through his own observations and to erect a glorious edifice to scientific medicine. This is in particular the duty of the clinical practitioner, because the clinic is medical practice raised to its highest power. The possession of a clinic in our time is thus immeasurably important, because the clinician nowadays has to be not only a scientific practitioner but also a researcher, an investigator.

It has been said that there are cases where the rift between scientific and general medicine is so great, that one can hold that the scholarly physician does nothing and the practical physician knows nothing. Lord Bacon said, *scientia est potentia.* That is not proper knowledge, when it cannot act upon what it knows, and what kind of dubious ability is it that does not know what it does! This rift between science and practice is relatively new; it has been brought about by our century and our country. Medicine could not go away empty-handed when an inner dissension ripped through all circumstances of German life! Who recognized a division between medicine, science, and medical practice at the time of Boerhaave [Hermann Boerhaave 1668-1738] and Haller [Albrecht von Haller 1708-1777]? Who back then recognized a division between the whole of natural science and medical practice? But then came years of deep spiritual hardship and then a period of the greatest distress in the inner life of the people; in such a time only the very great or very small men are able to turn away from the unbelievable changes in society to the miniscule phenomena of eternal nature. French medicine arose out of the storms of the Revolution stronger and better, for the French people actually completed one segment of their Revolution. English medicine has never broken the bond between science and practice, because the spirit of England proceeds unceasingly and unshakeably along the recognized path. In Germany philosophy was born along with the revolution, but a philosophy that turned away more and more from nature, and that made a return to nature possible only when it finally resolved itself. This return to nature is expressed in the history of medicine through three stages: the stage of natural philosphy, the stage of natural history, and that of natural science. Everyone knows the principles by which these three viewpoints have become valid in medicine. The importance of each stage is best measured according to the importance each concedes to hypothesis, just as they each express a transition from a convenient method to a less convenient one to an inconvenient one. The natural-philosophical school built its medical system, as is well recognized, on its philosophical system. As a consequence, this school held logical hypotheses to be the completely justified equivalent of observations. The next school styled itself very significantly the natural-historical school; in its development it absorbed a part of the view of the natural philosophers, and then developed proof by analogy to an unprecedented degree. And while it exploited as far as it was able all of nature known to it, including the present and the past of medicine, it erected with much spirit an edifice whose girders were in fact only hypotheses and analogies. Medicine afterwards came to a natural scientific viewpoint at a time when even philosophy had turned to nature and to life. Just as philosophy had vindicated its old rights to the senses, so had medicine thrown off belief, cashiered the authorities, and banned hypotheses to a domesticated still-life. Although one probably uses them when one is at home alone, one leaves them at home when one enters the market of public life. In this, medicine and philosophy are of the same kind, that only a serious study of life and its manifestations can assure medicine and philosophy a place of importance in life. Only an exact knowledge of the conditions of the life of an individual and the life of a people will make it possible to validate the laws of medicine and philosophy as general laws of the human race, and only then will the saying be fulfilled: *scientia est potentia!*

One Hundred Years of General Pathology

It does not appear necessary at this point to develop the basic principles of cellular pathology in a comprehensive fashion. They are readily available for everyone. This science, which naturally includes a cellular theory of the living, proceeds from the fact that cells are the actually operative parts of the body, the true elements themselves, and that all vital action proceeds from them. Just as life itself is only expressed by means of action, so is the knowledge of the various kinds of activity and its disturbances the actual task of pathology. This is by no means, in the sense of Lotze [Hermann Rudolf Lotze 1817-1881], a mechanical science, but rather a biological one. The mechanical occurrence of the individual life actions is thus in no way excluded; on the contrary, without an exact investigation of the mechanism at work, a disclosure of the fine details is not possible. Life does not suspend the physical and chemical laws, as was taught until quite recently; they only achieve their validity in another way, which occurs in a healthy life. Also, a power otherwise not available or otherwise repressed does not appear either in sickness or in convalescence. The same substance, which is the bearer of life, is also the bearer of sickness. Every spiritualistic impulse is excluded. Nothing hinders the characterization of even such a tendency as vitalism, but one should not forget that a particular life-force cannot be traced, and the vitalism does not necessarily mean either a spiritualistic or even a dynamic system. But even so one must remember that life is different from events in the rest of the world and that it cannot be reduced simply to physical or chemical powers.

Just as no other property brings this particular quality of the living so clearly into view, as does heredity in the transmission of life from one being to the next, so also the victory of cellular pathology has been secured through the proof of heredity in the history of plastic processes; or, as one could also express it, in the unfolding history of the new forms. Ever since it became clear that no cell originates without having, as one says in this case, a mother (matrix), which is or was itself a cell, the following proposition has become the recognized signature of biological cellular theory: *omnis cellula a cellula.* Blastemas have disappeared and matrices have taken their place. There are no longer histogenetic or organopoetic substances apart from cells.

This view is clearly ontological. That is to its benefit, not its detriment. An *ens morbi* does exist, just as there is an *ens vitae*; in both cases a cell or a cell complex is entitled to be so named. The *ens morbi* is at the same time a parasite in the sense of the natural historical school, not a parasite in the sense of the bacteriologists. We will return to this difference in a moment.

When I left Berlin in 1849 to accept the chair in Würzburg, I already carried with me the main ideas of cellular pathology, but they were not yet sufficiently clarified. Only the investigations of the next few years concerning connective tissue, and tissues closely related to it, enabled me to take a large step forward and to prove that the body is completely composed of cell territories.[1] In such cell territories I recognized possible "multitudes of disease". Thus a theoretical conclusion to the research begun by Morgagni [Giovanni Battista Morgagni 1682-1772] on the "seats of disease" was attained, and even in a much finer sense than the great anatomist of Padua had dreamed, but yet as a further development of his "anatomic thought". The point of departure from then on for every general pathological observation about the elementary processes had to be the altered cell territory. Most diseases are not elementary processes but rather compound processes where alterations of several or many cell territories co-exist or range themselves alongside each other. As a consequence, further investigation of the cells or cell groups under consideration, indeed a repeated investigation of the place or places of the disturbances, is required not only for special pathology, but also for the theory of disease in general, i.e., of the "where" of the disease, therefore of the anatomical parts involved thereby. This investigation is to be carried out not merely with the knife, but also according to the usual, authentic anatomical methods. It is generally necessary to use experimental and clinical investigation. To give a common example of this, one may consider ordinary fibrinous pneumonia. It is an obviously local infection, but it is at the same time so often associated with a so-called general infection, fever, that it was still classified as an inflammatory fever at the beginning of this century. The exact knowledge of the local course should not mislead us, any more than the dissolution of the concept of essential fevers, into studying only one side of this compound process. On the contrary, the local infection can be explored only by means of pathological anatomy, the fever only by means of clinical observation or experiment. But since fever leads back to a certain locale in the nervous system, this has no effect on the "anatomical thought."

Being impressed by such reflections, I further developed the cellular doctrine while in Würzburg. I have written an inclusive picture of my views at the time in the general part of my work on special pathology and therapy.[2] The bases of these views were expressed in a more complete and in many ways improved style in a series of demonstrative lectures,[3] which I gave to a fairly large group of physicians soon after my return to Berlin. Later came comprehensive lectures on morbid tumors (since 1863), as well as manifold individual investigations by me and my students. Worthy of particular mention is the pioneering work by my assistant, von Recklinghausen [Friedrich Daniel von Recklinghausen 1833-1910], on the motility of pus and connective tissue corpuscles (1863), and of Cohnheim [Julius Friedrich Cohnheim 1839–1884] on the migration of the white blood corpuscles (1867),which so completely altered the theory of exudates in the cellular pathological sense. If it were pertinent at the moment to write a comprehensive history of further detailed investigations, one would have to include a large number of papers written both here and abroad, the like of which no phase of earlier pathology produced. Yet none of these papers marked a return to earlier doctrines or an essential change in the direction of the cellular viewpoint. In order to elucidate this progress in pathology, it is not necessary to examine details, since at the present time the work of foreign researchers is turning more and more along the same path we are following.

The only important movement that has appeared and is taking another direction and sometimes even an opposing form is the bacteriological. Ever since Ferdinand Cohn [Ferdinand Julius Cohn 1824-1898] expanded the name of bacteria (which is not always identical with bacilli) from Ehrenberg's [Christian Gottfried Ehrenberg 1795-1876] rodlets to all possible forms of the smallest microscopic life forms, and even made globular bacteria out of cocci, bacteriology in everyday usage has come to mean almost the same as what I have termed mycotic diseases. Sprouting and filamentous fungi have to submit to the fact that they are classified with bacteria, just as others call the cocci fungi. Perhaps a more pertinent terminology will one day be found. For now there is nothing left except to adapt to this understanding even with its irrational terms.

All mycotic diseases have one thing in common, namely, that parasitic microorganisms come into the foreground of our attention. All investigations, therefore, have to strive for the final goal of determining the effect of these organisms and to clarify the particular kind of their parasitism. It is easy to see from the foregoing that this parasitism is something completely different from the parasitism of the natural historians. In actuality, this concerns the action, if not the invasion, of autonomous beings in the human body, so that from this point two or more lives are present, one beside the other. One thus arrives at a schema, as Paracelsus [Theophrastus Bombastus von Hohenheim 1493–1541] had advanced it, except that he interpreted the parasites as being pseudo-organizations springing from the body, not as independent plants arising from the outside. However, in the apparent similarity of these two things is the seduction towards a mistake into which many superficial minds of modern times have stumbled, a mistake about which one cannot be earnestly enough warned. It thus happens, as I have repeatedly set forth,[4] that there is the confusion of a being with a cause, of an *ens morbi* with a *causa morbi.* An actual parasite, whether it is plant or animal, can become the cause of a disease, but it can never exhibit the disease itself. Nothing demonstrates the necessity of this differentiation more than the fact that parasites in great numbers live even in the healthy body, and that in individual cases parasites can be harmless, even though they can act as pathogens (more strictly, pathogenetically) according to current usage. If this action does not take place, if e.g. diphtheria bacilli are in the throat of a healthy child, then there is no disease and therefore no *ens morbi* present. On the other hand, if one, along with the natural historians, calls an altered bodily part, e.g. a new formation (tumor), a parasite, then one easily reaches the notion of two parasites in the same body: the *causa viva* and the *ens morbi.*

In a paper on the condition and causes of disease I have fully discussed these circumstances with particular reference to cellular pathology.[5] I later defined the condition of the body in relation to the pathogenetic microorganisms as a battle between cells and bacteria.[6] For quite a while I have consistently stressed that this is not always a matter of microorganisms as such. Again and again I have pointed to the processes of fermentation, whose agents are obviously microorganisms, but microorganisms that are almost completely harmless for an animal organism. The noxiousness in fermentation lies in the alcohol or acetic acid, the products of the life functions of the fermentative fungi. In this sense, I have all along held fast to the theory that there can be harmful or even poisonous substances of a purely chemical nature along with the microorganisms, and that the disease, which arises as a result of the invasion of microorganisms, should not be regarded as an "effect of the fungus". In this same sense, I was the first to differentiate the category of "infectious diseases" and to give them a whole section in my large *Handbuch der speciellen Pathologie und Therapie.* Since that time a whole series of poisonous substances has been differentiated, primarily through Brieger [Ludwig Brieger 1849–1919], which have been called toxins, along with the ptomaines already described by Selmi [Francesco Selmi 1817–1881]. The number of infectious diseases has also been considerably broadened by means of new discoveries of pathogenic microorganisms, and it cannot be said whether still more discoveries are to be expected.

The last two decades have been filled to a great extent with work in this area. An account of what has been accomplished would take up much space without ever being able to be definitive in every case. The fact that, for a number of the most significant contagious and infectious diseases, it is possible to verify not only the invariable existence of microorganisms, but also the experimental proofs of their activity, is sufficient to show the great progress made by natural scientific knowledge in this difficult area, which only half a century ago was still endangered by the most arbitrary assumptions concerning the causes and conditions of pestilences and contagious diseases. We have not yet been successful in establishing that all contagious diseases have pathogenetic microorganisms; it even has not been scientifically determined whether there is a contagion without bacteria. One only need think of rabies, as well as of the many diseases in the neoplastic group, from carcinomas and sarcomas to enchondromas and myxomas, all of which act just like contagious diseases in their spread through the body. Nevertheless, it is conceivable that the hope of discovering the sought-after parasitic microorganisms has foundation in other than just the minds of sanguine researchers or dogma-loving disciples, and that every new twist in our knowledge of independent organisms (as e.g. of certain protozoa) under disease conditions does not lead just to for the most part arbitrary inductive amplification of dogmatic formulae. For the dispassionate observer this drive sometimes has something disturbing about it. But the great and consoling difference in contrast to the method of the earlier speculative and aprioristic pathologists lies in the fact that every step on the way of the contemporary researcher can be controlled exactly, and that even the greatest enthusiasts start from real things which are approachable by means of experimental criticism. The rich profusion of factual observations and the eagerness in pursuing even the smallest being is surely quite satisfying in contrast to the desolation and inertia which were the stamp of etiological investigation a hundred years ago.

It is most peculiar, however, that the latest developments in these investigations have resulted in completely unexpected successes for practice, but for theory it has produced a kind of relapse into long-forgotten formulae. Louis Pasteur [1822–1895], the very researcher who first taught in the most meticulous fashion the hereditary transmission of the smallest organisms and their mode of chemical activity, has also begun a bold undertaking, using the products of contagious organisms to control diseases produced by them, and to immunize the animal body against their activity in general. The long series of ever new attempts, from anthrax in ruminants and cholera in fowls to rabies, which have been carried out by him, ties in with the well-known method of Jenner [Louis Jenner 1866–1904], which led to cow-vaccine as a protection against smallpox. Since this is concerned in part with diseases in which pathogenetic microorganisms in general have not yet been found, the conception of the "lymph" has once again attained a certain degree of importance.

The renowned attempt of Robert Koch [1843–1910], the fortunate dis–coverer of some of the most important pathogenetic bacteria, to produce a "lymph" from pure cultures of tubercle bacteria, which "lymph" would act in a healing and immunising fashion on tuberculosis, led to a new direction that has finally brought *serum therapy* into the foreground of practical interest. This is concerned with a very complex procedure, one having a fairly typical model in vaccinia. Fluid obtained from pure cultures of bacteria, which contain the metabolic products of bacteria, as one says nowadays, is introduced first into the body or even directly into the blood stream of a healthy animal. After a relatively long time a change manifests itself in the animal, which can be recognized by the character of its serum. This proves itself to be an antitoxic serum, because it aids elimination of the corresponding disease and warrants a relative protection against its development. This has been demonstrated particularly in diphtheria, thanks to the careful experiments on which Behring [Emil A. von Behring 1854–1917] based his method. There is understandably a widespread hope that this experience can be broadened to include the treatment of other contagious diseases.

One cannot come to a definitive judgment at this point. Yet it has been a long time since a particular direction of therapy has won such great sympathy. The question of the implications of serum therapy for general pathology is much more difficult. Enthusiasts see in this final triumph of humoral pathology, obviously a completely different humoral pathology from any that has gone before. The old humoral pathology does not even come under consideration, rather one of the later versions, namely, hematopathology. But even this was concerned either with merely quantitative changes of blood "crases" or with quantitatively abnormal substances entering the blood either from outer or from inner parts. Putrescent substances are first among these, and they have for decades been the object of countless experiments. The theory of putrid infection (septicemia) long ago passed into general knowledge; everyone has assumed that putrescent substances have a harmful effect on the body and sometimes cause new putrescent processes. But no one had the right to assume that the tissues of the body—a shorter description could be cells—could be left out of consideration, and that putrid infection was nothing other than an abnormal condition of the blood. The cause of the tissue disturbance is contained in the blood only, but the disease is not in the blood, rather the disease is the effect of the cause on the cells (tissues).

1. Vgl. die Anmerkung zu meinen "Einheitsbestrebungen in der wissenschaftlichen Medicin" in den Gesammelten Abhandlungen. 1856. S. 50.

2. Handbuch der speciellen Pathologie und Therapie. Erlangen 1854. Bd. I. S. 2.

3. Die Cellularpathologie in ihrer Begründung auf physiologische und pathologische Gewebelehre. Berlin 1858.

4. Vgl. meine Rede zur Feier des Stiftungstages der militärärztlichen Bildungsanstalten am 2. August 1874: "Die Fortschritte in der Kriegsheilkunde, besonders im Gebiete der Infektionskrankheiten." (Gesammelte Abhandlungen aus dem Gebiete der öffentlichen Medicin und der Seuchenlehre. Berlin 1879. II. S. 185.)

5. Archiv f. path. Anat. u. Phys. 1880. Bd. 79. S. 1 und 185.

6. Ebendas. 1885. Bd. 101. S. 1.

2.6

Relations of Biological and Social Homeostasis, from *The Wisdom of the Body*

Walter B. Cannon

I

Are there not general principles of stabilization? May not the devices developed in the animal organism for preserving steady states illustrate methods which are used, or which could be used, elsewhere? Would not a comparative study of stabilizing processes be suggestive? Might it not be useful to examine other forms of organization—industrial, domestic or social—in the light of the organization of the body?

These are tempting questions. Many times in the history of philosophy and sociology similar questions have led to an examination of the analogies between the body physiologic and the body politic. The biologist is as subject to temptation in respect to these analogies as are the philosophers and sociologists. He may lack the philosophers' broad outlook and the sociologists' knowledge of the complex details of the social system. But as a unit of that system he is interested in it. And he looks on the analogies from the biological point of view. May not the new insight into the devices for stabilizing the human organism, which we have been examining in the foregoing chapters, offer new insight into defects of social organization and into possible modes of dealing with them? The details of bodily homeostasis are, of course, available to anyone who cares to see whether they offer any suggestions for the study of social conditions. As a stimulus to such suggestions it might not be amiss to consider some features of their apparent analogies.

II

In an earlier chapter I pointed out that the single-cell organism, living in a flowing stream, is dependent immediately on its surroundings; it has no means of controlling the environment and must submit wholly to what the environment imposes upon it. Only when cells grow in masses do they acquire the possibility of developing an internal organization, capable of separating them from the disturbances due to shifts of external circumstance.

We must not overlook the fact that when cells grow in masses they still remain living units. Like the isolated single cell, each cell in a complex organism has its own life processes. In our discussion of homeostasis, we have considered the environment—the internal environment—which is provided for these living units. We have not, however, regarded the events occurring within the units themselves. Each one takes in, from its fluid contact, water and salts and oxygen; it takes in food which it uses to build up or repair its own structure, or to elaborate new substances for special secretions, or to secure the energy needed in performing other special services for the organism as a whole; and finally it discharges the waste resulting from the wear and tear and from the débris of its own activities. All these complicated functions the cell normally carries on in a nicely adjusted manner, with not too much and not too little of either intake or output. And throughout the multitudes of exchanges which are involved it preserves in a marvelous manner its intimate texture and precise action.

In the one-cell organism all the vital functions—digestion, motion, reproduction—are performed by it alone. As cells grow in masses the phenomenon of division of labor appears. The cells are arranged in separate structures or organs for special services—muscles for pulling, nerves for conducting impulses, glands for secreting. Of course, these organs are not always active. For long periods, even in the waking state, many muscles and their controlling nerves may be idle. The digestive organs do not work steadily except when given work to do. Only the respiratory organs and the heart must keep persistently at their tasks; and the heart, when beating at the moderate rate of seventy pulses per minute, is actually contracting only nine hours in the twenty-four—rest periods after each contraction amount to fifteen hours every day. Even in the parts of an organ activity is not continuous; muscle fibers take turns in keeping up a long pull, capillaries are closed down when blood is not needed, and the glomeruli of the kidneys operate in shifts. The labor of internal organs (the viscera) is, as a rule, so well regulated by inherent automatisms that the phenomena of fatigue rarely appears—the waves course over the stomach at their routine rate, the kneading movements of the intestines cannot be made to go faster than their wont. The central nervous system alone can force activities to such a degree as to bring about the limitations and inefficiencies resulting from fatigue—and that system is almost wholly limited to a control of the muscles which pull on the bones. Furthermore, fatigue itself is a check on excessive activity. It is clear, then, that the processes going on in individual cells, as well as those going on in organs, are accompanied by a large amount of local self-regulation.

III

The centrally important fact is that with the division of labor, which is implicit in the massing of cells in great multitudes and their arrangement in specific organs, most of the individual units become fixed in place so that they cannot forage for themselves. Far removed from the sources of essential supplies, these segregated and specialized units would necessarily cease their activities and would soon die unless there was developed, at the same time with their development, a means of transportation and distribution which would assure these supplies. This transporting and distributing system we recognize as the fluid matrix of the organism—the rapidly flowing blood and the more slowly moving lymph. The existence of the fluid matrix at once simplifies the problem of the remotely situated cells engaged in particular tasks. Having that provision they need not be concerned with getting food, water and oxygen, avoiding too great heat or cold, and keeping clear of the dangers of accumulating waste. All these conditions are attended to by a special organization, which, as we have seen, holds the fluid matrix constant. So long as that constancy is preserved, the various kinds of cells in the different organs are free to give full time to their special services. The fluid matrix, therefore, is a prime requisite for the more complex organization of living units. It makes such organization possible. It gives such organization stability. And insofar as the constancy of the fluid matrix is evenly controlled, it is not only a means of liberating the organism as a whole from both internal and external limitations, as we have repeatedly noted, but it is an important measure of economy, greatly minimizing the need for separate governing agencies in the various organs.

We may remark in passing that the cells in the organs which control the constancy of the fluid matrix are themselves part of the total organization of the body. They do not act by imposing conditions from the outside. In maintaining steady states n the blood and lymph they work both for the welfare of the cells in other organs essential to the body, and also for their own welfare. In short they well illustrate the arrangements for mutual dependence; in spite of generous provision for factors of safety, the integrity of the organism as a whole rests on the integrity of its individual elements, and the elements, in turn, are impotent and useless, save as parts of the organized whole.

IV

In primitive conditions, small human groups living by the chase and by simple agriculture encountered circumstances not unlike those which prevail in the life of isolated single cells. Individuals were, indeed, free to move about over wide ranges and to forage for themselves, but they were dependent on what their immediate environment at the moment could furnish. They had little control over that environment. Of necessity they had to submit to the conditions which it determined.

Only when human beings are grouped in large aggregations, much as cells are grouped to form organisms, is there the opportunity of developing an internal organization which can offer mutual aid and the advantage, to many, of special individual ingenuity and skill. But with the development of larger and more complex social communities, just as with the evolution of the larger and more complex organisms, the phenomenon of division of labor becomes more and more pronounced. The list of special types of workers in a civilized society is almost unlimited. Again, like the division of labor in the animal organism, the division of labor in a complex social group has two noteworthy effects—it leads gradually to relative fixation of the individual members of the group in places where they perform their peculiar labor, and they may then be far removed from the sources of supply necessary for their continued existence. The expert mechanic in a large urban industry, for example, can neither grow his food, make his clothing, nor procure his fuel directly. He must rely on members of others groups for these things. He can do his part only so long as the others do theirs. Each one finds security in the general cooperation. Once more, just as in the body physiologic, so in the body politic, the whole and its parts are mutually dependent; the welfare of the large community and the welfare of its individual members are reciprocal.

It is obvious that at present nations have not yet achieved a full measure of success in maintaining constancy of the routine of existence or in assuring to the human elements a continuous provision for their essential needs. There is widespread search for the conditions which would diminish the anxieties and distress which are caused by the great ups and downs of economic fluctuations. Stability would free mankind from a vast amount of pain. In our own individual bodily organization we have an example of methods of successful achievement. By storage and release of material supplies, by altering the rate of continuous processes, by natural defenses against injury, and by a wide margin of safety in its functional arrangements, the normal organism protects itself for decades against perturbations. Through myriads of eons of experience, our bodies, though composed of extraordinarily labile material, have developed these devices for maintain stability. What have they to suggest?

V

At the outset it is noteworthy that the body politic itself exhibits some indications of crude automatic stabilizing processes. In the previous chapter I expressed the postulate that a certain degree of constancy in a complex system is itself evidence that agencies are acting or are ready to act to maintain that constancy. And moreover, that when a system remains steady it does so because any tendency towards change is met by increased effectiveness of the factor or factors which resist the change. Many familiar facts prove that these statements are to some degree true for society even in its present unstabilized condition. A display of conservatism excites a radical revolt and that in turn is followed by a return to conservatism. Loose government and its consequences bring the reformers into power, but their tight reins soon provoke restiveness and the desire for release. The noble enthusiasms and sacrifices of war are succeeded by moral apathy and orgies of self indulgence. Hardly any strong tendency in a nation continues to the stage of disaster; before that extreme is reached corrective forces arise which check the tendency and they commonly prevail to such an excessive degree as themselves to cause a reaction. A study of the nature of these social swings and their reversal might lead to valuable understanding and possibly to means of more narrowly limiting the disturbances. At this point, however, we merely note that the disturbances are roughly limited, and that this limitation suggests, perhaps, the early stages of social homeostasis.

As an analogous condition of affairs, we may recall that in the evolution of vertebrate animals, and also in the development of the individual organism, the physiological devices which preserve homeostasis are at first not well developed. Only among forms which show other signs of being highly evolved do we find the automatic processes of stabilization working promptly and effectively. I would point again to the strikingly greater control of the internal environment by the complex mammalian than by the relatively simple amphibian creatures; and associated therewith the much greater freedom and independence in the presence of disturbing conditions. Is it not possible that social organization, like that of the lower animals, is still in a rudimentary stage of development? It would appear that civilized society has some of the requirements for achieving homeostasis but that it lacks others, and because lacking them it suffers from serious and avoidable afflictions.

For the present adhering fairly strictly to physiological considerations (i.e., to the supplies of food, shelter, etc.) we are forced to recognize that the homeostasis of the individual human being is largely dependent on social homeostasis. There are certain essential needs which must be satisfied in order to preserve our personal health and efficiency. Some of the needs are satisfied gratuitously. Oxygen, and sometimes water also, we may have at will, without cost. It is noteworthy that in cities a supply of water is obtained only by community action and at public expense. There are other needs, however, which in the long run are quite as urgent as the needs for water and oxygen, and which at times cannot be satisfied because of the lack of social stability. These are the elementary requirements of food and of shelter (clothing, housing and warmth), and the benefits of medical care. To specialized workers in the social organization, limited and segregated as they are by their specialization, so that they must rely almost wholly on social homeostasis, disturbances of that homeostasis may be seriously harmful. Not only may the bodily needs be inadequately supplied, but in addition there may be suffering because of a loss of the sense of security. In the animal organism, as we have learned, the device which preserves homeostasis, which protects the cells in all parts from perturbations whether from within or without, is the controlled fluid matrix. What is the agency in civilized society which corresponds to that feature of our bodily arrangements?

VI

In a functional sense the nearest equivalent to the fluid matrix of animal organisms that is found in a state or a nation is the system of distribution in all its aspects—canals, rivers, roads and railroads, with boats, trucks and trains, serving, like the blood and lymph, as common carriers; and wholesale and retail purveyors, representing the less mobile portions of the system. In this vast and intricate stream, whose main channels and side branches reach more or less directly all communities, goods are placed, at their source, for carriage to other localities. These other localities are also sources of goods which likewise are placed in the stream. Thus the products of farm and factory, of mine and forest, are borne to and fro. But it is permissible to take goods out of the stream only if goods of equivalent value are put back in it. Ordinarily, of course, this immediate exchange does not occur. It would be highly awkward. To facilitate the process of exchange, money, which has generally recognized value, is employed. Or credit may temporarily be its substitute. By means of his money or his credit any individual can take from the stream whatever he needs or desires. Money and credit, therefore, become integral parts of the fluid matrix of society.

To assure the same degree of stability in the social organism that has been attained in the animal organism, the latter suggests such control of the fluid matrix that its constancy would be maintained. That would involve, in the first instance, the certainty of continuous delivery by the moving stream of the necessities of existence. Food, clothing, shelter, the means of warmth, and assistance in case of injury or disease are naturally among these necessities. Stability would involve also the assurance of continuous remuneration of individual labor—labor which would produce exchangeable goods and which would be paid a wage sufficient to allow the laborer to take from the stream the necessary things which he and those dependent on him require. I have stated the situation, for the present, in the lowest terms. *At least* these conditions should be met if stabilization of the social organism is to be achieved. In the light of biological experience social stabilization should be sought, not in a fixed and rigid social system, but in such adaptable industrial and commercial functions as assure continuous supplies of elementary human needs.

The social organism like the animal organism is subject to disturbances, some imposed from without, some due to its own activities. Droughts, floods, earthquakes, fires and pestilence may destroy immense accumulations of goods—crops and cattle, homes and workshops—and leave great numbers of men, women and children not only destitute of the prime requirements of life, but without the means of getting them, either directly or by going to the common stream. A new machine may be invented which, because it can do the work of thousands of laborers, throws thousands of laborers out of their jobs. Thus they lose for a time the opportunity to earn the money which they must have in order to take from the stream what they require. Or there may be excessive production of certain goods so that they do not move in the stream but accumulate; or such goods have a value so much reduced that they bring little in exchange, and consequently other exchangeable goods accumulate; or men may become apprehensive of future security so that money is not used to take goods from the stream but is hoarded, and again goods accumulate; or credit may be withdrawn, which has the same effect of retarding the usual processes of trading. In whatever way the movement of goods may be checked or hindered, the result is the same. The common stream becomes clogged, its rate of flow becomes slower, manufacture becomes hazardous, workmen are therefore unemployed, and being unemployed they cannot earn the wherewithal to secure what they must have. In these various types of disaster the individual members of the social organization are not responsible for the ills which circumstance forces them to endure. As more or less fixed units, performing specialized tasks in a complex system of tasks, they are incapable of making quick adjustments to new conditions as they arise. In the emergency they are impotent to modify the system to the advantage of all. Either type of remedy—new individual adjustments or modification of the general system—requires time and thoughtful planning.

VII

What does the stability of the organism suggest as to modes of solving the problem? Here we must be careful not to extend the principles of homeostatic orderliness at first to large and unwieldy administrative regions. If we assume a limited and fairly self-sufficient administrative region, we may suppose that the suggestions of the organism would be somewhat as follows.

The organism suggests that *stability is of prime importance*. It is more important than economy. The organism throws away not only water and salts, but also sugar, if they are present in excess in the fluid matrix. This rejection is uneconomical. The organism is driven into convulsions if the sugar supply runs too low, and the convulsions mark the acme of the manoeuvres which bring forth extra sugar from the hepatic reserves to restore the normal glycemic percentage. Violent shivering may be induced to develop the additional heat which prevents a fall of body temperature. All these extreme activities, which are wasteful of energy, are not ordinarily employed, because milder measures suffice; but they are ready, whenever they are needed, to keep uniform the internal environment. This evidence that in critical times economy is secondary to stability is supported by the generous provisions of factors of safety in the body. The status of blood volume, lung capacity, blood pressure and cardiac power, for example, is not set by economy, but by the chance of having to meet unusual demands which would disturb the fluid matrix of the body if they were not met.

The organism suggests, also, that there are early signs of disturbance of homeostasis which, if sought, can be found. These warning signals are little known in the social organism, and yet their discovery and the demonstration of their real value would make contributions to social science of first-rate importance. In the complexity of modern social interrelations the strategic control would appear to reside in the devices for distributing goods, in commerce, and the flow of money rather than in manufacture and production. Our bodily devices would indicate that the early warning signals, pointing to social and economic danger, should perhaps be sought in sensitive indicators of fluctuations of the commercial stream, though the causes of these fluctuations may be found in industry.

The organism suggests, furthermore, that the importance of stability warrants a specially organized control, invested by society itself with power to preserve the constancy of the fluid matrix, i.e., the processes of commerce. Does not this imply that when there is a prospect of social perturbation there should be a power to limit the production of goods to a degree which would reasonably adjust the supply to the demand? power to lay aside stores of goods which could be released if crises arise? power to require the accumulation of wage reserves which could be used at times of temporary unemployment? power to arrange emergency employment or training for new types of labor skill? and power to accelerate or retard the routine processes of both the production of goods and their distribution, in accordance with desirable adaptations to internal or external disturbing factors? It is noteworthy that in the bodily organism such powers as storing or releasing material reserves, hastening or checking continuous processes are exercised not by the cerebral cortex, where adaptive intelligence is mediated, but by lower centers of the brain which work in an automatic manner when appropriate signals call upon them to act.

The development of organisms indicates that the automatic devices which keep steady the internal environment have resulted from a long course of experience, possibly of experimental trial, error and correction. It seems reasonable to expect that the modes of assuring social stability, that may develop, will be the resultant of a similar evolution. Intelligence, and the example of successful stabilizing processes already in action, however, may make the evolution in society relatively rapid.

If cells of the bodily organism are injured, or are attacked by disease germs, the fluid matrix at once sets up procedures which are favorable to the restoration of the normal state. The conditions in the organism, therefore, point to the assurance of expert protective and restorative attention, through arrangements in the social group, so that the group shall not be weakened by the incapacity or ill health of its members.

We must take account of the fact that the adult organism represents a fairly fixed number of constituent cells, i.e., it is the equivalent of an adjusted population. It has no provision for any process which would be the equivalent of immigration into the social community. Nor has it any provision for unlimited growth, either as a whole or in its parts. Indeed, when some cells reproduce themselves in an uncontrolled manner, they form a malignant disease, endangering the welfare of the organism as a whole. Against such pathology the body has no protection. It appears, therefore, that any wisdom which the human organism has to offer to the social organism would be based on the proviso of a population which is adjusted to reasonably assured means of subsistence and which is undisturbed by large increases from either local or foreign sources.

A noteworthy difference between the social and the biological organism is the certainty of death in the latter. In the course of existence the cells lay down intracellular substance which becomes obstructive, or they become injured by accident in irreparable ways, or they degenerate with age, until finally an essential organ of which they are members fail to play its rôle and the failure of that organ ends the activities of the whole organism. Death is a means of ridding society of old members in order to yield places for the new. A state or a nation, therefore, does not need to contemplate its own end, because its units are ceaselessly refreshed. The stabilizing processes in a body politic, therefore, when once discovered and established, might be expected to continue in operation as long as the social organization itself, to which they apply, remains fairly stable in its growth.

VIII

It is of considerable significance that the sufferings of human creatures because of lack of stability in the social organism have more and more stimulated efforts directed towards improvement. Various schemes for the avoidance of economic calamities have been put forth not only by dreamers of Utopias but also by sociologists, economists, statesmen, labor leaders and experienced managers of affairs. In all such proposals a much greater control of credit, currency, production, distribution, wages, and workmen's welfare is anticipated than has been regarded as expedient or justifiable in the individualistic enterprises of the past.

Communists have offered their solution of the problem and are trying out their ideas on a large scale in Soviet Russia. The socialists have other plans for the mitigation of the economic ills of mankind. And in the United States where neither communism nor socialism has been influential, various suggestions have been offered for stabilizing the conditions of industry and commerce. Among these suggestions are the establishment of a national economic council or a business congress or a board of industries or of trade associations, representing key industries or the more highly concentrated industries, and endowed (in some of the schemes) with mandatory power to coördinate production and consumption for the benefit of wage earners; provision for regularity and continuity of employment, with national employment bureaus as an aid, with unemployment insurance as a safety device, and with planned public works as a means of absorbing idle workmen; incentives for the preservation of initial initiative and originality in spite of the dangers of fixed organization; shortening of the working time and prohibition of child labor; the raising of the average industrial wage; and the assuring of the general public through governmental regulation that in any arrangements which are made its interests will be protected.

The multiplicity of these schemes is itself proof that no satisfactory single scheme has been suggested by anybody. The projection of the schemes, however, is clear evidence that in the minds of thoughtful and responsible men a belief exists that intelligence applied to social instability can lessen the hardships which result from technological advances, unlimited competition, and the relatively free play of selfish interests.

By application of intelligence to medico-social problems, destructive epidemics such as the plague and smallpox have been abolished; fatal afflictions, e.g., diphtheria and tuberculosis, have been greatly mitigated and largely reduced; and vast areas of the earth's surface, formerly dangerous to man, have been made fit for safe and sanitary habitation because of the conquest of malaria, yellow fever and hookworm disease. These achievements all involve social organization, social control, and a lessening of the independence of the individual members. Economic and sociological programs, in which emphasis is laid on the well-being of the human elements in production as well as on material profits, have purposes similar to the medical programs just mentioned. They recognize that the social organism, like the bodily organism, cannot be vigorous and efficient unless its elements are assured the essential minimal conditions for healthful life and activity. And the possession of a mind by the human elements would require that these conditions include not only provision for the elementary needs which we have been considering, but also reasonable satisfaction of desires.

IX

In our study of the effects on the organism of a controlled stability of the fluid matrix we noted that just insofar as the stability is preserved the organism is released from the limitations imposed by internal and external disturbances. Is it not probable that similar results will flow from control and stabilization of the fluid matrix of the social organism? The hope is not unreasonable that the distress arising from catastrophes can be greatly mitigated, and that the suffering due to lack of necessary things which is attendant on great economic fluctuations can be obviated, by carefully planning and by intelligently regulating the processes of production and distribution. Banishment of this distress and suffering would bring freedom from fears, worries and anxieties concerning livelihood, which now may fill men with dark despair. As a Lord Chancellor of England has declared, and his declaration has been approved by a Justice of the United States Supreme Court, "Necessitous men are not, truly speaking, free men." The assurance of freedom *to men who are willing to work* would justify a larger control of economic processes, repugnant though that may seem, for it would be a sacrifice of lesser for greater values.

Bodily homeostasis, as we have learned, results in liberating those functions of the nervous system that adapt the organism to new situations, from the necessity of paying routine attention to the management of the details of bare existence. Without homeostatic devices we should be in constant danger of disaster, unless we were always on the alert to correct voluntarily what normally is corrected automatically. With homeostatic devices, however, that keep essential bodily processes steady, we as individuals are free from such slavery—free to enter into agreeable relations with our fellows, free to enjoy beautiful things, to explore and understand the wonders of the world about us, to develop new ideas and interests, and to work and play, untrammeled by anxieties concerning our bodily affairs. The main service of social homeostasis would be to support bodily homeostasis. It would therefore help to release the highest activities of the nervous system for adventure and achievement. With essential needs assured, the priceless unessentials could be freely sought.

There might be apprehension that social stabilization would tend towards dull monotony, that the excitements of uncertainty would be lacking. That would be true, however, only for the fundamental requirements of existence. There would still be the social disturbances of new inventions, the social interest in renowned exploits, in the discords of human nature, in reports of fresh ideas, in the intrigues of love and hate, and in whatever other events there may be that make life varied and colorful. Above all there might be apprehension that social stabilization would too greatly interfere with the free action of individuals. As repeatedly emphasized, however, steady states in society as a whole and steady states in its members are closely linked. Just as social stabilization would foster the stability, both physical and mental, of the members of the social organism, so likewise it would foster their higher freedom, giving them serenity and leisure, which are the primary conditions for wholesome recreation, for the discovery of a satisfactory and invigorating social *milieu*, and for the discipline and enjoyment of individual aptitudes.

2.7

The Evolution of the Concept of Disease

Professor Sir Henry Cohen,
M.D., D.Sc., LL.D., F.R.C.P.

"The very purpose of philosophy," wrote Whitehead in his *Adventures of Ideas*, "is to delve below the apparent clarity of human speech." The dominant trends in contemporary philosophy have been fashioned and profoundly influenced by semantic studies; they reject the Baconian precept that the study of words is "the first distemper of learning."

In medicine there are innumerable examples of words whose meaning has altered with the passage of time and increasing knowledge. For example, "artery" persists from the pre-Galenic days when that vessel was thought to contain air (αῆρ = air; τηρεῖν = to keep); the "phrenic" nerve supplied the diaphragm which was then regarded as the seat of the mind (Gk. φρην = mind); the "pituitary" gland owes its name to the mistaken notion that it secretes the nasal mucus (L. *pituita* = phlegm); the very different pathological states of osteomyelitis and myelitis share their common etymology from the days when the spinal cord was thought to be the bone-marrow (Gk. μυελός) of the vertebral column. These words, and an infinity of others, have varied in meaning with changes in contemporary knowledge and theory; their colour and content reflect the knowledge of the times in which they were introduced.

The word "disease" is no exception to this general rule. The notion or concept which it conveyed has varied with the ideas held about the *nature* of disease through the ages. The differentiation of disease as *dis-ease*, with its pain and suffering contrasted with health (O.E. *hal* = whole) has been recognized from the earliest times, though its existence has been denied by the Stoics in ancient times and, more recently, by quasi-religious cults. Primitive man was not deeply concerned with the *nature* or *cause* of disease. He sought its *cure*. And his purpose was not wholly selfish; sympathy for his fellows is revealed in his writings as one of the dominant human instincts.

The *cures* which he elaborated were based on crude supernatural magical doctrines, all of which, however, profoundly influenced later thought. Of these

Editors' note: footnotes omitted.

principles, those most widely known were the doctrines of *similars*, of *signatures*, of *analogy*, and of *contagion.*

The doctrine of *similars* was based on the principle that objects or circumstances similar in shape, colour, or sequence of events to those preceding or resulting from disease were effective in its treatment. For example, the appropriate remedy for greying hair was stewed raven because of its deep black features, whilst yellow birds were useful for jaundice.*

Those who based their practice on the doctrine of *signatures*, and it had a long sway, claimed that plants and animals have distinctive marks which indicate their medical properties. Thus trefoil was used in heart disease; the yellow celandine in jaundice; cyclamen for ear disease; flowers of the lily for gout; the roots of bryony (which resembled a swollen foot) for dropsy; thistle for a stitch in the side; walnut shells for head injuries; the spotted skin of the lizard for tumours. This doctrine was later to be the main basis of the therapeutic systems of Paracelsus and Culpeper.

The doctrine of the *analogy* had a more modern ring. The behaviour of ailing animals was observed, the food they took, whether, where and when they rested. Similar measures were then adopted in cases of human illness. Later analogy was extended to ill people. Special attention was paid to what happened to those who recovered. From analogy there came many useful contributions to knowledge; but it saw the birth in medicine of the *post hoc ergo propter hoc* fallacy whose baneful effects still influence treatment.

The doctrine of *contagion* was more recondite and took account of the alleged cause of disease. The object used in treatment was one which had been associated with this cause—for example, moonstone in mental disorders.

Except for the doctrine of contagion, none of these principles of treatment was based on theories concerning the nature of disease. From the earliest times to the present day two main concepts have dominated all writings on the nature of disease. These are (1) disease as a distinct entity; when a healthy man A falls ill he becomes A *plus* B, where B is "a disease." This view maintains that there are innumerable Bs, each with its individual and recognizable characters. And (2) disease as a deviation from the normal; a healthy man A, through the influence of any number of factors ($x_1, x_2, x_3 \ldots x_\infty$)—physical or mental—is changed and suffers; he is dis-eased (*A*). The appropriate formula is $A^{x_1, x_2, x_3 \ldots x_\infty} \rightarrow \mathit{A}$ when ill.

Many terms are used to cover these two concepts—*e.g., ontological*—indicating the independent self-sufficiency of diseases running a regular course and with a natural history of their own, as opposed to the *biographical* or *historical* which records the history of the patient. Other names arise from the

---

*This doctrine differs from that of Hahnemann's similars—*similia similibus curantur*—in that here a drug is advocated because it gives symptoms and signs similar and peculiar to those which the patient manifests. Hippocrates reveals his acceptance of this doctrine in the use of veratrum, but his writings show him as an eclectic who did not confine his therapy to one system.

founders of the schools of thought which appear to have given these concepts birth—*e.g., Platonic* and *Hippocratic*; from the site of their main temples, *Cnidian* and *Coan*; from the philosophies from which they are primarily derived—the contrasting *realist* and *nominalist*, *rationalist* and *empirical*, *conventional* and *naturalistic* schools. The names are of little importance. The two notions varying a little in content and occasionally overlapping have persisted, the dominance of the one or the other at different epochs reflecting either the philosophy of the time or the influence and teaching of outstanding personalities.

The earliest views on the nature of disease, its cause and its cure by eradicating the cause, stem from the fact that in the early history of mankind religion, philosophy and medicine were a single discipline. Religion recognized the multiplicity of gods, both good and evil; and philosophy accepted the influence of inanimate bodies, especially the sun, moon and stars, on living things. Thus arose the most primitive concept of the nature and cause of disease—namely, that it is due to the influence of evil spirits, a concept appropriately labelled *demoniacal*. But this idea had at least five variants. The simplest was that of an evil spirit entering the body directly and therein pursuing its nefarious purpose. For this, the appropriate prophylactic was the amulet, which took various forms, especially bracelets. Modern counterparts are by no means rare; witness the carrying of a new potato in the pocket or wearing a ring to ward off rheumatism. Once the spirit had entered the body, treatment consisted of exorcism by appropriate incantations, such as that of Marcellus in the fourth century, who is recorded as treating an ulcer of the eye by reiterating, "Fly, fly, a barley corn is pursuing you." One of the earliest known surgical operations—trephining of the skull—owed its rationale to this concept. Its intent was to facilitate the expulsion of the evil spirits from the diseased body.

But the evil spirit might indeed be a messenger of the gods and it then had to be placated or cajoled by burnt offerings or sacrifices. Or a human enemy might possess supernatural power influencing the diseased person; his machinations were to be warded off by sorcery and spells. The ideal of the "soul"—an *alter ego*—which arose from the attempt to interpret such phenomena as dreams, the shadows of objects and their reflections in water—gave rise to the idea that disease might be associated with offending spirits of the dead. It was from this that stemmed the family loyalties and ancestor worship of primitive peoples. The idea of the transmigration of "souls" was used not only in interpreting disease, but also for therapeutic purposes. The young lay with the old so that the more vital spirit of the young might pass over to the old. I well recall seeing, some twenty years ago, an Armenian patient with grave jaundice, and on entering the room, there was a repellent odour which I discovered to be due to a pigeon which had been slit open whilst alive and applied directly to the chest of the patient so that its "living principle" might enter the patient and sustain her.

The idea of diseases as separate entities springs in part from this demoniacal concept and was fostered by the description of "diseases" by the ancient writers. Hippocrates wrote essentially of disease in individuals—a biographical approach, and Aretaeus, the Cappadocian, in the second and third centuries A.D., gave careful pictures of patients with pneumonia, pleurisy with effusion (empyema), diabetes, tetanus, elephantiasis, the aura of epilepsy, cross paralysis from brain injury, etc. But these were records of individual cases. It is not until the ninth century that we detect the early glimmerings of generalization. It was then that Rhazes of Persia differentiated smallpox and measles.

After this many separate "diseases" began to be described. Glisson's description of rickets in 1650 is among the classical examples, and shortly after Glisson came the greatest of ontologists, Thomas Sydenham (1624–89), the "English Hippocrates", for whom diseases were "to be reduced to certain and determinate kinds with the same exactness as we see it done by botanic writers in their treatises of plants", and possessing "certain distinguishing signs which Nature has particularly affixed to every species." Illustrative of Sydenham's outlook is the following quotation:

> "Nature, in the production of disease, is uniform and consistent; so much so, that for the same disease in different persons the symptoms are for the most part the same; and the selfsame phenomena that you would observe in the sickness of a Socrates you would observe in the sickness of a simpleton. Just so the universal characters of a plant are extended to every individual of the species; and whoever (I speak in the way of illustration) should accurately describe the colour, the taste, the smell, the figure, etc., of one single violet, would find that his description held good, there or thereabouts, for all the violets of that particular species upon the face of the earth."

In the second half of the eighteenth century, classification of "diseases" became an obsession of medical writers largely due to the impetus given to taxonomy by Linnaeus' *Systema Naturae* (1735). This included the critical sentence—"Species tot sunt diversae quot diversae formae ab initio sunt creatae." In 1768 Francois Boissier de Sauvages, botanist and physician, published a detailed "Nosologia methodica sistens morborum classes, genera, et species" based on Linnaeus. He divided "diseases" into ten classes, subdivided these into forty orders, the orders into genera, and the genera into species—in all 2,400. Cullen and others were later to embellish this with even greater detail.

The concept of disease as a "clinical entity" still dominates much of our textbook descriptions, as illustrated by the so-called classical pictures of typhoid fever, influenza, disseminated sclerosis and the rest. Many of these are little more helpful in diagnosis than would be a composite portrait of a Cabinet or a Test Team in revealing whether a given individual is a member of either. And we will seek for pathognomonic signs as short cuts to diagnosis—

e.g., the staccato speech, intention tremor, and nystagmus of disseminated sclerosis; the thirst, polyuria, wasting and glycosuria of diabetes mellitus; the goitre, proptosis, tremor and tachycardia of Graves' disease. And we are even happier when these pathognomonic signs or specific tests are revealed by the exact instruments of a clinical laboratory, by X-rays or by a whole gamut of electrical recording machines. This way lies simplicity and directness; this way labour, time and thought can be conserved. But this way lies also error and unreason.

The concept of disease as a deviation from the normal owes its birth to the abstract nature of Greek thought. For the Greeks, reason was the master. Observation of nature was a low menial who could be disregarded if she contradicted the master. Indeed, pervading the whole of Greek thought is the attempt to conceive nature without an adequate knowledge of its parts; to generalize from inadequate particulars. In the abstract realms of mathematics the results were profound and indeed astounding when contrasted with the scientific knowledge of the age. There was, indeed, a perverse trend on the part of Greek philosophers to transcend experience by dialectics. But this was not confined to the Greeks. Indeed, as Sarton has written, history suggests that this is an intrinsic defect of the human mind. We have seen it in our own times in the works of such physicists as Eddington who have held that "the structure of the universe can be established on an *a priori* basis because of the structure of our mind."

In the fifth century B.C. Empedocles conceived the whole of Nature as derived from the four elements—fire, earth, air and water. In the later works of Hippocrates and Aristotle, we observe the development of the idea of four associated qualities—heat and cold, dryness and moisture, and of the four humours of the body—blood, phlegm, yellow bile and black bile.

It was Plato in "Timaeus" who first asserted that health was harmony, and disease discord of these four humours. He postulated that discord might arise from (1) an unnatural excess or defect of the four humours (a quantitative change) (2) a change in their natural place (site), and (3) the humours being of the wrong kind (a change in quality). But Plato argued also that disease might arise from a disturbance of the normal proportions of body and soul; when the soul is dominant, it leads to convulsions and "fills with disorders the whole inner nature of man"; but if the body is dominant, then the soul becomes dull, stupid and forgetful—ignorance and apathy result. It is in "Timaeus" that Plato's classification of disease based on these general principles is given.

Plato's theories led to the school of doctors which Galen labelled *Dogmatists*, which existed for at least a century after the death of Hippocrates. Its system had a twofold basis. Firstly, the *humoral* theory of disease which was to dominate medicine for 2,000 years was expanded, and provided the explanation for such later "diseases" as rheumatism (a flow of abnormal humours), gout (drops of humour appearing in abnormal situations), melancholia (the depression caused by an excess of black bile), and the splenetic and choleric disposition. Secondly, it relied on the magic of Pythagorean numbers, especially seven—*e.g.*, the Dogmatists stressed the significance of multiples of seven in the appearance of the second teeth at seven years, puberty at fourteen years, and hair on the beard area at twenty-one years.

During the second and third centuries B.C., the teachings of Aristotle, and their emphasis on observing nature, were exerting greater influence, and with this arose the school of *Empiricists*. Their rise was not simply a reaction to the rationalism of the Dogmatists. Two other happenings played a prominent rôle. Firstly, at that time Greece was extending her commerce to other Mediterranean countries, where were heard tales of wonder about the efficacy of drugs and the effects of poisons. And secondly, Pyrrho and the Sceptics were wielding greater influence. They taught that it was impossible to know the true nature of things, for perception shows us objects not as they are, but as they appear; so we must suspend judgment, since reason itself is futile (except apparently when reason seeks to demonstrate its own futility!). Hence the Empiricists observed the workings of Nature; unlike the Dogmatists, they did not aspire to unmask by reason the final causes of the things observed. Their observations were concerned essentially with treatment and it was here that their journeys abroad enriched their therapeutic resources. Their knowledge of the nature and cure of disease was based on the tripod of *autopsy*, *history* and *analogy*. For them, *autopsy* covered the patient's observations on himself; *history* meant learning from others—from teachers and from books; *analogy* implied observing similar events in others. Later, the Empiricists added a fourth method of attaining knowledge—*epilogism*—by which they meant inferring preceding events from present symptoms. But to their credit it must be conceded that in their teaching is to be found the germ of the idea of a "syndrome", and indeed it was on this that their analogies were based, and they defined disease as "a union of symptoms which are observed always in the same way in the human body," without, however, giving "disease" a strictly ontological interpretation. For the Empiricists, anatomy appeared quite unnecessary, and since they had no means of distinguishing *propter* from *post*, charlatanism was rife in their search for specifics, and the doctrine of signatures held unimpaired sway.

Rational Greek medicine reached its purest exposition in the school of the Methodists who applied the principles of Epicureanism to medicine. This school originated with Asclepiades of Bithynia (born in 124 B.C.), but it was more fully developed by his pupil, Themison of Laodicea (123–43 B.C.). The Methodists believed that the body of man was an infinity of atoms (small particles) and pores (the spaces between the particles). If the size, weight, shape, position and movement of the particles were normal, then health (symmetry) resulted. Themison held that disease resulted from disturbance of the pores. He recognized three communities of disease, (1) excessive relaxation or enlargement of the pores, (2) contraction of the pores, and (3) a mixed group. Both diagnosis and treatment were simple. If the disease resulted from relaxation of the pores, astringents such as cold baths, vinegar, alum, lead and chalk were indicated; whilst if contraction of the pores caused diseases, then laxatives such as venesection, cupping, leeches, poultices, fomentations and warmth were called for. They did not accept the doctrine of signatures; their therapeutic maxim was *contraria contrariis curantur*. The Methodists claimed to be the only begetters of the true faith. Like many who have devised systems since, they despised earlier knowledge and held that there was no medicine of any importance known before them. What had been taught by earlier schools had been they held inaccurate, and consequently, unduly complicated and prolix. Indeed, one of the protagonists of Methodism, Thessalus of Lydia, reversed the Hippocratic aphorism, holding rather that "art is short and life is long," and maintained that all medicine could be taught in six months. On a monument in the Appian Way he styles himself, "Conqueror of Physicians."

Anatomy and physiology in any modern sense had no place in the practice of the Dogmatists or the Methodists. But this practice was systematized and had a strong attraction for the rational mind.

Since their time, innumerable systems have had their day and then ceased to be. Even after Sydenham's appeal in the seventeenth century for a return to the study of the natural history of disease, many systems were evolved during the eighteenth century which reflected the ideas of the Methodists. In each of these the central idea was that of health being due to the just balance of two opposing tendencies; disease resulted from their imbalance. Two systems which exerted considerable influence were those of John Brown (1735–88) and of Broussais (1772–1838). The Brunonians regarded tone as the dominant characteristic of the body. Disease was *sthenic* (due to excessive tone) or *asthenic* (due to lack of tone). For the former opium, and for the latter alcohol were the appropriate, and to the patient most acceptable remedies. For Broussais the "irritability" of tissues was what determined health or disease. He was strongly opposed to delineating clinical pictures of disease and describing their "typical" course. "Those groups of symptoms," he wrote, "which are given out as diseases are metaphysical abstractions which by no means represent a constant, unchangeable, morbid condition.... They are factitious entities (*entités factices*)."

Typical of the kind of system developed during the eighteenth century was that of Theophilus Lobb (*Medical Principles and Cautions*, 1751), who wrote as follows:

> "The Causes of Diseases in general are the following, viz.
>
> i. Some Excess in the Quantity of one or other of the Animal Fluids; that is, an Excess either in the Quantity of the Blood, or of the Lymph, or of the

> nervous Liquid; which three general Fluids are always moving in all Parts of the Body.
> ii. Some *wrong Quality* of them.
> iii. Some *deficiency* in the Quantity of one or other of them; Or,
> iv. Some Combination of these causes.
> The Cause of every Disease that can happen to the human Body (how manifold soever they may be) is comprehended in one, or other of the Heads mentioned."

Those familiar with the history of endocrinology and of the "stress" syndrome will recognize from these examples the forerunners of the general theory pervading more modern concepts.

The significance of anatomy and physiology in medicine and in the interpretation of disease was but little appreciated before the nineteenth century. Surgery, it is true, had benefited from the studies of the early anatomists and such operations as amputation, lithotomy and the excision of tumours were designed on the basis of the anatomical knowledge then available. But even Vesalius' monumental work (*De Humani Corporis Fabrica*, 1543) and Harvey's classical demonstration of the circulation of the blood (*Exercitatio De Motu Cordis*, 1628) had but little direct influence on the rational practice of medicine. The emphasis, however, which these works placed on the lever-like action of muscles and joints, and the analogy of the circulation with pumps, valves, and conduits led to the concept of medicine which treated the body as a machine. The influence of Newton's *Principia* (1687), embodying the simple mechanical laws governing the universe, lent weight to this view. Indeed, Newton's work forms the basis of an interesting but neglected book by Thomas Morgan on *Philosophical Principles of Medicine* (1725). This book is divided into three parts. The first is "A Demonstration of the General Laws of Gravity with their Effects upon Animal Bodys." The second deals with "The More Particular Laws which Obtain in the Motion and Secretion of the Vital Fluids, Applied to the Principal Diseases and Irregularitys of the Animal Machine." And the third describes "The Primary and Chief Intentions of Medicine in the Cure of Diseases, Problematically Propos'd and Mechanically Resolv'd." In this preface, Dr.Morgan stresses:

> "That the animal Body is a pure Machine and that all its Operations and Phaenomena with the several changes which happen to it are the necessary result of its Organisation and Structure." This, he says, "is now generally known and confirmed beyond all contradiction by the modern Observations and Improvements in Anatomy." He explains "how necessary it is for a Physician to be well acquainted with the Principles and Laws of Motion together with the Constitution and Structure of animal Bodys and the application of one to the other. For since the animal Body is a Machine and Diseases are nothing else but its particular irregularitys, Defects and Disorders, a blind Man might as well pretend to regulate a piece of Clockwork, or a deaf Man to tune an Organ, as a

> Person ignorant of Mathematics and Mechanism to cure Diseases without understanding the natural Organisation, Structure, and Operations of the Machine which he undertakes to regulate."

Pitcairn and Mead were later among the staunch adherents and exponents of these iatromechanical doctrines.

The rôle of chemistry in medicine was first emphasized by van Helmont (1577–1644). He and his successors investigated the chemistry of the secretions and ferments of the body, whilst Boyle and Hook were contributing to the knowledge of respiration by their researches on air. On the work of these chemical pioneers developed the iatrochemical school, which was firmly established by the beginning of the eighteenth century.

Before long, however, a reaction to the iatromechanical and iatrochemical schools appeared. It stressed that mechanism and chemistry were not enough. Regard had to be paid to the "soul" in medicine. This movement found its early exposition in the works of Georg Ernst Stahl (1660–1734), who revived a Cartesianism which taught that all vital movement is derived from the soul, and that the body is simply a passive agent guided by this immortal soul. Friedrich Hoffman (1660–1742), a strong advocate of similar views, emphasized that the universe is pervaded by a vital substance "finer than all other matter, but not exactly spirit, soul or mind"; this subtle substance, he thought, maintained the body in a state of tonic equilibrium, and he then emphasized, as did the Methodists, that disease resulted from an excess of this tone (when sedatives were indicated) or a deficiency (when tonics were indicated). Excess of tone, he held, was usually an acute process, whereas deficiency was chronic. But Hoffman was not prepared to abandon wholly the humoral theory and he taught that there were changes in humoral balance which required alternatives for their correction and that there might also be faulty excretion of the humours which demanded evacuants.

During the eighteenth century not only normal anatomy but also the anatomy of disease rapidly advanced. For the first time with Morgagni (1682–1771) in his *De Sedibus et Causis Morborum* (1761) came a clear attempt at correlating clinical observation with post-mortem findings, thus laying the foundations of pathology as a fundamental medical science. The clinicopathological correlations then established acquired an added importance when, in the nineteenth century, Virchow related clinical syndromes not simply to organs but to cellular systems, such as the blood and haemopoietic tissues, which might be distributed through many organs. They continue to play an important part in more recent work, for example, in that of Klinge on rheumatism as a manifestation of connective tissue disturbance, and of Klemperer's correlation of the collagen diseases.

In 1828 with Wöhler's synthesis of urea occurred a revolution in the approach to vitalism. Then for the first time a product of living matter was synthetized in the laboratory. The instruments of physics and chemistry, rapidly increasing in sensitivity and complexity, were during the ensuing decades turned to the study of disease. Normal values were determined and deviations from the normal recognized. Hyperchlorhydria and hypochlorhydria, hypertension and hypotension, polycythaemia and anaemia were now capable of recognition and quantitative assessment. But minds still shackled with the concept of diseases as "entities" interpreted even these changes in terms of "diseases."

The distinctive contribution of the nineteenth century, however, to the concept of disease was the recognition of its causes. Bacteria as the necessary and specific causes of such diseases as typhoid, tuberculosis, and cholera, were unmasked; the significance of endocrine unbalance, of nutritional deficiencies, of genetic influences was soon recognized; the part played by social, occupational, and economic factors and the psychological contribution to the aetiology of disease were all made clearer.

With this background we are in a position to appraise the present status of the two concepts of disease which we earlier recognized as pervading the history of medicine in the past 3,000 years.

We no longer regard diseases as being capable of reduction "to certain and determinate kinds with the same exactness as we see it done by botanic writers in their treatises on plants" and possessing "certain distinguishing signs which Nature has particularly affixed to each species" (Sydenham). But "disease" labels remain convenient symbols in those recurrent clinical patterns which are frequently isomorphic, as for example, in acromegaly, though they are less satisfactory where the variability of the clinical picture is much more marked, as, for example, in rheumatoid arthritis. The dangers which the "entity" concept carries are (1) that it promotes a "penny-in-the-slot machine" approach to diagnosis by seeking for pathognomonic signs, especially the short cuts of the laboratory or instrument (2) that it suggests that diagnosis is arrived at by comparing an unknown with a catalogue of knowns: the method of recognizing an elephant by having seen one before (3) that it reduces thought to a minimum (4) that it is of little help and may be positively misleading where the disease process varies significantly from the usual, and (5) that it leads to all those dangers associated with a label which Cowper implied when he wrote of those—"who to the fascination of a name, Surrender judgment, hoodwinked."

The second concept—deviation from the normal—interprets disease rationally in terms of anatomy and physiology. The simplest changes are *quantitative deviations from the normal* such as hypertension, menorrhagia, hypoglycaemia, macroglossia, anencephaly. It is, of course, important to recognize that the normal is a range and not a rigid figure (we recognize this in regard to the length of the nose but less frequently with regard to the blood-pressure!); and that the range varies with age, sex, number, site. These simple quantitative deviations from the normal are, however, commonly combined in constantly recurring patterns (isomorphism); these we label "syndromes". Of these, three groups are clearly recognizable. The first is *anatomical—e.g.*, staccato speech, intention tremor and nystagmus are manifestations not of disseminated sclerosis but of a disorder of the cerebellar mechanism; the vomiting of huge quantities of fluid free from bile and containing food taken twenty-four hours earlier is evidence of pyloric obstruction. The second group of syndromes are *physiological* (and here we include also *psychological*); thirst, wasting, polyuria, glycosuria, are the signs not of a disease, diabetes mellitus, but of impaired carbohydrate tolerance. The division into anatomical and physiological is somewhat artificial; physiological disturbances may well reveal an anatomical site of disease; for example, the disturbances of sensation which localize disease in the parietal lobe. Thirdly, the syndrome might indicate *pathological changes—e.g.*, redness, swelling, heat and pain as evidence of inflammation; or *aetiology—e.g.*, the Hutchinsonian triad as evidence of congenital syphilis.

It is this concept which should dominate our teaching and our approach to medicine. In brief, it may be stated thus: (*a*) disease indicates deviations from the normal—these are its symptoms and signs (*b*) symptoms and signs are commonly found to recur in constant patterns; these are the "syndromes" or "symptom-complexes" (*c*) these syndromes always indicate one or more of three aspects of disease: (1) its site, (2) associated functional disturbances, (3) causative factors in terms of (i) morbid anatomy, physiology and psychology, and (ii) aetiology.

Galen desired that every true physician should be also a philosopher. Philosophical enquiry in medicine is apt to be regarded as an arduous eccentricity for which few physicians in our time have had either the opportunity or the inclination. Yet it is a worth-while pursuit, for a knowledge of the history of ideas has a moderating influence. It helps to keep a balance between undue dogmatism on the one hand and undue scepticism on the other; and above all in revealing the thoughts and expounding the works of some of the greatest minds in human history, it inculcates a humility which is the surest shield against intellectual arrogance.

2.8

Historical Reflections on the Changing Concepts of Disease

Ilza Veith, M.A., Ph.D.

One of the many aspects that makes the reading of Hippocratic medicine so superbly interesting is the fact that the ancient Greek medical writer had practically no medical terminology. Medical nomenclature developed slowly and gradually, in pace with the gradual development of medical knowledge; and so long as medical knowledge was restricted, a narrative, descriptive style was used to evoke a picture of a disease, where nowadays one word, a simple disease name, would suffice. From a literary point of view the Hippocratic method of medical writing was eminently more pleasing. But it was satisfactory also from a medical point of view, for many of the ancient descriptions were so succinct and detailed that they presented as graphic a picture of the disease under discussion as can now be found in the most modern medical textbook. This is perhaps best illustrated by the reading of one short excerpt. It deals with a disease whose name I need not mention, but which will be recognized by everyone in all its detail and ramification.

> In Thasus, early in spring.... Many had swellings beside the ears, either on one or both sides, in most cases without fever, and not necessitating confinement to bed; some, however, were a little heated. In all cases these swellings subsided without giving trouble, and none went on to suppuration as do those from other causes. In character they were flabby, large, diffuse, without inflammation or pain; in all cases they disappeared without a sign. These conditions occurred in youths, young men, and adults; mostly in such as took exercise in the wrestling schools and gymnasia; but they seldom attacked women. Many had dry coughs without expectoration; and hoarseness in speaking. Not long after, but in some cases a considerable time later, painful inflammation occurred in one or both testicles; fever in some cases, in others not. The condition was as a rule very

troublesome. In other respects they had no illnesses requiring medical attention.[1]

This passage gives emphasis to a phenomenon which is of great importance to our subject: The disease in question, mumps, is so well observed that it need not be named. It was described more than 2,000 years ago. And yet, it might be a description of a mumps epidemic of today. The same is true for most other diseases given in the Hippocratic writings. From this we must conclude that while in the nearly twenty-five hundred intervening years since the days of Hippocrates some diseases may have undergone slight changes or permutations, most of them have existed in their present form since the beginning of history. Thus, what is unchanged is disease. What did change, however, is the way in which disease was looked upon.

This change is twofold: first, it refers to the pathological, physiological, and etiological concepts and hence also to therapy. And second, it refers to the social aspect of disease in general and of individual diseases in particular.

The distinction which we now make between disease in general and individual disease or disease entities is a very important one. It did not come about automatically, nor early in the history of medicine but was the result of long experience and increasing sophistication in medical thought. Thus, while some individual diseases were known and recognized fairly early in the evolution of medicine, they were not looked upon as distinct entities but rather as manifestation of a state of disease that affected the human body *in toto*. This is, of course, particularly evident in primitive cultures, where all aspects of disease—etiology, pathology and therapy—were related to superhuman influences. Gods, evil spirits, demons did not send a sore throat or appendicitis or a broken leg; they sent disease, a state of illness which attacked the body in general, although it might be manifest in one particular spot only. Conversely, to treat disease, the exponents of primitive medicine, the shaman, or medicine man, did little for the affected parts of the body, but rather tried to appease the powers that had sent the disease. In doing so they acted entirely logically—even if not altogether rationally from our point of view. They avoided the treatment of the disease itself and went straight to the root of the evil, namely, to assuage the wrath of the powers that had caused it. With the appeasement of the superhuman powers by prayers, incantations and sacrifices, the manifestation of their anger—that is, the disease itself—was bound to disappear.

The eventual divorce of medicine from superhuman connections was finally and clearly pronounced in the Hippocratic writings (fifth to fourth century B.C.) and finds succinct expression in the treatise on epilepsy, entitled:

"ON THE SACRED DISEASE"

It is this with regard to the disease called *Sacred*: it appears to me to be nowise more divine nor more sacred than other diseases, but has a natural cause from

> which it originates like other affections. Men regard its nature and cause as divine from ignorance and wonder, because it is not at all like to other diseases. And this notion of its divinity is kept up by their inability to comprehend it. But if it is reckoned divine because it is wonderful, instead of one there are many diseases which would be sacred; for, as I will show, there are others no less wonderful and prodigious, which nobody imagines to be sacred.[2]

It is difficult to appreciate fully the impact and importance of this statement. It removed disease from the hazy spheres of the heavens and brought it down to earth and into the realm of the physician's responsibility. The physician's every act now became important and it was up to him, and no longer to the deities, to treat and cure the patient.

Of course, the removal of the gods from the concept of disease necessitated the formation of new frameworks of thought for the cause and the cure of illness. Since it was no longer the deities whose pleasure maintained the harmony of the human body and whose displeasure caused disharmony and disease, other bases for harmony and disharmony had to be found. The first of these bases was known as humoral pathology; it was the theory of the harmony or disharmony of the four elementary substances, the four humors (yellow bile, black bile, phlegm, and blood). The preponderance of each of these led to either the choleric, melancholic, phlegmatic, or the sanguine personality type. Another theory of health and disease was that of the so-called solid pathology of the atoms, the solid minute particles whose harmony—that is, whose even distribution and free flow—maintained health and whose stagnation or plethora caused disease and death.

Thenceforth, the scholarly physicians of Greece and of the later Graeco-Roman period distinguished illnesses not so much by their location and manifestation as by their supposed cause, whether a preponderance or lack of one of the four humors or an exaggerated constriction or relaxation of the atoms. Translated into practice, this meant that the physicians who believed in the pathology of solids gave constricting or relaxing remedies as the case might require (following the maxim of *contraria contrariis*). Those who adhered to the concept of humoral pathology attempted to supplement the deficient humor by related foods or to combat the superabundant humor by foods with opposing properties. Together with these measures, however, which were directed to the theory of disease, the physicians also attempted relief of the symptoms which actually represented the individual illness.

The medical theorists in Greece, that is, those who saw the cause of disease in dyscrasia of humors or an imbalance of atoms, maintained their point of view well into the first centuries of our era, and, indeed, the humoral theory continued to persist until the rise of modern medicine. Not only for physical disease was humoral imbalance considered responsible, but also in the attitudes toward mental health and disease this theory played an important role. The melancholic person in whom black bile (*melas cholé*) predominated, the choleric who was full of yellow bile, the sanguine person and the phlegmatic became prototypes of personality and behavior—often found in the plays of Shakespeare—and have remained so ever since.

DISEASE AS THE WORK OF WITCHES

The spirit peculiar to the Middle Ages, however, re-introduced a concept of disease that was strongly reminiscent of primitive medical thinking. Again a punishing deity began to send disease to chastise humanity with epidemics of a vast variety and unsurpassed severity—particularly the Black Death, that is, the plague. And again mankind attempted appeasement of the offended deity by means of prayers, fasting and incantations. Thus once again the practice of medicine was shared by the priest. Of course, a great many of the medieval monks were trained in the practice of medicine, and they could give medical care as well as spiritual. But it was largely the pure cleric, not the medically trained monk, who gave medieval medicine its superhuman stamp.

Perhaps the best example for this removal of all physical considerations from the realm of medicine can be found in a work that was actually composed during the Renaissance, but which is unsurpased as a prototype of medieval reasoning. This work, the *Malleus Maleficarum*[4]—the "Witches' Hammer"—stemmed from the pen of two Dominican monks, Johann Sprenger and Heinrich Kraemer, who had been appointed Inquisitors of Northern Germany by Pope Innocent VIII. Fortified by a Papal Bull of 1484, these two men composed a work in which any mental and physical aberration from the norm was ascribed to deviltry, witchery and evil. The volume became the guide-book for the Inquisition and went through nearly 20 editions within two centuries. The latest edition (of 1928) rendered it into English.

The "Witches' Hammer" is divided into three parts. The first is devoted to the proof of the existence of witchcraft, the second presents "clinical reports" of the manifestation of the various types of witches, and the third deals with legal aspects of establishing and sentencing witchery. In the course of the Middle Ages the differentiation between the mentally sick, the witch and the heretic had become less and less sharply defined; and in the 13th century they were considered synonymous by most persons. Eventually, however, all diseases came into the realm of witchery. This can be illustrated by the following statement emanating from the pen of a member of the Inquisition.

> "There is no part in our body that they [the witches] would not injure. Most of the time they make the human being possessed and thus they are left to the devils to be tortured with unheard of pains. They even get into carnal relations with them....Unfortunately, the number of such witches is very great in every province; more than that, there is no locality too small for a witch to find. Yet

> Inquisitors and Judges who could avenge these open offenses against God and Nature are so few and far between. Man and beast die as a result of the evil of these women and no one thinks of the fact that these things are perpetrated by witches. Many suffer constantly of severest diseases, and are not even aware that they are bewitched."

What, specifically, were the types of diseases that were removed from the responsibility of the physicians and put into the domain of religion? The "Witches' Hammer" enumerates them explicitly. The devil—or the witches—

> "have six ways of injuring humanity. And one is, to induce an evil love in a man for a woman, or in a woman for a man. The second is to plant hatred or jealousy in anyone. The third is to bewitch them so that a man cannot perform the genital act with a woman, or conversely a woman with a man; or by various means to procure an abortion. The fourth is to cause some disease in any of the human organs. The fifth, to take away life. The sixth, to deprive them of reason." (*Malleus Maleficarum*, p. 115).

It is clear that this listing comprises a very large part, if not most, of medicine, but some diseases are mentioned specifically for their demonic origin. Even the righteous monks felt that a special explanation was needed to make this plausible. The following is only one of many such examples.

> And, ". . . although greater difficulty may be felt in believing that witches are able to cause leprosy or epilepsy, since these diseases generally arise from some long-standing physical predisposition or defect, nonetheless it has sometimes been found that even these have been caused by witchcraft." And then they give an example.
>
> "For in the diocese of Basel, in the district of Alsace and Lorraine, a certain honest laborer spoke roughly to a certain quarrelsome woman, and she angrily threatened that she would soon avenge herself on him. He took little notice of her; but on the same night he felt a pustule grow upon his neck, and he rubbed it a little, and found his whole face and neck puffed up and swollen, and a horrible form of leprosy appeared all over his body. He immediately went to his friends for advice, and told them of the woman's threat, and said that he would stake his life on the suspicion that this had been done to him by the magic art of that same witch. In short, the woman was taken, questioned, and confessed her crime. But when the judge asked her particularly about the reason for it, and how she had done it, she answered: 'When that man used abusive words to me, I was angry and went home; and my familiar [advisor, the Devil] began to ask the reason for my ill humor. I told him, and begged him to avenge me on the man. And he asked what I wanted him to do to him; and I answered that I wished he would always have a swollen face. And the devil went away and afflicted the man even beyond my asking; for I had not hoped that he would infect him with such sore leprosy.' And so the woman was burned."

This is only one of many similar examples.

MONK'S THOUGHTS ON WOMEN

It is interesting that most of the victims of witchery were men, and that there were vastly more witches than wizards in the mental world of the Middle Ages and the two Inquisitors. While almost any known disease was described, and ascribed to witchery, the disturbances encountered most frequently relate to the reproductive organs. Sexual disorders, impotence and perversion, delusions of the loss of sexual organs occur with remarkable frequency. In view of the fact that the authors were monks and subordinate to the laws of celibacy, their preoccupation with these subjects is quite remarkable. Even more so, perhaps, is their attitude toward women, who, they felt, by their very nature, were disposed to enter into a compact with the devil. It almost appears as if they considered the state of femaleness a disease itself, when they exclaimed:

> "What else is woman but a foe to friendship, an unescapable punishment, a necessary evil, a natural temptation, a desirable calamity, a domestic danger, a delectable detriment, an evil of nature, painted with fair colours! Therefore, if it be a sin to divorce her when she ought to be kept, it is indeed a necessary torture; for either we commit adultery by divorcing her or we must endure daily strife."

Thus, women, inferior by nature, lying, vicious and hopelessly impure, are naturally the most serviceable and most willing tool of the devil. The *Malleus* supports its misogynous contentions by way of another characteristic excursion into infantile philology—the alleged derivation of the Latin word for woman, *femina*; the word is supposed to come from *fe* and *minus* (without faith), the latter designating a defect in nature. Woman is also proved to be constitutionally inferior, because

> "... it should be noted that there was a defect in the formation of the first woman, since she was formed from a bent rib, that is, a rib of the breast, which is bent as it were in a contrary direction to a man. And since through this defect she is an imperfect animal, she always deceives."

The digression into the *Malleus Maleficarum* has served to illustrate the concept of disease as it was held by many of the clergy during the Middle Ages and even the Renaissance. While these men were probably altogether representative of medieval attitudes toward mental illness, there were a few other more enlightened healers, as well as a great many lay physicians who attended to man's *physical* diseases.

What were their concepts of disease? As was mentioned earlier, it was the humoral concept that persisted for more than a millennium. But the dyscrasia of humors was not too satisfactory an explanation for the rise and spread of medieval epidemics, such as leprosy, the plague, St. Anthony's fire (ergotism), the English sweating sickness and others of equally devastating nature. Nor was it sufficient to explain the existence of syphilis, the new scourge of the Renaissance.

A TARDY UNDERSTANDING OF CONTAGION

From our modern point of view it seems difficult to understand that the phenomenon of contagion was not recognized with the appearance of the first contagious disease. Yet, even as keen an observer as the author of the Hippocratic description of mumps failed to see why it was the men who congregated in gymnasia who contracted the disease while the women who stayed at home in relative isolation remained free from it. In the absence of a recognition of contagion, all sorts of other explanations were sought to account for the spread of disease. Foulness of the air, as in the case of malaria (*mal aria*), swampy exhalations in the form of miasma, artificially poisoned water and other imaginary causes gained firmly convinced adherents. In consequence, treatment was also geared to these hypothetical causes. Protection from the foul air was sought by means of perfumed sponges, windows were kept closed to keep out the miasma, and the pogroms against Jews (and others suspected of evil intentions) were held to prevent the alleged poisoning of wells.

Personal contact was feared only in the case of leprosy. Whether this was so because of the well-known biblical injunctions in Leviticus XIII, or because the disease in its medieval form was of a more contagious nature than we know it now, will never be known. Nor will we ever know whether the many outcasts diagnosed as lepers by non-medical authorities were actually sufferers from what later became more precisely defined as Hansen's disease.

The first truly modern biological concept entered medical thinking only with the earliest clear statement on the existence of contagion. This came into being amazingly late if we consider the clear disease pictures of the earlier days. After all, Hippocrates' description of mumps contained a clear picture of a contagious disease which was contracted by the men who gathered in the gymnasia but more rarely by the women who spent their days in the seclusion of their homes. The first clear statement of contagion was pronounced by Girolamo Fracastoro (1478–1553) of Verona, a true Renaissance personality who was at the same time a physician, a poet, a physicist, an astronomer, and a pathologist. He is best known for his medical poem on syphillis, *Syphilis sive morbus gallicus* (Venice, 1530).[4] In this poem he coined the name of the disease and stresses its venereal cause. More important, however, is his treatise on contagion which was published in 1546. Here we find the first clear statement concerning the existence of microorganisms (*seminaria contagionum*), capable of reproduction in an appropriate media. To be sure, Fracastoro did not think of these imperceptible particles whose existence he divined but could not prove as living organisms (*contagia animata*) but we must consider that his work was done as early as 1530 and without the help of a microscope, in fact centuries before it was even invented. When we consider that Fracastoro worked solely on the basis of logical deduction, we must read in awed admiration his definition of contagion.

> "If we allow ourselves to sketch a sort of tentative definition of contagion, we shall define it as: A certain precisely similar corruption which develops in the substance of a combination, passes from one thing to another, and is originally caused by infection of the imperceptible particles.
>
> "In what follows they are called [*seminaria contagionum*, seeds or] 'germs of contagion.'
>
> "There are, it seems, three fundamentally different types of contagion: the first infects by direct contact only; the second does the same but in addition, leaves fomes [fomites], and this contagion may spread by means of that fomes [fomites]—for instance, scabies, phthisis, bald spots, elephantiasis and the like. By fomes I mean clothes, wooden objects, and things of that sort, which though not themselves corrupted can, nevertheless, preserve the original germs of the contagion and infect by means of these; third, there is a kind of contagion which is transmitted not only by direct contact or by fomes as intermediary, but also infects at a distance; for example, pestilent fevers, phthisis, certain kinds of ophthalmia, exanthemata of the kind called variolae, and the like. These different contagions seem to obey a certain law."

It is not surprising that so revolutionary a doctrine failed to catch the imagination of Fracastoro's contemporaries. Indeed, it altogether failed to make a decisive impact on medicine until the 19th century, when the theory of microorganism could be substantiated by scientific measurements and apparatus.

Instead, the medical scientists of the centuries that followed the Renaissance persisted in the search for general laws by which to explain the phenomenon of health and disease. In keeping with the scientific movements of the 17th century, the interest of the physicians was drawn either toward the mathematical and physical discoveries of men such as Copernicus, Kepler, Galileo and Newton or toward the work of chemists such as Boyle, Willis and Mayow. Depending on the bent of their interest, they began to explain all bodily function and dysfunction either on mathematical or chemical principles and became known as Iatro- (from the Greek *iatros* = physician) physicists (also known as Iatromathematicians) or as Iatro-chemists.

THE "SENSITIVE SOUL" THEORY OF DISEASE

As was to be expected, these two materialistic and mechanistic theories gave rise to a third, equally speculative but much more abstract, school of thought which began as "animism" and ended as "vitalism". It was conceived by Georg Ernst Stahl (1660–1734), a German who saw the "sensitive soul" as a source of all vital phenomena. Disease was a disturbance of the vital functions caused by the faulty activity of the soul. In fact, Stahl himself was a victim of this: he died in deep melancholia.

The idea of the soul as the source of life, as a regulator of physical function, and as a cause of pathological processes was immensely appealing to Stahl's contemporaries and successors. This idea can also be found in the writings of Barthez (1743–1806) of Montpellier, who coined the term "vital principle." It can also be found in the *élan vital*, by the philosopher Henri Bergson.

Even in the writings of Marie-Francois Xavier Bichat (1771–1802) this principle can be found. Bichat was the creator of descriptive anatomy and the founder of the field of histology. He examined the tissues of the body, unaided by the microscope, and defined 21 varieties of tissue. So far, he was a pure scientist, but then he concluded that each of the 21 tissues had its own specific vital property which made the tissue viable and gave it its specific character. Bichat, like the vitalists before him, regarded disease as an alteration of vital properties or principles. His definition of life, from which scientists still take an answer today, was "the sum of forces that resist death."

Perhaps it was not too astonishing that the somewhat mystic idea of vitalism persisted longest in Germany and had its most recent representative in the person of Hans Driesch in the early 20th century.

Vitalism, of course, is in conflict with science, with its search for measurable and demonstrable facts. Therefore, there is now no patience with or room for immeasurable or undemonstrable functions of the soul. Hence, the pendulum swings back to a more materialistic attitude toward the concept of disease. With the rise of chemistry and biochemistry, new concepts of disease came alive which are strongly remindful of the Iatrochemist of the 17th century who attempted to explain all physiology and pathology on chemical principles. And with the rise of physics and biophysics, we are again reminded of the Iatrophysicists of the 17th century.

However, there is one branch of medicine which is never able to dispense with the activities of the soul—and that is psychiatry. Stahl, the 18th century founder of vitalism, was also one of the early advocates of psychotherapy. He made striking observations of the effect of the mind upon the body, and his theory of the distraught psyche as a cause of disease contains more than a germ of Freud's teachings.

But even this sketchy outline of the history of the concepts of disease must make it evident that concepts rarely persist too long and that none of them ever remain unchallenged. Thus, even psychiatry, which deals with the psyche, the soul itself, is not left unshaken in its adherence to vitalist thought. Recent events in drug therapy have even brought the study of the treatment of the soul into the realm of the biochemist.

As an historian, I cannot project the history of the future. As a scholar, I cannot even venture to guess what concepts of disease are yet to arise. It is certain, however, that even our increasing knowledge of individual disease and our recognition of disease entities which have been unrecognized during the first two millennia of medical history, will not end the quest for the ultimate concepts of disease.

There will always be a search for an answer to all ills—perhaps in the hope that one day one school of thought will find the one true concept that has power over all disease.

REFERENCES

1. Hippocrates: Epidemics I (in Hippocrates with an English translation by W.H.S. Jones), Harvard University Press, Cambridge, 1948. Vol. I, pp. 147–149.
2. Edelstein, Emma J., and Edelstein, Ludwig: Asclepius, 2 vols., the Johns Hopkins Press, Baltimore, 1945.
3. Hippocrates, loc. cit., Vol. II. pp. 139–141.
4. Malleus Maleficarum, transl. with an Introduction, Bibliography and Notes by the Rev. Montague Summers, [Bungay, Suffolk], John Rodker, Publisher, 1928.
5. Hieronimi Fracastorii de Contagione.... Translation and Notes by Wilmer Cave Wright, G.P. Putnam and Sons, New York, 1930.
6. Fracastoro: Syphilis or the French Disease, with a Translation, Notes, and Appendix by Heneage Wynne-Finch, William Heinemann, London, 1935.
7. Bichat, Xavier: Recherches sur la vie et le mort, Paris, 1800, p. 1.
8. Garrison, Fielding H.: An Introduction to the History of Medicine, 4th Ed., W.B. Saunders Co., Philadelphia, 1929, p. 313.

2.9

Some Basic Explanations of Disease: An Historian's Viewpoint

Lester S. King

At the age of three or four a child begins to ask the question, "Why?" Insofar as we can think our way into the mind of a child, we might say that he is trying to understand the world around him and meets with puzzles that he cannot resolve. He is seeking an explanation. This word derives from the Latin *planus*, which means "flat" or "smooth." Explanation renders smooth that which formerly had been rough or uneven. Before a person seeks an explanation he must be aware of something rough or uneven, something troublesome in the flow of experience. The explanation, when accepted, removes that rough spot, and renders the flow of experience once more smooth.

Quite obviously, people vary in the degree to which they actively seek explanations, or, differently phrased, people vary in their sensitivity to rough spots. We do not need to talk about the princess and the pea, but I would offer the example of two men who may examine a knife edge that seems reasonably sharp. One looks at it with the naked eye and is quite satisfied, but the other examines the knife under a microscope, to find that the apparently smooth blade really has a jagged roughness. He wants to sharpen it further to get out the microscopic nicks not perceptible to the naked eye. One man is easily satisfied, the other actively hunts for irregularities that the first one misses. To transpose the metaphor we could say that the one has more curiosity and that he demands more detailed and far-reaching explanation than his less sensitive fellow. Those who are exquisitely sensitive to irregularity and unevenness are the philosophers and scientists. They are the ones for whom the world is full of puzzles. They are the ones who, in Browning's words

> ...welcome each rebuff
> That turns earth's smoothness rough,

and then they try to re-establish an intellectual smoothness. To do so they find explanations.

Why are some persons more curious than others and why does a given answer satisfy one person but not another? These questions involve the very fabric of intellectual life, but their exploration lies beyond the scope of the present analysis. More important for us is the distinction between the philosopher and the historian. Both deal with problems of explanation, but there are certain crucial differences between the two approaches, and these must be clarified if we want to avoid confusion.

In philosophy explanation is a complex process whose meaning many thinkers have tried to analyze and expound. Especially active in this regard have been the philosophers concerned with logic and the conceptual foundations of science.[1] These thinkers have sought criteria that, if fulfilled, would qualify an explanation as true or valid. They define what conditions must be satisfied for an explanation to be correct.

Historians of science have also touched upon the subtleties involved, but to a lesser degree and from a quite different viewpoint. Whereas the philosophers have sought the true meaning of explanation and the way to distinguish the true from the false, the historian tries to find out what past thinkers have offered as explanations. He is not concerned whether a given explanation is in fact true, but he tries to analyze the internal and external factors that led a particular writer to offer a particular theory as an explanation. And, in addition, the historian seeks the relation between an explanatory theory and any rival theory that succeeded it. Historians thus deal with the temporal sequence of theories and not with the intrinsic truth or error of any one of them.

The philosophers of science who study the problems of explanation have concerned themselves largely with physics and the physical sciences, especially as these have developed since the middle of the 19th century, and have for the most part paid relatively little attention to the biological sciences. To be sure, Darwin and the post-Darwinian concepts have had a good share of attention, but the biology of an earlier period—and this includes medicine—has been largely ignored. Yet the history of medicine furnishes a rich field for the study of explanation as a process and its relation to the history of ideas.

I

Explanations can vary in complexity, generality, and degree of systematization. I want first to discuss two explanatory theories of maximum generality, so general, indeed, that either of them may serve as a basic philosophy. I identify them by the two opposing terms, "supernatural," and "natural," representing concepts of ancient lineage. The two terms imply an opposition such that either is meaningless without the other, like the terms "up" and "down" or "in" and "out." Nevertheless, the basic ideas of each can be understood without circularity.

The term "supernatural" implies a personal will that brings about a specific event. This personal will belongs to some being of great power—or at least, much greater power than that possessed by mere man. This personal being, whose will operates in a particular case, is ordinarily called a god.

I want to avoid getting embroiled in the more general category of "animism," and for the purpose of this presentation I will offer a concrete example that involves a religious formulation, namely, the mature religious system that we find in Homer. We can see how this formulation serves to explain disease.

Let us refer to the beginning of the *Iliad.* Agamemnon, leader of the Greeks, had taken captive a beautiful Theban maiden whose father, Chryses, was a priest of Apollo. The father, vainly trying to get the release of his daughter, received only rebuffs from Agamemnon. Thereupon, Chryses, hoping to rescue his daughter, prayed to Apollo to wreak vengeance on the Greeks. In answer to the prayer Apollo let fly his arrows and afflicted the Grecian host with a grievous pestilence, affecting both animals and men. The Greeks, in despair, sought counsel from their own priests. A soothsayer indicated that the cause of the pestilence was Apollo's anger at Agamemnon. After complicated bickering and bitter quarrels among the Greeks, the captive girl was returned to her father and appropriate sacrifices made to Apollo, in expiation. Chryses then prayed again to Apollo who, satisfied, then removed the pestilence.

This incident can exemplify a supernatural explanation. The crucial feature is that a personal being, much more powerful than man, can by volition change the course of phenomena. By an act of will the god can bring about events that without his express intent would not have happened.

Equally important, the will of the god can be influenced by appropriate human behavior such as prayer or sacrifice. As a corollary, we may infer that the divine agent, although vastly more powerful than man, acts from motives comparable to those of man. A further corollary points to a divine inconstancy. In a given situation the god may or may not take action, and if he takes action at one time, we cannot be sure that he will do so again a second time. Divine behavior depends only in part on external events, but as much or more on divine motives that may lie far beyond human comprehension. Some men, for example, can influence the divine will more than others. But in any case there is a lack of constancy.

The view that disease has a "natural" causation contrasts strongly with the preceding view. This contrast we find sharply indicated in the Hippocratic text, "The Sacred Disease." Hippocrates—and I use that name regardless of who actually wrote the treatise—declared that this disease, epilepsy, is not "any more divine or more sacred than other diseases, but has a natural cause."[2]

According to Hippocrates, those practitioners who alleged a divine origin to epilepsy were unable to understand the disease and were comparable to faith healers and quacks who cloaked their own ignorance under a divine attribution. These charlatans prescribed their remedies in the same way. The Hippocratic text does not reject the gods but denies that the various symptoms can be attributed to gods or that special healers, by magical rites, sacrifices, and incantations, can cure the disease.

Instead, Hippocrates held that epilepsy is like all other diseases and has a natural causation. Each disease has its own nature, its own character, which is intelligible and subject to investigation. Hippocrates analyzed the physiological or, as we might say today, its pathophysiological basis—the chain of physiological events that lead to a seizure. His formulation he couched in terms of the then prevailing humoral theory which, in modern terms, was wrong in virtually every respect. But this is not important for our purposes. The important aspect was his emphasis on nature.

This term, of course, is kaleidoscopic in its meanings. For the present context I would stress certain selected aspects—that the phenomena of disease are regular and predictable, not affected by capricious volition of divine beings, but uniform, intelligible, and dependable. Phenomena can be studied, their behavior formulated into generalizations. To use terms that arose much later, we can perhaps speak of "uniformity of nature" and "natural law." In contrast, belief in the personal action of gods provided no uniformity and permitted no generalizations. The investigation of nature that Hippocrates so clearly grasped was the method of science. It was one method of total explanation.

II

The conflict between these alternative methods of explanation, namely, between what is "natural" and what is "supernatural," has persisted throughout all of intellectual history. For our purposes I want to jump to the end of the 17th century. The polytheism of Homer had been replaced by Christianity whose concept of a single all-powerful God was elaborated into a complex theological system. In contrast, the classical atomism of Democritus and Epicurus had revived in the 17th century and gradually superseded the Aristotelian philosophy that had dominated scientific inquiry. In the resurgent philosophy, material particles, in motion, undergoing various combinations and recombinations, served as the basic stuff for creating explanatory theories. But the existence of the immaterial still remained dominant in its own sphere. God was immaterial, so was the soul and the mind of man, and as we shall see, so was the devil.

In the course of the 17th century what we call the mechanical philosophy served as the major explanatory theory for various aspects of experience, and firmly established the significance of "nature" and "natural" explanations.

Any detailed approach would be out of place in the present exposition and I will content myself with some references to Robert Boyle. In his treatise, "A free Inquiry into the received Notion of Nature,"[3] he offered a series of analyses showing the extreme complexity of the term "Nature" and the various meanings that had accrued to it. He discussed especially the relations between nature and God—between the material and the immaterial. Boyle can also serve as the spokesman for the dominant thinking of the century.

His definition, offered rather tentatively and discursively, declares nature to be "the aggregate of the bodies, that make up the world"; and that these bodies "are enabled to act upon, and fitted to suffer from one another, according to the settled laws of motion"; and furthermore the laws of motion "are prescribed by the Author of things," that is, God.[4] His discussion contains three essential features. First, that nature involves the corporeal universe, made up of matter in motion; second, that these motions proceed according to definite laws; and third, that these laws were established by God who, of course, is immaterial and quite distinct from the material universe.

Boyle made quite clear that nature in his sense is not a separate being; not an *ens* in the scholastic sense; not a demiurge or subordinate deity; not an agent or director; not a being with wisdom, skill, or power.[5] Instead, nature is compared to a machine, like the familiar clockwork mechanism, whose modes of action and behavior were established by the divine artificer. The glory and power of God were thus preserved and so too the concept of "supernatural."

Ordinary experience—and I must stress the word "ordinary"—fell into the category of nature. Nature as an explanatory theory referred events to material particles in motion and therefore was mechanistic, lawful, subject to scientific investigation. But what of "extraordinary" experience—that is, events that seem not to conform to the patterns of natural laws, events that apparently run directly counter to the ordinary predictability and regularity that govern the rest of nature? Such events might be considered miracles. The sharp distinction between God and nature provided a ready explanation. God, the all powerful creator who established the laws of nature, can suspend these laws whenever he wishes. God is above nature, truly supernatural, and his miracles are supernatural events. A miracle must be explained not by natural law but by the specific will of God that upset these laws. In the 17th century no religious person questioned the genuine existence of miracles or their supernatural explanation.

God is good, and miracles, expressing his special will, are beneficial. But many extraordinary events could occur that, far from being beneficial, might be positively harmful or degrading. Various witnesses attested such alleged events as the transformation of humans into animals and back again, the calling up of spirits from the dead, the transportation of bodies through the air, the prevision of future events, the possession of knowledge that could not come by any natural means, the misfortunes that sometimes overtake the virtuous and seem to result from a personal malevolence—these and innumerable other events all seemed to violate the known laws of nature.

The orthodox explanation attributed such events to the will of a supernatural agent, not God but the devil. God is beneficent, the devil malevolent. The devil supposedly acted through the agency of certain humans called witches and warlocks, and in the 15th, 16th, and 17th centuries there occurred that intense persecution of witches that forms such an important part of intellectual history.

Explanatory theories that involved the devil and witchcraft collided with the explanatory theories of science and "natural" causation. But the persecutions that swept over Western Europe and the New World had aroused not only the passions of man but also his critical faculties. The growth of science strengthened the hand of those who wanted to apply "natural" explanations to phenomena. Perhaps the events attributed to witches really had a natural explanation.

By the end of the 17th century the witchcraft persecutions had diminished in Europe, even if not in Massachusetts, but the theoretical implications of alleged witchcraft and the relationships to scientific inquiry still needed resolution. Such an attempt at resolution we find in a little known document, published in 1703 by one of the outstanding physicians of the century.

III

In the 17th and 18th centuries the degree of doctor of medicine ordinarily required a dissertation. Customarily the professor wrote the dissertation and the student defended it in public disputation. These dissertations were included in the *Opera Omnia* of the professor. In this instance the professor was Friedrich Hoffmann who, with Boerhaave and Stahl, dominated medicine in the early 18th century. The dissertation bears the title "De Potentia Diaboli in Corpore,"[6] and deals quite specifically with the problems of explaining particular events and deciding what might be attributed to the supernatural powers of the devil and what to the activities of nature.

Concerning the existence of the devil there was no question. Hoffman, like most intellectual leaders of the period, believed in God as beneficent and omnipotent, and also in the devil as malevolent but limited in power. What can the devil accomplish? How much can he do and how might he do it? In part, Hoffmann reasoned from definitions, in what is really a scholastic method. God is all powerful. God established nature and its laws and only God could abrogate these laws. The devil cannot negate the works of God. Hence the devil cannot perform miracles.

He cannot bring about events that run counter to the laws of nature. The devil cannot make witches fly through the air, he cannot transform bodies, he cannot bring the dead to life, he cannot create living creatures out of inanimate objects. But if the devil cannot break the laws of nature, he can, so to speak, *bend* them. He can use the laws of nature and direct them for evil purposes.

The metaphysical support for this concept, and the rationale that provides its explanatory force, lie in the concept of intermediate substances. There is latent here a form of neoplatonic doctrine, namely, a scheme of transitions or intermediaries between purely immaterial being and the completely material. How can the devil, for example, who is immaterial, act on body which is material? The answer lay through an intermediate subtle matter or spirit, that is so fine that it shares in the properties of the immaterial, and yet not so fine that it is completely removed from the material world.

In the great world or macrocosm this intermediate substance comprises the air or ether that acts as connecting link between the totally immaterial and the completely material. The devil, who is immaterial, can directly affect the air or ether that is almost immaterial. The air, in turn, brings about changes in the weather and all the phenomena that depend upon the weather (such as, for example, certain plagues and pestilences), and these in turn affect man. When, for example, the devil brings about disturbances in the atmosphere and thereby causes hail or destructive storms, he is not performing miracles. He is only using nature to accomplish evil ends. By his *will* he directs the natural forces to produce harm. He is bending nature, not breaking natural law.

The devil acts on man in analogous fashion. Comparable to air or ether in the great world, there is in man an extremely subtle and delicate fluid, the animal spirits, that mediates action of the nervous system. All sensory impressions, as well as the actions of will that produce voluntary movement, are mediated through this subtle fluid; and the mental activities of intellection and imagination also depend on the subtle spirit.

With this concept everything falls into a neat system. In the great world there is the ether, in man the animal spirits. The devil, by acting on the animal spirits, can affect virtually all mental activity and the behavior of man. By affecting the animal spirits the devil can induce bodily motions such as convulsions, bodily states such as trances, and can distort the imagination to produce various beliefs and illusions.

We might at this point re-examine the original distinction between natural and supernatural explanations. The devil cannot bring about supernatural events in the same sense as God, but the devil can bring about what we may call preternatural events—that is, events that would not have happened without the specific malevolent will that used the laws of nature for its own purposes. The important distinction is not whether we deal with supernature or with nature, but whether we deal with volition or intent on the onc hand, or impersonal "law" on the other.

In one system of explanation the concept of personality represents the critical feature. Personality carries with it the power of volition, of bringing about certain actions through the process of will. With humans this power is sharply limited, but God's will is totally unlimited. The devil, however, seems to be intermediate—his will is more powerful than man's, less powerful than God's. In the present context, "power" means the ability to control those events that comprise nature, understood in the sense as discussed above—that is, an orderly system, obeying the laws that God established and that only God can change or suspend.

A naturalistic explanation, on the other hand, holds that matter and motion are sufficient to explain events, even unusual events, and that non-human volition need not be invoked as an explanatory factor. Yet, the mechanical philosophy—a generalized term for various naturalistic explanations—tried to avoid the pitfall of materialism and atheism. The philosophers who held to mechanistic explanations were careful not to deny the reality of the immaterial—that is, the existence of God and of man's soul and mind. While the mechanical philosophy could readily apply to inanimate objects, plants, lower animals, and much of human physiology, the mind and soul of man were explicitly excepted.[7] The *mens* and *anima* of man, that have played such a dominant role in the history of thought, proved a real stumbling block in the mechanical philosophy.

Terms such as mind, thought, imagination, knowledge, will—concepts that philosophers had wrestled with without ever reaching a consensus—were sufficiently vague that they could be compatible with quite diverse explanatory theories. Did the laws of nature apply to the mind of man? If so, to what extent? totally or only partially? From our 20th century viewpoint we would say that in this area the philosophers simply lacked adequate positive knowledge to reach any reasonable conclusion. But such a statement does not accurately reflect the contemporary viewpoint. Philosophers and philosophically-minded physicians of the early 18th century would certainly have admitted that there is much that they did not know, but they nevertheless did create detailed formulations to cover the problems they faced. We might say that no generation ever appreciates the abyss of ignorance in which it rests, an abyss apparent only to subsequent generations. This applies to 1974 as well as 1703.

In this paper I am interested in the way that alternative explanations gradually get sharpened and better defined. How did medical thinkers deal with such topics as abnormal physical and mental states? How did they evaluate evidence? What was the status of skepticism? The definition of nature? The concepts of divinity? We cannot take up these aspects in a systematic fashion at this time, but they furnish a backdrop for my presentation.

IV

Hoffman's paper attempted to harmonize various factors. Hoffmann was a scientist. He had already published his *Fundamenta Medicinae*,[8] a text that expounded the scientific basis of medicine. His whole doctrine he built on the basis of the mechanical philosophy, and yet he had to take account of other factors prevalent in the intellectual climate. Various mental phenomena, and physical phenomena clearly related to mental states, were calling for explanation. In regard to the problems of demonic influence Hoffman, like a good scientist, did not rest content with generalities but sought specific explanations for specific events. He tried to construct a theory that harmonized with both the mechanical philosophy and the concept of non-human will that could control events. Hoffman tried to harmonize conflicting views. There is no question of a rigid *either . . . or* type of explanation—either purely naturalistic or purely demonic. Rather he tried to explain facts by a synthesis of different theories.

However, when we try to invoke the role of the devil to explain particular facts, we come up against a difficult problem that haunts all explanations, namely, in any individual case, what *are* the facts? In the controversies over witchcraft some writers had accepted as true various reports of alleged remarkable events. Other writers, however, more skeptical, branded the reports as falsehoods and the alleged events as frauds and chicanery. Joseph Glanvill, staunch believer in witchcraft, had defined a witch as one "who can do or seems to do strange things, beyond the known Power or Art and ordinary Nature, by vertue of a confederacy with Evil Spirits."[9] He then added, that these "strange things" were "*really* performed, and were not all Imposture and Delusion." On the other hand, there was abundant evidence of deliberate imposture. Reginald Scot, in 1584, without denying the existence of the devil, gave many examples of proven fraud. He satirized some of the events allegedly due to witchcraft. Thus, if on the farm the cream would not turn into butter, the farmer's wife might blame a witch. But, said Scot, ". . . chearne as long as you list, your butter will not come; especiallie, if either the maids had eaten up the creame; or the goodwife have sold the butter before in the market."[10]

But even if many cases of alleged demonic influence were shown to be fraud and imposture, this did not disprove the power of the devil and the existence of witches. Meric Casaubon forcefully declared, "there is no truth, no nor virtue, but is attended with a counterfeit, often mistaken for the true."[11] And elsewhere he wrote, "let no man . . . discredit the truth or reality of any business that is controverted, because the thing is liable to abuse and imposture . . . For what is it, if well look'd into that is not liable to abuse and imposture?"[12] And Glanvill summed up the situation forcefully, when he declared it is not valid to infer "That because there are some Cheats and

Impostures, that therefore there are no Realities."[13] From particular negative instances a universal negative cannot be logically inferred.[14]

Hoffmann did not take at face value most of the reports that alleged demonic activity, yet these reports were not necessarily fraudulent attempts at imposture. Ground existed intermediate between fact and fraud. Allegations of remarkable phenomena might represent not a deliberate falsehood but a disordered imagination, and the demonic activity might have produced this disorder of imagination. But how?

The answer involves an analysis of the imagination, to determine how much this function was purely naturalistic, consistent with the mechanical philosophy, and how much it might be subject to preternatural will. We must remember that what we now call psychology, as one of the natural sciences, was then in its infancy.

The imagination depends partly on the mind, partly on the body, that is, on the sense organs that receive external impressions. Sensation reaches the mind by intermediation of the animal spirits. Hence the devil, by acting on these spirits, can affect the sensorium and the imagination, and can induce illusions such as attendance at the witches' Sabbath, ecstasies, transmutation into animals, and the like.[15] Such a formulation made a harmonious correlation between imagination, demonic activity, empirical observations, and naturalistic explanations.

If the devil, by affecting the animal spirits, can distort the imagination, why does this happen only in some persons and not in others? There must be some difference in receptivity to the devil's influence and Hoffmann, like any scientist, tried to define these variables. Because he adhered to the main tenets of the mechanical philosophy, he, like most of the early 18th century physicians, relied heavily on the circulation of the blood to provide an explanation. Thus, he declared that persons whose blood is abundant and thick and circulates sluggishly through the cerebral vessels, are more susceptible to the activities of the devil than are those whose blood is thin, motile, and florid. Other factors such as sex, age, diet, and climate also affect the susceptibility to demonic illusion. In France, where people drink wine and engage in intellectual pursuits, there is little talk of witchcraft, but in cold northern regions, and in areas where the diet is harsh—beans, heavy bread, pork—we have many witches and abundant "demonic illusion." Hoffman analyzed various factors but we do not need to repeat details here. Suffice it to emphasize that the devil can affect persons such as witches *only if there is some prior disposition*. The power of the devil is "bound to certain laws, to a certain disposition of the body and the blood."[16] Given this disposition the devil can then exert some dominion by acting on the animal spirits.

But clearly, we must not ascribe to the devil all the delusions of the imagination that occur in every disease or that may result from the use of drugs.[17] On the other hand, we cannot eliminate demonic influence merely because physical factors are requisite and operative. Attacks that have a physical basis are not necessarily due to that cause alone. The physical disturbances can furnish the environment, and the physical defect can offer the *occasion* for the devil to exert his power.[18] This power relates especially to inducing such conditions as convulsions, spasms and violent movements, and states where the disturbance is clearly in the animal spirits.[19] In this regard, the devil can not only increase the force of the animal spirits, as is the case in convulsions, but also diminish the flow of spirits to produce privative states such as deafness or sexual impotence.

Many authors had held that diseases ascribed to demonic origin were due entirely to natural causes. Hoffman was fully aware of this viewpoint. He also referred to the Hippocratic text on epilepsy, the "sacred disease" deemed purely natural. It is a difficult task, said Hoffmann, to distinguish so-called natural diseases having purely physical and mechanical causes from those having "magical" origin. By this he meant diseases that arose from "higher, supernatural and moral [i.e., psychological] causes."[20]

How can we discriminate between these different categories and distinguish one from the other? To help with the differential diagnosis Hoffmann provided seven criteria that to his mind indicated a demonic causation: a sudden attack in a previously healthy man, such that suspicion of poison might arise; the use of blasphemy and obscenity; foreknowledge of the future and of secret events, especially in unlearned persons; knowledge of foreign languages that the affected person had never heard; vast physical strength that greatly surpasses the normal; the excretion or expulsion of various monstrous and heterogeneous objects, such as nails, hair, wood, flint, bones, and teeth; and finally, the failure of established remedies.[21]

V

Although more than 2500 years separated the writings of Homer from those of Friedrich Hoffmann, their attempts at explanation have much in common. Homer tried to explain an epidemic that afflicted the Greeks, Hoffman some disorders of the imagination, especially those affecting certain women known as witches. For both Homer and Hoffmann the explanation involved an act of will—Apollo in the one case, the devil in the other—and without the specific volition the particular events would not have happened. Neither Homer nor Hoffman implied that all diseases of whatever type resulted from some act of will. Hoffman, indeed, was most explicit on this score—most disorders, he emphasized, had a purely natural causation, but certain ailments, in certain individuals, at certain times, could be attributed to demonic activity. The powers of the devil were sharply limited. The devil could not cause any disease whatever but only specific abnormal states. Homer did not discuss any such specific limitations for Apollo but seems to imply that the god might have caused any disease he wished.

Although an act of will serves as "ultimate" explanation, there were important intermediate steps. Apollo implemented his will through his arrows while the devil's will involved a far more complicated process, namely, particles in motion obeying certain mechanical laws, then especially fine particles, called "animal spirits," and finally an immaterial entity called the mind, all in a complex but nevertheless direct chain of connection.

Homer, in attributing disease to the arrows of Apollo, did not offer any details that today would serve as "pathogenesis." Did Apollo's arrows, *by themselves*, convey the disease? Were they the specific disease-causing agent in and for themselves, an agent that Apollo merely directed? Would these arrows have caused the disease if someone else had directed them—if, say, Mercury had stolen them and then shot them in jest?

If we answer these questions affirmatively, then we approach a naturalistic explanation. The alternative holds that the arrows were simply an *ad hoc* agency of Apollo's will which the god could have implemented in many other ways. For example, he might have scattered handfuls of pebbles or sprinkled drops of water, and conveyed the pestilence just as well. Did the potency reside in the object, so that arrows served instead of the bacteria or viruses of a much later era; or did potency reside entirely in the personal will of the preternatural being— in this case, Apollo? Homer did not discuss this point specifically but the general tenor suggests that the arrows did not themselves exert power. All depended on the personal will of Apollo.[22]

With Hoffmann, on the other hand, the pathogenetic mechanisms were sketched out through a chain of events involving natural forces. Sometimes demonic will initiated the sequence that led to disease, but any other event that could have started the causal chain would have produced a similar result. Drugs, for example, might induce similar delusions but on a purely natural basis.

Even though totally incorrect, Hoffmann's schema indicates the formal character of an explanation. Homer's account of the epidemic (and epizootic), wrong as it is, also represents a formally valid explanation and is, I maintain, similar to Hoffmann's. To maintain this position I would offer a brief exposition of the nature of explanation.

Let me add a few additional examples of causal assertions. Thus, (1) Why did Jane lose her temper? *Because* she was upset at failing the test in school. (2) Why did John catch cold? *Because* he went out in the rain without his rubbers. (3) Why is foxglove good for certain kinds of "dropsy"? *Because* it "strengthens" the action of the heart. (4) Why did Job suffer so many misfortunes? *Because* God permitted Satan to afflict him.

In all of these we start with some phenomenon—the *explicandum*—Job's boils, Jane's temper tantrums, Uncle Henry's dropsy, John's coryza, the Homeric pestilence, the trance or convulsions of the witch.

This explicandum I might call "Area 1." When we want to explain it, we enlarge it by adding on a quite different area or, as the logicians call it, a different universe of discourse. This I designate the *explication* and will call it "Area 2." Whether the explication be "factual" or "conceptual" is not important. Area 2 may be simple or complex, factual or conceptual, but the important feature is, that Area 1 and Area 2 should join in a smooth and acceptable fashion. Area 1 and Area 2 enter into an acceptable relationship that satisfies the curiosity of the questioner. If this takes place, Area 1 is explicated by Area 2, and the conjunction of the two areas *is* the explanation. In metaphorically spatial terms we say that the conjunction makes things smooth; the questioner can pass from Area 1 to Area 2 and back with ease and satisfaction. If he cannot do so, then no explanation exists.

There is no requirement that the explication should be "correct," for judgments regarding correctness are relative to historical contexts. It is necessary, however, that there be a smooth transition, and smoothness is a subjective factor.

The historian has the task of mapping out the various areas that I designate as 1 and 2, and analyzing why at certain times men could find the passage from one to the other quite smooth, while at a later time what once seemed smooth has become mountainous and impassable, and is no longer satisfactory as an explanation.

Since all explanations are not equal, we must introduce *value* and distinguish good explanations from bad. And the historian, realizing that evaluation changes with time, must explain—I use the word advisedly—why what seems good at one time seems bad at another.

Obviously this theme has extensive ramifications but at the moment there is no opportunity to follow out the many open pathways. I expect to develop these further in subsequent studies. For the present I must rest with showing some relations of medical history to the problems of explanation.

NOTES

* This study was supported by a grant from the Public Health Service Research Grant LM 01804-01.

1. There is an enormous literature on the philosophical problems of explanation. A few of the major works that have been helpful include C. G. Hempel, *Aspects of Scientific Explanation and Other Essays in the Philosophy of Science* (Glencoe: Free Press, 1965); Georg Henrik von Wright, *Explanation and Understanding* (Ithaca, N. Y.:

Cornell University Press, 1971); Ernest Nagel, *The Structure of Science: Problems in the Logic of Scientific Explanation* (London: Routledge and Kegan Paul, 1971); Karl R. Popper, *The Logic of Scientific Discovery* (London: Hutchinson, 1959); Mary B. Hesse, *Models and Analogies in Science* (Notre Dame, Ind.: University of Notre Dame Press, 1966).

2. *Hippocrates*, with an English translation by W. H. S. Jones, Loeb Library edition, 4 vols. (London: William Heinemann, 1923), II, 139.
3. *The Works of the Honourable Robert Boyle*, ed. by Thomas Birch, 6 vols. [Facsimile edition, London, W. Johnston et al., 1772 (Hildesheim: Georg Olms, 1966), V, 158.
4. Boyle, V, 177.
5. *Ibid.*, pp. 162–165 and *passim*, 175, 191.
6. The original dissertation of 1703 bears, on the title page, "Praeside Friderico Hoffmann... submittit Godofredus Bueching, Halle, Gruner." In Hoffmann's collected works (*Opera Omnia*, in 6 vols. with 2 supplements [11 vols. in all], (Geneva: De Tournes, 1741–1750), the essay appears in vol. V, pp. 94–103, the title is slightly altered to *De Diaboli Potentia in Corpora* and Bueching's name does not appear. The text shows some polishing and stylistic improvements, compared with the original edition. I have taken the quotations from the edition appearing in the *Opera Omnia*.
7. Boyle, V, 166.
8. Friedrich Hoffmann, *Fundamenta Medicinae* [1695], trans. by Lester S. King (London: Macdonald, and New York: American Elsevier, 1971).
9. Joseph Glanvill, *Saducismus Triumphatus, or Full and Plain Evidence Concerning Witches and Apparitions* [1689] (Gainesville, Florida: Scholars' Facsimiles and Reprints, 1966), p. 269.
10. Reginald Scot, *The Discoverie of Witchcraft* [1584] (1930; reprint ed., New York: Dover Publications, 1972), p. 6.
11. Meric Casaubon, *Of Credulity and Incredulity in Things Natural, Civil, and Divine* (London: T. Garthwait, 1668), p. 31.
12. *Ibid.*, pp. 164–5.
13. Glanvill, p. 87.
14. Before we apply an explanatory theory we should be quite clear just what we are trying to explain. To use current jargon, in any given instance what are the "facts" of the case? "Facts"—I must enclose the word in quotation marks—come in bundles and clusters. For a given cluster we may find a satisfactory explanation. But if to that cluster of events we add a few additional facts, we may produce thereby a totally different situation, so that the explanation satisfactory before the addition might not suffice for the newly constituted bundle. The data relevant to witchcraft furnished many obvious examples. To use the illustration that Scot offered almost four centuries ago, if the dairy maid cannot make cream turn into butter, perhaps a malevolent spirit had influenced the result. But if we add the additional fact that the girl had drunk most of the cream before starting to churn, then we have a new situation and we will find some alternative explanation more satisfactory. The problems of explanation, in large part, depend on what cluster of events we try to explain.

15. Hoffmann, *De Diaboli Potentia...*, § 18.
16. *Ibid.*, § 19.
17. *Ibid.*, § 19.
18. § 20
19. § 21.
20. § 24.
21. § 24.
22. In this connection see the discussion in my *The Growth of Medical Thought* (Chicago: University of Chicago Press, 1963), pp. 13–17.

2.10

The Scientific Approach to Disease: Specific Entity and Individual Sickness

Owsei Temkin

I

This paper should perhaps be described as the thoughts of an historian of medicine on a subject that is not, in itself, historical. We are not dealing here with the historical development of the concept, or of the typology, of disease, for which we can refer to a series of competent publications.[1] Nor shall we try to evaluate the interplay of external and internal factors, since this has been done by Mr. Shryock[2] whose comments appear below. Rather we shall discuss some historical illustrations of the role which the notions of specific entity and individual sickness have played in the scientific approach to disease.

The basic situation involved is a perennial one. When a man is ill, that is when he feels dis-ease, he has experiences which are partly his own, partly open to others. This is his individual sickness which in exactly this particular form with all its details will never repeat itself in others or even in himself. But the sick man, his family, and neighbours, the physician (if there is one), all will try to understand what is happening to him. When Job was smitten by Satan he complained:

> ...wearisome nights are appointed to me. When I lie down, I say, When shall I arise, and the night be gone? and I am full of tossings to and fro unto the

[1]Of the very large literature dealing with, or related to, this subject, I name here Emanuel Berghoff, *Entwicklungsgeschichte des Krankheitsbegriffes* (2nd ed., Vienna, 1947); Friedrich Curtius, *Individuum und Krankheit, Grundzüge einer Individualpathologie* (Berlin, 1959); Lester S. King, "What is Disease?", *Philosophy of Science*, XXI (1954) 193–203; Richard Koch, *Die ärztliche Diagnose* (Wiesbaden, 1917); L. J. Rather, "Towards a Philosophical Study of the Idea of Disease," *The Historical Development of Physiological Thought*, ed. Chandler McC. Brooks and Paul F. Cranefield (New York, 1959) 351–73; Walther Riese, *The Conception of Disease, its History, its Versions and its Nature* (New York, 1953). A few additional items will be cited below, with my apologies to the very numerous authors whose publications I am unable to mention.

[2]Richard H. Shryock, "The interplay of social and internal factors in the history of modern medicine," *The Scientific Monthly*, LXXVI (1953) 221–30.

> dawning of the day. My flesh is clothed with worms and clods of dust; my skin is broken, and become loathsome.... When I say, My bed shall comfort me, my couch shall ease my complaint; Then thou searest me with dreams, and terrifiest me through visions: So that my soul chooseth strangling and death rather than my life. I would not live alway: let me alone; for my days are vanity.[1]

This is part of the way in which Job, the sick man, tries to express what he feels, sees, and thinks when being diseased. The narrator of the book puts it more briefly: "Satan... smote Job with sore boils from the sole of his foot unto his crown."[2] This is the diagnosis of a disease: generalized sore boils caused by Satan.

Speaking of 'sickness', or 'illness', or 'disease', we have introduced a conceptual denominator uniting many such individual events. The individual may not think of himself as being ill or dis-eased. By thus labelling him, his friends, physician, or society, have classified his experience. From here on it becomes possible to approach the matter scientifically. But the introduction of the label has also determined the reply. The person's experience has become the sickness of X. Use of the term disease raises the question of the nature of disease. Here we may avail ourselves of the observation of Lord Cohen of Birkenhead that two main ideas have been dominant: disease as an entity that befalls a healthy person, and "disease as a deviation from the normal," where a number of factors have influenced a man so as to make him suffer. To this observation Lord Cohen adds:

> Many terms are used to cover these two concepts—e.g., *ontological*—indicating the independent self-sufficiency of diseases running a regular course and with a natural history of their own, as opposed to the *biographical* or *historical* which records the history of the patient. Other names arise from the founders of the schools of thought which appear to have given these concepts birth—e.g., *Platonic* and *Hippocratic*; from the philosophies from which they are primarily derived—the contrasting *realist* and *nominalist*, *rationalist* and *empirical*, *conventional* and *naturalistic* schools. The names are of little importance. The two notions varying a little in content and occasionally overlapping have persisted, the dominance of the one or the other at different epochs reflecting either the philosophy of the time or the influence and teaching of outstanding personalities.[3]

Without inquiring into the historical emergence of these two ideas which, for brevity's sake, we shall here refer to as the 'ontological' and the 'physio-

---

[1]Job, vii, 3–5 and 13–16.

[2]Ibid. ii, 7.

[3]Henry Cohen, "The evolution of the concept of disease," in *Concepts of Medicine*, ed. Brandon Lush (Oxford, 1960) 160.

logical', I shall make a few comments on their interplay, and this will also lead us to other aspects.

II

Ontologists find themselves hard pressed when asked what exactly they mean by the existence of specific diseases. In the case of 'demoniac possession' the answer is reasonably clear. The demon which has entered a person struggles with his personality: it speaks out of the mouth of the possessed; it makes him commit unusual acts, it inflicts pain which causes the possessed to cry or to wrestle with the demon.[1] Ontologists have, therefore, been suspected of clinging to a demoniac aetiology of disease, even if the demon was replaced by a bacterium. Indeed there are analogies between the demonistic and bacteriological interpretation, at least where bacteriology appears in the crude assumption of a specific micro-organism as *the* cause of the specific disease. In both cases the entrance of a certain living being is made responsible for the disease, and the expulsion or killing of this being is considered the essential part of therapy. In both cases there is a clear-cut difference between health and disease.

But even the extreme bacteriologist of the nineteenth century had to deviate from this ideal of medical ontology. The bacterium might be made responsible for all the symptoms of the disease, yet it could cause the symptoms only by damaging parts or organs of the body or otherwise interfering with their normal functions. The disease was represented by the injured organism which the bacterium had poisoned. With the elimination of crude and one-sided modes of thinking, the bacteriologist had to visualize the relationship between parasite and host as an interaction, and it was this interaction which manifested itself as the disease.

In the history of medical ontology, specific aetiology is not a constitutive element. The ancient Empiricists, a sect founded in the third century B.C., did not believe that nature could be understood, and they rejected aetiological research beyond such evident causes as hunger and cold. They concentrated on "pathognomonic syndromes" as Galen tells us.[2] A Greek author of the sixth century indicates that the Empiricists thought of diseases as species. "Of symptoms," he writes,

> some constitute species of the diseases and definitely appear together with them. The Empiricists call them 'pathognomonic' as characterizing the nature of the

[1] T. K. Oesterreich, *Possession, Demoniacal and Other* (London, 1930).

[2] The passages are conveniently available in Karl Deichgräber, *Die griechische Empirikerschule* (Berlin, 1930), see Index *s.v. syndrome.*

> species (*idea*) of the diseases: for instance, cough, fever, dyspnea, and stabbing pain in pleurisy. Other symptoms, foreign [to the idea of the disease] appear later....[1]

Since the scepticism of the Empiricists regarding the comprehensibility of nature reflects the scepticism of the Academy, as Edelstein has shown,[2] their belief in species of disease as Platonic ideas would not be improbable.

Sydenham, the arch-ontologist of modern times, also disparaged the search for the remote causes of diseases. He claimed that "Nature, in the production of disease, is uniform and consistent; so much so, that for the same disease in different persons the symptoms are for the most part the same..."[3] other hand,

> a disease, however much its cause may be adverse to the human body, is nothing more than an effort of Nature, who strives with might and main to restore the health of the patient by the elimination of the morbific matter.[4]

Put together, this amounts to the definition of diseases as uniform patterns of the organism's attempt to restore its health. The "concatenation of symptoms"[5] is nature's method for the elimination of the peccant matter. This is not very far removed from a very recent statement that "physicians now consider most diseases to be distinct from one another insofar as they represent patterned responses or adaptations to noxious forces in the environment."[6]

The difficulty inherent in the ontological idea of the separate existence of diseases is matched by the difficulty of making the diseases or patterned responses conform to the variety of individual sickness. Sub-divisions that made the distinction between disease and symptom illusory had to be assigned in the nosological schemes of Boissier de Sauvages, Cullen, and Pinel. In the first half of the nineteenth century, pathological anatomy helped to weed out a number of diseases and to secure the position of others. But many contemporary investigators recognized that the anatomical changes, though they might account for a number of clinical symptoms, were products of the disease

---

[1] Stephanus, "Commentarii in priorem Galeni librum therapeuticum ad Glauconem," *Apollonii Citiensis, Stephani, Palladii, Theophili, Meletii, Damascii, Ioannis, aliorum scholia in Hippocratem et Galenum*, ed. F. R. Dietz (Regimontii Prussorum, 1834) I, 233–344 (p. 267).

[2] *Ludwig Edelstein, "Empirie und Skepsis in der griechischen Empirikerschule," Quellen und Studien zur Geschichte der Naturwissenschaften und der Medizin*, III, 4 (1933) 45–53.

[3] *The Works of Thomas Sydenham, M.D.*, trans. R. G. Latham (London, 1848) I, 18.

[4] Ibid. p. 29.

[5] Ibid.

[6] Stewart Wolf, "Disease as a way of life: neural integration in systemic pathology," *Perspectives in Biology and Medicine*, IV (1961) 288–305 (p. 288).

rather than the disease itself.[1] This led to a discussion of the nature of the disease behind anatomical and clinical symptoms. In this discussion ontologists fared badly until bacteriologists were believed to have discovered the source of disease outside the body and geneticists inside it.

The hope that bacteriology would allow a reliable classification on the basis of specific causes, at least in the realm of infectious diseases, also proved doubtful. If this principle were pushed to the logical extreme, there should be as many specific diseases as there are pathogenic organisms, or even strains.

The weakness of a bacteriological definition of specific diseases is shared by the definitions based on other aetiological classifications. There should be as many specific deficiency diseases as there are substances whose absence can affect the body adversely. Finally, there should also be as many hereditary diseases as there are different genes representing abnormal submolecular chemical structures. A person with haemoglobin-C genes, we are informed, will suffer from so-called homozygous haemoglobin-C disease. If he has one haemoglobin-C gene only, while the other is a haemoglobin-S gene (sickle-cell-anemia gene) "he suffers from a disease that has been given the name haemoglobin-C: sickle-cell anemia."[2] Since about twenty kinds of abnormal human haemoglobin are said to exist, the number of combinations and possible 'specific diseases' in this one province seems very large. In short, if based on causative principles such as micro-organisms, absence of nutritive substances, or inherited genes, danger arises lest specific diseases be postulated which have no clinical reality, or, vice versa, that clinically important entities like appendicitis have no logical place in the nosological scheme.

III

The weaknesses of ontology are avoided by the physiological idea of disease. This has been cultivated by Hippocrates and his scientific (in contrast to the purely empirical) successors from Galen to our own times. When we turn to the Hippocratic *Epidemics*, it is true, disease entities are accepted as a matter of course and referred to by names, such as "phthisis," which had probably been in common popular usage. Hippocrates, or whoever the physicians were whom this name connotes, is outstanding for having seen disease as a process in time, not as a mere stationary picture.[3] The book *On the Sacred Disease*, that is epilepsy, is probably the earliest monograph on a disease, describing its pathogenesis, symptoms, pathological physiology, and prognosis. Diseases

---

[1] Knud Faber, *Nosography* (2nd ed., New York, 1930) 53.

[2] Linus Pauling in *Disease and the Advancement of Basic Science*, ed. Henry K. Beecher (Cambridge, Mass., 1960) 3.

[3] Owsei Temkin, "Greek Medicine as science and art," *Isis*, XLIV (1953) 213–25 (p. 223).

have their nature; but they are seen as rooted in the general nature of man. There is neither a studious exclusion of disease entities nor a one-sided concentration on them. In judging diseases we are told to take into account "the peculiar nature of each individual."[1] Most of the patient's activities, mental and physical, are considered, from thoughts and dreams to eructation and flatulence. The list of things to be observed included diseases and symptoms as well as functions and discharges such as respiration and urine. This allows the gathering of a very large number of data in each case. Since the totality of these data will vary from patient to patient, each will have a description of symptoms fitting him only.

But the ancient followers of Hippocrates did not believe that Hippocrates had given them a science of the individual. Galen, the last of the ancient Hippocratics, and Galen's Byzantine successors ended on a sceptical note.[2] They thought Hippocrates right in demanding that the nature of the disease as well as of the individual be studied. The nature of disease was to be found in man's temperament, the structure of his parts, his physiological and his psychological dynamism. Thus the nature of disease was grounded in the nature of man. All men have humours and divers parts and organs; they all digest and possess sensation and mobility. Consequently, they also have diseases in common. But no two men will be completely alike. The individual differences are "ineffable and cannot be subjected to concepts."[3] Therefore, it was concluded, there is no science of the individual, and medicine suffers from a fundamental contradiction: its practice deals with the individual while its theory grasps universals only.[4]

Ancient medicine had a particular reason for this scepticism.[5]. The physician possessed an approximate picture of the behaviour and appearance of healthy individuals.[6] He could compare his patient to this picture of the normal and decide what was "according to nature" (*kata physin*) and what "against nature" (*para physin*). But just because of the physician's strongly individualizing inclination, such a comparison was considered insufficient. For instance, his patient's face might indicate a morbid discolouration. If the patient's colour always had been like this, the finding was meaningless, while in a new patient, the physician had nothing to refer to. It was advisable that the doctor be his patient's friend and know him intimately.[7] Such intimate knowledge was

---

[1]Hippocrates, "Epidemics", I, 10, *The Genuine Works of Hippocrates*, trans. Francis Adams (London, 1849) I, 367.

[2]For the following see Galen, *Ad Glauconem de medendi methodo* I, *I, Opera*, ed. C. G. Kü (Leipzig, 1821 ff.) XI, 1 ff., and the commentary on this work by Stephanus, op. cit.

[3]Stephanus, op. cit. p. 235.

[4]Ibid.

[5]The nature of the medical scepticism of the Hippocratic authors as rooted in their individualistic approach has been brought out by Edelstein, op. cit.

[6]Celsus, *De medicina*, 1, 2, 4.

[7]Ibid., Prooem., 73.

possible in private practice only, and, according to Celsus, where it was impossible, medicine of an inferior kind was practised because it relied on the features common to many diseases:

> For in like manner those who treat cattle and horses, since it is impossible to learn from dumb animals particulars of their complaints, depend only upon common characteristics; so also do foreigners, as they are ignorant of reasoning subtleties, look rather to common characteristics of disease. Again, those who take charge of large hospitals, because they cannot pay full attention to individuals, resort to these common characteristics.[1]

Celsus made this remark in discussing the ancient sect of the Methodists who judged disease according to whether it exhibited a *status strictus*, *laxus*, or *mixtus*. Thessalus, a Methodist of the time of Nero, boasted of teaching medicine to anybody within six months.[2] Methodism was popular in the Roman Empire, and it would be of interest to find out whether it had its social roots among military surgeons and in the latifundia, since such hospitals (*valetudinaria*) as existed in Antiquity were for soldiers and slaves.

Few things mark the chasm between ancient and modern medicine as impressively as does the different character of the hospitals. The ancient hospital, just because it housed many patients, was looked down upon as neglecting individual sickness. The modern hospital, just because it houses many patients, has developed into an institution where individual sickness can be described with some degree of precision.

In the hospitals of the nineteenth century it became possible to observe many cases of the same disease, clinically as well as anatomically, and thus to strengthen the diagnosis of 'diseases'. At the same time, it became possible to establish standards of what was normal, and to elaborate tests which expressed numerical agreement with, or deviation from the norm. The norm here was a value found in a smaller or greater number of healthy persons. Without this norm, measurements were of little avail. The ever lengthening chart of data accumulating in the course of medical examinations, from pulse rate and temperature curve, to X-ray pictures, chemical, physical, bacteriological and immunological tests, mirrors this development which has been traced admirably by Knud Faber for the nineteenth and early twentieth centuries. A modern physician has at his disposal infinitely more objective data concerning particular patient than the Greek doctor could ever dream of. Ophthalmoscope, bronchoscope, etc. allow him a direct view of the conditions of many parts. Experimental medicine enables the physician to interpret his findings so as to translate the language of symptoms and tests into the

---

[1]Ibid., 65; Celsus, *De Medicina*, with an English translation by W. G. Spencer (London, 1935 ff.) I, 35.

[2]Galen, *De sectis ad eos qui introducentur*, VI, refers to Methodists in general, but seems to have Thessalus in mind.

language of physiological processes. Here then is a scientific approach to individual sickness.

Thus it might appear that modern medicine has succeeded where ancient medicine failed. This success is due to giving statistical attention to what is normal and abnormal. The Ancients did not evaluate statistically what was "according to nature" and "contrary" to it. Still, there is a significant parallel between their attempt to explain certain diseases as an imbalance of qualities or humours and our numerical occupation with the normal and abnormal. The parallel can be formulated in the question: what deviation constitutes sickness? We know that 'the normal individual' is a construct, not to be found in nature. Likewise, the Galenists realized that a complete balance of the four humours and their qualities represented an ideal temperament. We allow variations within the normal;[1] the Ancients conceived of temperaments where the predominance of one or the other humour characterized the still healthy organism. But where exactly was, and is, the line to be drawn where imbalance or variation becomes disease?

Galen defined health as a condition "in which we neither suffer pain nor are hindered in the functions of daily life."[2] In as far as this definition is concerned with impeded function, it leads to the equation of disease with *functio laesa*, popular among the academic physiologists of modern times. "The condition of the living body whereby the ability of exercising any one function is abolished, is called disease," writes Boerhaave in his *Institutions*, and he adds the following comment to the word disease: "we correctly define it as 'functio laesa'. . . ."[3] In speaking of the functions, Boerhaave had in mind the traditional natural, vital, and psychic functions, all of which could be diminished to the point of disappearance.

But, if the ontologist was rightly challenged by the demand that disease must be understandable as a process of life, the physiologist was challenged to show cause why the endless variations of form and gradations of function should somewhere admit classification as healthy and diseased.[4] It is a truism to designate 'health' and 'disease' as medical categories. It is not easy to decide whether these categories themselves, though relating to biological phenomena, still belong in biology. Following in the footsteps of Broussais,[5] the young Virchow referred to disease as life under changed circumstances. But Virchow himself later admitted that a man in prison also lived under

---

[1]John A. Ryle, "The meaning of normal," *Concepts of Medicine*, op. cit. pp. 137–49.

[2]Galen, *De sanitate tuenda*, I, 5.

[3]Hermann Boerhaave, *Praelectiones academicae in proprias institutiones rei medicae*, ed. Albertus Haller (Turin, 1742 ff.) V, 4 and 10.

[4]This problem has been dealt with very lucidly by G. W. Pickering, "The concept of essential hypertension," *Concepts of Medicine*, op. cit. pp. 170–6.

[5]Erwin H. Ackerknecht, *Rudolf Virchow* (Madison, 1953) 50–1.

changed circumstances without therefore necessarily being ill.[1] The answer may depend on the biologist's philosophical orientation. If he excludes all teleology, he may, with Ricker, believe that health and disease are not scientific terms.[2] If he does not mind using teleological notions, he may find it pertinent to pay attention to those states where nature fails in two of its main aims, as Galen had them, assurance of the life of the individual and of the species.[3]

But disease does not necessarily threaten life. To supplement his teleological biology, Galen added nature's aim of assuring a "good life."[4] A blind man might be able to live and to have progeny, yet he would not live well. But there are no limits to the "good life." For man, the good life extends far into his mental and social well being. This is best illustrated by Galen's reference to pain in his definition of health and in his explanation of the functions of daily life as our ability "to take part in government, to bathe, drink, and eat, and do the other things we want."[5] Participation in government and frequenting the bath were activities of the member of the ancient city state. In another civilization, different functions might be required for health, or, if absent, mark disease.

Examples for this are most easily adduced from the field of mental abnormalities. Theologians of the Renaissance persecuted witches as confederates of the devil, and the worldly authorities executed them because of their alleged danger to society. The defence of witches could claim that the devil was powerless to bring about the evil deeds ascribed to witches, themselves victims of the devil who caused their illusions. This argument was a theological one,[6] which explains the accusation made against Weyer, the defender of witches, that he meddled in things which were none of his, the physician's, concern. Instead of being victims of Satan, witches could be declared to suffer from a natural disease, preferably hysteria. Similarly, convulsions, often taken as demonstrations of demoniac possession or of divine enthusiasm, were diagnosed as *grande hystérie* by the school of Charcot.[7]

In contrast, Charcot's own time tended to refuse recognition to disease where it existed. It is not so very long ago that people who felt ill, or who suspected illness, would consult a physician to be told after a thorough

---

[1]Virchow, "Über die heutige stellung der Pathologie," in Karl Sudhoff, *Rudolf Virchow und die Deutschen Naturforscherversammlungen* (Leipzig, 1922) 77–97 (p. 91); see also Paul Diepgen, "Die Universalität von Rudolf Virchows Lebenswerk", *Virchows Archiv.*, CCCXXII (1952) 221–32 (p. 228).

[2]Ricker distinguishes between medical and scientific thinking; cf. also Claudius F. Mayer, *"Metaphysical trends in modern pathology," Bulletin of the History of Medicine*, XXVI (1952) 70–81.

[3]Galen, *De usu partium*, VI, 7; ed. G. Helmreich (Leipzig, 1907) I, 318.

[4]Ibid: *τὸ καλῶς ζῆν*.

[5]Galen, *De sanitate tuenda*, I, 5.

[6]Gregory Zilboorg, *The Medical Man and the Witch During the Renaissance* (Baltimore, 1935) 117.

[7]Owsei Temkin, *The Falling Sickness* (Baltimore, 1945) 321.

physical examination that there was nothing wrong with them, and that they could go home. Thomas Huxley who suffered from "the blue devils and funk" could not make out what it was and suggested "liver."[1] Disease in the second half of the nineteenth century meant somatic disease, if one disregarded the frank psychoses. This attitude reflected the prevailing materialistic philosophy which Huxley himself had helped to shape. It also reflected the conviction that there is a science of disease separable from medicine as the art of healing. Men of this persuasion might have much human sympathy for the sick, but they were not easily influenced in their scientific work by vague subjective complaints. A whole realm of disease was in danger of losing the right to existence because of the dissociation between the sick person's complaint and the physician's philosophical outlook.

Functio laesa is not a self-explanatory definition of disease in man. The ontologist avoids this difficulty by accepting entities which are set apart from health or 'normal' functioning. However he may define disease, it is something strange to man in his ordinary life: it enters or befalls him. In this respect, the ontologist's weakness is also his strength. There is a tendency in ontology to consider disease entities as persistent and to corroborate the specific nature of a disease by tracing its existence through the ages. Bretonneau said of diphtheria, "because during a long series of centuries it remained so constantly the same that in each of the epochs where it appeared it was recognized in the admirable description of Aretaeus,"[2] giving this among the arguments for diphtheria as a specific affection. Since, according to Charcot, *grande hystérie* was "a perfectly well characterized morbid entity," his school tried to prove its existence long before its scientific discovery.[3]

The ontological bias of the perennial existence of the specific diseases can express itself moreover in a reluctance to admit the appearance of new diseases or the existence of specific diseases during a short period of time. The plague of Thucydides has challenged diagnostic acumen and has been variously interpreted as plague, smallpox, typhus, measles. Without denying the possibility of identifying it with some disease of our modern nosological catalogue, I still fail to see proof of the necessity. Similarly, the "sweating sickness" which appeared in epidemic waves, chiefly in England, between 1485 and 1551, is but reluctantly acknowledged as a disease unknown to modern nosology.

The ontologist thus avoids a difficulty which the radical physiologist must face. The difference in attitude between the two is expressed in the encounter

---

[1] Leonard Huxley, *Life and Letters of Thomas Henry Huxley* (New York, 1901) II, 112–13.

[2] Pierre-Fidèle Bretonneau, *Traités de la dothinentérie et de la spécificité*, publiés, etc. par le Dr. Louis Dubreuil-Chambardel (Paris, 1922) 309.

[3] Cf. above, p. 639, n. 1.

between Michel Peter and Pasteur as told by René Dubos. Peter claimed that "Disease is in us, of us, by us," whereas

> Pasteur emphasized that contagion and disease could be the expression of the living processes of foreign microbial parasites, introduced from the outside, descending from parents identical to themselves, and incapable of being generated *de novo*.[1]

Pasteur made it clear that contagious disease was the expression of a foreign life. But if disease has to be looked for in our own nature it has to be accounted for differently. If we attribute it to genes we still have recourse to ontology, as I indicated previously, an 'internal' ontological orientation in contrast to the external of the bacteriologist. It is probably neither possible nor advisable to renounce ontology completely. The wisdom of Hippocrates documents itself in accepting such popular disease entities as were known, rather than denouncing them. The danger which the physiologist faces, as well as the consequences which may ensue, are illustrated by Freud's work—if it is permissible to broaden the term physiology so as to admit his psychological method.

In the meaning of our context, Freud offered a physiological explanation of neuroses by explaining them as the result of a reaction between psychic urges and restriction imposed upon them. He believed himself to be dealing with psychological phenomena like the one symbolized as the Oedipus complex, necessarily engendered in all civilized human beings. This being the case, everybody was fundamentally neurotic, the intensity and particular turn of the neurosis depending on the experiences of the individual's life. Psycho-analysis thus succumbed to the danger of what the Greeks called *aeipatheia*, perpetual illness.

Psycho-analysis insisted upon a minute scrutiny of the patient's life in order to find, and to make conscious, those experiences with which the patient had been unable to cope successfully. This meant that the disease was not due to some accident. More than others, Freud and his followers leaned on the biographical approach, on the detailed case history of the patient. Finally, as the name indicates, psycho-analysis originated from Freud's therapeutic activity. Freud gained his insight into neuroses while treating patients. Since the contact between patient and psycho-analyst invariably involved an emotional engagement (on the patient's side at least), the psycho-analysis had to affect the patient. Thereby Freud ran counter to one of the scientific ideals of his time: the study of an object without interfering with it.

Whatever the merits of psycho-analysis may be, I believe that it was consistent (though possibly wrong) in imputing neurosis to everybody, looking

---

[1]René J. Dubos, *Louis Pasteur, Free Lance of Science* (Boston, 1950) 246.

for the vicissitudes of man's neurosis in his biography, making the judgment of manifest disease dependent on the patient's inability to cope with the aims of society or of himself, and avoiding a gulf between the diagnostic and therapeutic activity of the physician who deals with individual sickness.

Consistency is not necessarily a virtue, but it has the advantage of laying bare what may otherwise pass unnoticed. I believe that Freud elucidated the part played by the case history and therapy in the comprehension of individual sickness.[1]

IV

Case histories form one of the glories of Hippocratic medicine; they mark the appearance of the form by which the physician tries to deal with an individual illness. The Hippocratic case histories are remarkable for what they contain, a passionless description of the symptoms and outcome of the case, and for what they largely lack, details as to the patient's diet and therapy.

In course of time, the case history changed, especially with the introduction of the new clinical teaching methods in Leyden. The diagnosis, usually meaning a disease entity, was incorporated, the treatment was registered, and, if available, a post mortem report was added in cases with fatal outcome. Detailed case histories emanated from the hospitals of the Old Vienna School of the eighteenth century. In the nineteenth century, a separation between the subjective history of the patient and the objective examination by the physician became noticeable. The objective signs of percussion and auscultation were the early core of the examination; temperature curves, and the results of the ever increasing tests and special examinations, followed. Thus the case history has come to incorporate all the data obtained through the scientific progress of medicine.[2]

As the member of a profession, the physician has used case histories to contribute to the spread or advance of medical knowledge. This, probably, was already the function of the Hippocratic case histories. All cases that are unusual because of the patient's illness, or its outcome, or the treatment employed, reveal new possibilities regarding human disease. The case history therefore has played a great role in the history of medicine. As casuistic material in combination with the post mortem protocol, it led to the rise of pathological anatomy for reasons which become clearer when this development is compared with the rise of normal anatomy.

[1]In thus summarily dealing with Freud and psycho-analysis, I am conscious of some degree of historical and material oversimplification for the sake of brevity.

[2]On the history of the case history see: Pedro Lain Entralgo, *La historia clinica* (Madrid, 1950); Walther Riese, "The structure of the clinical history," *Bull. Hist. Med.* XVI (1944) 437–49; O. Temkin, "Studien zum 'Sinn'—Begriff in der Medizin," *Kyklos*, II (1929) 43–59.

The study of anatomy as based on dissection did not derive from the opening of many bodies. Both Galen and Vesalius described the structure of *the* body (of animal or man). They were aware of variations which, it is true, could be established as such by repeated autopsies only. Yet it is fair to say that both expected an immediate insight into the body, as God or nature had willed it, that is into the norm. This insight was then cleared by discounting individual variations or morbid changes.[1]

Although some of the ancient physicians had the idea of a pathological anatomy, pathological anatomy, as we know it, began with the medieval *anatomia privata*. This was a dissection performed in an individual case to establish the cause of death, especially if foul play was suspected. It differed from the *anatomia publica* where the fabric of man's body was demonstrated to a large audience. Benivieni's little book of 1507 from which we conventionally date the literary beginning of pathological anatomy, was named significantly: "On Some Hidden and Singular (*mirandis*) Causes of Diseases and Cures," the causes being revealed by the autopsy. Bonet's *Sepulchretum* of 1679 was a huge collection of casuistic material culled from the literature. Morgagni's *De sedibus et causis morborum* was to be a revised edition of Bonet's *Sepulchretum*, and the work as it finally emerged in 1761 still shows its descent. Its backbone is the hundreds of case histories elucidated by post mortem findings. It differs from its predecessors by having overcome the limitation of the singular and remarkable. It systematically applies the method to diseases in all parts of the body, *a capite ad calcem*, and tries to draw generally valid inferences. Thereby it marked the beginning of something new. After Morgagni, it became more convenient to envisage the pathological anatomy of disease processes, a trend that culminated in Rokitansky's *Manual* of the 1840's. Here too a huge casuistic material was utilized, yet it was integrated into a work which dealt with disease entities.[2]

It is not immediately clear why the anatomical interpretation of disease had to follow the road from case histories to disease entities. The idea of an anatomical substratum of disease was not unheard of. Pneumonia and pleurisy, as their names indicate, were differentiated by ancient authors according to the organs involved.[3] Dysentery was described by Aretaeus as due to ulcers of the intestine.[4] Medieval textbooks names quite a number of diseases. Conceivably, one might have started out by describing the anatomy of disease after disease, following the example of normal anatomy. One or a very few cases should have sufficed to give an insight into the particular

---

[1]William L. Straus, jr. and O. Temkin, "Vesalius and the problem of variability", *Bull. Hist. Med.* XIV (1943) 609–33.

[2]Strictly speaking it deals with the pathological anatomy of tissues and organs.

[3]Cf. Galen, *Opera*, ed. Kühn, op. cit. XI, 77.

[4]Aretaeus, *The Extant Works*, ed. and trans. Francis Adams (London, 1856) 353.

disease; nor is it likely that such private anatomies would have met with external obstacles. The obstacles were of a different nature. It was assumed that diseases were sufficiently known, so that only the unusual was worth investigating. Moreover, the traditional disease entities were not sufficiently suited to such an anatomical analysis.

The role of the case history in a particular phase of medical development elucidates further the notion of the abnormal in medicine. Even if expressed in numerical values it retains the character of something that is not as nature or man would have it. To bring a person back to normal, therefore, means to bring him back to where he should be. But where should he be?

To this query the old formula of complete curative success gave a superb answer: *in integrum restitutus est*, he has been restored to his former condition. The formula leaves it undecided whether this connotes health or simply the state before the physician was called in. In either case the answer is a doubtful one; treatment may have made the patient 'a changed person' as the saying goes. The sickness which brought the patient to the doctor may even reveal a lack of previous health, and the cure of a neurotic patient may consist in not restoring him *in integrum*. Each patient's sickness is truly individual in the role it plays in his life; it has a meaning for him. But here where disease melts into the patient's whole life, science finds its limits. In bringing a patient back to health the physician will take as his frame of reference what is commonly considered as health. The patient is cured when he feels well, when his life is not in danger, and when he can safely do what healthy people generally do. This will often require far-reaching adaptations. If a person who was close to death undergoes a religious conversion, this in itself is outside the physician's concern. The physician traditionally is not supposed to judge his patient's morality or to influence his religion.[1] The case history is the form in which the physician links the science, which does not deal with the unique directly, and the patient, who requires attention as an individual. Replete with scientific data and possibly utilized to serve the advance of medical science, the case history documents the physician's art. It is the closest approach to an individual's sickness, yet it does not become the whole life story of a person while sick. Job fell ill and was restored to health and wealth. But the *Book of Job* is not a case history: the 'meaning' of Job's illness is not of medical concern.[2]

V

Nevertheless, the interdependence of treatment and of the idea of disease is

---

[1] O. Temkin, "Medicine and the problem of moral responsibility," *Bull. Hist. Med* XXIII (1949) 1–20.

[2] For arguments against the metaphysical interpretation of sickness by the physician see Curtius, op. cit. and his "Hippokrates und die moderne Medizin," *Tägliche Praxis*, II (1961) 1–19.

a very real one. It is by no means true that treatment is always adapted to the nature of the disease. Treatment can determine how disease should be considered. The rise of pathological anatomy at the turn of the eighteenth to the nineteenth century was stimulated by the growing influence of the surgeons and of their localistic point of view.[1] Ontologists have been inclined to favour the treatment of diseases and to look for possible specifics. Sydenham hoped for plants with specific actions on specific diseases, such as cinchona upon malaria.[2] While localized pathology was favoured by surgeons, specifics were favoured by the apothecaries who liked to sell drugs that promised cures of symptoms, syndromes, or diseases. By contrast, the physician of the physiological school opposed the routine use of standard treatments. At the end of the fifteenth century, Leoniceno warned doctors against trying to cure the French disease with the same medicine in all cases, in imitation of "a bad cobbler who tries to fit everybody with the same shoe."[3]

Similar notions are at the bottom of the maxim to treat the patient, not the disease. This is reinforced by the declaration that only sick individuals exist, that diseases are mere abstractions. Most physicians are likely to subscribe to this declaration, even if they find the abstractions useful. It is not altogether by chance that Hippocrates figures as the author of the case histories of the *Epidemics* and of the Hippocratic *Oath*. There is reason to doubt this authorship, especially that of the *Oath*.[4] But the fact remains that the *Oath* formulates classically the ethics of the doctor-patient relationship. Until not so very long ago, 'medicine' was the domain of the physician who treated patients, privately or in the hospital. The medical sciences too were cultivated by men nearly all of whom were engaged in medical practice. Somewhat over a hundred years ago, a change took place: medical scientists, chiefly professors at German universities, began to separate themselves from practical medical work and to devote themselves 'full time' to anatomy, physiology, or pathology. The change set in at about the same time as the abandonment of the traditional therapy. Therapeutic nihilism and autonomy of the full-time medical scientist are, in my opinion, but two aspects of the same movement. Therapeutic nihilism was a passing phase, while the growth of the basic sciences was accelerated with the development of bacteriology, immunology, and experimental pharmacology, and the increasing alliance with industry. As a result, medicine ceased to be the exclusive domain of the physician who

---

[1] O. Temkin, "The role of surgery in the rise of modern medical thought", *Bull. Hist. Med.* XXV (1951) 248–59.

[2] Sydenham, op. cit. I, 23.

[3] Karl Sudhoff, *The Earliest Printed Literature on Syphilis*, adapted by Charles Singer (Florence, 1925), 172.

[4] Ludwig Edelstein, *The Hippocratic Oath* (Baltimore, 1943).

[5] I have dealt with this matter in more detail in my Josiah Trent Lecture at Duke University, 1960, which now awaits publication.

treated patients. The contributions of the chemist Pasteur were fundamental, as well as symbolic, for the things to come.

Pasteur invented an anti-rabies vaccine the effectiveness of which he tested in dogs. In the scientific part of this discovery the rabies virus and the possibility of counter-acting it were under consideration. But from the practical point of view it was the disease embodying a well-known course with fatal outcome that was to be combated. In the background here was Jenner's discovery of the prevention of smallpox by vaccination with cowpox. In contrast to Jenner, who was a physician, Pasteur was not qualified to vaccinate; the boy Joseph Meister, who had been bitten by a mad dog, was vaccinated by physicians associated with Pasteur. Although the actual treatment, preventive or therapeutic, may still be applied or supervised by the physician, there is behind him a growing organization of persons and institutions who are screened from individual patients, yet work towards the cure and prevention of disease. In the scientific part of their work, 'the disease' may play no role at all; their minds may be occupied with bacteriological, immunological, and chemical details. Yet the work is directed against diseases as the public health officer, rather than the practitioner, sees them. There are laws aimed at preventing smallpox, and Jenner discovered a means of preventing it. Thousands of children are vaccinated against a disease which, at the time, may not show a single sufferer in the country. In all this work and in campaigns to eradicate this or that disease, the picture of the disease as an entity devoid of individual features has a very real existence, though we must leave it to the metaphysician to determine the nature of this particular form of existence.

We began with a denunciation of ontology and end with its reassertion. In between we discussed the strength and weakness of the physiological approach and the case history in which the physician's art comes closest to individual sickness. We would like to draw the inference that in the scientific approach to disease the notions of both specific entity and individual sickness play their roles. The question: does disease exist or are there only sick persons? is an abstract one and, in that form, does not allow a meaningful answer. Disease is not simply either the one or the other. Rather it will be thought of as the circumstances require. The circumstances are represented by the patient, the physician, the public health man, the medical scientist, the pharmaceutical industry, society at large, and last but not least, the disease itself. For our thinking about disease is not only influenced by internal and external factors, it is also determined by the disease situation in which we find ourselves. Sydenham, the ontologist, lived at the time of the great plague of London, and the plague, I understand, has little concern with individual variations. In contrast, the practitioner of our time, who has to deal with degenerative disorders and neuroses demanding much individual attention, may have little use for disease entities. He may be inclined to leave them to the laboratory or the public health man for prevention.[1] With the changing disease situation our thoughts about disease change too. As Hippocrates said, "The art consists in three things—the disease, the patient, and the physician."[2] To the historian's mind, the histories of all three are bound up in the history of the art itself.

---

[1]For concepts of disease in social medicine see Iago Galdston, *The Meaning of Social Medicine* (Cambridge, Mass., 1954) 73 and *passim*.

[2]Hippocrates, *Epidemics* I, Sect. 2, 5, in *Works*, op. cit. I, 360.

Part 3

Disease Versus Values: Sex, Race, Addiction, and Sexual Preference

The pursuit of conceptual clarity regarding the concepts of health and disease is not simply an intellectual exercise. Labeling a condition or state as a disease has had, and continues to have, serious political, economic, and social consequences. If a particular behavior or problem is approached as a matter of health and disease, the medical profession is thereby conceptually licensed to diagnose, treat, and otherwise intervene. It is thus no small matter to the person who uses drugs or who engages in various forms of sexual activity whether such behavior is viewed as indicative of disease, criminality, taste, or immorality. Liability and responsibility are often waived when a physiological condition or behavior is labeled as a disease or illness, often to be replaced by involuntary treatment, institutional confinement, and surgical or pharmacological manipulation.

As the selections in this section reveal, medicine has often deemed it appropriate to classify various sexual activities, habits, and ethnic differences as diseases. The importation of biases and prejudices into medical classifications of disease has had disastrous consequences for various social groups. The danger that subjective perferences and tastes can masquerade as objective scientific judgments is a danger requiring vigilant and critical conceptual attention. Moreover, where matters of sex, race, drugs, or ethnicity are concerned, these selections reveal the health professions to be subject to all the same ideological, political, and moral influences and concerns that affect other segments of society.

Decisions about whether a condition or behavior is best conceived of as a disease or as indicative of health are not made in a social vacuum. As social conditions change, persons who once struggled to establish certain behaviors, for example, homosexuality, heroin addiction, gambling, or alcoholism, as diseases may find themselves arguing that such states ought not to be so classified. The history of the medical profession's activities regarding sensitive areas of personal behavior and lifestyle should give the reader pause as to whether current medical attitudes toward disease reflect an uncritical acceptance of views based only upon tradition, and the extent to which the concepts of health and disease are conceptually independent from moral and value choices and justifications.

3.1

The Disease of Masturbation: Values and the Concept of Disease*

H. Tristram Engelhardt, Jr.

Masturbation in the 18th and especially in the 19th century was widely believed to produce a spectrum of serious signs and symptoms, and was held to be a dangerous disease entity. Explanation of this phenomenon entails a basic reexamination of the concept of disease. It presupposes that one think of disease neither as an objective entity in the world nor as a concept that admits of a single universal definition: there is not, nor need there be, one concept of disease.[1] Rather, one chooses concepts for certain purposes, depending on values and hopes concerning the world.[2] The disease of masturbation is an eloquent example of the value-laden nature of science in general and of medicine in particular. In explaining the world, one judges what is to be significant or insignificant. For example, mathematical formulae are chosen in terms of elegance and simplicity, though elegance and simplicity are not attributes to be found in the world as such. The problem is even more involved in the case of medicine which judges what the human organism should be (i.e., what counts as "health") and is thus involved in the entire range of human values. This paper will sketch the nature of the model of the disease of masturbation in the 19th century, particularly in America, and indicate the scope of this "disease entity" and the therapies it evoked. The goal will be to outline some of the interrelations between evaluation and explanation.

The moral offense of masturbation was transformed into a disease with somatic not just psychological dimensions. Though sexual overindulgence

---

*Read at the 46th annual meeting of the American Association for the History of Medicine, Cincinnati, Ohio, May 5, 1973. I am grateful for the suggestions of Professor John Duffy, and the kind assistance of Louanna K. Bennett and Robert S. Baxter, Jr.

[1]Alvan R. Feinstein, "Taxonomy and logic in clinical data," *Ann. N. Y. Acad. Sci.*, 1969, *161*: 450–459.

[2]Horacio Fabrega, Jr., "Concepts of disease: logical features and social implications," *Perspect. Biol. Med.*, 1972 *15*: 583–616.

generally was considered debilitating since at least the time of Hippocrates,[3] masturbation was not widely accepted as a disease until a book by the title *Onania* appeared anonymously in Holland in 1700 and met with great success.[4] This success was reinforced by the appearance of S. A. Tissot's book on onanism.[5] Tissot held that all sexual activity was potentially debilitating and that the debilitation was merely more exaggerated in the case of masturbation. The primary basis for the debilitation was, according to Tissot, loss of seminal fluid, one ounce being equivalent to the loss of forty ounces of blood.[6] When this loss of fluid took place in an other than recumbent position (which Tissot held often to be the case with masturbation), this exaggerated the ill effects.[7] In attempting to document his contention, Tissot provided a comprehensive monograph on masturbation, synthesizing and appropriating the views of classical authors who had been suspicious of the effects of sexual overindulgence. He focused these suspicions clearly on masturbation. In this he was very successful, for Tissot's book appears to have widely established the medical opinion that masturbation was associated with serious physical and mental maladies.[8]

There appears to have been some disagreement whether the effect of frequent intercourse was in any respect different from that of masturbation. The presupposition that masturbation was not in accordance with the dictates of nature suggested that it would tend to be more subversive of the constitution than excessive sexual intercourse. Accounts of this difference in terms of the differential effect of the excitation involved are for the most part

---

[3]For example, Hippocrates correlated gout with sexual intercourse, *Aphorisms*, VI, 30. Numerous passages in the *Corpus* recommend the avoidance of overindulgence especially during certain illnesses.

[4]René A. Spitz, "Authority and masturbation. Some remarks on a bibliographical investigation." *Yb. Psychoanal.*, 1953, *9*: 116. Also, Robert H. MacDonald, "The frightful consequences of onanism: notes on the history of a delusion." *J. Hist. Ideas*, 1967, *28*: 432–431.

[5]Simon-André Tissot, *Tentamen de Morbis ex Manustrupatione* (Lausannae: M. M. Bousquet, 1758). An anonymous American translation appeared in the early 19th century: *Onanism* (New York: Collins & Hannay, 1832). Interestingly, the copy of Tissot's book held by the New York Academy of Medicine was given by Austin Flint. Austin Flint in turn was quoted as an authority on the effects of masturbation; see Joseph W. Howe's *Excessive Venery, Masturbation and Continence* (New York:Bermingham, 1884), p. 97. Also the American edition of Tissot's book, to show its concurrence with an American authority, added in a footnote a reference to Benjamin Rush's opinion concerning the pernicious consequences of masturbation. See Tissot, *Onanism*, p. 19, and Benjamin Rush's *Medical Inquiries and Observations Upon the Diseases of the Mind* (Philadelphia: Kimber and Richardson, 1812), pp. 348–349; also Tissot, *Onanism*, p. 21.

[6]Simon-André Tissot, *Onanism* (New York: Collins & Hannay, 1832), p. 5.

[7]*Ibid.*, p. 50.

[8]E. H. Hare, "Masturbatory insanity: the history of an idea," *J. Mental Sci.*, 1962, *108*: 2–3. It is worth noting that Tissot, as others, at times appears to have grouped together female masturbation and female homosexuality. See Vern L. Bullough and Martha Voght, "Homosexuality and its confusion with the 'secret sin' in pre-Freudian America." *J. Hist. Med. All. Sci.*, 1973, *28*: 143–155.

obscure. It was, though, advanced that "during sexual intercourse the expenditure of nerve force is compensated by the magnetism of the partner."[9] Tissot suggested that a beautiful sexual partner was of particular benefit or was at least less exhausting.[10] In any event, masturbation was held to be potentially more deleterious since it was unnatural, and, therefore, less satisfying and more likely to lead to a disturbance or disordering of nerve tone.

At first, the wide range of illnesses attributed to masturbation is striking. Masturbation was held to be the cause of dyspepsia,[11] constrictions of the urethra,[12] epilepsy,[13] blindness,[14] vertigo, loss of hearing,[15] headache, impotency, loss of memory, "irregular action of the heart," general loss of health and strength,[16] rickets,[17] leucorrhea in women,[18] and chronic catarrhal conjunctivitis.[19] Nymphomania was found to arise from masturbation, occurring more commonly in blonds than in brunettes.[20] Further, changes in the external genitalia were attributed to masturbation: elongation of the clitoris, reddening and congestion of the labia majora, elongation of the labia minora,[21] and a thinning and decrease in size of the penis.[22] Chronic masturbation was held to lead to the development of a particular type, including enlargement of the superficial veins of the hands and feet, moist and clammy hands, stooped shoulders, pale sallow face with heavy dark circles around the eyes, a "draggy" gait, and acne.[23] Careful case studies were

---

[9] Howe, *op. cit.* (n. 5 above), pp. 76–77.

[10] Tissot, *op. cit.* (n. 6 above), p. 51.

[11] J. A. Mayes, "Spermatorrhoea, treated by the lately invented rings," *Charleston Med. J. & Rev.*, 1854, *9*: 352.

[12] Allen W. Hagenbach, "Masturbation as a cause of insanity," *J. Ner. Ment. Dis.*, 1879, *6*: 609.

[13] Baker Brown, *On the Curability of Certain Forms of Insanity, Epilepsy, Catalepsy, and Hysteria in Females* (London: Hardwicke, 1866). Brown phrased the cause discreetly in terms of "peripheral irritation, arising originally in some branches of the pudic nerve, more particularly the incident nerve supplying the clitoris...." (p. 7).

[14] F. A. Burdem, "Self pollution in children," *Mass. Med. J.*, 1896, *16*: 340.

[15] Weber Liel, "The influence of sexual irritation upon the diseases of the ear," *New Orleans Med. & Surg. J.*, 1884, *11*: 786–788.

[16] Joseph Jones, "Diseases of the nervous system," *Trans. La. Med. Soc.* (New Orleans: L. Graham & Son, 1889), p. 170.

[17] Howe, *op. cit.* (n. 9 above), p. 93.

[18] J. Castellanos, "Influence of sewing machines upon the health and morality of the females using them," *South. J. Med. Sci.*, 1866–1867, *1*: 495–496.

[19] Comment, "Masturbation and ophthalmia," *New Orleans Med. & Surg. J.*, 1881–1882, *9*: 67.

[20] Howe, *op. cit.* (n. 5 above), pp. 108–111.

[21] *Ibid.*, pp. 41, 72.

[22] *Ibid.*, p. 68.

[23] *Ibid.*, p. 73.

published establishing masturbation as a cause of insanity,[24] and evidence indicated that it was a cause of hereditary insanity as well.[25] Masturbation was held also to cause an hereditary predisposition to consumption.[26] Finally, masturbation was believed to lead to general debility. "From health and vigor, and intelligence and loveliness of character, they became thin and pale and cadaverous; their amiability and loveliness departed, and in their stead irritability, moroseness and anger were prominent characteristics.... The child loses its flesh and becomes pale and weak."[27] The natural history was one of progressive loss of vigor, both physical and mental.

In short, a broad and heterogeneous class of signs and symptoms were recognized in the 19th century as a part of what was tantamount to a syndrome, if not a disease: masturbation. If one thinks of a syndrome as the concurrence or running together of signs and symptoms into a recognizable pattern, surely masturbation was such a pattern. It was more, though, in that a cause was attributed to the syndrome providing an etiological framework for a disease entity. That is, if one views the development of disease concepts as the progression from the mere collection of signs and symptoms to their interrelation in terms of a recognized causal mechanism, the disease of masturbation was fairly well evolved. A strikingly heterogeneous set of signs and symptoms was unified and comprehended under one causal mechanism. One could thus move from mere observation and description to explanation.

Since the signs and symptoms brought within the concept of masturbation were of a serious order associated with marked debility, it is not unexpected that there would be occasional deaths. The annual reports of the Charity Hospital of Louisiana in New Orleans which show hospitalizations for masturbation over an eighty-six year period indicate that, indeed, two masturbators were recorded as having died in the hospital. In 1872, the reports show that there were two masturbators hospitalized, one of whom was discharged, the other one having died.[28] The records of 1887 show that of the five masturbators hospitalized that year two improved, two were unimproved, and one died.[29] The records of the hospital give no evidence concerning the patient who died in 1872. The records for 1887, however, name the patient, showing him to have been hospitalized on Tuesday, January 6, 1887, for masturbation. A forty-five year old native of Indiana, a resident of New

---

[24]Hagenbach, *op. cit.* (n. 12 above), pp. 603–612.

[25]Jones, *op. cit.* (n. 16 above), p. 170.

[26]Howe, *op. cit.* (n. 5 above), p. 95.

[27]Burdem, *op. cit.* (n. 14 above), pp. 339, 341.

[28]*Report of the Board of Administrators of the Charity Hospital to the General Assembly of Louisiana* [for 1872] (New Orleans: The Republican Office, 1873), p. 30.

[29]*Report of the Board of Administrators of the Charity Hospital to the General Assembly of Louisiana* [for 1887] (New Orleans: A. W. Hyatt, 1888), p. 53.

Orleans for the previous thirty-five years, single, and a laborer, he died in the hospital on April 8, 1887.[30] There is no indication of the course of the illness. It is interesting to note, though, that in 1888 there was a death from anemia associated with masturbation, the cause of death being recorded under anemia. The records indicate that the patient was hospitalized on August 17, 1887, and died on February 11, 1888, was a lifelong resident of New Orleans, and was likewise a laborer and single.[31] His case suggests something concerning the two deaths recorded under masturbation: that they, too, suffered from a debilitating disease whose signs and symptoms were referred to masturbation as the underlying cause. In short, the concept of masturbation as a disease probably acted as a schema for organizing various signs and symptoms which we would now gather under different nosological categories.

As with all diseases, there was a struggle to develop a workable nosology. This is reflected in the reports of the Charity Hospital of Louisiana (in New Orleans) where over the years the disease was placed under various categories and numerous nomenclatures were employed. In 1848, for example, the first entry was given as "masturbation," in 1853 "onanism" was substituted, and in 1857 this was changed to "onanysmus."[32] Later, as the records began to classify the diseases under general headings, a place had to be found for masturbation. Initially in 1874, the disease "masturbation" was placed under the heading "Male Disease of Generative Organs." In 1877 this was changed to "Diseases of the Nervous System," and finally in 1884 the disease of "onanism" was classified as a "Cerebral-Spinal Disease." In 1890 it was reclassified under the heading "Diseases of the Nervous System," and remained classified as such until 1906 when it was placed as "masturbation" under the title of "Genito-Urinary System, Diseases of (Functional Disturbances of Male Sexual Organs)." It remained classified as a functional disturbance until the last entry in 1933. The vacillation in the use of headings probably indicates hesitation on the part of the recorders as to the nature of the disease. On the one hand, it is understandable why a disease, which was held to have such grossly physical components, would itself be considered to have some variety of physical basis. On the other hand, the recorders appear to have been drawn by the obviously psychological aspects of the phenomenon of masturbation to classify it in the end as a functional disturbance.

As mentioned, the concept of the disease of masturbation developed on the

---

[30]Record Archives of the Charity Hospital of Louisiana [in New Orleans] M S, "Admission Book #41 from December 1, 1885 to March 31, 1888 Charity Hospital," p. 198. I am indebted to Mrs. Eddie Cooksy for access to the record archives.

[31]*Ibid.*, p. 287.

[32]This and the following information concerning entries is taken from a review of the *Report of the Board of Administrators of the Charity Hospital*, New Orleans, Louisiana, from 1848 to 1933. The reports were not available for the years 1850–1851, 1854–1855, 1862–1863, and 1865.

basis of a general suspicion that sexual activity was debilitating.[33] This development is not really unexpected: if one examines the world with a tacit presupposition of a parallelism between what is good for one's soul and what is good for one's health, then one would expect to find disease correlates for immoral sexual behavior.[34] Also, this was influenced by a concurrent inclination to translate a moral issue into medical terms and relieve it of the associated moral opprobrium in a fashion similar to the translation of alcoholism from a moral into a medical problem.[35] Further, disease as a departure from a state of stability due to excess or under excitation offered the skeleton of a psychosomatic theory of the somatic alterations attributed to the excitation associated with masturbation.[36] The categories of over and under excitation suggest cogent, basic categories of medical explanation: over and under excitation, each examples of excess, imply deleterious influences on the stability of the organism. Jonathan Hutchinson succinctly described the etiological mechanism in this fashion, holding that "the habit in question is very injurious to the nerve-tone, and that it frequently originates and keeps up maladies which but for it might have been avoided or cured."[37] This schema of causality presents the signs and symptoms attendant to masturbation as due to "the nerveshock attending the substitute for the venereal act, or the act itself, which, either in onanism or copulation frequently indulged, breaks men down."[38] "The excitement incident to the habitual and frequent indulgence of

[33]Even Boerhaave remarked that "an excessive discharge of semen causes fatigue, weakness, decrease in activity, convulsions, emaciation, dehydration, heat and pains in the membranes of the brain, a loss in the acuity of the senses, particularly of vision, *tabes dorsalis*, simplemindedness, and various similar disorders." My translation of Hermanno Boerhaave's *Institutiones Medicae* (Viennae: J. T. Trattner, 1775), p. 315, paragraph 776.

[34]"We have seen that masturbation is more pernicious than excessive intercourse with females. Those who believe in a special providence, account for it by a special ordinance of the Deity to punish this crime." Tissot, *op. cit.* (n. 6 above), p. 45.

[35]". . . the best remedy was not to tell the poor children that they were damning their souls, but to tell them that they might seriously hurt their bodies, and to explain to them the nature and purport of the functions they were abusing." Lawson Tait, "Masturbation. A clinical lecture," *Med. News*, 1888, *53*: 2.

[36]Though it has not been possible to trace a direct influence by John Brown's system of medicine upon the development of accounts of the disease of masturbation, yet a connection is suggestive. Brown had left a mark on the minds of many in the 18th and 19th centuries, and given greater currency to the use of concepts of over and under excitation in the explanation of the etiology of disease. Guenter B. Risse, "The quest for certainty in medicine: John Brown's system of medicine in France," *Bull. Hist. Med.*, 1971, *45*: 1–12.

[37]Jonathan Hutchison, "On circumcision as preventive of masturbation," *Arch. Surg.*, 1890–1891, *2*: 268.

[38]Theophilus Parvin, "The hygiene of the sexual functions," *New Orleans Med. & Surg. J.*, 1884, *11*: 606.

the unnatural practice of masturbation leads to the most serious constitutional effects...."[39] The effects were held to be magnified during youth when such "shocks" undermined normal development.[40]

Similarly, Freud remarks in a draft of a paper to Wilhelm Fliess dated February 8, 1893, that "Sexual exhaustion can by itself alone provoke neurasthenia. If it fails to achieve this by itself, it has such an effect on the disposition of the nervous system that physical illness, depressive affects and overwork (toxic influences) can no longer be tolerated without [leading to] neurasthenia.... *neurasthenia in males* is acquired at puberty and becomes manifest in the patient's twenties. Its source is masturbation, the frequency of which runs completely parallel with the frequency of male neurasthenia."[41] And Freud later stated, "It is the prolonged and intense action of this pernicious sexual satisfaction which is enough on its own account to provoke a neurasthenic neurosis...."[42] Again, it is a model of excessive stimulation of a certain quality leading to specific disabilities. This position of the theoreticians of masturbation in the 19th century is not dissimilar to positions currently held concerning other diseases. For example, the first Diagnostic and Sta-

---

[39]Jones, *op. cit.* (n. 16 above), p. 170. It is interesting to note that documentation for the constitutional effects of masturbation was sought even from post-mortem examination. A report from Birmingham, England, concerning an autopsy on a dead masturbator, concluded that masturbation "...seems to have acted upon the cord in the same manner as repeated small haemorrhages affect the brain, slowly sapping its energies, until it succumbed soon after the last application of the exhausting influence, probably through the instrumentality of an atrophic process previously induced, as evidenced by the diseased state of the minute vessels" ([James] Russell, "Cases illustrating the influence of exhaustion of the spinal cord in inducing paraplegia," *Med. Times & Gaz., Lond.*, 1863, *2*: 456). The examination included microscopic inspection of material to demonstrate pathological changes. Again, the explanation of the phenomena turned on the supposed intense excitement attendant to masturbation. "In this fatal vice the venereal passion is carried at each indulgence to the state of highest tension by the aid of the mind, and on each occasion the cord is subjected to the strongest excitement which sensation and imagination in combination can produce, for we cannot regard the mere secretion of the seminal fluid as constituting the chief drain upon the energies of the cord, but rather as being the exponent of the nervous stimulation by which it has been ejaculated" (*Ibid.*, p. 456). The model was one of the mental tension and excitement "exhausting" the nervous system by "excessive functional activity" leading to consequent "weakening" of the nervous system. Baker Brown listed eight stages in the progress of the disease in females: hysteria, spinal irritation, hysterical epilepsy, cataleptic fits, epileptic fits, idiocy, mania and finally death; Brown, *op. cit.* (n. 13 above), p. 7.

[40]"Any shock to this growth and development, and especially that of masturbation, must for a time suspend the process of nutrition; and a succession of such shocks will blast both body and mind, and terminate in perpetual vacuity." Burdem, *op. cit.* (n. 14 above), p. 339. In this regard, not only adolescent but childhood masturbation was the concern of 19th century practitioners; e.g., Russell, *op. cit.* (n. 39 above), p. 456.

[41]Sigmund Freud, *The Standard Edition of the Complete Psychological Works of Sigmund Freud*, I (London: The Hogarth Press, 1971), p. 180.

[42]*Ibid.*, III, "Heredity and the Aetiology of the Neuroses," p. 150.

tistical Manual of the American Psychiatric Association says with regard to "psychophysiologic autonomic and visceral disorders" that "The symptoms are due to a chronic and exaggerated state of the normal physiological expression of emotion, with the feeling, or subjective part, repressed. Such long continued visceral states may eventually lead to structural changes."[43] This theoretical formulation is one that would have been compatible with theories concerning masturbation in the 19th century.

Other models of etiology were employed besides those based upon excess stimulation. They, for the most part, accounted for the signs and symptoms on the basis of the guilt associated with the act of masturbation. These more liberal positions developed during a time of reaction against the more drastic therapies such as Baker Brown's use of clitoridectomy.[44] These alternative models can be distinguished according to whether the guilt was held to be essential or adventitious. Those who held that masturbation was an unnatural act were likely to hold that the associated guilt feelings and anxiety were natural, unavoidable consequences of performing an unnatural act. Though not phrased in the more ethically neutral terms of excess stimulation, still the explanation was in terms of a pathophysiological state involving a departure from biological norms. "The masturbator feels that his act degrades his manhood, while the man who indulges in legitimate intercourse is satisfied that he has fulfilled one of his principal natural functions. There is a healthy instinctive expression of passion in one case, an illegitimate perversion of function in the other."[45] The operative assumption was that when sexual activity failed to produce an "exhilaration of spirits and clearness of intellect" and when associated with anxiety or guilt it would lead to deleterious effects.[46] This analysis suggested that it was guilt, not excitation, which led to the phenomena associated with masturbation. "Now it happens in a large number of cases, that these young masturbators sooner or later become alarmed at their practices, in consequence of some information they receive. Often this latter is of a most mischievous character. Occasionally too, the religious element is predominant, and the mental condition of these young men becomes truly pitiable.... The facts are nearly these: Masturbation is not a

---

[43]*Diagnostic and Statistical Manual: Mental Disorders* (Washington, D. C.: American Psychiatric Association, 1952), p. 29.

[44]"Mr. Baker Brown was not a very accurate observer, nor a logical reasoner. He found that a number of semi-demented epileptics were habitual masturbators, and that the masturbation was, in women, chiefly effected by excitement of the mucous membrane on and around the clitoris. Jumping over two grave omissions in the syllogism, putting the cart altogether before the horse, he arrived at the conclusion that removal of the clitoris would stop the pernicious habit, and therefore cure the epilepsy." Tait, *op. cit.* (n. 35 above), p. 2.

[45]Howe, *op. cit.* (n. 5 above), p. 77.

[46]*Ibid.*, p. 77.

crime nor a sin, but a vice."[47] Others appreciated the evil and guilt primarily in terms of the solitary and egoistic nature of the act.

Such positions concerning etiology graded over into models in which masturbation's untoward signs and symptoms were viewed as merely the result of guilt and anxiety felt because of particular cultural norms, which norms had no essential basis in biology. "Whatever may be abnormal, there is nothing unnatural."[49] In short, there was also a model of interpretation which saw the phenomena associated with masturbation as mere adventitious, as due to a particular culture's condemnation of the act. This last interpretation implied that no more was required than to realize that there was nothing essentially wrong with masturbation. "Our wisest course is to recognize the inevitableness of the vice of masturbation under the perpetual restraints of civilized life, and, while avoiding any attitude of indifference, to avoid also an attitude of excessive horror, for that would only lead to the facts being effectually veiled from our sight, and serve to manufacture artificially a greater evil than that which we seek to combat."[50] This last point of view appears to have gained prominence in the development of thought concerning masturbation as reflected in the shift from the employment of mechanical and surgical therapy in the late 19th century to the use of more progressive means (i.e., including education that guilt and anxiety were merely relative to certain cultural norms) by the end of the century and the first half of the 20th century.[51]

To recapitulate, 19th-century reflection on the etiology of masturbation led to the development of an authentic disease of masturbation: excessive sexual stimulation was seen to produce particular and discrete pathophysiological changes.[52] First, there were strict approaches in terms of disordered nerve-tone due to excess and/or unnatural sexual excitation. Over-excitation was seen to lead to significant and serious physical alterations in the patient, and in

---

[47]James Nevins Hyde, "On the masturbation, spermatorrhoea and impotence of adolescence," *Chicago Med. J. & Exam.*, 1879, *38*: 451–452.

[48]"There can be no doubt that the habit is, temporarily at least, morally degrading; but if we bear in mind the selfish, solitary nature of the act, the entire absence in it of aught akin to love or sympathy, the innate repulsiveness of intense selfishness or egoism of any kind, we may see how it may be morally degrading, while its effect on the physical and mental organism is practically nil." A. C. McClanahan, "An investigation into the effects of masturbation," *N. Y. Med. J.*, 1897, *66*: 502.

[49]*Ibid.*, p. 500.

[50]Augustin J. Himel, "Some minor studies in psychology, with special reference to masturbation," *New Orleans Med. & Surg. J.*, 1907, *60*: 452.

[51]Spitz, *op. cit.* (n. 4 above), esp. p. 119.

[52]That is, masturbation as a disease was more than a mere collection of signs and symptoms usually "running together" in a syndrome. It became a legitimate disease entity, a causally related set of signs and symptoms.

this vein a somewhat refined causal model of the disease was developed. Second, there were those who saw the signs and symptoms as arising from the unavoidable guilt and anxiety associated with the performance of an unnatural act. Third, there were a few who appreciated masturbation's sequelae as merely the response of a person in a culture which condemned the activity.

Those who held the disease of masturbation to be more than a culturally dependent phenomenon often employed somewhat drastic therapies. Restraining devices were devised,[53] infibulation or placing a ring in the prepuce was used to make masturbation painful,[54] and no one less than Jonathan Hutchinson held that circumcision acted as a preventive.[55] Acid burns or thermoelectrocautery[56] were utilized to make masturbation painful and, therefore, to discourage it. The alleged seriousness of this disease in females led, as Professor John Duffy has shown, to the employment of the rather radical treatment of clitoridectomy.[57] The classic monograph recommending clitoridectomy, written by the British surgeon Baker Brown, advocated the procedure to terminate the "long continued peripheral excitement, causing frequent and increasing losses of nerve force, . . ."[58] Brown recommended that "the patient having been placed completely under the influence of chloroform, the clitoris [be] freely excised either by scissors or knife—I always prefer the scissors."[59] The supposed sequelae of female masturbation, such as sterility, paresis, hysteria, dysmenorrhea, idiocy, and insanity, were also held to be remedied by the operation.

Male masturbation was likewise treated by means of surgical procedures. Some recommended vasectomy[60] while others found this procedure ineffective and employed castration.[61] One illustrative case involved the castration of a physician who had been confined as insane for seven years and who subsequently was able to return to practice.[62] Another case involved the

---

[53]C. D. W. Colby, "Mechanical restraint of masturbation in a young girl," *Med. Record in N. Y.*, 1897, *52*: 206.

[54]Louis Bauer, "Infibulation as a remedy for epilepsy and seminal losses," *St. Louis Clin. Record*, 1879, *6*: 163–165. See also Gerhart S. Schwarz, "Infibulation, population control, and the medical profession," *Bull. N. Y. Acad. Med.*, 1970, *46*: 979, 990.

[55]Hutchinson, *op. cit.* (n. 37 above), pp. 267–269.

[56]William J. Robinson, "Masturbation and its treatment," *Am. J. Clin. Med.*, 1907, *14*: 349.

[57]John Duffy, "Masturbation and clitoridectomy. A nineteenth-century view," *J.A.M.A.*, 1963, *186*: 246–248.

[58]Brown, *op. cit.* (n. 37 above), pp. 267–269.

[59]*Ibid.*, p. 17.

[60]Timothy Haynes, "Surgical treatment of hopeless cases of masturbation and nocturnal emissions," *Boston Med. & Surg. J.*, 1883, *109*: 130.

[61]J. H. Marshall, "Insanity cured by castration," *Med. & Surg. Reptr.*, 1865, *13*: 363–364.

[62]"The patient soon evinced marked evidences of being a changed man, becoming quiet, kind, and docile." *Ibid.*, p. 363.

castration of a twenty-two year old epileptic "at the request of the county judge, and with the consent of his father... the father saying he would be perfectly satisfied if the masturbation could be stopped, so that he could take him home, without having his family continually humiliated and disgusted by his loathsome habit."[63] The patient was described as facing the operation morosely, "like a coon in a hollow."[64] Following the operation, masturbation ceased and the frequency of fits decreased. An editor of the *Texas Medical Practitioner*, J. B. Shelmire, added a remark to the article: "Were this procedure oftener adopted for the cure of these desperate cases, many, who are sent to insane asylums, soon to succumb to the effects of this habit, would live to become useful citizens."[65] Though such approaches met with ridicule from some quarters,[66] still various novel treatments were devised in order to remedy the alleged sequelae of chronic masturbation such as spermatorrhea and impotency. These included acupuncture of the prostate in which "needles from two to three inches in length are passed through the perineum into the prostate gland and the neck of the bladder.... Some surgeons recommend the introduction of needles into the testicles and spermatic cord for the same purpose."[67] Insertion of electrodes into the bladder and rectum and cauterization of the prostatic urethra were also utilized.[68] Thus, a wide range of rather heroic methods were devised to treat masturbation and a near fascination developed on the part of some for the employment of mechanical and electrical means of restoring "health."

There were, though, more tolerant approaches, ranging from hard work and simple diet[69] to suggestions that "If the masturbator is totally continent, sexual intercourse is advisable."[70] This latter approach to therapy led some physicians to recommend that masturbators cure their disease by frequenting houses of prostitution,[71] or acquiring a mistress.[72] Though these treatments would appear ad hoc, more theoretically sound proposals were made by many physicians in terms of the model of excitability. They suggested that the disease and its sequelae could be adequately controlled by treating the

---

[63]R. D. Potts, "Castration for masturbation, with report of a case," *Texas Med. Practitioner*, 1898, *11*: 8.

[64]*Ibid.*, p. 8.

[65]*Ibid.*, p. 9.

[66]Editorial. "Castration for the relief of epilepsy," *Boston Med. & Surg. J.*, 1859, *60*: 163.

[67]Howe, *op. cit.* (n. 5 above), p. 260.

[68]*Ibid.*, pp. 254–255, 258–260.

[69]Editorial, "Review of European legislation for the control of prostitution," *New Orleans Med. & Surg. J.*, 1854–1855, *11*: 704.

[70]Robinson, *op. cit.* (n. 56 above), p. 350.

[71]Parvin, *op. cit.* (n. 38 above), p. 606.

[72]Mayes, *op. cit.* (n. 11 above), p. 352.

excitation and debility consequent upon masturbation. Towards this end, "active tonics" and the use of cold baths at night just before bedtime were suggested.[73] Much more in a "Brownian" mode was the proposal that treatment with opium would be effective. An initial treatment with 1/12 of a grain of morphine sulfate daily by injection was followed after ten days by a dose of 1/16 of a grain. This dose was continued for three weeks and gradually diminished to 1/30 of a grain a day. At the end of a month the patient was dismissed from treatment "the picture of health, having fattened very much, and lost every trace of anaemia and mental imbecility."[74] The author, after his researches with opium and masturbation, concluded, "*We may find in opium a new and important aid in the treatment of the victims of the habit of masturbation by means of which their moral and physical forces may be so increased that they may be enabled to enter the true physiological path.*"[75] This last example eloquently collects the elements of the concept of the disease of masturbation as a pathophysiological entity: excitation leads to physical debilitation requiring a physical remedy. Masturbation as a pathophysiological entity was thus incorporated within an acceptable medical model of diagnosis and therapy.

In summary, in the 19th century, biomedical scientists attempted to correlate a vast number of signs and symptoms with a disapproved activity found in many patients afflicted with various maladies. Given an inviting theoretical framework, it was very conducive to think of this range of signs and symptoms as having one cause. The theoretical framework, though, as has been indicated, was not value free but structured by the values and expectations of the times. In the 19th century, one was pleased to think that not "one bride in a hundred, of delicate, educated, sensitive women, accepts matrimony from any desire of sexual gratification: when she thinks of this at all, it is with shrinking, or even with horror, rather than with desire."[76] In contrast, in the 20th century, articles are published for the instruction of women in the use of masturbation to overcome the disease of frigidity or orgasmic dysfunction.[77] In both cases, expectations concerning what should be significant structure the appreciation of reality by medicine. The variations are not due to mere fallacies of scientific method,[78] but involve a basic dependence of the logic of

---

[73] Haynes, *op. cit.* (n. 60 above), p. 130.

[74] B. A. Pope, "Opium as a tonic and alternative; with remarks upon the hypodermic use of the sulfate of morphia, and its use in the debility and amorosis consequent upon onanism," *New Orleans Med. & Surg. J.*, 1879, *6*: 725.

[75] *Ibid.*, p. 727.

[76] Parvin, *op. cit.* (n. 38 above), p. 607.

[77] Joseph LoPiccolo and W. Charles Lobitz, "The role of masturbation in the treatment of orgasmic dysfunction," *Arch. Sexual Behavior*, 1972, *2*: 163–171.

[78] E. Hare, *op. cit.* (n. 8 above), pp. 15–19.

scientific discovery and explanation upon prior evaluations of reality.[79] A sought-for coincidence of morality and nature gives goals to explanation and therapy.[80] Values influence the purpose and direction of investigations and treatment. Moreover, the disease of masturbation has other analogues. In the 19th century, there were such diseases in the South as "Drapetomania, the disease causing slaves to run away," and the disease "Dysaesthesia Aethiopis or hebetude of mind and obtuse sensibility of body—a disease peculiar to negroes—called by overseers 'rascality'."[81] In Europe, there was the disease of *morbus democritus*.[82] Some would hold that current analogues exist in diseases such as alcoholism and drug abuse.[83] In short, the disease of masturbation indicates that evaluations play a role in the development of explanatory models and that this may not be an isolated phenomenon.

This analysis, then, suggests the following conclusion: although vice and virtue are not equivalent to disease and health, they bear a direct relation to these concepts. Insofar as a vice is taken to be a deviation from an ideal of human perfection, or "well-being," it can be translated into disease language. In shifting to disease language, one no longer speaks in moralistic terms (e.g., "You are evil"), but one speaks in terms of a deviation from a norm which implies a degree of imperfection (e.g., "You are a deviant"). The shift is from an explicitly ethical language to a language of natural teleology. To be ill is to fail to realize the perfection of an ideal type; to be sick is to be defective rather than to be evil. The concern is no longer with what is naturally, morally good, but what is naturally beautiful. Medicine turns to what has been judged to be naturally ugly or deviant, and then develops etiological accounts in order to explain and treat in a coherent fashion a manifold of displeasing signs and symptoms. The notion of the "deviant" structures the concept of disease providing a purpose and direction for explanation and for action, that is, for

---

[79]Norwood Hanson, *Patterns of Discovery* (London: Cambridge University Press, 1965).

[80]Tissot, *op. cit.* (n. 6 above), p. 45. As Immanuel Kant, a contemporary of S.-A. Tissot remarked, "Also, in all probability, it was through this moral interest [in the moral law governing the world] that attentiveness to beauty and the ends of nature was first aroused." (*Kants Werke*, Vol. 5, *Kritik der Urtheilskraft* [Berlin: Walter de Gruyter & Co., 1968], p. 459, A 439. My translation.) That is, moral values influence the search for goals in nature, and direct attention to what will be considered natural, normal, and non-deviant. This would also imply a relationship between the aesthetic, especially what was judged to be naturally beautiful, and what was held to be the goals of nature.

[81]Samuel A. Cartwright, "Report on the diseases and physical peculiarities of the negro race," *New Orleans Med. & Surg. J.*, 1850–1851, *7*: 707–709. An interesting examination of these diseases is given by Thomas S. Szasz, "The sane slave," *Am. J. Psychoth.*, 1971, *25*: 228–239.

[82]Heinz Hartmann, "Towards a concept of mental health," *Brit. J. Med. Psychol.*, 1960, *33*: 248.

[83]Thomas S. Szasz, "Bad habits are not diseases: a refutation of the claim that alcoholism is a disease," *Lancet*, 1972, *2*: 83–4; and Szasz, "The ethics of addiction," *Am. J. Psychiatry*, 1971. *128*: 541–546.

diagnosis and prognosis, and for therapy. A "disease entity" operates as a conceptual form organizing phenomena in a fashion deemed useful for certain goals. The goals, though, involve choice by man and are not objective facts, data "given" by nature. They are ideals imputed to nature. The disease of masturbation is an eloquent example of the role of evaluation in explanation and the structure values give to our picture of reality.

3.2

The Female Animal: Medical and Biological Views of Woman and Her Role in Nineteenth-Century America

Carroll Smith-Rosenberg
and
Charles Rosenberg

Since at least the time of Hippocrates and Aristotle, the roles assigned women have attracted an elaborate body of medical and biological justification. This was especially true in the nineteenth century as the intellectual and emotional centrality of science increased steadily. Would-be scientific arguments were used in the rationalization and legitimization of almost every aspect of Victorian life, and with particular vehemence in those areas in which social change implied stress in existing social arrangements.

This essay is an attempt to outline some of the shapes assumed by the nineteenth-century debate over the ultimate bases for woman's domestic and child-bearing role.[1] In form it resembles an exercise in the history of ideas; in

[1]For historical studies of women's role and ideological responses to it in nineteenth-century America, see William L. O'Neill, *Everyone was Brave: A History of Feminism in America* (Chicago, 1969); William Wasserstrom, *Heiress of all Ages: Sex and Sentiment in the Victorian Tradition* (Minneapolis, 1959); Eleanor Flexner, *Century of Struggle: The Woman's Rights Movement in the United States* (New York, 1968); Aileen S. Kraditor, *The Ideas of the Woman Suffrage Movement, 1890–1920* (New York, 1965). For studies emphasizing the interaction between social change and sex role conflict see, Carroll Smith Rosenberg, "Beauty, the Beast and the Militant Woman: A Case Study in Sex Roles and Social Stress in Jacksonian America," *American Quarterly*, XXIII (Oct. 1971), 562–84; Carroll Smith Rosenberg, "The Hysterical Woman: Sex Roles and Role Conflict in 19th-Century America," *Social Research*, XXXIX (Winter, 1972), 652–78. The problem of sexuality in the English-speaking world has been a particular subject of historical concern. Among the more important, if diverse, attempts to deal with this problem are Peter T. Cominos, "Late-Victorian Sexual Respectability and the Social System," *Internation Review of Social History*, VIII (1963), 18–48, 216–50; Stephen Nissenbaum, "Careful Love: Sylvester Graham and the Emergence of Victorian Sexual Theory in America, 1830–1840" (doctoral dissertation, University of Wisconsin, 1968); Graham Barker-Benfield, "The Horrors of the Half Known Life: Aspects of the Exploitation of

intent it represents a hybrid with social and psychological history. Biological and medical views serve as a sampling device suggesting and illuminating patterns of social continuity, change, and tension.

The relationships between social change and social stress are dismayingly complex and recalcitrant to both psychological theorists and to the historian's normal modes of analysis. In an attempt to gain insight into these relationships the authors have chosen an analytic approach based on the study of normative descriptions of the female role at a time of widespread social change; not surprisingly emotion-laden attempts to reassert and redefine this role constitute one response to the stress induced by such social change.

This approach was selected for a variety of reasons. Role definitions exist on a level of prescription beyond their embodiment in the individuality and behavior of particular historical persons. They exist rather as a formally agreed upon set of characteristics understood by and acceptable to a significant proportion of the population. As formally agreed upon social values they are, moreover, retrievable from historical materials and thus subject to analysis. Such social role definitions, however, have a more than platonic reality; for they exist as parameters with which and against which individuals must either conform or define their deviance. When inappropriate to social, psychological, or biological reality such definitions can themselves engender anxiety, conflict, and demands for change.

During the nineteenth century, economic and social forces at work within Western Europe and the United States began to compromise traditional social roles. Some women at least began to question—and a few to challenge overtly—their constricted place in society. Naturally enough, men hopeful of preserving existing social relationships, and in some cases threatened themselves both as individuals and as members of particular social groups, employed medical and biological arguments to rationalize traditional sex roles as rooted inevitably and irreversibly in the prescriptions of anatomy and physiology. This essay examines the ideological attack mounted by prestigious and traditionally minded men against two of the ways in which women expressed their dissatisfaction and desire for change: women's demands for improved educational opportunities and their decision to resort to birth control and abortion. That much of this often emotionally charged debate was oblique and couched in would-be scientific and medical language and metaphor makes it even more significant; for few spokesmen could explicitly and consciously confront those changes which impinged upon the bases of their particular emotional adjustment.

Women by Men" (doctoral dissertation, University of California, Los Angeles, 1968); Nathan G. Hale, Jr., *Freud and the Americans: The Beginnings of Psychoanalysis in the United States, 1876–1917* (New York, 1971), 24–46; David M. Kennedy, *Birth Control in America: The Career of Margaret Sanger* (New Haven, 1970), 36–71; Steven Marcus, *The Other Victorians: A Study of Sexuality and Pornography in Mid-Nineteenth-Century England* (New York, 1966). See also Charles E. Rosenberg, "Sexuality, Class and Role in 19th-Century America," *American Quarterly*, XXV (May 1973), 131–54.

The Victorian woman's ideal social characteristics—nurturance, intuitive morality, domesticity, passivity, and affection—were all assumed to have a deeply rooted biological basis. These medical and scientific arguments formed an ideological system rigid in its support of tradition, yet infinitely flexible in the particular mechanisms which could be made to explain and legitimate woman's role.

Woman, nineteenth-century medical orthodoxy insisted, was starkly different from the male of the species. Physically, she was frailer, her skull smaller, he muscles more delicate. Even more striking was the difference between the nervous system of the two sexes. The female nervous system was finer, "more irritable," prone to overstimulation and resulting exhaustion. "The female sex," as one physician explained in 1827,

> is far more sensitive and susceptible than the male, and extremely liable to those distressing affections which for want of some better term, have been denominated nervous, and which consist chiefly in painful affections of the head, heart, side, and indeed, of almost every part of the system.[2]

"The nerves themselves," another physician concurred a generation later, "are smaller, and of a more delicate structure. They are endowed with greater sensibility, and, of course, are liable to more frequent and stronger impressions from external agents or mental influences."[3] Few if any questioned the assumption that in males the intellectual propensities of the brain dominated, while the female's nervous system and emotions prevailed over her conscious and rational faculties. Thus it was only natural, indeed inevitable, that women should be expected and permitted to display more affect than men; it was inherent in their very being.

Physicians saw woman as the product and prisoner of her reproductive system. It was the ineluctable basis of her social role and behavioral characteristics, the cause of her most common ailments; woman's uterus and ovaries controlled her body and behavior from puberty through menopause. The male reproductive system, male physicians assured, exerted no parallel degree of control over man's body. Charles D. Meigs, a prominent Philadelphia gynecologist, stated with assurance in 1847 that a woman is "a moral, a sexual,

---

[2]Marshall Hall, *Commentaries on some of the more important of the Diseases of Females*, in three parts (London, 1827), 2. Although this discussion centers on the nineteenth century, it must be understood that these formulations had a far longer pedigree.

[3]Stephen Tracy, *The Mother and her Offspring* (New York, 1860), xv; William Goodell, *Lessons in Gynecology* (Philadelphia, 1879), 332; William B. Carpenter, *Principles of Human Physiology: With Their Chief Applications to Pathology, Hygiène, and Forensic Medicine* (4th ed., Philadelphia, 1850), 727. In mid-nineteenth century many of these traditional views of woman's peculiar physiological characteristics were restated in terms of the currently fashionable phrenology. For example, see Thomas L. Nichols, *Woman, in All Ages and Nations: A Complete and Authentic History of the Manners and Customs, Character and Condition of the Female Sex in Civilized and Savage Countries, from the Earliest Ages to the Present Time* (New York, *ca.* 1849), xi.

a germiferous, gestative and parturient creature."[4] It was, another physician explained in 1870, "as if the Almighty, in creating the female sex, had taken the uterus and built up a woman around it."[5] A wise deity had designed woman as keeper of the hearth, as breeder and rearer of children.

Medical wisdom easily supplied hypothetical mechanisms to explain the interconnection between the female's organs of generation and the functioning of her other organs. The uterus, it was assumed, was connected to the central nervous system; shocks to the nervous system might alter the reproductive cycle—might even mark the gestating fetus—while changes in the reproductive cycle shaped emotional states. This intimate and hypothetical link between ovaries, uterus, and nervous system was the logical basis for the "reflex irritation" model of disease causation so popular in middle and late nineteenth-century medical texts and monographs on psychiatry and gynecology. Any imbalance, exhaustion, infection, or other disorders of the reproductive organs could cause pathological reactions in parts of the body seemingly remote.[6] Doctors connected not only the paralyses and headaches of the hysteric to uterine disease but also ailments in virtually every part of the body. "These diseases," one physician explained, "will be found, on due investigation, to be in reality, no disease at all, but merely the sympathetic reaction or the symptoms of one disease, namely, a disease of the womb."[7]

Yet despite the commonsensical view that many such ailments resulted from childbearing, physicians often contended that far greater difficulties could be expected in childless women. Motherhood was woman's normal destiny, and those females who thwarted the promise immanent in their body's design must expect to suffer. The maiden lady, many physicians argued, was fated to a greater incidence of both physical and emotional disease than her married

---

[4]Charles D. Meigs, *Lecture on Some of the Distinctive Characteristics of the Female. Delivered before the Class of the Jefferson Medical College, January 5, 1847* (Philadelphia, 1847), 5.

[5]M. L. Holbrook, *Parturition without Pain: A Code of Directions for Escaping from the Primal Curse* (New York, 1882), 14–15. See also Edward H. Dixon, *Woman, and her Diseases, from the Cradle to the Grave: Adapted Exclusively to her Instruction in the Physiology of her System, and all the Diseases of her Critical Periods* (New York, 1846), 17; M. K. Hard, *Woman's Medical Guide: Being a Complete Review of the Peculiarities of the Female Constitution and the Derangements to which it is Subject. With a Description of Simple yet Certain Means for their Cure* (Mt. Vernon, Ohio, 1848), 11.

[6]In the hypothetical pathologies of these generations, the blood was often made to serve the same function as that of the nerves; it could cause general ills to have local manifestations and effect systemic changes based on local lesions. By mid-century, moreover, physicians had come to understand that only the blood supply connected the gestating mother to her child.

[7]M. E. Dirix, *Woman's Complete Guide to Health* (New York, 1869), 24. So fashionable were such models in the late-nineteenth century that America's leading gynecologist in the opening years of the present century despaired of trying to dispel such exaggerated notions from his patients' minds. It is difficult," he explained, "even for a healthy girl to rid her mind of constant impending evil from the uterus and ovaries, so prevalent is the idea that woman's ills are mainly 'reflexes' from the pelvic organs." Gynecological therapy was the treatment of choice for a myriad of symptoms. Howard A. Kelly, *Medical Gynecology* (New York, 1908), 73.

sisters and to a shorter life-span.[8] Her nervous system was placed under constant pressure, and her unfulfilled reproductive organs—especially at menopause—were prone to cancer and other degenerative ills.

Woman was thus peculiarly the creature of her internal organs, of tidal forces she could not consciously control. Ovulation, the physical and emotional changes of pregnancy, even sexual desire itself were determined by internal physiological processes beyond the control or even the awareness of her conscious volition.[9] All women were prisoners of the cyclical aspects of their bodies, of the great reproductive cycle bounded by puberty and menopause, and by the shorter but recurrent cycles of childbearing and menstruation. All shaped her personality, her social role, her intellectual abilities and limitations; all presented as well possibly "critical" moments in her development, possible turning points in the establishment—or deterioration—of future physical and mental health. As the president of the American Gynecological Society stated in 1900: "Many a young life is battered and forever crippled in the breakers of puberty; if it crosses these unharmed and is not dashed to pieces on the rock of childbirth, it may still ground on the ever-recurring shallows of menstruation, and lastly, upon the final bar of the menopause ere protection is found in the unruffled waters of the harbor beyond the reach of sexual storms."[10]

Woman's physiology and anatomy, physicians habitually argued, oriented her toward an "inner' view of herself and her worldly sphere. (Logically enough, nineteenth-century views of heredity often assumed that the father was responsible for a child's external musculature and skeletal development, the mother for the internal viscera, the father for analytical abilities, the mother for emotions and piety.[11]) Their secret internal organs, women were told, determined their behavior; their concerns lay inevitably within the home.[12] In a passage strikingly reminiscent of some mid-twentieth-century

---

[8][Dr. Porter,] *Book of Men, Women, and Babies. The Laws of God applied to Obtaining, Rearing, and Developing the Natural, Healthful, and Beautiful in Humanity* (New York, 1855), 56; Tracy, *Mother and Offspring*, xxiii; H. S. Pomeroy, *The Ethics of Marriage* (New York, 1888), 78.

[9]On the involuntary quality of female sexuality, see Alexander J. C. Skene, *Education and Culture as Related to the Health and Diseases of Women* (Detroit, 1889), 22.

[10]George Engelmann, *The American Girl of To-Day: Modern Education and Functional Health* (Washington, 1900), 9–10.

[11]Alexander Harvey, "On the Relative Influence of the Male and Female Parents in the Reproduction of the Animal Species," *Monthly Journal of Medical Science*, XIX (Aug. 1854), 108–18; M. A. Pallen, "Heritage, or Hereditary Transmission," *St. Louis Medical & Surgical Journal*, XIV (Nov. 1856), 495. William Warren Potter, *How Should Girls be Educated? A Public Health Problem for Mothers, Educators, and Physicians* (Philadelphia, 1891), 9.

[12]As one clerical analyst explained, "All the spare force of nature is concerned in this interior nutritive system, unfitting and disinclining the woman for strenuous muscular and mental enterprise, while providing for the shelter and nourishment of offspring throughout protracted periods of embryo and infancy." William C. Conant, "Sex in Nature and Society," *Baptist Quarterly*, IV (April 1870), 183.

writings, a physician in 1869 depicted an idealized female world, rooted in the female reproductive system, sharply limited socially and intellectually, yet offering women covert and manipulative modes of exercising power.

> Mentally, socially, spiritually, she is more interior than man. She herself is an interior part of man, and her love and life are always something interior and incomprehensible to him.... Woman is to deal with domestic affections and uses, not with philosophies and sciences.... She is priest, not king. The house, the chamber, the closet, are the centres of her social life and power, as surely as the sun is the centre of the solar system.... Another proof of the interiority of woman, is the wonderful secretiveness and power of dissimulation which she possesses.... Woman's secrecy is not cunning; her dissimulation is not fraud. They are intuitions of spiritual perceptions, full of tact and wisdom, leading her to conceal or reveal, to speak or be silent, to do or not to do, exactly at the right time and in the right place.[13]

The image granted women in these hypothetical designs was remarkably consistent with the social role traditionally allotted them. The instincts connected with ovulation made her by nature gentle, affectionate, and nurturant. Weaker in body, confined by menstruation and pregnancy, she was both physically and economically dependent upon the stronger, more forceful male, to whom she necessarily looked up to with admiration and devotion.

Such stylized formulae embodied, however, a characteristic yet entirely functional ambiguity. The Victorian woman was more spiritual than man, yet less intellectual, closer to the divine, yet prisoner of her most animal characteristics, more moral than man, yet less in control of her very morality. While the sentimental poets placed woman among the angels and doctors praised the transcendent calling of her reproductive system, social taboos made woman ashamed of menstruation, embarrassed and withdrawn during pregnancy, self-conscious and purposeless during and after menopause. Her body, which so inexorably defined her personality and limited her role, appeared to woman often degrading and confining.[14] The very romantic rhetoric which tended to suffocate nineteenth-century discussions of femininity only underlined with irony the distance between behavioral reality and the forms of conventional ideology.

The nature of the formalistic scheme implied as well a relationship between the fulfilling of its true calling and ultimate social health. A woman who lived

---

[13]William H. Holcombe, *The Sexes here and hereafter* (Philadelphia, 1869), 201–01. William Holcombe was a Swedenborgian, and these contrasting views of the masculine and feminine also reflect New Church doctrines.

[14]In regard to pregnancy many middle-class women "sought to hide their imagined shame as long as possible," by tightening corsets and then remaining indoors, shunning even the best of friends—certainly never discussing the impending event. Henry B. Hemenway, *Healthful Womanhood and Childhood: Plain Talks to Non-Professional Readers* (Evanston, Ill., 1894); Elizabeth Evans, *The Abuse of Maternity* (Philadelphia, 1875), 28–29.

"unphysiologically"—and she could do so by reading or studying in excess, by wearing improper clothing, by long hours of factory work, or by a sedentary, luxurious life—could produce only weak and degenerate offspirng. Until the twentieth century, it was almost universally assumed that acquired characteristics in the form of damage from disease and improper life-styles in parents would be transmitted through heredity; a nervous and debilitated mother could have only nervous, dyspeptic, and undersized children.[15] Thus appropriate female behavior was sanctioned not only by traditional injunctions against the avoidance of individual sin in the form of inappropriate and thus unnatural modes of life but also by the higher duty of protecting the transcendent good of social health, which could be maintained only through the continued production of healthy children. Such arguments were to be invoked with increasing frequency as the nineteenth century progressed.

In mid-nineteenth-century America it was apparent that women—or at least some of them—were growing dissatisfied with traditional roles. American society in mid-nineteenth century was committed—at least formally—to egalitarian democracy and evangelical piety. It was thus a society which presumably valued individualism, social and economic mobility, and free will. At the same time it was a society experiencing rapid economic growth, one in which an increasing number of families could think of themselves as middle class and could seek a life-style appropriate to that station. At least some middle-class women, freed economically from the day-to-day struggle for subsistence, found in these values a motivation and rationale for expanding their roles into areas outside the home. In the Jacksonian crusades for piety, for temperance, for abolition, and in pioneering efforts to aid the urban poor, women played a prominent role, a role clearly outside the confines of the home. Women began as well to demand improved educational opportunities—even admission to colleges and medical schools. A far greater number began, though more covertly, to see family limitation as a necessity if they would preserve health, status, economic security, and individual autonomy.

Only a handful of nineteenth-century American women made a commitment to overt feminism and to the insecurity and hostility such a commitment implied. But humanitarian reform, education, and birth control were all issues which presented themselves as real alternatives to every respectable churchgoing American woman.[16] Contemporary medical and biological

---

[15]For a brief summary of late nineteenth-century assumptions in regard to human genetics, see Charles E. Rosenberg, "Factors in the Development of Genetics in the United States: Some Suggestions," *Journal of the History of Medicine*, XXII (Jan. 1967), 31–33.

[16]Since both male and female were ordinarily involved in decisions to practice birth control, the cases are not strictly analogous. Both, however, illustrate areas of social conflict organized about stress on traditional role characteristics. This discussion emphasizes only those aspects of birth control debate which placed responsibility on woman. Commentators did indeed differ in such emphases; in regard to abortion, however, writers of every religious and ideological persuasion agreed in seeing the matter as woman's responsibility.

arguments identified, reflected, and helped to eliminate two of these threats to traditional role definitions: demands by women for higher education and family limitation.

Since the beginnings of the nineteenth century, American physicians and social commentators generally had feared that American women were physically inferior to their English and Continental sisters. The young women of the urban middle and upper classes seemed in particular less vigorous, more nervous than either their own grandmothers or European contemporaries. Concern among physicians, educators, and publicists over the physical deterioration of American womanhood grew steadily during the nineteenth century and reached a high point in its last third.

Many physicians were convinced that education was a major factor in bringing about this deterioration, especially education during puberty and adolescence. It was during these years that the female reproductive system matured, and it was this process of maturation that determined the quality of the children which American women would ultimately bear. During puberty, orthodox medical doctrine insisted, a girl's vital energies must be devoted to development of the reproductive organs. Physicians saw the body as a closed system possessing only a limited amount of vital force; energy expended in one area was necessarily removed from another. The girl who curtailed brain work during puberty could devote her body's full energy to the optimum development of its reproductive capacities. A young woman, however, who consumed her vital force in intellectual activities was necessarily diverting these energies from the achievement of true womanhood. She would become weak and nervous, perhaps sterile, or more commonly, and in a sense more dangerously for society, capable of bearing only sickly and neurotic children—children able to produce only feebler and more degenerate versions of themselves.[17] The brain and ovary could not develop at the same time. Society, mid-century physicians warned, must protect the higher good of racial health by avoiding situations in which adolescent girls taxed their intellectual faculties in academic competition. "Why," as one physician pointedly asked, "spoil a good mother by making an ordinary grammarian?"[18]

Yet where did America's daughters spend these years of puberty and adolescence, doctors asked, especially the daughters of the nation's most

---

[17]"The results," as Edward H. Clarke put it in his widely discussed polemic on the subject, "are monstrous brains and puny bodies; abnormally active cerebration, and abnormally weak digestion; flowing thought and constipated bowels; lofty aspirations and neuralgic sensations...." Edward H. Clark, *Sex in Education: Or, a Fair Chance for Girls* (Boston, 1873), 41. Thomas A. Emmett, in his widely used textbook of gynecology, warned in 1879 that girls of the better classes should spend the year before and two years after puberty at rest. "Each menstrual period should be passed in the recumbent position until her system becomes accustomed to the new order of life." Thomas Addis Emmett, *The Principles and Practice of Gynecology* (Philadelphia, 1879), 21.

[18]T. S. Clouston, *Female Education from a Medical Point of View* (Edinburgh, 1882), 20; Potter, *How Should Girls be Educated?* 9.

virtuous and successful middle-class families? They spent these years in schools; they sat for long hours each day bending over desks, reading thick books, competing with boys for honors. Their health and that of their future children would be inevitably marked by the consequences of such unnatural modes of life.[19] If such evils resulted from secondary education, even more dramatically unwholesome was the influence of higher education upon the health of those few women intrepid enough to undertake it. Yet their numbers increased steadily, especially after a few women's colleges were established in the East and state universities in the Midwest and Pacific Coast began cautiously to accept coeducation. Women could now, critics agonized, spend the entire period between the beginning of menstruation and the maturation of their ovarian systems in nerve-draining study. Their adolescence, as one doctor pointed out, contrasted sadly with those experienced by healthier, more fruitful forebears: "Our great-grandmothers got their schooling during the winter months and let their brains lie fallow for the rest of the year. They knew less about Euclid and the classics than they did about housekeeping and housework. But they made good wives and mothers, and bore and nursed sturdy sons and buxom daughters and plenty of them at that."[20]

Constant competition among themselves and with the physically stronger males disarranged the coed's nervous system, leaving her anxious, prey to hysteria and neurasthenia. One gynecologist complained as late as 1901:

> the nervous force, so necessary at puberty for the establishment of the menstrual function, is wasted on what may be compared as trifles to perfect health, for what use are they without health? The poor sufferer only adds another to the great army of neurasthenia and sexual incompetents, which furnish neurologists and gynecologists with so much of their material... bright eyes have been dulled by the brain-fag and sweet temper transformed into irritability, crossness and hysteria, while the womanhood of the land is deteriorating physically.
>
> She may be highly cultured and accomplished and shine in society, but her future husband will discover too late that he has married a large outfit of headaches, backaches and spine aches, instead of a woman fitted to take up the duties of life.[21]

---

[19]The baleful hereditary effects of woman's secondary education served as a frequent sanction against this unnatural activity. Lawrence Irwell, "The Competition of the Sexes and its Results," *American Medico-Surgical Bulletin*, X (Sept. 19, 1896), 319–20. All the doyens of American gynecology in the late-nineteenth century—Emmett, J. Marion Sims, T. Gaillard Thomas, Charles D. Meigs, William Goodell, and Mitchell—shared the conviction that higher education and excessive development of the nervous system might interfere with woman's proper performance of her maternal functions.

[20]William Goodell, *Lessons in Gynecology* (Philadelphia, 1879), 353.

[21]William Edgar Darnall, "The Pubescent Schoolgirl," *American Gynecological & Obstetrical Journal*, XVIII (June 1901), 490.

Such speculations exerted a strong influence upon educators, even those connected with institutions which admitted women. The state universities, for example, often prescribed a lighter course load for females or refused to permit women admission to regular degree programs. "Every physiologist is well aware," the Regents of the University of Wisconsin explained in 1877, "that at stated times, nature makes a great demand upon the energies of early womanhood and that at these times great caution must be exercised lest injury be done. . . . Education is greatly to be desired," the Regents concluded:

> but it is better that the future matrons of the state should be without a University training than that it should be produced at the fearful expense of ruined health; better that the future mothers of the state should be robust, hearty, healthy women, than that, by over study, they entail upon their descendants the germs of disease.[22]

This fear for succeeding generations born of educated women was widespread. "We want to have body as well as mind," one commentator noted, "otherwise the degeneration of the race is inevitable."[23] Such transcendent responsibilities made the individual woman's personal ambitions seem trivial indeed.

One of the remedies suggested by both educators and physicians lay in tempering the intensely intellectualistic quality of American education with a restorative emphasis on physical education. Significantly, health reformers' demands for women's physical education were ordinarily justified not in terms of freeing the middle-class woman from traditional restrictions on bodily movement, but rather as upgrading her ultimate maternal capacities. Several would-be physiological reformers called indeed for active participation in house-cleaning as an ideal mode of physical culture for the servant-coddled American girl. Bedmaking, clothes scrubbing, sweeping, and scouring provided a varied and highly appropriate regimen.[24]

Late nineteenth-century women physicians, as might have been expected, failed ordinarily to share the alarm of their male colleagues when contemplating the dangers of coeducation. No one, a female physician commented sardonically, worked harder or in unhealthier conditions than the washer-

---

[22]Board of Regents, University of Wisconsin, *Annual Report, for the Year Ending, September 30, 1877* (Madison, 1877), 45.

[23]Clouston, *Female Education*, 19.

[24]James E. Reeves, *The Physical and Moral Causes of Bad Health in American Women* (Wheeling, W.Va., 1875), 28; John Ellis, *Deterioration of the Puritan Stock and its Causes* (New York, 1884), 7; George Everett, *Health Fragments or, Steps Toward a True Life: Embracing Health, Digestion, Disease, and the Science of the Reproductive Organs* (New York, 1874), 37; Nathan Allen, "The Law of Human Increase; Or Population based on Physiology and Psychology," *Quarterly Journal of Psychological Medicine*, II (April 1868), 231; Nathan Allen, "The New England Family," *New Englander* (March 1882), 9–10; Pye Henry Chavasse, *Advice to a Wife on the Management of her Own Health. And on the Treatment of Some of the Complaints Incidental to Pregnancy, Labour and Suckling with an Introductory Chapter especially Addressed to a Young Wife* (New York, 1886), 73–75.

woman; yet, would-be saviors of American womanhood did not inveigh against this abuse—washing, after all, was appropriate work for women. Women doctors often did agree with the general observation that their sisters were too frequently weak and unhealthy; however, they blamed not education or social activism but artificialities of dress and slavery to fashion, aspects of the middle-class woman's life-style which they found particularly demeaning. "The fact is that girls and women can bear study," Alice Stockham explained, "but they cannot bear compressed viscera, tortured stomachs and displaced uterus," the results of fashionable clothing and an equally fashionable sedentary life. Another woman physician, Sarah Stevenson, wrote in a similar vein: " 'How do I look?' is the everlasting story from the beginning to the end of woman's life. Looks, not books, are the murderers of American women."[25]

Even more significant than this controversy over woman's education was a parallel debate focusing on the questions of birth control and abortion. These issues affected not simply a small percentage of middle- and upper-middle-class women, but all men and women. It is one of the great and still largely unstudied realities of nineteenth-century social history. Every married woman was immediately affected by the realities of childbearing and child rearing. Though birth control and abortion had been practiced, discussed—and reprobated—for centuries, the mid-nineteenth century saw a dramatic increase in concern among spokesmen for the ministry and medical profession.[26]

Particularly alarming was the casualness, doctors charged, with which seemingly respectable wives and mothers contemplated and undertook abortions and how routinely they practiced birth control. One prominent New York gynecologist complained in 1874 that well-dressed women walked into his consultation room and asked for abortions as casually as they would for a

---

[25]Sarah H. Stevenson, *The Physiology of Woman, Embracing Girlhood, Maternity and Mature Age* (2nd ed., Chicago, 1881), 68, 77; Alice Stockham, *Tokology: A Book for Every Woman* (rev. ed., Chicago, 1887), 257. Sarah H. Stevenson noted acidly that "the unerring instincts of woman have been an eloquent theme for those who do not know what they are talking about." Stevenson, *Physiology of Woman*, 79. The dress reform movement held, of course, far more significant implications than one would gather from the usually whimsical attitude with which it is normally approached; clothes were very much a part of woman's role. Health reformers, often critical as well of the medical establishment whose arguments we have—essentially—been describing, were often sympathetic to women's claims that not too much, but too little, mental stimulation was the cause of their ills, especially psychological ones. M. L. Holbrook, *Hygiene of the Brain and Nerves and the Cure of Nervousness* (New York, 1878), 63–64, 122–23; James C. Jackson, *American Womanhood: Its Peculiarities and Necessities* (Dansville, N.Y., 1870), 127–31.

[26]For documentation of the progressive drop in the white American birth rate during the nineteenth century, and some possible reasons for this phenomenon, see Yasukichi Yasuba, *Birth Rates of the White Population in the United States, 1800–1860: An Economic Study* (Baltimore, 1962); J. Potter, "American Population in the Early National Period," Paul Deprez, ed., *Proceedings of Section V of the Fourth Congress of the International Economic History Association* (Winnipeg, Canada, 1970), 55–69. For a more general background to this trend, see A. M. Carr-Saunders, *World Population: Past Growth and Present Trends* (London, 1936).

cut of beefsteak at their butcher.[27] In 1857, the American Medical Association nominated a special committee to report on the problem; then appointed another in the 1870s; between these dates and especially in the late 1860s, medical societies throughout the country passed resolutions attacking the prevalence of abortion and birth control and condemning physicians who performed and condoned such illicit practices. Nevertheless, abortions could in the 1870s be obtained in Boston and New York for as little as ten dollars, while abortifacients could be purchased more cheaply or through the mail. Even the smallest villages and rural areas provided a market for the abortionist's services; women often aborted any pregnancy which occurred in the first few years of marriage. The Michigan Board of Health estimated in 1898 that one third of all the state's pregnancies ended in abortion. From 70 to 80 percent of these were secured, the board contended, by prosperous and otherwise respectable married women who could not offer even the unmarried mother's "excuse of shame."[28] By the 1880s, English medical moralists could refer to birth control as the "American sin" and warn against England's women following in the path of America's faithless wives.[29]

---

[27] A. K. Gardner, *Conjugal Sins against the Laws of Life and Health* (New York, 1874), 131. H. R. Storer of Boston was probably the most prominent and widely read critic of such "conjugal sins." Abortion had in particular been discusssed and attacked since early in the century, though it was not until the postbellum years that it became a widespread concern of moral reformers. Alexander Draper, *Observations on Abortion. With an Account of the Means both Medicinal and Mechanical, Employed to Produce that Effect*... (Philadelphia, 1839); Hugh L. Hodge, *On Criminal Abortion; A Lecture* (Philadelphia, 1854). Advocates of birth control routinely used the dangers and prevalence of abortion as one argument justifying their cause.

[28] *Report of the Suffolk District Medical Society On Criminal Abortion and Ordered Printed... May 9, [1857]* (Boston, 1857), 2. The report was almost certainly written by Storer. The Michigan report is summaried in William D. Haggard, *Abortion: Accidental, Essential, Criminal.* Address before the Nashville Academy of Medicine, Aug. 4, 1898 (Nashville, Tenn., 1898), 10. For samples of contemporary descriptions of prevalence, cheapness, and other aspects of abortion and birth control in the period, see Ely Van De Warker, *The Detection of Criminal Abortion, and a Study of Foeticidal Drugs* (Boston, 1872); Evans, *Abuse of Maternity*; Horatio R. Storer, *Why Not? A Book for Every Woman* (2nd ed., Boston 1868); [N. F. Cook,] *Satan in Society: By A Physician* (Cincinnati, 1876); Discussion, *Transactions of the Homeopathic Medical Society of New York*, IV (1866), 9–10; H. R. Storer and F. F. Heard, *Criminal Abortion* (Boston, 1868); H. C. Ghent, "Criminal Abortion, or Foeticide," *Transactions of the Texas State Medical Association at the Annual Session 1888–89* (1888–1889), 119–46; Hugh Hodge, *Foeticide, or Criminal Abortion: A Lecture Introductory to the Course on Obstetrics, and Diseases of Women and Children. University of Pennsylvania* (Philadelphia, 1869), 3–10. Much of the medical discussion centered about the need to convince women that the traditional view that abortion was no crime if performed before quickening was false and immoral and to pass and enforce laws and medical society proscriptions against abortionists.

[29] Compare the warning of Pomeroy, *Ethics of Marriage*, v, 56, with editorial, "A Conviction for Criminal Abortion," *Boston Medical & Surgical Journal*, CVI (Jan. 5, 1882), 18–19. It is significant that discussions of birth control in the United States always emphasized the role and motivations of middle-class women and men; in England, following the canon of the traditional Malthusian debate, the working class and its needs played a far more prominent role. Not until late in the century did American birth control advocates tend to concern themselves with the needs and welfare of the working population. It is significant as well that English birth control advocates often used the prevalence of infanticide as an argument for birth control; in America this was rarely discussed. And one doubts if the actual incidence of infanticide was substantially greater in London than New York.

So general a phenomenon demands explanation. The only serious attempts to explain the prevalence of birth control in this period have emphasized the economic motivations of those practicing it—the need in an increasingly urban, industrial, and bureaucratized society to limit numbers of children so as to provide security, education, and inheritance for those already brought into the world. As the nineteenth century progressed, it has been argued, definitions of appropriate middle-class life-styles dictated a more and more expansive pattern of consumption, a pattern—especially in an era of recurring economic instability—particularly threatening to those large numbers of Americans only precariously members of the secure economic classes. The need to limit offspring was a necessity if family status was to be maintained.[30]

Other aspects of nineteenth-century birth control have received much less historical attention. One of these needs only to be mentioned for it poses no interpretative complexities; this was the frequency with which childbirth meant for women pain and often lingering incapacity. Death from childbirth, torn cervixes, fistulae, prolapsed uteri were widespread "female complaints" in a period when gynecological practice was still relatively primitive and pregnancy every few years common indeed. John Humphrey Noyes, perhaps the best-known advocate of family planning in nineteenth-century America, explained poignantly why he and his wife had decided to practice birth control in the 1840s:

> The [decision] was occasioned and even forced upon me by very sorrowful experiences. In the course of six years my wife went through the agonies of five births. Four of them were premature. Only one child lived.... After our last disappointment, I pledged my word to my wife that I would never again expose her to such fruitless suffering....[31]

The Noyeses' experience was duplicated in many homes. Young women were simply terrified of having children.[32]

Such fears, of course, were not peculiar to nineteenth-century America. The dangers of disability and death consequent upon childbirth extended back to the beginning of time, as did the anxiety and depression so frequently associated with pregnancy. What might be suggested, however, was that

---

[30]For a guide to literature on birth control in nineteenth-century America, see Norman Himes, *Medical History of Contraception* (Baltimore, 1936). See also J. A. Banks, *Prosperity and Parenthood: A Study of Family Planning among the Victorian Middle Classes* (London, 1954), and J. A. and Olive Banks, *Feminism and Family Planning in Victorian England* (Liverpool, 1964); Margaret Hewitt, *Wives and Mothers in Victorian Industry* (London, *ca.* 1958). For the twentieth century, see David M. Kennedy, *Birth Control in America*.

[31]John Humphrey Noyes, *Male Continence* (Oneida, N.Y., 1872), 10–11.

[32]It is not surprising that the design for a proto-diaphragm patented as early as 1846 should have been called "The Wife's protector." J. B. Beers, "Instrument to Prevent Conception, Patented Aug. 28th, 1846," design and drawings (Historical Collections, Library of the College of Physicians of Philadelphia).

economic and technological changes in society added new parameters to the age-old experience. Family limitation for economic and social reasons now appeared more desirable to a growing number of husbands; it was, perhaps, also, more technically feasible. Consequently married women could begin to consider, probably for the first time, alternative life-styles to that of multiple pregnancies extending over a third of their lives. Women could begin to view the pain and bodily injury which resulted from such pregnancies not simply as a condition to be borne with fatalism and passivity, but as a situation that could be avoided. It is quite probable, therefore, that, in this new social context, increased anxiety and depression would result once a woman, in part at least voluntarily, became pregnant. Certainly, it could be argued, such fears must have altered women's attitudes toward sexual relations generally. Indeed the decision to practice birth control must necessarily have held more than economic and status implications for the family; it must have become an element in the fabric of every marriage's particular psycho-sexual reality.[33]

A third and even more ambiguous aspect of the birth control controversy in nineteenth-century America relates to the way in which attitudes toward contraception and abortion reflected role conflict within the family. Again and again, from the 1840s on, defenders of family planning—including individuals as varied and idealistic as Noyes and Stockham, on the one hand, and assorted quack doctors and peddlers of abortifacients, on the other—justified their activities not in economic terms, but under the rubric of providing women with liberty and autonomy. Woman, they argued with remarkable unanimity, must control her own body; without this she was a slave not only to the sexual impulses of her husband but also to endless childbearing and rearing. "Woman's equality in all the relations of life," a New York physician wrote in 1866, "implies her absolute supremacy in the sexual relation....it is her absolute and indefeasible right to determine when she will and when she will not be exposed to pregnancy." "God and Nature," another physician urged, "have given to the female the complete control of her own person, so far as

---

[33]In some marriages, for example, even if the male had consciously chosen, indeed urged, the practice of birth conrol, he was effectively deprived of a dimension of sexual pleasure and of the numerous children which served as tangible and traditional symbols of masculinity as well as the control over his wife which the existence of such children implied. In some marriages, however, birth control might well have brought greater sexual fulfillment because it reduced the anxiety of the female partner. Throughout the nineteenth century withdrawal was almost certainly the most common form of birth control. One author described it as "a practice so universal that it may well be termed a national vice, so common that it is unblushingly acknowledged by its perpetrators, for the commission of which the husband is even eulogized by his wife." [Cook,] *Satan in Society*, 152. One English advocate of birth control was candid enough to argue that "the real objection underlying the opposition, though it is not openly expressed, is the idea of the deprivation of pleasure supposed to be involved." Austin Holyyoake, *Large or Small Families* (London, 1892), 11.

sexual congress and reproduction are concerned."[34] The assumption of all these writers was clear and unqualified: women, if free to do so, would choose to have sexual relations less frequently, and to have far fewer pregnancies. Implied in these arguments as well were differences as to the nature and function of sexual intercourse. Was its principal and exclusively justifiable function, as conservative physicians and clergymen argued, the procreation of children, or could it be justified as an act of love, of tenderness between individuals? Noyes argued that the sexual organs had a social, amative function separable from their reproductive function. Sex was justifiable as an essential and irreplaceable form of human affection; no man could demand this act unless it was freely given.[35] Nor could it be freely given in many cases unless effective modes of birth control were available to assuage the woman's anxieties. A man's wife was not his chattel, her individuality to be violated at will, and forced—ultimately—to bear unwanted and thus almost certainly unhealthy children.

Significantly, defenders of women's right to limit childbearing employed many of the same arguments used by conservatives to attack women's activities outside the home; all those baleful hereditary consequences threatened by over-education were seen by birth control advocates as resulting from the

---

[34] *R. T. Trall, Sexual Physiology: A Scientific and Popular Exposition of the Fundamental Problems in Sociology* (New York, 1866), xi, 202. As women awoke to a realization of their own "individuality," as a birth control advocate explained it in the 1880s, they would rebel against such "enforced maternity." E. B. Foote, Jr., *The Radical Remedy in Social Science: Or, Borning Better Babies* (New York, 1886), 132. See also Stevenson, *Physiology of Women*, 91; T. L. Nichols, *Esoteric Anthropology* (New York, 1824); E. H. Heywood, *Cupid's Yokes: Or, the Binding Force of Conjugal Life* (Princeton, Mass., 1877); Stockham, *Tokology*, 250; Alice Stockholm, *Karezza: Ethics of Marriage* (Chicago, 1896); E. B. Foote, *Medical Commonsense Applied to the Causes, Prevention and Cure of Chronic Diseases and Unhappiness in Marriage* (New York, 1864), 365; J. Soule, *Science of Reproduction and Reproductive Control. The Necessity of Some Abstaining from Having Children. The Duty of all to Limit their Families According to their Circumstances Demonstrated. Effects of Continence Effects of Self-Pollution—Abusive Practices. Seminal Secretion—Its Connection with Life. With all the Different Modes of Preventing Conception, and the Philosophy of Each* (n.p., 1856), 37; L. B. Chandler, *The Divineness of Marriage* (New York, 1872). To radical feminist Tennie C. Claflin, man's right to impose his sexual desires upon woman was the issue underlying all opposition to woman suffrage and the expansion of woman's role. Tennie C. Claflin, *Constitutional Equality: A Right of Woman: Or a Consideration of the Various Relations Which She Sustains as a Necessary Part of the Body of Society and Humanity; With Her Duties to Herself—together with a Review of the Constitution of the United States, Showing that the Right to Vote Is Guaranteed to All Citizens. Also a Review of the Rights of Children* (New York, 1871), 63. Particularly striking are the letters from women desiring birth control information. Margaret Sanger, *Motherhood in Bondage* (New York, 1928); E. B. Foote, Jr., *Radical Remedy*, 114–20; Henry C. Wright, *The Unwelcome Child; or, the Crime of an Undesigned and Undesired Maternity* (Boston, 1858). This distinction between economic, "physical," and role consideration, is, quite obviously, justifiable only for the sake of analysis; these considerations must have coexisted within each family in particular configuration.

[35] Noyes, *Male Continence*, 16; Frederick Hollick, *The Marriage Guide, Or Natural History of Generation; A Private Instructor for Married Persons and Those About to Marry, Both Male and Female* (New York, *ca.* 1860), 348; Trall, *Sexual Physiology*, 205–06.

bearing of children by women unwilling and unfit for the task, their vital energies depleted by excessive childbearing. A child, they argued, carried to term by a woman who desired only its death could not develop normally; such children proved inevitably a source of physical and emotional degeneracy. Were women relieved from such accustomed pressures, they could produce fewer but better offspring.[36]

Many concerned mid-nineteenth-century physicians, clergymen, and journalists failed to accept such arguments. They emphasized instead the unnatural and thus necessarily deleterious character of any and all methods of birth control and abortion. Even coitus interruptus, obviously the most common mode of birth control in this period, was attacked routinely as a source of mental illness, nervous tension, and even cancer. This was easily demonstrated. Sex, like all aspects of human bodily activity, involved an exchange of nervous energy; without the discharge of such accumulated energies in the male orgasm and the soothing presence of the male semen "bathing the female reproductive organs," the female partner could never, the reassuring logic ran, find true fulfillment. The nervous force accumulated and concentrated in sexual excitement would build up dangerous levels of undischarged energy, leading ultimately to a progressive decay in the unfortunate woman's physical and mental health. Physicians warned repeatedly that condoms and diaphragms—when the latter became available after mid-century—could cause an even more startlingly varied assortment of ills. In addition to the mechanical irritation they promoted, artificial methods of birth control increased the lustful impulse in both partners, leading inevitably to sexual excess. The resultant nervous exhaustion induced gynecological lesions, and then through "reflex irritation" caused such ills as loss of memory, insanity, heart disease, and even "the most repulsive nymphomania."[37]

Conservative physicians similarly denounced the widespread practice of inserting sponges impregnated with supposedly spermicidal chemicals into the vagina immediately before or after intercourse. Such practices, they warned, guaranteed pelvic injury, perhaps sterility. Even if a woman seemed in good health despite a history of practicing birth control, a Delaware physician explained in 1873 that "...as soon as this vigor commences to decline...

---

[36]Indeed, in these post-Darwinian years it was possible for at least one health reformer to argue that smaller families were a sign of that higher nervous evolution which accompanied civilization. [M. L. Holbrook,] *Marriage and Parentage* (New York, 1882). For the eugenic virtues of fewer but better children, see E. R. Shepherd, *For Girls: A Special Physiology: Being a Supplement to the Study of General Physiology. Twentieth Edition* (Chicago, 1887), 213; M. L. Griffith, *Ante-Natal Infanticide* (n.p. [1889]), 8.

[37]See Louis François Étienne Bergeret, *The Preventive Obstacle: Or Conjugal Onanism*, P. de Marmon, trans. (New York, 1870); C. H. F. Routh, *Moral and Physical Evils Likely to Follow if Practices Intended to Act as Checks to Population be not Strongly Discouraged and Condemned* (2nd ed., London, 1879), 13; Goodell, *Lessons in Gynecology*, 371, 374; Thomas Hersey, *The Midwife's Practical Directory; Or Woman's Confidential Friend: Comprising, Extensive Remarks on the Various Casualties and Forms of Diseases Preceding, Attending and Following the Period of Gestation, with appendix* (2nd ed., Baltimore, 1836), 80; William H. Walling, *Sexology* (Philadelphia, 1902), 79.

about the fortieth year, the disease [cancer] grows as the energies fail—the cancerous fangs penetrating deeper and deeper until, after excruciating suffering, the writhing victim is yielded up to its terrible embrace."[38] Most importantly, this argument followed, habitual attempts at contraception meant—even if successful—a mother permanently injured and unable to bear healthy children. If unsuccessful, the children resulting from such unnatural matings would be inevitably weakened. And if such grave ills resulted from the practice of birth control, the physical consequences of abortion were even more dramatic and immediate.[39]

Physicians often felt little hesitation in expressing what seems to the historian a suspiciously disproportionate resentment toward such unnatural females. Unnatural was of course the operational word; for woman's presumed maternal instinct made her primarily responsible for decisions in regard to childbearing.[40] So frequent was this habitual accusation that some medical authors had to caution against placing the entire weight of blame for birth control and abortion upon the woman; men, they reminded, played an important role in most such decisions.[41] In 1871, for example, the American Medical Association Committee on Criminal Abortion described women who patronized abortionists in terms which conjured up fantasies of violence and punishment:

> She becomes unmindful of the course marked out for her by Providence, she overlooks the duties imposed on her by the marriage contract. She yields to the

---

[38]J. R. Black, *The Ten Laws of Health; Or, How Disease Is Produced and Can be Prevented* (Philadelphia, 1873), 251. See also C. A. Greene, *Build Well. The Basis of Individual, Home, and National Elevation. Plain Truths Relating to the Obligations of Marriage and Parentage* (Boston, *ca.* 1885), 99; E. P. LeProhon, *Voluntary Abortion, or Fashionable Prostitution, with Some Remarks upon the Operation of Craniotomy* (Portland, Me., 1867), 15; M. Solis-Cohen, *Girl, Wife, and Mother* (Philadelphia, 1911), 213.

[39]There is an instructive analogy between these ponderously mechanistic sanctions against birth control and abortion and the psychodynamic arguments against abortion used so frequently in the twentieth century; both served precisely the same social function. In both cases, the assumption of woman's childbearing destiny provided the logical basis against which a denial of this calling produced sickness, in the nineteenth century through physiological, and ultimately, pathological processes—in the twentieth century through guilt and psychological but again, ultimately, pathological processes.

[40]A. K. Gardner, for example, confessed sympathy for the seduced and abandoned patron of the abortionist, "but for the married shirk, who disregards her divinely-ordained duty, we have nothing but contempt. . . ." Gardner, *Conjugal Sins*, 112. See also E. Frank Howe, *Sermon on Ante-Natal Infanticide delivered at the Congregational Church in Terre Haute, on Sunday Morning, March 28, 1869* (Terre Haute, Inc., 1869); J. H. Tilden, *Cursed before Birth* (Denver, *ca.* 1895); J. M. Toner, *Maternal Instinct, or Love* (Baltimore, 1864), 91.

[41]It must be emphasized that this is but one theme in a complex debate surrounding the issue of birth control and sexuality. A group of more evangelically oriented health reformers tended to emphasize instead the responsibility of the "overgrown, abnormally developed and wrongly directed amativeness of the man" and to see the woman as victim. John Cowan, Henry C. Wright, and Dio Lewis were widely read exemplars of this point of view. This group shared a number of assumptions and presumably psychological needs, and represents a somewhat distinct interpretive task. John Cowan, *The Science of A New Life* (New York, 1874), 275.

> pleasures—but shrinks from the pains and responsibilities of maternity; and, destitute of all delicacy and refinement, resigns herself, body and soul, into the hands of unscrupulous and wicked men. Let not the husband of such a wife flatter himself that he possesses her affection. Nor can she in turn ever merit even the respect of a virtuous husband. She sinks into old age like a withered tree, stripped of its foliage; with the stain of blood upon her soul, she dies without the hand of affection to smooth her pillow.[42]

The frequency with which attacks on family limitation in mid-nineteenth-century America were accompanied by polemics against expanded roles for the middle-class woman indicates with unmistakable clarity something of one of the motives structuring such jeremiads. Family limitation necessarily added a significant variable within conjugal relationships generally; its successful practice implied potential access for women to new roles and a new autonomy.

Nowhere is this hostility toward women and the desire to inculcate guilt over women's desire to avoid pregnancy more strikingly illustrated than in the warnings of "race suicide" so increasingly fashionable in the late-nineteenth century. A woman's willingness and capacity to bear children was a duty she owed not only to God and husband but to her "race" as well.[43] In the second half of the nineteenth century, articulate Americans forced to evaluate and come to emotional terms with social change became, like many of their European contemporaries, attracted to a world view which saw racial identity and racial conflict as fundamental. And within these categories, birthrates became all-important indices to national vigor and thus social health.

In 1860 and again in 1870, Massachusetts census returns began to indicate that the foreign born had a considerably higher birthrate than that of native Americans. Indeed, the more affluent and educated a family, the fewer children it seemed to produce. Such statistics indicated that native Americans in the Bay State were not even reproducing themselves. The social consequences seemed ominous indeed.

The Irish, though barely one quarter of the Massachusetts population, produced more than half of the state's children. "It is perfectly clear," A Boston clergyman contended in 1884, "that without a radical change in the religious ideas, education, habits, and customs of the natives, the present population

[42]W. L. Atlee and D. A. O'Donnell, "Report of the Committee on Criminal Abortion," *Transactions of the American Medical Association*, XXII (1871), 241.

[43]The most tireless advocate of these views was Nathan Allen, a Lowell, Massachusetts, physician and health reformer. Nathan Allen, "The Law of Human Increase; Or Population based on Physiology and Psychology," *Quarterly Journal Psychological Medicine*, II (April 1868), 209–66; Nathan Allen, *Changes in New England Population. Read at the Meeting of the American Social Science Association, Saratoga, September 6, 1877* (Lowell, Mass., 1877); Nathan Allen, "The Physiological Laws of Human Increase," *Transactions of the American Medical Association*, XXI (1870), 381–407; Nathan Allen, "Physical Degeneracy," *Journal of Psychological Medicine*, IV (Oct. 1870), 725–64; Nathan Allen, "The Normal Standard of Woman for Propagation," *American Journal of Obstetrics*, IX (April 1876), 1–39.

and their descendants will not rule that state a single generation."[44] A few years earlier a well-known New England physician, pointing to America's still largely unsettled western territories, had asked: "Shall they be filled by our own children or by those of aliens? This is a question that our own women must answer; upon their loins depends the future destiny of the nation." Native-born American women had failed themselves as individuals and society as mothers of the Anglo-Saxon race. If matters continued for another half century in the same manner, "the wives who are to be mothers in our republic must be drawn from trans-Atlantic homes. The Sons of the New World will have to re-act, on a magnificent scale, the old story of unwived Rome and the Sabines."[45]

Such arguments have received a goodly amount of historical attention, especially as they figured in the late-nineteenth and early twentieth centuries as part of the contemporary rationale for immigration restriction.[46] Historians have interpreted the race suicide argument in several fashions. As an incident in a general Western acceptance of racism, it has been seen as product of a growing alienation of the older middle and upper classes in the face of industrialization, urbanization, and bureaucratization of society. More specifically, some American historians have seen these race suicide arguments as rooted in the fears and insecurities of a traditionally dominant middle class as it perceived new and threatening social realities.

Whether or not historians care to accept some version of this interpretation—and certainly such motivational elements seem to be suggested in the rhetorical formulae employed by many of those bemoaning the failure of American Protestants to reproduce in adequate numbers—it ignores another element crucial to the logical and emotional fabric of these arguments. This is the explicit charge of female sexual failure. To a significant extent, contemporaries saw the problem as in large measure woman's responsibility; it was America's potential mothers, not its fathers, who were primarily responsible for the impending social cataclysm. Race suicide seemed a problem in social gynecology.

---

[44]Ellis, *Deterioration of Puritan Stock*, 3; Storer, *Why Not?* 85.

[45]Clarke, *Sex in Education*, 63. For similar warnings, see Henry Gibbons, *On Feticide* (San Francisco, 1878), 4; Charles Buckingham, *The Proper Treatment of Children, Medical or Medicinal* (Boston, 1873), 15; Edward Jenks, "The Education of Girls from a Medical Stand-Point," *Transactions of the Michigan State Medical Society*, XIII (1889), 52–62; Paul Paquin, *The Supreme Passions of Man* (Battle Creek, Mich., 1891), 76.

[46]These arguments, first formulated in the 1860s, had become clichés in medical and reformist circles by the 1880s. See Barbara Miller Solomon, *Ancestors and Immigrants: A Changing New England Tradition* (Cambridge, Mass., 1956); John Higham, *Strangers in the Land: Patterns of American Nativism, 1860–1925* (New Brunswick, N.J., 1955). Such arguments exhibited a growing consciousness of class as well as of ethnic sensitivity; it was the better-educated and more sensitive members of society, anti-Malthusians began to argue, who would curtail their progeny, while the uneducated and coarse would hardly change their habits. H. S. Pomeroy, *Is Man Too Prolific? The So-Called Malthusian Idea* (London, 1891), 57–58.

Though fathers played a necessary role in procreation, medical opinion emphasized that it was the mother's constitution and reproductive capacity which most directly shaped her offspring's physical, mental, and emotional attributes. And any unhealthy mode of life—anything in short which seemed undesirable to contemporary medical moralists, including both education and birth control—might result in a woman becoming sterile or capable of bearing only stunted offspring. Men, it was conceded, were subject to vices even more debilitating, but the effects of male sin and imprudence were, physicians felt, "to a greater extent confined to adult life; and consequently do not, to the same extent, impair the vitality of our race or threaten its physical destruction." Women's violation of physiological laws implied disaster to "the unborn of both sexes."[47]

Though such social critics tended to agree that woman was at fault, they expressed some difference of opinion as to the nature of her guilt. A few felt that lower birthrates could be attributed simply to the conscious and culpable decision of American women to curtail family size. Other physicians and social commentators, while admitting that many women felt little desire for children, saw the roots of the problem in somewhat different—and perhaps even more apocalyptic—terms. It was not, they feared, simply the conscious practice of family limitation which resulted in small families; rather the increasingly unnatural life-style of the "modern American woman" had undermined her reproductive capacities so that even when she would, she could not bear adequate numbers of healthy children. Only if American women returned to the simpler life-styles of the eighteenth and early nineteenth centuries could the race hope to regain its former vitality; women must from childhood see their role as that of robust and self-sacrificing mothers. If not, their own degeneration and that of the race was inevitable.

Why the persistence and intensity of this masculine hostility, of its recurring echoes of conflict, rancor, and moral outrage? There are at least several possible, though by no means exclusive, explanations. One centers on the hostility implied and engendered by the sexual deprivation—especially for the male—implicit in many of the modes of birth control employed at this time. One might, for example, speculate—as Oscar Handlin did some years ago—that such repressed middle-class sexual energies were channeled into a xenophobic hostility toward the immigrant and the black and projected into fantasies incorporating the enviable and fully expressed sexuality of these alien groups.[48] A similar model could be applied to men's attitudes toward women as well; social, economic, and sexual tensions which beset late nineteenth-

---

[47] Ellis, *Deterioration of Puritan Stock*, 10.

[48] Oscar Handlin, *Race and Nationality in American Life* (5th ed., Boston, 1957), 139–66.

century American men might well have caused them to express their anxieties and frustrations in terms of hostility toward the middle-class female.[49]

Such interpretations are, however, as treacherous as they are inviting. Obviously, the would be scientific formulations outlined here mirror something of post-bellum social and psychic reality. Certainly some middle-class men in the late-nineteenth century had personality needs—sexual inadequacies or problems of status identification—which made traditional definitions of gender roles functional to them. The hostility, even the violent imagery expressed toward women who chose to limit the number of children they bore indicates a significant personal and emotional involvement on the part of the male author. Some women, moreover, obviously used the mechanisms of birth control and, not infrequently sexual rejection, as role-sanctioned building blocks in the fashioning of their particular adjustment. Their real and psychic gains were numerous: surcease from fear and pain, greater leisure, a socially acceptable way of expressing hostility, and a means of maintaining some autonomy and privacy in a life which society demanded be devoted wholeheartedly to the care and nurturance of husband and children. Beyond such statements, however, matters become quite conjectural. At this moment in the development of both historical methodology and psychological theory great caution must be exercised in the development of such hypotheses—especially since the historians of gender and sexual behavior have at their disposal data which from a psychodynamic point of view is at best fragmentary and suggestive.[50]

What the nineteenth-century social historian can hope to study with a greater degree of certainty, however, is the way in which social change both caused and reflected tensions surrounding formal definitions of gender roles. Obviously, individuals as individuals at all times and in all cultures have experienced varying degrees of difficulty in assimilating the prescriptions of expected role behavior. When such discontinuities begin to affect comparatively large numbers and become sufficiently overt as to evoke a marked

---

[49]One might postulate a more traditionally psychodynamic explanatory model, one which would see the arguments described as a male defense against their own consciousness of sexual inadequacy or ambivalence or of their own unconscious fears of female sexual powers. These emphases are quite distinct. The first—though it also assumes the reality of individual psychic mechanisms such as repression and projection—is tied very much to the circumstances of a particular generation, to social location, and to social perception. The second kind of explanation is more general, time-free, and based on a presumably ever-recurring male fear of female sexuality and its challenge to the capacity of particular individuals to act and live an appropriately male role. For the literature on this problem, see Wolfgang Lederer, *The Fear of Women* (New York, 1968).

[50]At this time, moreover, most psychiatric clinicians and theoreticians would agree that no model exists to extend the insights gained from individual psychodynamics to the behavior of larger social groups such as national populations or social classes.

ideological response one can then speak with assurance of having located fundamental cultural tension.[51]

Students of nineteenth-century American and Western European society have long been aware of the desire of a growing number of women for a choice among roles different from the traditional one of mother and housekeeper. It was a theme of Henry James, Henrik Ibsen, and a host of other, perhaps more representative if less talented, writers. Women's demands ranged from that of equal pay for equal work and equal education for equal intelligence to more covert demands for abortion, birth control information, and sexual autonomy within the marriage relationship. Their demands paralleled and were in large part dependent upon fundamental social and economic developments. Technological innovation and economic growth, changed patterns of income distribution, population concentrations, demographic changes in terms of life expectancy and fertility all affected woman's behavior and needs. Fewer women married; many were numbered among the urban poor. Such women had to become self-supporting and at the same time deal with the changed self-image that self-support necessitated. Those women who married generally did so later, had fewer children, and lived far beyond the birth of their youngest child. At the same time ideological developments began to encourage both men and women to aspire to increased independence and self-fulfillment. All these factors interacted to create new ambitions and new options for American women. In a universe of varying personalities and changing economic realities, it was inevitable that some women at least

[51]Most societies provide alternative roles to accommodate the needs of personality variants—as, for example, the shaman role in certain Siberian tribes or the accepted man-woman homosexual of certain American Indian tribes. In the nineteenth-century English-speaking world such roles as that of the religious enthusiast and the chronic female invalid or hysteric may well have provided such modalities. But a period of peculiarly rapid or widespread social change can make even such available role alternatives inadequate mechanisms of adjustment for many individuals. Others in the same society may respond to the same pressures of change by demanding an undeviating acceptance of traditional role prescriptions and refusing to accept the legitimacy of such cultural variants. The role of the hysterical woman in late nineteenth-century America suggests many of the problems inherent in creating such alternative social roles. While offering both an escape from the everyday duties of wife and mother, and an opportunity for the display of covert hostility and aggression, this role inflicted great bodily (though non-organic) pain, provided no really new role or interest, and perpetuated—even increased—the patient's dependence on traditional role characteristics, especially that of passivity. The reaction of society, as suggested by the writings of most male physicians, can be described as at best an unstable compromise between patronizing tolerance and violent anger. See Carroll Smith Rosenberg, "The Hysterical Woman: Sex Roles and Role Conflict in 19th-Century America," 652–78. For useful discussions of hysteria and neurasthenia, see Ilza Veith, *Hysteria: The History of a Disease* (Chicago, 1965); Henri F. Ellenberger, *The Discovery of the Unconscious: The History and Evolution of Dynamic Psychiatry* (New York, 1970); Charles E. Rosenberg, "The Place of George M. Beard in Nineteenth-Century Psychiatry," *Bulletin of the History of Medicine*, XXXVI (May-June 1962), 245–59; John S. Haller, Jr., "Neurasthenia: The Medical Profession and the 'New Woman' of Late Nineteenth-Century," *New York State Journal of Medicine*, LXXI (Feb. 15, 1971), 473–82. Esther Fischer-Homberger has recently argued that these diagnostic categories masked an endemic male-female conflict: "Hysterie und Mysogynie—ein Aspekt der Hysteriegeschichte," *Gesnerus*, XXVI (1969), 117–27.

would—overtly or covertly—be attracted by such options and that a goodly number of men would find such choices unacceptable. Certainly for the women who did so the normative role of home-bound nurturant and passive woman was no longer appropriate or functional, but became a source of conflict and anxiety.

It was inevitable as well that many men, similarly faced with a rapidly changing society, would seek in domestic peace and constancy a sense of the continuity and security so difficult to find elsewhere in their society. They would—at the very least—expect their wives, their daughters, and their family relationships generally to remain unaltered. When their female dependents seemed ill-disposed to do so, such men responded with a harshness sanctioned increasingly by the new gods of science.

3.3

Report on the Diseases and Physical Peculiarities of the Negro Race

Samuel A. Cartwright, M.D.

Gentlemen:—On the part of the Committee, consisting of Doctors Copes, Williamson, Browning and myself, to investigate the diseases and physical peculiarities of our negro population, we beg leave TO REPORT—

That, although the African race constitutes nearly a moiety of our southern population, it has not been made the subject of much scientific investigation, and is almost entirely unnoticed in medical books and schools. It is only very lately, that it has, in large masses, dwelt in juxta position with science and mental progress. On the Niger and in the wilds of Africa, it has existed for thousands of years, excluded from the observation of the scientific world. It is only since the revival of learning, that the people of that race have been introduced on this continent. They are located in those parts of it, not prolific in books and medical authors. No medical school was ever established near them until a few years ago; hence, their diseases and physical peculiarities are almost unknown to the learned. The little knowledge that Southern physicians have acquired concerning them, has not been derived from books or medical lectures, but from facts learned from their own observation in the field of experience, or picked up here and there from others.

Before going into the peculiarities of their diseases, it is necessary to glance at the anatomical and physiological differences between the negro and the white man; otherwise their diseases cannot be understood. It is commonly taken for granted, that the color of the skin constitutes the main and essential difference between the black and the white race; but there are other differences more deep, durable and indelible, in their anatomy and physiology, than that of mere color. In the albino the skin is white, yet the organization is that of the negro. Besides, it is not only in the skin, that a difference of color exists between the negro and white man, but in the membranes, the muscles, and tendons and in all the fluids and secretions. Even the negro's brain and nerves, the chyle and all the humors, are tinctured with a shade of the pervading darkness. His bile is of a deeper color and his blood is blacker than the white man's. There is the same difference in the flesh of the white and black man, in regard to color, that exists between the flesh of the rabbit and the hare. His bones are whiter and harder than those of the white race, owing to their containing more phosphate of lime and less gelatine. His head is hung on the atlas differently from the white man; the face is thrown more upwards and the neck is shorter and less oblique; the spine more inwards, and the pelvis more obliquely outwards; the thigh-bones larger and flattened from before backwards; the bones more bent; the legs curved outwards or bowed; the feet flat; the gastrocnemii muscles smaller; the heel so long, as to make the ankle appear as if planted in the middle of the foot; the gait, hopper-hipped, or what the French call *l'allure déhanchée*, not unlike that of a person carrying a burden. The projecting mouth, the retreating forehead, the broad, flat nose, thick lips and wooly hair, are peculiarities that strike every beholder. According to Soemmerring and other anatomists, who have dissected the negro, his brain is a ninth or tenth less than in other races of men, his facial angle smaller, and all the nerves going from the brain, as also the ganglionic system of nerves, are larger in proportion than in the white man. The nerves distributed to the muscles are an exception, being smaller than in the white race. Soemmerring remarks, that the negro's brain has in a great measure run into nerves. One of the most striking differences is found in the much greater size of the *foramen magnum* in the negro than the white man. The foramen, or orifice between the brain and the spinal marrow, is not only larger, but the medulla oblongata, and particularly the nerves supplying the abdominal and pelvic viscera. Although the nose is flat, the turbinated bones are more developed, and the pituitary membrane, lining the internal cavities of the nose, more extensive than in the white man, and causing the sense of smell to be more acute. The negro's hearing is better, his sight is stronger, and he seldom needs spectacles.

The field of vision is not so large in the negro's eye as in the white man's. He bears the rays of the sun better, because he is provided with an anatomical peculiarity in the inner canthus, contracting the field of vision, and excluding the sun's rays,—something like the membrana nictitans, formed by a preternatural development of the plica lunaris, like that which is observed in apes. His imitative powers are very great, and he can agitate every part of the body at the same time, or what he calls *dancing all over*. From the diffusion of the brain, as it were, into the various organs of the body, in the shape of nerves to minister to the senses, everything, from the necessity of such a conformation, partakes of sensuality, at the expense of intellectuality. Thus, music is a mere sensual pleasure with the negro. There is nothing in his music addressing the understanding; it has melody, but no harmony; his songs are mere sounds, without sense or meaning—pleasing the ear, without conveying a single idea to the mind; his ear is gratified by sound, as his stomach is by food. The great development of the nervous system, and the profuse distribution of nervous matter to the stomach, liver and genital organs, would make the Ethiopian race entirely unmanageable, if it were not that this excessive nervous development is associated with a deficiency of red blood in the pulmonary and arterial systems, from a defective atmospherization or arterialization of the blood in the lungs—constituting the best type of what is called the lymphatic temperament, in which lymph, phlegm, mucus, and other humors, predominate over the red blood. It is this defective hematosis, or atmospherization of the blood, conjoined with a deficiency of cerebral matter in the cranium, and an excessive nervous matter distributed to the organs of sensation and assimilation, that is the true cause of that debasement of mind, which has rendered the people of Africa unable to take care of themselves. It is the true cause of their indolence and apathy, and why they have chosen, through countless ages, idleness, misery and barbarism, to industry and frugality,—why social industry, or associated labor, so essential to all progress in civilisation and improvement, has never made any progress among them, or the arts and sciences taken root on any portion of African soil inhabited by them; as is proved by the fact that no letters, or even hieroglyphics—no buildings, roads or improvements, or monuments of any kind, are any where found, to indicate that they have ever been awakened from their apathy and sleepy indolence, to physical or mental exertion. To the same physiological causes, deeply rooted in the organization, we must look for an explanation of the strange facts, why none of the languages of the native tribes of Africa, as proved by ethnographical researches, have risen above common names, standing for things and actions, to abstract terms or generalizations;—why no form of government on abstract principles, with divisions of power into separate departments, has ever been instituted by them;—why they have always preferred, as more congenial to their nature, a government combining the legislative, judicial and executive powers in the same individual, in the person of a petty king, a chieftain or master;—why, in America, if let alone, they always prefer the same kind of government of their forefathers, as it gives them more tranquility and sensual enjoyment, expands the mind and improves the morals, by arousing them from that natural indolence so fatal to mental and moral progress. Even if they did not prefer slavery, tranquility and sensual enjoyment, to liberty, yet their organization of mind is such, that if they had their liberty, they have not the industry, the moral virtue, the courage and vigilance to maintain it, but would relapse into barbarism, or into slavery, as they have done in Hayti. The reason of this is founded in unalterable physiological laws. Under the compulsive power of the white man, they are made to labor or exercise, which makes the lungs perform the duty of vitalizing the blood more perfectly than is done when they are left free to indulge in idleness. It is the red, vital blood, sent to the brain, that liberates their mind when under the white man's control; and it is the want of a sufficiency of red vital blood, that chains their mind to ignorance and barbarism, when in freedom.

The excess of organic nervous matter, and the deficiency of cerebral—the predominance of the humors over the red blood, from defective atmospherization of the blood in the lungs, impart to the negro a nature not unlike that of a new-born infant of the white race. In children, the nervous system predominates, and the temperament is lymphatic. The liver, and the rest of the glandular system, is out of proportion to the sanguineous and respiratory systems, the white fluids predominating over the red; the lungs consume less oxygen, and the liver separates more carbon, than in the adult age. This constitution, so well marked in infancy, is the type of the Ethiopian constitution, of all ages and sexes. It is well known, that in infancy, full and free respiration of pure fresh air in repose, so far from being required, is hurtful and prejudicial. Half smothered by its mother's bosom, or the cold external air carefully excluded by a warm room or external covering over the face, the infant reposes—re-breathing its own breath, warmed to the same temperature as that of its body, and loaded with carbonic acid and aqueous vapor. The natural effect of this kind of respiration is, imperfect atmospherization of the blood in the lungs, and a hebetude of intellect, from the defective vitalization of the blood distributed to the brain. But it has heretofore escaped the attention of the scientific world, that the defective atmospherization of the blood, known to occur during sleep in infancy, and to be the most congenial to their constitutions, is the identical kind of respiration most congenial to the negro constitution, of all ages and sexes, when in repose. This is proved by the fact of the universal practice among them of covering their head and faces, during sleep, with a blanket, or any kind of covering that they can get hold of. If they have only a part of a blanket, they will cover their faces when about to go to sleep. if they have no covering, they will throw their hands or arms across the mouth and nose, and turn on their faces, as if with an instinctive design to obstruct the entrance of the free external air into the lungs during sleep. As in the case with infants, the air that negroes breathe, with their faces thus smothered with blankets or other covering, is not so much the external air as their own breath, warmed to the same temperature as that of their bodies, by confinement and reinspiration. This instinctive and universal method of breathing, during sleep, proves the similarity of organization and physiological laws existing between negroes and infants, as far as the important function of respiration is concerned. Both are alike in re-breathing their own breath, and in requiring it to be warmed to their own temperature, by confinement which would be insupportable to the white race after passing the age of infancy. The inevitable effect of breathing a heated air, loaded with carbonic acid and aqueous vapor, is defective hematosis and hebetude of intellect.

Negroes, moreover, resemble children in the activity of the liver and in their strong assimilating powers, and in the predominance of the other systems over the sanguineous; hence they are difficult to bleed, owing to the smallness of their veins. On cording the arm of the stoutest negro, the veins will be found scarcely as large as a white boy's of ten years of age. They are liable to all the convulsive diseases, cramps, spasms, colics, etc., that children are so subject to.

Although their skin is very thick, it is as sensitive, when they are in perfect health, as that of children, and like them they fear the rod. They resemble children in another very important particular; they are very easily governed by love combined with fear, and are ungovernable, vicious and rude under any form of government whatever, not resting on love and fear as a basis. Like children, it is not necessary that they be kept under the fear of the lash; it is sufficient that they be kept under the fear of offending those who have authority over them. Like children, they are constrained by unalterable physiological laws, to love those in authority over them, who minister to their wants and immediate necessities, and are not cruel or unmerciful. The defective hematosis, in both cases, and the want of courage and energy of mind as a consequence thereof, produces in both an instinctive feeling of dependence on others, to direct them and to take care of them. Hence, from a law of his nature, the negro can no more help loving a kind master, than the child can help loving her who gives it suck.

Like children, they require government in every thing; food, clothing, exercise, sleep—all require to be prescribed by rule, or they will run into excesses. Like children, they are apt to over-eat themselves or to confine their diet too much to one favorite article, unless restrained from doing so. They often gorge themselves with fat meat, as children do with sugar.

One of the greatest mysteries to those unacquainted with the negro character, is the facility with which an hundred, even two or three hundred, able-bodied and vigorous negroes are kept in subjection by one white man, who sleeps in perfect security among them, generally, in warm weather, with doors and windows open, with all his people, called slaves, at large around him. But a still greater mystery is the undoubted fact of the love they bear to their masters, similar in all respects to the love that children bear to their parents, which nothing but severity or cruelty in either case can alienate. The physiological laws on which this instinctive and most mysterious love is founded in the one case, are applicable to the other. Like children, when well-behaved and disposed to do their duty, it is not the arbitrary authority over them that they dread, but the petty tyranny and imposition of one another. The overseer among them, like the school-master among children, has only to be impartial, and to preserve order by strict justice to all, to gain their good will and affections, and to be viewed, not as an object of terror, but as a friend and protector to quiet their fears of one another.

There is a difference between infant negroes and infant white children; the former are born with heads like gourds, the fontinelles being nearly closed and the sutures between the various bones of the head united,—not open and permitting of overlapping, as in white children. There is no necessity for the overlapping of the bones of the head in infant negroes, as they are smaller, and the pelvis of their mothers larger than in the white race. All negroes are not equally black—the blacker, the healthier and stronger; any deviation from the black color, in the pure race, is a mark of feebleness or ill health. When heated from exercise, the negro's skin is covered with an oily exudation that gives a dark color to white linen, and has a very strong odor. The odor is strongest in the most robust; children and the aged have very little of it.

I have thus hastily and imperfectly noticed some of the more striking anatomical and physiological peculiarities of the negro race. The question may be asked, Does he belong to the same race as the white man? Is he a son of Adam? Does his peculiar physical conformation stand in opposition to the Bible, or does it prove its truth? These are important question, both in a medical, historical and theological point of view. They can better be answered by a comparison of the facts derived from anatomy, physiology, history and theology, to see if they sustain one another. We learn from the Book of Genesis, that Noah had three sons, Shem, Ham and Japheth, and that Canaan, the son of Ham, was doomed to be servant of servants unto his brethren. From history, we learn, that the descendants of Canaan settled in Africa, and are the present Ethiopians, or black race of men; that Shem occupied Asia, and Japheth the north of Europe. In the 9th chapter and 27th verse of Genesis, one of the most authentic books of the Bible, is this remarkable prophecy: 'God shall enlarge Japheth, and he shall dwell in the tents of Shem; and Canaan *shall be* his servant.' Japheth has been greatly enlarged by the discovery of a new world, the continent of America. He found in it the Indians, whom natural history declares to be of Asiatic origin, in other words, the descendants of Shem: he drove out Shem, and occupied his tents: and now the remaining part of the prophecy is in the process of fulfilment, from the facts every where before us, of Canaan having become his servant. The question arises, Is the Canaanite, or Ethiopian, qualified for the trying duties of servitude, and unfitted for the enjoyment of freedom? If he be, there is both wisdom, mercy and justice in the decree dooming him to be servant of servants, as the decree is in conformity to his nature. Anatomy and physiology have been interrogated, and the response is, that the Ethiopian, or Canaanite, is unfitted, from his organization and the physiological laws predicated on that organization, for the responsible duties of a free man, but, like the child, is only fitted for a state of dependence and subordination. When history is interrogated, the response is that the only government under which the negro has made any improvement in mind, morals, religion, and the only government under which he has led a happy, quiet and contented life, is that under which he is subjected to the arbitrary power of Japheth, in obedience to the Divine decree. When the original Hebrew of the Bible is interrogated, we find, in the significant meaning of the original name of the negro, the identical fact set forth, which the knife of the anatomist at the dissecting table has made appear; as if the revelations of anatomy, physiology and history, were a mere re-writing of what Moses wrote. In the Hebrew word 'Canaan,' the original name of the Ethiopian, the word *slave by nature*, or language to the same effect, is written by the inspired penman. Hence there is no conflict between the revelations of the science of medicine, history, and the inductions drawn from the Baconian philosophy, and the authority of the Bible; one supports the other.

As an illustration, it is known that all the Hebrew names are derived from verbs, and are significant. The Hebrew verb *Canah*, from which the original name of the negro is derived, literally means *to submit himself—to bend the knee.* Gesenius, the best Hebrew scholar of modern times, renders both the Kal, Hiphil and Niphal form of the verb from which Canaan, the original name of the negro is derived, in the following Latin: *Genu flexit*—he bends the knee; *in genua procidet*—he falls on his knees; *depressus est animus*—his mind is depressed; *submisse se gessit*—he deports himself submissively; *fractus est*—he is crouched or broken; or in other words, *slave by nature*, the same thing which anatomy, physiology, history, and the inductions drawn from philosophical observations, prove him to be.

A knowledge of the great primary truth, that the negro is a slave by nature, and can never be happy, industrious, moral or religious, in any other condition than the one he was intended to fill, is of great importance to the theologian, the statesman, and to all those who are at heart seeking to promote his temporal and future welfare. This great truth, if better known and understood, would go far to prevent the East Indian Company and British government from indulging in any expectation of seeing their immense possessions in Asia enhanced in value, by the overthrow of slave labor in America, through the instrumentality of northern fanaticism; or of seeing the Union divided into two or more fragments, hostile to each other; or of gaining any advantages, that civil commotion on this side of the Atlantic would give to the tottering monarchies of Europe. With the subject under this aspect, the science of Medicine has nothing to do, further than to uncover its light, to show truth from error.

Without a knowledge of the physical differences between the Ethiopian and the Caucasian, the Queen of England's medical advisers would not be much better qualified to prescribe for a negro, than her parliament to legislate for him; or her subjects to dictate to us what position he should occupy in our republican Union of Sovereign States.

THE DISEASES OF NEGROES—PULMONARY CONGESTIONS, PNEUMONIA, ETC.

One of the most formidable complaints among negroes, and which is more fatal than any other, is congestion of the lungs, or what European writers would call false pleurisy, or peri-pneumonia notha. It is often called cold plague, typhus pneumonia, bilious pleurisy, etc., according to its particular type, and the circumstances attending it; sometimes the head complains more than any other part, and it then bears the misnomer, 'head pleurisy.' It occurs, mostly, in winter and spring, but is met with at every season of the year, when cold nights succeed to warm days. It is more common among those who sleep in open houses, without sufficient fires to keep them warm and comfortable. It is seldom observed among negroes who inhabit log cabins, with cemented or clay floors, or warm houses made of brick, or any material to exclude the cold wind and air. The frame houses, with open weather-boarding and loose floors, admitting air both at the sides and from below, are buildings formed in ignorance of the peculiar physiological laws of the negro's organization, and are the fruitful sources of many of his most dangerous diseases.

Want of sufficient fires and warm blankets, is also another cause of thoracic complaints. The negro's lungs, except when the body is warmed by exercise, are very sensitive to the impressions of cold air. When not working or taking exercise, they always crowd around a fire, even in comparatively warm weather, and seem to take a positive pleasure in breathing heated air and warm smoke. In cold weather, instead of sleeping with their feet to the fire, as all other kinds of people do, whether civilized or savage, they turn their head to the fire—evidently for the satisfaction of inhaling warm air, as congenial to their lungs, in repose, as it is to infants. In bed, when disposing themselves for sleep, the young and old, male and female, instinctively cover their heads and faces, as if to insure the inhalation of warm, impure air, loaded with carbonic acid and aqueous vapor. The natural effect of this practice is imperfect atmospherization of the blood—one of the heaviest chains that binds the negro to slavery. In treating, therefore, their pulmonary affections, the important fact should be taken into consideration, that cold air is inimical to the lungs of healthy negroes, when the body is in repose, and not heated by exercise, and consequently more prejudicial in the diseases of those organs. A small, steady fire, a close room, and plenty of thick blanket covering, aided with hot stimulating teas, are very essential means in the treatment of the pulmonary congestions to which their lungs are so prone. An accurate diagnosis, whether the complaint be a mere congestion, pleuritis or pneumonia, is not of much practical importance in the first instance, because, whether it be one or the other, warm air is equally essential, and warm stimulating teas, to determine to the surface. It is proper, first to warm the body by external means and stimulating drinks, after which, an emetic, followed by a purgative of a mild kind, will be beneficial. When there is pain in taking a full inspiration, a moderate blood-letting from the arm, followed by half grain or grain doses of tartar emetic, repeated at intervals of an hour or two, and combined with a little anodyne, to prevent its running off by the bowels, will be found a very effectual remedy in subduing inflammation and promoting expectoration. In the typhoid forms of pneumonia, the quinine, in efficient doses, combined with camphor, aromatics and calomel, is generally the best practice. Bleeding is not admissible in this form of pneumonia, otherwise they bear blood-letting in chest complaints much better than any others. But even in these, they will not bear repeated blood-letting, as the white race do.

BILIOUS AND ADYNAMIC FEVERS—REMITTENTS AND INTERMITTENTS

The next class of complaints to which they are mostly liable, are bilious and adynamic fevers—remittents and intermittents. Evacuating the stomach and bowels by a mild emetico-cathartic, combined with a weak anodyne carminative, to prevent its excessive action, is generally the best medicine to begin with; for, whatever be the type of the fever, as negroes are hearty eaters, it will be an advantage, in the after treatment of the case, to have the *prima via* cleared of their load of undigested food, and the superabundant mucosities poured out into the alimentary canal of a people so phleghmatic, when attacked with a fever suspending digestion, and interrupting absorption.

For this purpose, a combination of ipecacuanha, rhubarb and cream of tartar, each half a drachm, and a tea-spoonful of paregoric, in ginger or pepper tea, is a very safe and effectual medicine. It will vomit, if there be bile or much mucosity, and will afterwards act on the bowels, promote secretion of urine, and determine to the surface; after which, a dose or two of quinine will generally effect a cure. Calomel is used too indiscriminately in the treatment of their diseases; nevertheless, in obstinate cases, it is not to be dispensed with. Negroes are very liable to become comatose, particularly after watery operations, or in torpid states of the liver. Such cases are best treated by a combination of calomel, camphor, capsicum, quinine and laudanum, and a blister to the back of the neck. Cold water to the head is dangerous. Nearly all their complaints bear stimulating, aromatic substances much better than similar affections among white people, and will not tolerate evacuations so well. The pure anti-phlogistic treatment by evacuations, cold air, starvation and gum water, so effectual in the inflammatory complaints of the hematose white man, will soon sink them into hopeless collapse. Even under the use of anti-phlogistics in their inflammatory complaints, pepper or ginger tea, or some stimulant, is necessary to support the vital actions, which would soon fail under such insipid drinks as gum water. The reason of this is, that the fluids and all the secretions are more acrid than those of the white man. In the latter, the lungs consume more oxygen; the blood is redder and more stimulating, and all the fluids more bland and sweet: whereas, in the negro, the deficient hematosis renders the blood less stimulating, and requires acrid and piquant substances addressed to the digestive system, to supply the stimulus that would otherwise be derived from the air in the lungs. Although they are so liable to congestive and bilious fevers—remittents and intermittents—they are not liable to the dreaded *el vomito*, or yellow fever. At least, they have it so lightly, that I have never seen a negro die with black vomit, although I have witnessed a number of yellow fever epidemics. This is a strong proof against the identity of yellow fever and the other fevers just named.

SCROFULA, ETC.

Like children, negroes are very liable to colics, cramps, convulsions, worms, glandular and nervous affections, sores, biles, warts, and other diseases of the skin. Scrofula is very common among them. Rickets, diseases of the spine and hip joint, and white swellings, are not uncommon. They are also subject to the goitre. All very fat negroes, except women who have passed the prime of life, are unhealthy and scrofulous. The great remedy for the whole tribe of their scrofulous affections, without which all other remedies do very little good, is *sunshine*. The solar rays is one of the most efficient therapeutic agents in the treatment of many other affections to which they are liable. A good, wholesome, mixed diet, warm clothing, warm, dry lodgings, and inunction of the skin, with oleaginous substances, and occasional tepid baths of salt and water, are also very necessary remedies. The limits of this report will not permit me to go into details of familiar treatment, as the use of iodine, and the usual remedies.

FRAMBAESIA, PIAN, OR YAWS.

The Frambaesia, Pian, or Yaws, is a disease thought to be peculiar to negroes. I have seen it in its worst forms, in the West Indies. I have occasionally met with it in its modified form, in the States of Mississippi and Louisiana, where it is commonly mistaken for syphilis. It is a contagious disease, communicable by contact among those who greatly neglect cleanliness. Children are liable to it, as well as adults. It is supposed to be communicable, in a modified form, to the white race, among whom it resembles pseudo-syphilis, or some disease of the nose, throat or larynx. Further observations are wanting in regard to it. It is said to be very prevalent in Tamaulipas, in Mexico. Attacking the nose and throat, in the first instance, very similar to secondary syphilitic affections, without ever having appeared on the genital organs at all, except in the shape of a slight herpes preputialis. According to my experience, no other remedies have been found to make the least impression upon it but the deuto-chloride of mercury, combined with guaiacum and dulcamara. Our planters do not go to the North or to Europe to learn the art of making sugar, cotton, rice, and tobacco, but they send their sons there to study medicine in the hospitals, where nearly all the diseases they see arise from causes unknown on our plantations—want of food, fire, and the common necessaries of life. Very good physicians they might be, if they staid there; but, on returning home, they have to study Medicine over again, in the school of experience, before they can practice with success, particularly among negroes. It would be very strange, that among the whole multitude of medical schools in the United States, there is not one that has made any special provision for instruction in regard to three millions of people in the Southern States, and representing half the value of Southern property, differently organized in mind and body from any other people, and having diseases requiring peculiar treatment,—if it were not for the well-known fact of the predominance of a most erroneous hypothesis among statesmen, divines, and other classes of people nearly everywhere, 'That there are no radical or physical differences in mankind, other than those produced by external circumstances, and that the treatment applicable to the white man would be just as good, under similar external circumstances, for the negro.' This false hypothesis is at the root of the doctrine that the liberty and political institutions so beneficial to the white man, would be equally beneficial to the negro— and that there is no internal or physical difference between the two races. The every-day experience of the Southern people, where the two races dwell together, prove this hypothesis to be unfounded; whereas its fallacy is not so apparent to the people of the North and of Europe, where only one race of mankind is found in numbers sufficient to make comparisons between the two. Hence they have not the data to arrive at the truth, and nothing to correct the erroneous views that a false dogma has given them in regard to negro slavery. But it is most strange that our institutions for medical learning, South, should be doing nothing, with such ample materials around them, to overturn an hypothesis, founded in gross ignorance of the anatomy and physiology of the African race—an hypothesis threatening to cause a disruption of our federal government, and that could be disproved and put down forever at the dissecting table; as it also could be by contrasting the phenomena, drawn from daily observations taken among three millions of negroes, in health and disease, with the phenomena already drawn from observations of the white race; and thereby proving the difference of organization in mind and body between the two races. Stranger still, that our Southern schools in Medicine should be content to linger behind those of the North, without even hope of rivaling them in the numbers of their students, when a provision for rivaling them in the numbers of their students, when a provision for including, in their course of instruction, the three millions of people in our midst, not cared for by any school, would, in time, put them far a-head, by attracting the current of students South, who have heretofore been attracted to the North. Some provision in our schools especially devoted to the anatomy and physiology of our negroes,—to the treatment of their diseases,—to the best means to prevent sickness among them,—to improve their condition, and at the same time to make them more valuable to their owners, and governed with more ease and safety,—would be sending Science into a new and wide field of usefulness, to reap immense benefits for the millions of both races inhabiting the South.

NEGRO CONSUMPTION.

Negro consumption is a disease almost unknown to medical men of the Northern States and Europe. A few Southern physicians have acquired some valuable information concerning it, from personal experience and observation; but this knowledge is scattered in fragments about, and has never been condensed in a form to make it of much practical utility. It is hoped that Dr. Fenner's Southern Reports will collect the experience of our physicians, and make that experience more available than it has heretofore been; some physicians, looking upon negro consumption through Northern books, suppose it to be a variety of phthisis pulmonalis—but it has no form or resemblance to the phthisis of the white race, except in the emaciation, or when it is complicated with the relics of pneumonia, or a badly-cured pleurisy. Others regard it as a dyspepsia, or some disease of the liver or stomach; the French call it *mal d'estomac*. But dyspepsia is not a disease of the negro; it is, *par excellence*, a disease of the Anglo-Saxon race; I have never seen a well-marked case of dyspepsia among the blacks. It is a disease that selects its victims from the most intellectual of mankind, passing by the ignorant and unreflecting.

The popular opinion is, that negro consumption is caused by *dirt-eating*. The eating of dirt is not the cause, but only one of the effects—a mere symptom, which may or may not attend it. As in pica, there is often a depraved appetite for substances not nutritious, as earth, chalk, lime, etc.; but oftener, as in malacia, a depraved appetite, for nutritious substances to a greater degree, than for nonnutritious. In negro consumption, the patients are generally hearty eaters of all kinds of food; but there are exceptions.

The disease may be detected, at a very early stage of its existence, by the pale, whitish color of the mucous membrane lining the gums and the inside of the mouth, lips and cheeks: so white are the mucous surfaces, that some overseers call it the paper-gum disease. It can be detected, however, in its incipient state, by making the patient ascend a flight of stairs; the pulse will be accelerated from eighty or ninety beats, to an hundred and thirty or forty. All kinds of active exercise will greatly accelerate the pulse, that of walking up hill or up stairs more than any other. The skin is ashy, pale and dry; the veins of the head are distended, and show more than in health; occasionally during the day, there is some heat of the skin, and febrile excitement; the blood is poor, pale and thin, in the advanced stages, containing a very few red globules; but the pathognomonic symptoms of the complaint are the acceleration of the pulse on exercise, and the whiteness of the lining membrane of the cheeks, lips and gums; the lining membrane of the eye-lids is also pale and whitish. It is of importance to know the pathognomic signs in its early stages, not only in regard to its treatment, but to detect impositions, as negroes afflicted with the complaint are often for sale; the acceleration of the pulse on exercise incapacitates them for labor, as they quickly give out and have to leave their work. This induces their owners to sell them, although they may not know the cause of their inability to labor. Many of the negroes brought south for sale are in the incipient stage of the disease; they are found to be inefficient laborers, and are sold in consequence thereof.

In order to be able to prevent or cure any malady, it is necessary to know its cause, and its seat. The seat of negro consumption is not in the lungs, stomach, liver or any organ of the body, but in the mind, and its cause is generally mismanagement or bad government on the part of the master, and superstition on the part of the negro. The patients themselves believe that they are poisoned; they are right, but it is not the body, but the mind that is poisoned. Negroes are very jealous and suspicious; hence, if they are slighted or imposed on in any way, or over-tasked, or do not get what they call their rights, they are apt to fall into a morbid state of mind, with sulkiness and dissatisfaction very plainly depicted in their countenances. It is bad government to let them remain in this sulky, dissatisfied mood, without inquiring into its causes, and removing them; otherwise, its long continuance leads to the disease under consideration. They fancy, that their fellow-servants are against them, that their master or overseer cares nothing for them, or is prejudiced against them, and that some enemy on the plantation or in the neighborhood has tricked them, that is, laid poison for them to walk over, or given it to them in their food or drinks. On almost every large plantation, there are one or more negroes, who are ambitious of being considered in the character of conjurers—in order to gain influence, and to make the others fear and obey them. The influence that these pretended conjurers exercise over their fellow servants, would not be credited by persons unacquainted with the superstitious mind of the negro. Nearly all, particularly those who have passed the age of puberty, are at times kept in constant dread and terror by the conjurers. These impostors, like all other impostors, take advantage of circumstances to swell their importance, and to inculcate a belief in their miraculous powers to bring good or evil upon those they like or dislike. It may be thought that the old superstition about conjuration has passed away with the old stock of native Africans; but it is too deeply radicated in the negro intellect to pass away: intelligent negroes believe in it, who are ashamed to acknowledge it. The effect of such a superstition—a firm belief that he is poisoned or conjured—upon the patient's mind, already in a morbid state, and his health affected from hard usage, over-tasking or exposure, want of wholesome food, good clothing, warm comfortable lodging, and the distressing idea, that he is an object of hatred or dislike, both to his master and fellow servants, and has no one to befriend him, tends directly to generate that erythism of mind, which is the essential cause of negro consumption. This erythism of mind, like the erythism of the gravid uterus in delicate females, often causes a depraved appetite for earth, chalk, lime, and such indigestible substances. The digestive passages, in both cases, become coated with acescent mucosities, or clogged with saburricious matters. Natural instinct leads such patients to absorbents, to correct the state of the stomach.

In the depraved appetite caused by pregnancy, or in young women afflicted with leuchorrhoea, true art improves upon instinct, or the natural medication of the patients themselves, by substituting magnesia, cathartics, bitters and tonics. But for the same morbid appetite in negro consumption, the natural medication, resorted to by the instinctive wants of the patient, is mistaken for the cause of the disease. It is not only earth or clay that the patients have an appetite for, but, like chlorotic girls, they desire vinegar, pepper, salt, and stimulants. Their skins are dry, proving want of cutaneous exhalation; very little aqueous vapor is thrown off from the lungs, owing to their inability to take exercise. Consequently, defluxions occur on the mucous coat of the digestive passages, from want of action of the skin and lungs; the mucosity, lining the intestinal canal, interrupts the absorption of chyle—the blood becomes impoverished, and the body wastes away from interstitial absorption and want of nutriment.

As far as medication is concerned, I have found a combination of tartar emetic half grain, capsicum five grains, a tea-spoonful of charcoal, a table-spoonful of tincture of gum guaiacum, three times a-day, a good remedy; also, rubbing the whole surface of the body over with some oily substance. But these, as various other remedies, as purgatives, tonics, etc., should be assisted by removing the original cause of the dissatisfaction or trouble of mind, and by using every means to make the patient comfortable, satisfied and happy.

DRAPETOMANIA, OR THE DISEASE CAUSING SLAVES TO RUN AWAY

Drapetomania is from δραπέτης, a runaway slave, and μανια, *mad or crazy*. It is unknown to our medical authorities, although its diagnostic symptom, the absconding from service, is well known to our planters and overseers, as it was to the ancient Greeks, who expressed by the single word δραπέτης the fact of the absconding, and the relation that the fugitive held to the person he fled from. I have added to the word meaning runaway slave, another Greek term, to express the disease of the mind causing him to abscond. In noticing a disease not heretofore classed among the long list of maladies that man is subject to, it was necessary to have a new term to express it. The cause, in the most of cases, that induces the negro to run away from service, is as much a disease of the mind as any other species of mental alienation, and much more curable, as a general rule. With the advantages of proper medical advice, strictly followed, this troublesome practice that many negroes have of running away, can be almost entirely prevented, although the slaves be located on the borders of a free State, within a stone's throw of the abolitionists. I was born in Virginia, east of the Blue Ridge, where negroes are numerous, and studied medicine some years in Maryland, a slave State, separated from Pennsylvania, a free State, by Mason & Dixon's line—a mere air line, without wall or guard. I long ago observed that some persons, considered as very good, and others as very bad masters, often lost their negroes by their absconding from service; while the slaves of another class of persons, remarkable for order and good discipline, but not praised or blamed as either good or bad masters, never ran away, although no guard or forcible means were used to prevent them. The same management which prevented them from walking over a mere nominal, unguarded line, will prevent them from running away anywhere.

To ascertain the true method of governing negroes, so as to cure and prevent the disease under consideration, we must go back to the Pentateuch, and learn the true meaning of the untranslated term that represents the negro race. In the name there given to that race, is locked up the true art of governing negroes in such a manner that they cannot run away. The correct translation of that term declares the Creator's will in regard to the negro; it declares him to be the submissive knee-bender. In the anatomical conformation of his knees, we see '*genu flexit*' written in the physical structure of his knees, being more flexed or bent, than any other kind of man. If the white man attempts to oppose the Deity's will, by trying to make the negro anything else than '*the submissive knee-bender*,' (which the Almighty declared he should be,) by trying to raise him to a level with himself, or by putting himself on an equality with the negro; of if he abuses the power which God has given him over his fellowman, by being cruel to him or punishing him in anger, or by neglecting to protect him fom the wanton abuses of his fellow-servants and all others, or by denying him the usual comforts and necessaries of life, the negro will run away: but if he keeps him in the position that we learn from the Scriptures he was intended to occupy, that is, the position of submission, and if his master or overseer be kind and gracious in his bearing towards him, without condescension, and at the same time ministers to his physical wants and protects him from abuses, the negro is spell-bound, and cannot run away. '*He shall serve Japheth*; he shall be his servant of servants;'—on the conditions above mentioned—conditions that are clearly implied, though not directly expressed. According to my experience, the 'genu flexit'—the awe and reverence, must be exacted from them, or they will despise their masters, become rude and ungovernable and run away. On Mason and Dixon's line, two classes of persons were apt to lose their negroes; those who made themselves too familiar with them, treating them as equals, and making little or no distinction in regard to color; and, on the other hand, those who treated them cruelly, denied them the common necessaries of life, neglected to protect them against the abuses of others, or frightened them by a blustering manner of approach, when about to punish them for misdemeanors. Before negroes run away, unless they are frightened or panic-struck, they become sulky and dissatisfied. The cause of this sulkiness and dissatisfaction should be inquired into and removed, or they are apt to run away or fall into the negro consumption. When sulky and dissatisfied without cause, the experience of those on the line and elsewhere was decidedly in favor of whipping them out of it, as a preventive measure against absconding or other bad conduct. It was called whipping the devil out of them.

If treated kindly, well fed and clothed, with fuel enough to keep a small fire burning all night, separated into families, each family having its own house—not permitted to run about at night, or to visit their neighbors, or to receive visits, or to use intoxicating liquors, and not overworked or exposed too much to the weather, they are very easily governed—more so than any other people in the world. When all this is done, if any one or more of them, at any time, are inclined to raise their heads to a level with their master or overseer, humanity and their own good require that they should be punished until they fall into that submissive state which it was intended for them to occupy in all after time, when their progenitor received the name of Canaan, or 'submissive knee-bender.' They have only to be kept in that state, and treated like children, with care, kindness, attention and humanity, to prevent and cure them from running away.

DYSAESTHESIA AETHIOPIS, OR HEBETUDE OF MIND AND OBTUSE SENSIBILITY OF BODY—A DISEASE PECULIAR TO NEGROES—CALLED BY OVERSEERS, 'RASCALITY'

Dysaesthesia Aethiopis is a disease peculiar to negroes, affecting both mind and body, in a manner as well expressed by dysaesthesia, the name I have given it, as could be by a single term. There is both mind and sensibility, but both seem to be difficult to reach by impressions from without. There is partial insensibility of the skin, and so great a hebetude of the intellectual faculties as to be like a person half asleep, that is with difficulty aroused and kept awake. It differs from every other species of mental disease, as it is accompanied with physical signs or lesions of the body, discoverable to the medical observer, which are always present and sufficient to account for the symptoms. It is much more prevalent among free negroes living in clusters by themselves, than among slaves on our plantations, and attacks only such slaves as live like free negroes in regard to diet, drinks, exercise, etc. It is not my purpose to treat of the complaint as it prevails among free negroes, nearly all of whom are more or less afflicted with it, that have not got some white person to direct and to take care of them. To narrate its symptoms and effects among them would be to write a history of the ruins and dilapidation of Hayti and every spot of earth they have ever had uncontrolled possession over for any length of time. I propose only to describe its symptoms among slaves.

From the careless movements of the individuals affected with the complaint, they are apt to do much mischief, which appears as if intentional, but is mostly owing to the stupidness of mind and insensibility of the nerves induced by the disease. Thus, they break, waste and destroy everything they handle,—abuse horses and cattle,—tear, burn or rend their own clothing, and paying no attention to the rights of property, they steal other's to replace what they have destroyed. They wander about at night, and keep in a half-nodding sleep during the day. They slight their work,—cut up corn, cane, cotton or tobacco when hoeing it, as if for pure mischief. They raise disturbances with their overseers and fellow servants without cause or motive, and seem to be insensible to pain when subjected to punishment. The fact of the existence of such a complaint, making man like an automaton or senseless machine, having the above or similar symptoms, can be clearly established by the most direct and positive testimony. That it should have escaped the attention of the medical profession, can only be accounted for because its attention has not been sufficiently directed to the maladies of the negro race. Otherwise, a complaint of so common occurrence on badly-governed plantations, and so universal among free negroes, or those who are not governed at all,—a disease radicated in physical lesions and having its peculiar and well-marked symptoms, and its curative indications, would not have escaped the notice of the profession. The northern physicians and people have noticed the symptoms, but not the disease from which they spring. They ignorantly attribute the symptoms to the debasing influence of slavery on the mind, without considering that those who have never been in slavery, or their fathers before them, are the most afflicted, and the latest from the slave-holding South the least. The disease is the natural offspring of negro liberty—the liberty to be idle, to wallow in filth, and to indulge in improper food and drinks.

In treating of the anatomy and physiology of the negro, I showed that his respiratory system was under the same physiological laws as that of an infant child of the white race; that a warm atmosphere, loaded with carbonic acid and aqueous vapor, was the most congenial to his lungs during sleep, as it is to the infant; that, to insure the respiration of such an atmosphere, he invariably, as if moved by instinct, shrouds his head and face in a blanket or some other covering, when disposing himself to sleep; that if sleeping by the fire in cold weather, he turns his head to it, instead of his feet, evidently to inhale warm air; that when not in active exercise, he always hovers over a fire in comparatively warm weather, as if he took a positive pleasure in inhaling hot air and smoke when his body is quiescent. The natural effect of this practice, it was shown, caused imperfect atmospherization or vitalization of the blood in the lungs, as occurs in infancy, and a hebetude or torpor of intellect—from blood not sufficiently vitalized being distributed to the brain; also, a slothfulness, torpor and disinclination to exercise, from the same cause—the want of blood sufficiently areated or vitalized in the circulating system. When left to himself, the negro indulges in his natural disposition to idleness and sloth, and does not take exercise enough to expand his lungs and to vitalize his blood, but dozes out a miserable existence in the midst of filth and uncleanliness, being too indolent and having too little energy of mind to provide for himself proper food and comfortable lodging and clothing. The consequence is, that the blood becomes so highly carbonized and deprived of oxygen, that it not only becomes unfit to stimulate the brain to energy, but unfit to stimulate the nerves of sensation distributed to the body. A torpor and insensibility pervades the system; the sentient nerves distributed to the skin lose their feeling to so great a degree, that he often burns his skin by the fire he hovers over, without knowing it, and frequently has large holes in his clothes, and the shoes on his feet burnt to a crisp, without having been conscious of when it was done. This is the disease called dysaesthesia—a Greek term expressing the dull or obtuse sensation that always attends the complaint. When aroused from his sloth by the stimulus of hunger, he takes anything he can lay his hands on, and tramples on the rights, as well as on the property of others, with perfect indifference as to consequences. When driven to labor by the compulsive power of the white man, he performs the task assigned him in a headlong, careless manner, treading down with his feet, or cutting with his hoe the plants he is put to cultivate—breaking the tools he works with, and spoiling everything he touches that can be injured by careless handling. Hence the overseers call it 'rascality,' supposing that the mischief is intentionally done. But there is no premediated mischief in the case,—the mind is too torpid to meditate mischief, or even to be aroused by the angry passions to deeds of daring. Dysaesthesia, or hebetude of sensation of both mind and body, prevails to so great an extent, that when the unfortunate individual is subjected to punishment, he neither feels pain of any consequence, or shows any unusual resentment, more than by a stupid sulkiness. In some cases, anaesthesiae would be a more suitable name for it, as there appears to be an almost total loss of feeling. The term 'rascality,' given to this disease by overseers, is founded on an erroneous hypothesis and leads to an incorrect empirical treatment, which seldom or ever cures it.

The complaint is easily curable, if treated on sound physiological principles. The skin is dry, thick and harsh to the touch, and the liver inactive. The liver, skin and kidneys should be stimulated to activity, and be made assist in decarbonising the blood. The best means to stimulate the skin is, first, to have the patient well washed with warm water and soap; then, to anoint it all over with oil, and to slap the oil in with a broad leather strap; then to put the patient to some hard kind of work in the open air and sunshine, that will compel him to expand his lungs, as chopping wood, splitting rails or sawing with the cross-cut or whip saw. Any kind of labor will do that will cause full and free respiration in its performance, as lifting or carrying heavy weights, or brisk walking; the object being to expand the lungs by full and deep inspirations and expirations, thereby to vitalize the impure circulating blood by introducing oxygen and expelling carbon. This treatment should not be continued too long at a time, because where the circulating fluids are so impure as in this complaint, patients cannot stand protracted exercise without resting frequently and drinking freely of cold water or some cooling beverage, as lemonade, or alternated with pepper tea sweetened with molasses. In bad cases, the blood has always the appearance of blood in scurvy, and commonly there is a scorbutic affection to be seen on the gums. After resting until the palpitation of the heart caused by the exercise is allayed, the patient should eat some good wholesome food, well seasoned with spices and mixed with vegetables, as turnip or mustard salad, with vinegar. After a moderate meal, he should resume his work again, resting at intervals, and taking refreshments and supporting the perspiration by partaking freely of liquids. At night he should be lodged in a warm room with a small fire in it, and should have a clean bed, with sufficient blanket covering, and be washed clean before going to bed; in the morning, oiled, slapped and put to work as before. Such treatment will, in a short time, effect a cure in all cases which are not complicated with chronic visceral derangements. The effect of this or a like course of treatment is often like enchantment. No sooner does the blood feel the vivifying influences derived from its full and perfect atmospherization by exercise in the open air and in the sun, than the negro seems to be awakened to a new existence, and to look grateful and thankful to the white man whose compulsory power, by making him inhale vital air, has restored his sensation and dispelled the mist that clouded his intellect. His intelligence restored and, his sensations awakened, he is no longer the *bipedum nequissimus*, nor arrant rascal, he was supposed to be, but a good negro that can hoe or plow, and handle things with as much care as his other fellow-servants.

Contrary to the received opinion, a northern climate is the most favorable to the intellectual development of negroes, those of Missouri, Kentucky, and the colder parts of Virginia and Maryland, having much more mental energy, more bold and ungovernable than in the Southern lowlands; a dense atmosphere causing a better vitalization of their blood.

Although idleness is the most prolific cause of dysaesthesia, yet there are other ways that the blood gets deteriorated. I said before that negroes are like children, requiring government in everything. If not governed in their diet, they are apt to eat too much salt meat and not enough bread and vegetables, which practice generates a scorbutic state of the fluids and leads to the affection under consideration. This form of the complaint always shows itself in the gums, which become spongy and dark, and leave the teeth. Uncleanliness of skin and torpid liver also tend to produce it. A scurvy set of negroes means the same thing, in the South, as a disorderly, worthless set. That the blood, when rendered impure and carbonaceous from any cause, as from idleness, filthy habits, unwholesome food or alcoholic drinks, affects the mind, is not only known to physicians, but was known to the Bard of Avon when he penned the lines—'We are not ourselves when Nature, being oppressed, commands the mind to suffer with the body.'

According to unalterable physiological laws, negroes, as a general rule, to which there are but few exceptions, can only have their intellectual faculties awakened in a sufficient degree to receive moral culture, and to profit by religious or other instruction, when under the compulsatory authority of the white man; because, as a general rule, to which there are but few exceptions, they will not take sufficient exercise, when removed from the white man's authority, to vitalize and decarbonize their blood by the process of full and free respiration, that active exercise of some kind alone can effect. A northern climate remedies, in a considerable degree, their naturally indolent disposition; but the dense atmosphere of Boston or Canada can scarcely produce sufficient hematosis and vigor of mind to induce them to labor. From their natural indolence, unless under the stimulus of compulsion, they doze away their lives with the capacity of their lungs for atmospheric air only half expanded, from the want of exercise to superinduce full and deep respiration. The inevitable effect is, to prevent a sufficient atmospherization or vitalization of the blood, so essential to the expansion and the freedom of action of the intellectual faculties. The black blood distributed to the brain chains the mind to ignorance, superstition and barbarism, and bolts the door against civilization, moral culture and religious truth. The compulsory power of the white man, by making the slothful negro take active exercise, puts into active play the lungs, through whose agency the vitalized blood is sent to the brain, to give liberty to the mind, and to open the door to intellectual improvement. The very exercise, so beneficial to the negro, is expended in cultivating those burning fields in cotton, sugar, rice and tobacco, which, but for his labor, would, from the heat of the climate, go uncultivated, and their products lost to the world. Both parties are benefitted—the negro as well as his master—even more. But there is a third party benefitted—the world at large. The three millions of bales of cotton, made by negro labor, afford a cheap clothing for the civilized world. The laboring classes of all mankind, having less to pay for clothing, have more money to spend in educating their children, and in intellectual, moral and religious progress.

The wisdom, mercy and justice of the decree, that Canaan shall serve Japheth, is proved by the disease we have been considering, because it proves that his physical organization, and the laws of his nature, are in perfect unison with slavery, and in entire discordance with liberty—a discordance so great as to produce the loathsome disease that we have been considering, as one of its inevitable effects,—a disease that locks up the understanding, blunts the sensations and chains the mind to superstition, ignorance and barbarism. Slaves are not subject to this disease, unless they are permitted to live like free negroes, in idleness and filth—to eat improper food, or to indulge in spirituous liquors. It is not their masters' interest that they should do so; as they would not only be unprofitable, but as great a nuisance to the South, as the free negroes were found to be in London, whom the British government, more than half a century ago, colonized in Sierra Leone to get them out of the way. The mad fanaticism that British writers, lecturers and emissaries, and the East India Company, planted in our Northern States, after it was found by well-tried experiments, that free negroes in England, in Canada, in Sierra Leone and elsewhere, were a perfect nuisance, and would not work as free laborers, but would retrograde to barbarism, was not planted there in opposition to British policy. Whatever was the motive of Great Britain in sowing the whirlwind in our Northern States, it is now threatening the disruption of a mighty empire of the happiest, most progressive and Christian people, that ever inhabited the earth—and the only empire on the wide earth that England dreads as a rival, either in arts or in arms.

Our Declaration of Independence, which was drawn up at a time when negroes were scarcely considered as human beings, '*That all men are by nature free and equal*,' and only intended to apply to white men, is often quoted in support of the false dogma that all mankind possess the same mental, physiological and anatomical organization, and that the liberty, free institutions, and whatever else would be a blessing to one portion, would, under the same external circumstances, be to all, without regard to any original or internal differences, inherent in the organization. Although England preaches this doctrine, she practises in opposition to it every where. Instance, her treatment of the Gypsies in England, the Hindoos in India, the Hottentots at her Cape Colony, and the aboriginal inhabitants of New Holland. The dysaesthesia aethiopis adds another to the many ten thousand evidencies of the fallacy of the dogma that abolitionism is built on; for here, in a country where two races of men dwell together, both born on the same soil, breathing the same air, and surrounded by the same external agents—liberty, which is elevating the one race of people above all other nations, sinks the other into beastly sloth and torpidity; and the slavery, which the one would prefer death rather than endure, improves the other in body, mind and morals; thus proving the dogma false, and establishing the truth that there is a radical, internal, or physical difference between the two races, so great in kind, as to make what is wholesome and beneficial for the white man, as liberty, republican or free institutions, etc., not only unsuitable to the negro race, but actually poisonous to its happiness.

3.4

Should the Morphine Habit Be Classed as a Disease

J. M. Fort, M.D.

[Read before the North Texas Medical Association.]

Mr. President:—At the last meeting of this Association a very entertaining paper was read upon the subject and treatment of the morphine habit. The writer took the position that this habit, when persisted in for any considerable length of time, or when unusually large doses of the drug were necessary to gratify the acquired appetite and systemic demands of the patient, that the morbid condition became a disease, and should be treated as such. There was but little discussion upon the paper. One gentleman, however, was very emphatic in expressing the opinion that the morphine habit was not a disease, and that it should not be classed as such. I now propose to discuss this proposition briefly, to wit:

SHOULD THE MORPHINE HABIT BE CLASSED AS A DISEASE?

Are we to conclude, Mr. President, that the use of narcotic poisons, such as opium, morphine, cocaine, alcohol, etc., when persisted in for months and years, until in fact the system not only tolerates, but demands excessive doses of these toxic agents to satisfy its cravings, do not result in, or become diseases, in the general acceptation of the term?

If disease means dis-ease, or if you please ill-at-ease, then most assuredly this class of suffering humanity are entitled to all the nomenclature means, for of all people, perhaps, they are the most miserable. Each repeated dose of the drug bringing them into a sphere of exalted nervous exhiliration, accompanied by delightful sensations, for which they are repaid by a more protracted season in a sphere far more infamous in torture than purgatory or the theologian's Gehenna.

In support of the negative side of this proposition it is argued that the morphine habit (and I suppose the cocaine and alcohol habit as well) does not constitute disease because it is not accompanied by what we call a visible, local lesion of brain tissue.

When we use this word "lesion" to designate a pathological condition we too frequently throw unwarranted restrictions around its true meaning. This term embraces not only a separation, or destruction of continuity of tissues, such as is produced by wounds, ulcers, or a disintegration of the parts from inflammatory processes or otherwise; but it also embraces any morbid change of function, or any diversion, or alteration from a physiological to a pathological condition. Nor are we to infer that such an abnormality, or pathological condition, does not exist simply because we are not able, in the present status of medical science, to demonstrate or elucidate in what the abnormality consists. Such a conclusion would lead us to presume that medical science has reached that degree of perfection which enables it to comprehend all the mysterious occult laws of our being, when in fact we stand but on the threshold or border land of such knowledge. This ultimatum conclusion would exclude from our field of research and investigation lesions not yet demonstrated. St. Paul gives us a line of argument upon this subject which it would be well for us to follow in these cases. He says in a letter written to some friends in Rome: "That the invisible things of him from the creation of the world—are clearly seen—how Paul?—being understood by the things that are seen" Rom:1-20.

Certainly no one will dare say that epilepsy, catalepsy, and perhaps other nervous affections are not worthy of a place in the list of diseases, or that there are not lesions, or morbid changes of some character in such cases. It may be an ill arranged molecular structure, or atrophy of brain cells, or a deficiency of vital force or energy of certain groups of cells, or a disruption of etherial wave motion or of an electric current, or some other unknown morbid condition. Can it be said that lesions do not, or can not, exist simply because microscopists and pathologists have not been able as yet to determine their nature and character?

From a practical standpoint it matters not, in the cases under consideration whether the physician regards the mind, comprising the intellectual and emotional part of our being, as the product or offspring of brain action, or rather of brain forces, or whether he regards the cerebral mass as merely the home or reservoir of thought, so long as we know that it requires a normal, active, vital condition of the brain to perform healthy functions and send out normal manifestations or rational thought.

It would be useless for me to give in detail the long train of symptoms indicating the morbid conditions, physical, mental, and moral, resulting from the long continued used of this class of narcotic poisons, as these symptoms and morbid conditions are perfectly familiar to each and every one present. Every practitioner of medicine has observed with feelings of mingled regret and mortification, the debasing and demoralizing effects of these noxious agents upon the mental and moral attributes of their unfortunate patients, who, by habitual use have allowed themselves to be brought under their baneful influence.

I believe, Mr. President, that the organicity of the mental faculties, as well as their localization, is no longer a mooted question. In the great majority of these cases certain inhibitory or acquired faculties of the mind seem to lose their vital energy and inhibitory powers, being overridden and subordinated by the more *enduring inherent faculties*. Prior to the use of the drug these acquired attributes or mental faculties perform their functions with equal energy with the other faculties, sustaining a happy equilibrium and co-ordination of mental forces, a condition essential to the well balanced, well rounded, symmetrical character. But alas, this castle of thought, this citadel of refinement and culture, this store house of knowledge is ruthlessly invaded by this enemy and robbed of some of its richest treasures, the hitherto untarnished jewel "character" is bound in fetters, despoiled, wrecked and ruined. The honest man becomes a thief, and the refined, truthful woman a base fabricator. Truth, honor, sobriety and every refining, elevating, acquired attribute which ennobles and enriches the human mind are dominated and brought into subjection by the baser animal propensities and proclivities inherent in all animality. Wild, ungoverned and ungovernable passion, or appetite, now sways, controls and governs the unfortunate victim of this habit. Impelled by an irresistible desire, an exaggerated and intensified craving, an insatiate demon whose cry is ever give me more, give me more," the poor unfortunate creature finally ceases all resistance and yields himself a conquered victim, a willing slave. He not only feels that he is bound in fetters, but realizes his degradation and humiliation and yet, perhaps, more keenly than all else, he comprehends his utter helplessness and total inability to save himself. Experiments upon animals in whom these inhibitory faculties have never been developed only to the extent of domestication, demonstrate the fact that some of these toxic agents arouse their vicious, savage natures to the extent of making them dangerous companions.

Now, Mr. President, can a normal mind, with its intellectual and moral faculties well developed and cultivated, forming a complete, symmetrical character stored with the rich treasures of honor, truth, virtue, and nobility of soul, become thus perverted and disjointed, its appetites vitiated, its passions uncontrolled and its propensities unrestrained; I repeat, can this wonderful metamorphosis, this intellectual degeneracy, take place independent of either organic or functional lesions? In other words, does not this retrograde movement in mental evolution justify the conclusion that it can only be brought about by a destructive influence exerted upon the brain tissue by the continued action of this deleterious agent.

I am aware that criminology and sociology are as yet undeveloped sciences, and what may be regarded as a debasing habit or even a crime by the inhabitants of one country, may be regarded as a commendable virtue by the inhabitants of another, but our patients are of our own people, having the same manners, habits, practices, etc. as ourselves.

In this connection permit me to say that it is an historic fact, admitted and acknowledged by every one, that we have all come up by a process of evolution from a state of barbarism and savagery. Our ancestry in the ages of the past were not only ignorant, superstitious savages and barbarians, but the basest of criminals as well. Cannibalism, which is regarded as the lowest degree of human depravity, is practiced in some countries, and by some races, even at the present day. Now, if we take the cannibal as a type of the lowest specimen of mankind, as a starting point, or as one end of the long line of humanity, we will find that the world furnishes us samples of peoples in every stage of evolution and development, reaching from the degraded cannibal, up the scale, step by step, higher and higher, to the loftiest plane of thought as found among the most enlightened and civilized nations of the day. This same law of evolution applies with equal truth and force to the human mind, and more, when it ceases to move forward on the road of progress, either for want of healthy nutriment in the way of education and culture, or from disease, or from the decrepitude and decay incident to old age, it, like nations, begins its backward march over a road of degeneracy. Another important fact to be remembered in this connection is, that on this road of unceasing evolution and progress, there is no resting place or halting ground. Nations are either marching forward or retreating, they are either advancing or retrograding. Take Egypt, Greece and Rome for examples. Each of these countries after reaching the zenith of their national greatness and glory, from some cause, be it what it may, began a retrograde movement and now their greatness is only a matter of history. When one looks upon the pyramids or the yet more wonderful labyrinth (in the oases of Fayum), or the temples of Karnak and Luxor in Egypt; or the Parthenon, the Erictheon or the temple of Thesius in Greece; or the Colosseum, the tower of Trajan and the baths of Caracalla in Rome, I repeat, when one looks upon these once grand and imposing works of sculpture and art, and when we see their magnificent paintings and read their literature in the works of their orators, poets and statesmen, it takes no great effort of the imagination to comprehend to what heights of culture and refinement these ancient people achieved in all of the essential elements of true greatness and enlightened civilization. Then we have but to see their descendants, many of whom are now living in mud huts, suffering the pangs of poverty and want, and blinded by ignorance and superstition, to comprehend in all its fulness the reality, truth and force, of this law of progress and degeneracy.

This law of progress and degeneracy holds good throughout all nature. The degrees of development vary both in the animal and vegetable kingdom as it does in races of people, and also in individuals, in proportion to the inherited capacity for development and their environments in after life.

Another factor to be considered in this connection in the case of individuals, is that acquired mental attributes or qualifications are the first to desert the mind when this retrogression begins, no matter by what produced. With the aged this is most apparent in the loss of memory and judgement, the old become fickle and childish but happily retain their moral attributes. They live their childhood over again, the time when their attributes were most deeply planted in the mind. "Once a man and twice a child" applies with peculiar force to this class of people.

It is unnecessary for me to say to you, and yet I would have you bear in mind, that these acquired attributes are the inhibitory or restraining faculties which by a slow but gradual development have led the superior races out of, and away from the world's midnight, a time in history when all mankind were enveloped and shrouded in the darkness of ignorance and superstition. They are the faculties which are now leading us along the pathway of honor, truth and virtue, to a holier and purer life and to a higher and more exalted civilization. These are the faculties of the mind whose physiological functions seem for the most part to be injured by the continuous narcosis kept up by this and allied agents. The brain cells or brain forces being kept in a state of abnormal passivity, atrophied degeneration, to a degree at least, follows as a necessary result. In this degeneration of function, if not of the anatomical organs, I locate the lesion in these cases.

Unfortunately for mankind the first effect of this class of agents upon the mental faculties is one of excitation and exhilaration. It lifts the individual out of himself and above himself, transports him into a realm of ecstatic bliss and happiness, "Behold old things have passed away and all things become new," pain and suffering, trouble and sorrow, poverty and want, are banished as by magic. The pendulum swings high into a world of enchantment, filled with weird phantasms, a world created by unduly exalted overwrought emotional sensations. This spell of dreamy bliss and happiness, however, is of but short duration, reaction follows, the pendulum drops back, and the patient now enters a land, first, of ease and quiet, followed by a delightful sensation of contentment and satisfaction, but passes on to a condition of torpor and indifference, followed by stupefaction and sleep, or drunken semi delirium, in other words it carries him first to Heaven then to hell, or after the habit is acquired, to hell and then to Heaven.

Do we not find here, Mr. President, in this continued preternatural exaltation and depression, this persistent stupefaction, ample grounds for believing that although unseen even by the aid of the microscope, that there exists lesions, and lesions of a grave character, inaugurated and perpetuated in the functional disturbance, if not in the anatomical structure, of the brain itself, in this class of cases.

SUMMARY OF CONTENTS

We argue that heredity throughout the long line of animality transmits the baser propensities and proclivities we find dominant in the lower order of animals, and also in the untutored and barbarous races.

We believe that the cause of crime in the majority of instances grows out of a want of development and culture of the rudamentary mental faculties.

We regard the inhibitory or restraining faculties to be acquired by the process of evolution in the march of civilization and progress.

We believe these faculties to be the first impaired in this class of cerebral diseases, as evidenced by the disregard of moral and social restraint by patients afflicted with these disorders.

Lastly: We believe that the persistent use of morphine, and other narcotic poisons, in inordinate doses, inaugurate functional and perhaps organic lesions in the manner indicated in this paper. And may I not add that a serious injury is done the race by the transmission of these defective organs to posterity.

In conclusion, Mr. President, if I accomplish no other good in reading this paper than to warn the young practitioner against the danger which lurks, like a hidden serpent, in the protracted use of these remedial agents I shall feel that my labor has not been in vain.

3.5

Homosexuality as a Mental Illness

Richard Green

In this article I will address myself to an issue which will become increasingly topical as some groups, traditionally passive acceptors of their societal role, adopt more assertive postures. One such group is the Gay Liberation movement, the outspoken faction of men and women whose preferred sexual partners are those of the same anatomic sex. Though their voices may be still relatively few, and occasionally harsh, they will become increasingly loud and articulate and will unavoidably be heard. They raise for the theory, practice, and public policy of psychiatry questions which cannot be dismissed in a cavalier manner, but demand careful attention and responsible consideration.

Before proceeding, I will define, for the purpose of this article, what is meant by homosexuality. Clinicians from the time of Freud (1905) have differentiated between exclusive (obligatory) homosexuality and situational (facultative) homosexuality. The latter term applies to someone engaging in a genital relationship with a same-sexed person, but whose sexual preference is for an opposite-sexed person. Temporarily, under conditions of deprivation (prison, long voyage at sea), he will engage in homosexual behavior. Psychiatrists generally do not consider such persons sexually disordered and in need of treatment. It is with those persons who exclusively or predominantly want sexual experiences with people of the same sex that psychiatry, and thus this article, concerns itself.

DEFINITIONS OF ILLNESS

Is homosexuality a mental illness? The current American Psychiatric

Association official diagnostic nomenclature does not use the words *illness* or *disease*, but rather speaks of *disorders. Disorder* is defined in the Random House dictionary as "lack of order or regular arrangement, confusion, an irregularity, a public disturbance, a derangement of physical or mental health or functions." Synonyms include *malady*, *illness*, and *sickness*. *Disease*, which has *disorder* as a synonym, is defined as "a condition in which there is an incorrect function... any deranged or depraved condition of the mind." Thus when we speak of disorder, we are speaking of disease and illness.

The arbitrariness of defining a pattern of behavior as health or illness has been stressed by Hoffman (1968):

> ...the diagnosis of mental illness is the result of a process of social definition ...certain individuals in society, usually psychiatrists, are granted the prerogative of making this definition. The standard which the psychiatrist has to use is determined by the general consensus among the community of his colleagues. Thus, he can, as is presently the case, define homosexuality *per se* as a mental illness merely because a large number of his colleagues have agreed that it is so.

BIOLOGICAL CONSIDERATIONS

The bases on which homosexuality has been categoried as an illness, a disorder, a defect, or unnatural behavior are varied. A prominent one is the biological: Man, as all other currently existing animals, has survived the hazardous evolutionary trail because of significant biologically adaptive mechanisms not possessed by those organisms which have perished. Thus "natural selection" has provided a definition of what is "natural," "normal," adaptable, or serviceable. Clearly, any species, not hermaphroditic, which would uniformly select for sexual expression only those other species members not biologically suited for reproduction would soon become extinct.

I am unaware of the existence of any society in which the majority of persons exclusively practiced homosexuality with just enough heterosexual individuals to insure the society's survival. It could be that in the history which is evolution, the process of insuring species survival demanded a dominant program for heterosexual mating. This dominance would emerge irrespective of social experience. A science fiction experiment to test this hypothesis would be raising a child in total isolation from other individuals, much in the manner in which Harlow (1962) raised monkeys. Would the child still automatically emerge as heterosexual? Harlow's monkeys do not. But neither are they homosexual. They are so interpersonally stunted from lack of other-monkey experience that they do not channel their sexual drive toward other living things. However, monkeys do appear to have an innate heterosexual orientation. They need not resolve their oedipal conflict to be heterosexual; nor need they be so taught by their parents; nor, for that matter, need they even have to *see* their parents. If the only other monkey contact they have while growing up is other young male and female monkeys (*also* raised without parents), their heterosexuality will emerge. Thus, at least in the rhesus monkey, there is a biologic program for heterosexuality. It would indeed be a rather inefficient attribute for heterosexuality to be entirely *learned*, if by its presence or absence hinged propagation of the species!

If, in fact, there is a biologic, evolution-derived basis for innate heterosexuality, can this be considered an absolute criterion by which to judge sexual behavior? If there is agreement that heterosexuality is indispensable to insure viability and that universal homosexuality would be catastrophic, must homosexual behavior by *many* people *some* of the time or a *few all* the time be considered unnatural or disordered? Furthermore, can an argument which favors one type of behavior on the basis of its possessing evolutionary merit remain equally valid when its teleologic footing is currently only barely applicable? Exclusive heterosexual adaptability is hardly necessary for continuation of the species at present and, in fact, in its present exhuberance, perils it. But is there here an absolute timeless value on which temporal events bear little influence?

To what extent can man consider himself dissociated from his two- and four-legged predecessors? Subhuman species are generally considered to manifest a series of automatic biologic responses, their central nervous system turning on to the distinctive smell or perceptual configuration of another animal, with biologic juices and neuronal circuits carrying them relentlessly on to consummate the copulatory act. It is often stated that as animals ascend the evolutionary scale, they become less and less automatically responsive to this biologic program. Yet the degree to which man, by his extraordinary capacity to remember, symbolize, and abstract, is divorced from these mechanisms is not clear. The basic animal nervous system remains. The limbic system, the endocrine glands, and their secretions have not been abandoned along the evolutionary trail. Rather they have been overlaid with additional components.

Clinical examples of persons who show dramatically altered patterns of sexual behavior concomitant with stimulation or destruction of specific brain parts are several. They demonstrate the extent to which basic mechanisms lay hidden behind that great façade of cortical matter. A few of these examples will be cited. Two provocative case reports emanate from the Maudsley Hospital in London. One is of a safety-pin fetishist with temporal lobe epilepsy (Mitchell, Falconer, and Hill, 1954). In this case, a "perverse form of erotic gratification, the contemplation of a safety pin, became attached to the onset of the epileptic seizure. . . ." A left anterior temporal lobectomy removed both the epilepsy and the fetishism. The second report describes a young adult male, with no childhood or adolescent history of transvestism, who developed an overwhelming desire to cross-dress in association with cerebral calcifications due to cysticercosis (Davies and Morganstern, 1960).

Another case report describes a female with "sexual seizures" in association with atrophy of the right temporal lobe (Freeman and Nevis, 1969). During these seizures she would experience the sensation of a red-hot poker being inserted into her vagina and would loudly verbalize sexual needs. These episodes, for which she would later be amnesic, were brought under some control with anticonvulsant medication. Another case report describes nymphomania in association with seizures and a vascular brain tumor. Removal of the hemangioma restored her previously typical sexual behavior (Erickson, 1945). Both hypersexuality and hyposexuality have been linked with temporal lobe epilepsy in a series of reports from the Johns Hopkins Hospital in Baltimore (Blumer and Walker, 1967; Blumer, 1969).

In a more recent controversial report, four adult males, sexually attracted to adolescent and preadolescent boys, were described as successfully treated by destruction of the ventromedial nucleus of the hypothalamus in the nondominant hemisphere (Roeder and Muller, 1969).

To what extent, then, *is* man dissociated from his prehuman heritage? Fifty percent? Twenty percent? Eighty percent? How much dissociation is required for man to be considered *free?* If it *is* there, all humans should be *predominantly* heterosexual and none exclusively homosexual because the best census-taker of animal sexuality, Frank Beach (personal communication), says that, while many animals will *at times* show "homosexual" behavior, there are no examples of animals that are *exclusively* "homosexual." Where are the 4 percent Kinsey (Kinsey *et al.,* 1948) found for human males?

Since most animals show *some* degree of "homosexual" behavior, could *exclusive* heterosexuality in man be argued to be an inhibition of homosexuality or, at least, an inhibition of ambisexual expression? Why should man, *among all the animals,* show *exclusive heterosexuality?* Perhaps this question can be raised to the counterargument that, since man is the only species that evinces *exclusive homosexuality* (if such is true), it must therefore follow that this is an experientially derived, "unnatural" phenomenon.

If indeed there *is* a basis for an evolution-derived biologic heritage, an "instinctive" predisposition to heterosexuality (of whatever magnitude), does it necessarily follow that those whose gross behavior does not manifest this tendency must therefore be ill, defective, malformed, or immature? At what point, if any, does the nonemergence of an innate tendency signify *disorder*, and how much innate tendency must there be present before this assumption can be made?

If there *is* a biologic basis for heterosexuality, is there also one for homosexuality? Though scientists have argued for decades over whether there exists a biologic basis for homosexuality, it has only been in recent years that any significant measure of understanding has existed as to what such as basis might be. An area of particular research interest has been the influence of sex hormones on the prenatally developing organism in permanently modifying sexual and social behavior. It has, for example, been shown that depriving a male rat fetus of the male hormone for a brief period allows for the later adult expression of female-type behavior, and that exposing a female rhesus monkey fetus to male hormone promotes postnatal male-type behavior. It is believed that male hormone organizes the prenatally developing central nervous system, at least at the level of the hypothalamus, to mediate masculine behavior postnatally. Can these findings be applicable to man?

Until recently, there have been no reports of male hormone abnormality in association with human homosexuality. There are now a few, as yet unconfirmed, reports, which must be interpreted with caution, but which are provocative enough to warrant scrutiny and attempts at replication. In the first, a group of twenty male homosexuals were discriminated from a group of twenty male heterosexuals on the basis of their twenty-four-hour urine content of two stereoisomeric androgen metabolites, androsterone and etiocholanolone (Margolese, 1970). In the second, urine assays of three male and four female homosexuals were reported. Urinary testosterone levels were abnormally low, compared to heterosexual controls, in the two males who practiced exclusive homosexuality and in the normal range for a third, who engaged in both heterosexual and homosexual behavior. In the females, levels of testosterone were raised, while those of estrogens, particularly estrone, were lower than the heterosexual female controls (Loraine *et al.,* 1970). The most compelling study to date has compared thirty young-adult male homosexuals with fifty male heterosexuals for plasma testosterone levels and additionally has examined semen of the homosexuals. Those males who were exclusively or almost exclusively homosexual has testosterone levels approximately one-half that of the heterosexuals. Additionally, there was a significant correlation between sperm count and degree of homosexuality, with fewer sperm being associated with a greater degree of homosexual orientation (Kolodny *et al.,* 1971). These preliminary findings are raised because of the possibility that one of these or some *other* biologic basis of homosexuality will one day be demonstrated.

Genetic studies have been cited as also lending support to an innate predisposition to homosexuality. Kallman's study (1952) found 100 percent concordance for homosexuality in thirty-seven pairs of probably monozygotic twins compared to twelve percent concordance in twenty-six dizygotic twin pairs. These figures have been criticized by many, including Kallman, but cannot be simply dismissed. Heston and Shields (1968) studied the Maudsley twin registry and found twelve male twins with a primary or secondary diagnosis of homosexuality. Two of the five monozygotic twin pairs (40 percent) were concordant for homosexuality. In a third pair, the co-twin had delusions of changing sex. Only one of the seven dizygotic twins (14 percent) were concordant for homosexuality. Also reported in this paper was a family with three monozygotic twin pairs—two concordant for homosexuality and one for heterosexuality.

If some day homosexuality *were* revealed to be a behavioral difference caused by a difference in neuroendocrine function, or a genetically influenced variable, and not by early pathologic family relationships, what effect on psychiatric theory would this have? Clearly, there would be less social pressure put on the person to change. But would homosexuality still be a psychiatric disorder? If Down's syndrome (with its chromosomal excess) and phenylketonuria (with its enzyme deficiency) are to be listed as psychiatric disorders (as they are at present), then homosexuality could remain so as well. For here we would have three conditions in which a noninterpersonally derived anomaly leads to a behavioral phenomenon. But with homosexuality, the problem is confounded with the finding that in some cases homosexual behavior is modifiable by an interpersonal experience—psychotherapy (Bieber et al., 1962; Socarides, 1968; Hatterer, 1970; and Bancroft, 1970). And if there should be a biologic basis for homosexuality (or for some cases of homosexuality), would this necessarily be incompatible with change via psychotherapy? Consider right cerebral dominance (left-handedness) and its amenability to environmental training.

That biologic substrates do not always win out over experiential ones in determining sexual object choice is demonstrated by the studies of pseudohermaphroditic children by Money and the Hampsons (1955) and Stoller (1967). These studies were of children born with ambiguous appearing or misleading genitalia, so that some infants who were choromosomal and gonadal males were designated female and reared as girls, and some, who possessed many of the anatomic attributes of females—ovaries, female chromosomal pattern—but male-appearing external genitalia, were designated male and reared as boys. In the overwhelming majority of cases these children matured into adulthood in the gender and sexual role typical of the sex to which they had been assigned and reared. Thus a chromosomal male, consistently reared as a girl, was subsequently sexually attracted to males, and a chromosomal female, consistently reared as a boy, was subsequently attracted to females. Both believed themselves to be normally heterosexual. Thus, it appears that consistently invoked experiential influences can, in many cases, override whatever biologic drive exists behind a heterosexual object choice, at least in individuals who are biologically intersexed. If indeed there were *no* biologic predisposition toward heterosexuality, then by what criteria would it be justifiable to conclude that experiences that result in homosexual preferences have produced "unnatural" psychosexual development?

PSYCHOLOGICAL CONSIDERATIONS

Another basis on which homosexuality is considerd a disorder, an illness, or a mark of psychologic immaturity rests on dynamic theories of psychosexual development. Classic psychoanalytic theory sees the male child taking as its first love-object its mother; then engaging in a period of intense sexual rivalry with the father for the mother's love, a rivalry he fears will cost him his penis in an act of paternal retaliation; and finally, at about age five–six, in the successful resolution of this conflict, identifying with the father to later seek out females other than the mother (Freud, 1920). Successful resolution of this oedipal conflict is seen as the universal rite of passage to healthy adult sexuality. An example of many elaborations on this basic theme is that the little boy's fear of castration is the consequence of his phallic impulse to penetrate the mother's vagina, of which he has *unconscious* knowledge. The danger of the mother's vagina is due to the presence of the father's penis. The boy's attitude to the father's penis inside the mother conceals oral and anal sadistic designs on it. These sadistic wishes are then displaced on the cavity supposed to contain the penis, so that penetration into the vagina exposes the boy's penis to as much danger as his father's penis would face if it entered the boy's sadistic mouth (Jones, 1933). Essentially, homosexuality is seen as a disorder because it is presumed to be a carry-over of conflict from an earlier life phase and functions as a defense against unresolved fears of penile loss. In some more recent theories, a life period prior to the oedipal phase is viewed as the crucial time during which interpersonal events form the *anlage* of normal or abnormal sexual development (Stoller, 1968 and Socarides, 1968). Thus a current theory states that unresolved fear of engulfment by the mother during the preoedipal period is responsible for inhibiting heterosexual development and may lead to homosexual behavior (Socarides, 1968).

The empirical data from which such theories derive are difficult to evaluate. First, they emanate from patients who are maladaptive to the extent of seeking extended, expensive psychiatric treatment. Second, they are reported by clinicians who ascribe to a psychologic philosophy that takes *as givens* certain universal, instinctual, incestuous drives, coupled with fears of genital mutilation, and who then interpret patient behavior in light of that theoretical matrix.

There are other theories of psychosexual development as well. The social-learning theory states that children like to be rewarded and that their parents like to see them do culturally appropriate, gender-typic things. Therefore, the parents will reward certain aspects of behavior and punish, or not reward, others (Mischel, 1966). Gradually, the boy or girl is shaped into behaving in a manner typical for a boy or girl of that culture. There is no mention in this theory of instinctual sexual drives, the desire by the small child to have sexual intercourse with the opposite-sexed parent, or of castration fear. To what extent can one deduce from *this* theory that a person not showing the culturally derived, normal gender role and sexual behavior is manifesting a mental disorder? If a mother and father were to selectively reward feminine behavior in a boy, so that he developed a feminine identification, does it legitimately follow that the child has a mental disorder? If the psychologic principles on which his sexual identity has been formed—for example, the desire for parental approval and selective reinforcement—are the same as in the masculine boy with parents holding to a different value system, is the femininely oriented boy manifesting mental illness? Or has he developed a conflict-free personality attribute on the same basis as the masculine boy? Are the *parents* the ones to be considered mentally ill? If so, can the child be similarly branded?

Both psychoanalytic and social-learning models of psychosexual development, in the scientific sense, are theories. Along with variations on their themes, they have behind them, to a greater or lesser degree, supporting evidence and, to lesser degree, some bases on which to test them. To some extent, each has components that are untestable and therefore unprovable. No one theory is universally accepted. Considering the theoretic status of many of these constructs, as well as the lack of consensual agreement as to their validity, even as *theories,* is it legitimate to extrapolate from them and categorically draw conclusions as to the state of a person's mental health or illness?

SOCIOLOGICAL CONSIDERATIONS

Yet another argument in support of homosexuality as an illness is that to develop culturally deviant behavior must be considered evidence of disorder. Thus, if the overwhelming majority of persons mature through childhood as heterosexual, then the person who evolves as homosexual must be choosing an alternative minority path for neurotic meanings. In a culture in which persons were heterosexual half the time (and enough to keep the species viable) and homosexual half the time, would children in their nonneurotic oedipal resolution be ambisexual? In such a culture would the exclusive heterosexual or exclusive homosexual then be the one suffering neurotic conflict?

Difficulties in defining "normality" or "nondeviancy" in male sexual behavior were put to poignant demonstration by the Institute for Sex Research. Their data on the sex histories of twelve thousand American men revealed the great disparity in the "normal" sex practices dependent on such factors as, for example, years of formal education (Kinsey et al., 1948). Consider "male mouth-female breast" contact during sex play by married couples. This is quite "normal" for persons with thirteen or more years of education (four out of five), but "abnormal" for those with eight or less years (one out of three). To quote Kinsey and his co-workers: "The upper level male considers it *natural* that the female breast should interest him, and that he should want to manipulate it, both by hand and by mouth . . . Many lower level males rate such mouth-breast contacts as *perversions* . . . " (italics added). "Male mouth-female genital" contact is fairly "normal" behavior for persons with thirteen or more years schooling (one in two), but abnormal for those with nine–twelve years education (one in six) or eight years or less (one in twenty-five). Similar standards of normalcy exist for "female mouth-male genital" contact. Petting to climax before marriage appears to be "normal" for the better educated (three of five), but not for the lesser educated (one of six). And it is relatively "normal" to sleep nude if you are twenty-six to forty-five years old and have had at least thirteen years schooling (one in two), but decidedly "abnormal" if you have had eight or less years (one in seven).

With respect to homosexuality, frequency of such behavior appears to be related to religion, age, educational status, and residence (urban or rural). Thus the degree to which it is "abnormal" varies for different people, at different times, and in different places.

In reviewing their study, Kinsey and co-workers observed that it:

> . . . raises a question as to whether the terms "normal" and "abnormal" belong in a scientific vocabulary. At the best, abnormal may designate certain individuals whose rates of activity are less frequent or whose sources of sexual outlet are not as usual in the population as a whole; but in that case, it is preferable to refer to such persons as rare, rather than abnormal. Moreover, many items in human sexual behavior which are labelled abnormal, or perversions, in textbooks, prove,upon statistical examination, to occur in as many as 30 or 60 or 75 percent of certain populations.

Indeed, in a comprehensive cross-cultural survey, Ford and Beach (1951) reported on some seventy-six societies and found that forty-nine (64 percent) considered homosexual activity "of one sort or another to be normal and socially acceptable for certain members of the community." In fact, in some societies, males who became the wives of important members of the community were credited with magical powers and accorded great respect. Additionally, among other cultures all men and boys were noted to engage in anal intercourse, and those who did not indulge in homosexual activities were singled out as peculiar.

CONTROLLED STUDIES OF PSYCHOLOGIC FUNCTIONING

Still another argument, relevant to whether homosexuality is a manifestation of an illness, rests on the level of social adaptability and effectiveness such persons show, outside the direction of their sexual drive. Degree of social adaptability, interpersonal effectiveness, and neurotic symptomatology are reasonably well-accepted criteria for mental health. The backward schizophrenic may be unable to keep himself alive in an industrialized culture, and so he is confined. The backward schizophrenic is an extreme example and is considered, by most psychiatrists, a profoundly disordered or ill person. Depression is clearly a significant degree of unhappiness, which is internally and externally maladaptive. The depressed person hurts and also functions poorly. Can the same things necessarily be said for the homosexual?

General impressions by psychiatrists of the state of psychologic healthiness of homosexually oriented persons derive from their patient population. A reviewer of my patient experience might conclude that *homosexuality* is a phenomenon of seeking emotional and sexual gratification in a genital relationship between two persons of the same sex, associated, to a considerable degree, with symptoms of anxiety, depression, drug abuse, phobias, and unfulfilled dependency needs. The same reviewer of my patient experience might also conclude that *heterosexuality* is a phenomenon of seeking emotional and sexual gratification in a genital relationship between two persons of the opposite sex, associated, to a considerable degree, with symptoms of anxiety, depression, drug abuse, phobias, and unfulfilled dependency needs.

Promiscuity and instability of relationships are probably more frequent in the male homosexual world. To those who want stable relationships, this is a source of concern. To what extent are the limitations in the ability of homosexual couples to establish long-term meaningful relationships (offered as evidence of the homosexual's psychic instability) a product of their mutually serious defect in emotional development, or the result of the extraordinary societal pressures working against such a union? One could argue that it takes a significant measure of ego strength to be in a homosexual "marriage" in a culture that so heavily condemns such activity.

What controlled experimental data exist do not support the contention that persons identified as homosexual are less psychologically healthy or adjusted than those identified as heterosexuals. In a recent study, eighty-nine male homosexuals were compared with thirty-five unmarried heterosexual males. Subjects were compared on several psychiatric states, including anxiety neurosis, hysteria, obsessional neurosis, schizophrenia, antisocial personality, neurosis, hysteria, obsessional neurosis, schizophrenia, antisocial personality, phobic neurosis, paranoid personality, alcoholism, and affective disorders. Forty-four percent of the homosexuals, compared with 51 percent of the heterosexuals, had no definable disorder (not statistically significant). Twenty-nine percent of the homosexuals had affective disorders, compared with 26 percent of the heterosexuals. Thirty percent of the homosexuals and 20 percent of the heterosexuals experienced excessive and problem drinking, and 11 percent of the homosexuals and 8 percent of the heterosexuals experienced an anxiety or phobic neurosis. Thus, "when differences did occur they were in the direction of more difficulties among the homosexual subjects than among the heterosexual controls," although results showed "an absence of striking differences between them and the unmarried control group. . . ." The authors (Saghir et al., 1970) observed further, "The homosexual subjects were able to achieve an educational, occupational, and economic status similar to that of the controls and significantly higher than that of single employed males."

In another study of one hundred male homosexuals seen in private practice (Curran and Parr, 1957), it was found that:

> . . . in spite of the probability that any group of homosexuals referred to a psychiatrist might be expected to be heavily weighted in the direction of psychiatric abnormality, no fewer than 51% were considered to be free from gross personality disorder, neurosis, or psychosis during their adult lives. They included a number of important and talented individuals of high integrity, successful, efficient, and respected members of the community. . . . Only half the patients showed significant psychiatric abnormality other than their sexual deviation, and such associated abnormalities were often slight. Moreover, many of these abnormalities were explicable as a reaction to the difficulties of being homosexual.

An investigation focusing on female homosexuals matched twenty-four female homosexuals with twenty-four female heterosexuals on the basis of age, intelligence, and education (Hopkins, 1969). The homosexuals were members of England's "minorities Research Group." Subjects were given Cattell's Sixteen Personality-Factor Questionnaire, a multifactor personality inventory. The homosexuals were found to be more independent, resilient, reserved, dominant, bohemian, self-sufficient, and composed.

Most recently, 307 male homosexuals were contrasted with 137 heterosexuals, using factor analytic techniques and psychologic test instruments. The homosexuals, of whom one-half were members of the Mattachine Society, scored higher on tender-mindedness, submissiveness, and anxiety and scored lower on depression. Homosexuals were also higher on goal-directedness, self-acceptance, sense of self, and nurturance. There was no difference on alienation, trust, dependency, or neuroticism (Siegelman, 1972).

These studies should be viewed with the same degree of caution as those that derive from case files of psychiatrists in private practice or from any setting which draws as its sample persons who come for therapy. Studies of nontreatment homosexuals generally draw their subjects from homophile organizations. These are composed of persons who are willing to publicly acknowledge their homosexuality and who are motivated and socially conscious enough to join a civic-action organization. They are usually of a higher educational and socioeconomic level than the average person. In these organizations there is generally a weighting toward those with a college education and stable employment (One, Inc., 1969). Both the latter are measures of general psychologic effectiveness and would be expected to enhance scores of measures of psychologic and psychiatric funtioning. However, Siegelman (1972), comparing his Mattachine Society and nonhomophile organization homosexuals, found very little difference and no evidence that society members biased their results more positively. If anything, they appeared somewhat more depressed and generally neurotic.

Although the above studies may not be definitive in describing the homosexual as either more healthy than or equally healthy as the heterosexual, neither should statements by therapists who treat unhappy homosexuals be considered to settle the issue. Furthermore, if, in fact, some homosexuals in all personality features (except sexual object choice) are not different from heterosexuals, does this necessarily mean they are not mentally ill? The argument has been raised, on the basis of the above studies, that unless one chooses to define homosexuality *per se* as an illness, these persons are healthy. Is it legitimate to argue that something, apart from possessing a particular attribute, is something else? A situation could exist for heart-transplant recipient in which it is asserted that, apart from the fact that his transplanted heart was rejected, he was in perfect condition. Was he, therefore, in good health when he died? Such an argument fails to come to grips with the essential issue as to whether or not the given state or attribute—for example, homosexuality—is *in itself* an illness, not whether all other systems are in order.

TREATMENT: WHY?

It may not be particularly helpful to debate which term to apply to a behavioral state. The more relevant issue may be whether that state is believed to represent something less desirable than its alternative(s) *and* whether those licensed to treat "disease" or "disorder" have and/or ought to have within their purview authorization and responsibility for effecting change to an alternative.

If a homosexual wants to become a heterosexual via psychotherapy, should this goal be granted or denied him? It is doubtful that many psychiatrists would object to undertaking therapy with such a goal in mind. But it might also be appropriate to examine the reasons for the desire to be heterosexual. One might ask whether there are any reasons for being heterosexual considered neurotic enough as to questions the goal of heterosexuality. Is it to conform to societal expectation and to avoid risking exposure and social disapproval? How rational a treatment motivation is this? Is the motivation the desire to be a father and to live in a suburban home? If so, then there is a clear necessity for a durable heterosexual union. However, before launching a program of vaginal penetration, it might be wise to examine the course of the patient's motivation for having a family. Is it to please parents or society? If so, is this an unneurotic motivation?

Maximum flexibility of emotional response is frequently a goal of insight-oriented or dynamic therapies. With respect to sexual relations, what is appropriately flexible, adaptive behavior? Is an exclusive reliance on orgastic release with one type of human restrictive? Some predominantly homosexual or ambisexual persons argue that exclusive reliance on heterosexual orgasms is restrictive of a wider breadth of genital and interpersonal experience in the same manner psychiatry argues the converse. Is ambisexuality evidence of a fuller range of interpersonal experience? Furthermore, is the anatomic configuration of the sexual object the only or even the critical variable? Or is it more in the quality of the relationship? One might argue that exclusive sexuality in either direction is by definition restrictive. What should be the psychiatrist's responsibility if consulted by a *heterosexual* who wants to overcome some of his *homosexual* inhibitions? Consider that such a person's reasons were to increase his means of sexual satisfaction and promote a more extensive manner of relating with men—motivation of reasonable merit, when comparably advanced by the homosexual who wishes to overcome heterosexual inhibitions. Would many (any) psychiatrists be willing to work with the patient toward such a goal?

The question of whether homosexuality is a "disease" was discussed earlier. *Dis*-ease implies *dis*-comfort. Whence the discomfort? Is it from internal conflict concomitant with a psychic defect or secondary to societal opprobrium? The recent National Institute of Mental Health Task Force on Homosexuality notes: "The extreme opprobrium that our society has attached to homosexual behavior, by way of criminal statutes and restrictive employment practices, has done more social harm than good. . . ." It is difficult to find a comparable sexual dilemma with which to compare this situation, but perhaps an out-of-wedlock pregnancy illustrates a related conflict. Is the distressed woman, who contemplates abortion and suffers with anxiety and depression, distressed because her psychic immaturity renders her incapable of effective function or because she is increasingly stigmatized with each passing day of gestation?

When is guilt considered appropriate and when, the object of treatment? The presence of guilt in a patient due to his practicing homosexuality is positively correlated with conversion to heterosexuality during the course of treatment (Hatterer, 1970). It may be asserted that this is primarily due to the fact that a person unhappy with what he is doing is more likely to change his behavior. One might question guilt *per se* as an inherent virtue to be harnessed for change. Psychiatry frequently helps assuage guilt in sexual matters. The woman incapable of enjoying intercourse because of early parental-religious prohibitions is helped overcome her guilt. Here guilt seems to be working against the good. Should guilt be reinforced or harnessed for behavioral change if it does not derive from behavior that is harmful to others? The psychopathic swindler could benefit from a heaping tablespoon of superego or conscience each morning, but is this also good medicine for the homosexual?

When is a pattern of behavior a life style to be considered by philosophers; when is it a social phenomenon to be considered by jurists or sociologists; and when is it a disease to be considered by physicians or other healers? Most psychiatrists justify treatment of schizophrenia by observing that schizophrenics are grossly unadaptable in this world. The more statistically unusual their behavior, the less likely they are to be employable or particularly sought after socially. Thus intervention by one human into the behavioral patterns of another is "morally" justified. Can the same justification be applied to the treatment of homosexuality? How should such a value system be established? When should the psychiatrist (or anyone else for that matter) be in a position to define a standard of behavior for another person when it comes to style of *living* or style of *loving?* There are some broad limits of behavioral freedom, involving clear-cut invasion of a person's rights, that require control to insure the freedom of others. But is there evidence that such infringement could come about by sexual object choice in mutually agreeable consorting?

Much of the value system on which heterosexuality is judged superior to homosexuality is the apparently given, greater virtue of marriage and children. The cultural norm for the adult is to be married with two to three children. Failure to comply makes one abnormal in the statistical sense. More recently, having four children has become evidence of *less* responsible behavior. For a number of political, economic, and emotional reasons, marriage has evolved as a common denominator of adult human interpersonal relations. So vital has maintenance of the marital configuration been that societies have posed considerable obstacles—in many cases, totally insurmountable—to efforts to separate the union, even when desired by *both* parties. Thus man, by fiat, has joined company with geese and the painted shrimp, who by instinct effect lifelong matings.

Recent modifications in this value system have weakened the footings on which such beliefs are based. Greater freedom from the equation, copulation = conception, and increasing disillusion with the equation, marriage = happiness, are bringing about change. Greater numbers of people are having sexual relations for love, not children, or simply because it is pleasurable, and are living together while the relationship is exuberant and fulfilling, rather than ultimately contributing to a divorce rate which runs 40 percent in some states. And it is heterosexual reproductive behavior, along with international diplomacy, that many people believe loom as the greatest threats to man's survival.

A Gay Liberation position is that psychiatry should be more concerned with "treating" *public values* than an individual's behavior. What can psychiatry do to change social values about homosexuality? Gay Liberation would like to see us strike homosexuality as a disorder from the *Diagnostic and Statistical Manual.* What would be the consequences to psychiatry of its no longer adhering to the position that homosexuality is a disorder, an immaturity, or a perversion? To what extent do psychiatrists, by their writings, shape societal values and the persons living them? Would societal values be affected if psychiatry were to no longer consider homosexuality a "disease" with prospect for "recovery"? To what extent does societal value shape psychiatric value (psychiatrists being a component of society)?

Without the present value system, how would approaches differ with the homosexual patient? Psychiatrists frequently state (or at least, many analysts do) that they have no goals for their patient, that the patient sets the goals, and that they assist the patient in achieving them. Yet, in their writing, most authorities on homosexuality clearly align themselves with the view that homosexuality is an illness or disorder. There is a clear value system in which conversion toward heterosexuality is the mark of therapeutic success and adjustment to the homosexual way of life, palliative at best. Homosexual behavior, by definition, is considered a less adequate means of sexual expression. To what extent can this value system supervene over one that defines the value of an interpersonal relationship by the extent to which it meets each person's needs and is free from intrusion on those of others? By what standard does one judge whether the one-night stand in a straight bar is of higher interpersonal value than one in a gay bar? Should there be an American Psychiatric Association (APA) diagnosis for this as well—that is, for "quality" of sexuality or only for *direction?* By not classifying such behavior as a disorder (though it is frequently treated), are we placing a higher value judgment on the heterosexual one-night stand than on the homosexual liaison of six-months duration? Are the sad representatives of the gay world, who stand about in homosexual bars on a Saturday night, any less depressing than the straights who attend "over-thirty and single" dances in any metropolitan area? Both are examples of persons who have not established meaningful, lasting relations with persons on whom they can be emotionally and sexually dependent. Their pain is severe and grants little discount for preferred sexual object choice.

What would be the effect of a consumer boycott? What if homosexuals were to cease defining themselves as ill and were to stop consulting psychiatrists? If they were to shop elsewhere for their health, education, and welfare, what would result? Furthermore, what would the impact be on psychiatry, as a theory and practice, if all homosexual psychiatrists in America were to openly acknowledge their sexual preference? The number of homosexual psychiatrists is unknown, but, if the percentage is comparable to that of the general population (4 percent), there would be some eight hundred exclusively homosexual psychiatrists. There would be an additional one thousand who prefer homosexual relations. It is an additionally provocative thought to consider an APA task force, composed of homosexual psychiatrists, preparing a report addressed to the prevailing theories of the etiology of homosexuality (written, for the most part, by heterosexuals). In all likelihood, the patients of a homosexual therapist rarely know that he is homosexual. Do these therapists tell their patients? If so, what effect does it have on the goals and processes of treatment? Is a homosexual therapist in a better or poorer position (all other things being equal) to treat the homosexual whose goal is either to live with it or to convert to heterosexuality?

CONCLUSION

I have concerns that in my inability to see the Emperor's beautiful clothes, I am casting myself in a dubious professional position. It can be argued that a homosexual psychiatrist would evince special pleading in defensive favor of his own defect and promulgate a similar argument. But for a heterosexual psychiatrist, to take such a position surely must be a sign of naïveté or antiauthoritarianism. It is of some comfort to me to quote from persons for whom I have considerable respect, on grounds other than that I find in their statements some support for this unsettled position.

A half-century ago Freud (1920) wrote: "[homosexuality] is found in peoples who exhibit no other serious deviations from the normal. It is similarly found in people whose efficiency is unimpaired. . . ." Thirty-seven years ago, in his letter to a mother of an American homosexual, Freud (1935) wrote:

> Homosexuality is assuredly no advantage, but is nothing to be ashamed of, no vice, no degradation; it cannot be classified as an illness: we consider it to be a variation of the sexual functions produced by a certain arrest of sexual development.

Thus Freud did not consider homosexuality an illness (whatever meaning that might have implied), though he clearly saw it as something short of psychologic maturity and, thus, perfection.

Marmor, a contemporary psychoanalyst, has observed (1965):

> The scientist must approach his data non-evaluatively; homosexual behavior and heterosexual behavior are merely different areas on a broad spectrum of human sexual behavior... and neither can be assured to be intrinsically more or less "natural" than the other.

Other psychoanalysts (Socarides, 1970) however, regard homosexuality as:

> ... a medical disorder which has reached epidemiologic (sic) proportions; its frequency of incidence surpasses that of the recognized major illnesses in the nation... a conservative estimate is that between 2,500,000 and 4,000,000 adult American males suffer from this condition. By way of comparison a Public Health Service report estimates the four major illnesses in this country (1963 to 1965) as: heart disease, 3,619,000; arthritis and rheumatism, 3,481,000; impairment (except paralysis) of the back and spine, 1,769,000; mental and nervous disease, 1,767,000.

(Apparently the Public Health Service census did not include homosexuality as a mental or nervous disease, for this would have considerably bolstered the ranks of the last category.)

Clearly, the issue remains clouded. At the risk of being charged with heresy, I have asked the above questions in a friendly, but troubled, spirit. They are not challenges, although they may be experienced as such by those for whom the issues have long since been decided. They are questions to which I invite considered, scholarly answers. As a scientist, I feel many questions must be asked and procedures established for the answering before truth is known and order is drawn. To my thinking, in this issue there has been premature closure and premature order. I believe it is again time for inquiry and questioning of accepted, comfortable givens. To heterosexual psychiatrists, I suppose it is a comfort to feel we have matured well in our psychosexuality. Perhaps we experience a measured sense of competence and comfort when we find evidence of defect or illness in others which merit our treatment. To what extent do all heterosexuals, not only psychiatrists, have an emotional investmeant in maintaining the given that homosexuality is a disease or is at least inferior, in the traditional manner that any majority has an investment in maintaining a conviction of superiority over a threatening minority?

What I question in this essay is the given state of "knowledge" that homosexuality is by definition a "disorder," a "disease," or an "illness." I question the given state of "knowledge" that orgasms between males *and* females are by definition better than between females and females or males and males, that the components comprising the major factor, "love," are by definition superior between males *and* females to between males and males or females and females. I am not convinced we have the data by which to base these judgments. I question them because they are not proved.

REFERENCES

1. American Psychiatric Association (1968), *Diagnostic and Statistical Manual of Mental Disorders.* Washington, D.C.
2. Bancroft, J. (1970), A comparative study of aversion therapy and desensitization in the treatment of homosexuality. In *Behavior Therapy in the 1970's.* Bristol: John Wright.
3. Beach, F. Personal communication.
4. Bieber, I. et al. (1962), *Homosexuality.* New York: Basic Books.
5. Blumer, D. (1969), Hypersexuality in temporal lobe epilepsy. Paper presented at annual A.P.A. meeting.
6. Blumer, D. and Walker, A. (1967), Sexual behavior in temporal lobe epilepsy. In *Archives of Neurology,* 16:37–43.
7. Curran, D. and Parr, D. (1957), Homosexuality: an analysis of 100 male cases seen in private practice. *British Medical J.*, 1:797–801.
8. Davies, B. and Morganstern, F. A. (1960), Case of cysticercosis, temporal lobe epilepsy and transvestism. *J. Neurology, Neurosurgery and Psych.*, 23:247–249.
9. Erickson, T. (1945), Erotomania (nymphomania) as an expression of cortical epileptiform discharge. *Archives of Neurology and Psych.,* 53:226.
10. Ford, C. and Beach, F. (1951), *Patterns of Sexual Behavior.* New York: Harper.
11. Freeman,F. and Nevis, A. (1969), Temporal lobe sexual seizures. *Neurology,* 19:87–90.
12. Freud, S. (1920), *A General Introduction to Psychoanalysis.* New York: Boni and Liveright.
13. ______ (9 April 1935), Letter to an American mother. *Amer.J.Psych.,* 107:786–787, 1951.
14. ______ (1905), *Three Contributions to the Theory of Sex.* New York: Random House, 1938.
15. Harlow, H. (1962), The heterosexual affectional system in monkeys. *American Psychologist,* 17:1–9.
16. Hatterer, L. (1970), *Changing Homosexuality in the Male.* New York: McGraw-Hill.
17. Heston, L. and Shields, J. (1968), Homosexuality in twins. *Archives of General Psych.,* 18:149–160.
18. Hoffman, M. (1968), *The Gay World. Male Homosexuality and the Social Creation of Evil.* New York: Basic Books.
19. Hooker, E. (1957), The adjustment of the male overt homosexual. *J. Projective Techniques,* 21:18–31.
20. ______ et al. (1969), Final Report of the NIMH Task Force on Homosexuality.
21. Hopkins, J. (1969), The lesbian personality. *British J. Psych.,* 115:1433–1436.
22. Jones, E. (1933), The phallic phase. *Int. J. Psycho-Anal.,* 114:1–33.
23. Kallman, F. (1952), Comparative twin study on the genetic aspects of male homosexuality. *J. of Nervous and Mental Disorders,* 115:283–298.
24. Kinsey, A., Pomeroy, W., and Martin C. (1948), *Sexual Behavior in the Human Male.* Philadelphia: W. B. Saunders.
25. Kolodny, R., Masters, W., Hendryx, J. and Toro, G. (1971), Plasma testosterone and semen analysis in male homosexuals. *New England J. of Medicine,* 285:1170–1174.

26. Loraine, J., Ismail, A., Adamopoulos, D., and Dove, G. (1970), Endocrine function in male and female homosexuals. *British Medical J.,* 4:406–408.
27. Margolese, M. (1970), Homosexuality: a new endocrine correlate. *Hormones and Behavior,* 1:151–155.
28. Marmor, J., ed. (1965), *Sexual Inversion.* New York: Basic Books.
29. Mischel, W. (1966), A social-learning view of sex differences in behavior. In *The Development of Sex Differences,* ed. E. Maccoby. Stanford: Stanford University Press.
30. Mitchell, W., Falconer, M., and Hill, D. (1954), Epilepsy with fetishism relieved by temporal lobectomy. *Lancet,* 2:626–630.
31. Money, J., Hampson, J.G., and Hampson, J.L. (1955), An examination of some basic sexual concepts: the evidence of human hermaphroditism. *Bulletin of Johns Hopkins Hospital.* 97:301–319.
32. One, Inc. (1969). Unpublished data.
33. Roeder, F. and Muller, D. (1969), The stereotaxic treatment of paedophiliac homosexuality. *German Medical Monthly.* 14:265–271.
34. Saghir, M., Robins, E., Walbran, B., and Gentry, K. (1970), Homosexuality III. Psychiatric disorders and disability in the male homosexual. *Amer. J. Psych.,* 126:1079–1086.
35. Siegelman, M. (1972), Adjustment of male homosexuals and heterosexuals. *Archives of Sexual Behavior.* (In press)
36. Socarides, C. (1968), *The Overt Homosexual.* New York: Grune and Stratton.
37. ______ (1970), Homosexuality and medicine, *JAMA* 212:1199–1202.
38. Stoller, R.J. (1967), The intersexed patient: counsel and management. In *Sexual Problems: Diagnosis and Treatment in Medical Practice,* ed. C.W. Wahl. New York: Free Press.
39. ______ (1968), *Sex and Gender: The Development of Masculinity and Femininity.* New York: Science House.
40. Young, W., Goy, R., and Phoenix, S. (1964), Hormones and sexual behavior. *Science,* 143:212–218.

Part 4

Disease versus Values: Mental Health and Illness

The greatest challenge to the view that a univocal concept of either health or disease can be located and defined has arisen over the nature of mental health and mental illness. Questions as to the adequacy and utility of somatic conceptions of health and disease, whether understood in terms of dysfunction, deviance, or adaptation for understanding mental health, continue to divide the medical profession.

The issue of whether mental and physical health and disease are amenable to a single type of conceptual analysis touches upon central philosophical issues in ontology, epistemology, and logic. The questions of whether mind and body are fundamentally different categories and whether different predicates and descriptions are appropriate for describing the mental and the physical are at the heart of the dispute about the autonomy of mental health and disease.

Theories of mental illness, as many of this section's authors note, are not as well developed as are theories of illness in other areas of medicine. It is difficult to know whether the concepts of health and disease used in somatic medicine seem less applicable to mental phenomena as a consequence of fundamental ontological differences between mental and physical phenomena or as a result of theoretical immaturity.

Much of the resistance to lumping mental problems under the same conceptual analysis as physical illness and health centers around concerns about the autonomy and freedom of persons. The independence and responsibility of a person often seem to many to be more closely tied to assessments of mental health than physical health. Mentally ill persons often are thought incapable of looking out for their own best interests and of participating fully in interpersonal relationships. Mental competency is often regarded as a prerequisite for maintaining moral and social status within a community. Those viewed as mentally ill are, as some of the authors point out, treated less as free moral agents and more as subjects in need of help and protection. The category of mental illness is the conceptual terrain over which many of our most basic assumptions about freedom, personhood, autonomy, and paternalism are battled out. Those who argue that mental health is more ambiguous than, or categorically distinct from, physical health often find themselves embroiled in disputes about what it means to be a free human being in a particular society. The power inherent in being in a position to define someone as a person or non-person requires that the debate about the reality and autonomy of mental health and disease receive serious, critical attention.

4.1

On Irritation and Insanity—Preface

F. J. V. Broussais

trans. by Thomas Cooper

After many vacillations in its course, Medicine has at length taken the only road which can lead to truth; that is, the observation of the relations of man with external modifiers,* and of the organs of man, one with another. This method now universally prevails in writings, and in practice, whether it be avowed or not. This is the physiological method; because it must be followed by studying the phenomena of life, which alone render the bodily organs thus modifiable. Let us, however, beware of mistake; it is not the abstraction, Life, which is to be studied, but the living organs. If the observer wearies himself with investigations of properties or forces, considered independently of these living organs, or the natural bodies which have an influence over them, he will take much labor indeed, but he will fail in his object; he will know neither organs nor agents; he will know only the dreams of his imagination; his head will be filled with illusions. It is thus that the ancients went astray, as will be seen in this work. The moderns have not escaped the snare; and the same snare is even now preparing to be spread in the path of our contemporaries.

Since then, true medical observation is that of the organs and their modifiers, it is in fact an observation of the body itself, and can be pursued only by means of the senses: hence the senses must furnish materials, and it belongs to the judgment to draw conclusions from them. But here a difficulty presents itself; if the physician draws false conclusions, or if he be so unfortunate as to forget the true source from whence they should proceed, he loses himself, and deviates into that mistaken road of which we have just spoken. Such an aberration is the more easy in the present day, as this false route is sanctioned by some distinguished men; by names that command respect and inspire confidence in the doctrines they advance. It is under the auspices of these respectable names, some of them dear to France, that

*Modificateurs. Whatever acts upon and excites any part of the animal frame, producing any alteration whatever in its antecedent state.—*Trans.*

education, by means of the senses, is depreciated, and threatened with discredit. Do not let us pass over an important distinction, and a practical truth. If the abstract words, rights, lawfulness, disinterestedness, elevation of soul, are adapted to produce actions, praiseworthy, useful to the public good and to the national glory, it is not the same with the words vital properties, vital forces, vis medicatrix, specifics, contagion, and others of the same kind, which, in like manner, paint the abstractions of the human intellect; for nothing is more easy than to abuse these expressions; that is to say, to impress under their sanction, on the living body, modifications hurtful to the health of particular men, and injurious to the good of society. Such a method of philosophising, although it may succeed in politics or diplomacy, is not always applicable to medicine; and if it be sufficient in those two sciences, to abandon ourselves to the sentiment of the beautiful, the sublime, and the just, without searching very profoundly in what manner we have arrived at these ideas, it is not so in medicine, where it becomes necessary to prescribe the regimen and treatment of a suffering fellow-creature, or to judge of questions that relate to the public health. These questions cannot be resolved by sentiment or inspiration; the motions cannot be resolved by sentiment or inspiration; the modifying medicaments prescribed, will not act directly upon vital force, upon nature, upon principle: they do not influence these abstractions, until after they have acted upon the organs; and if these last are injured by a blow, the evil which the abstract idea would have produced, will be in future without remedy. In politics, on the contrary, the results of the application of a false principle may be calculated before the existence of society is compromitted; for nations are much more robust than individuals; some victims there will be, but their sufferings will be perceived if the press be respected, and the mass of society may be preserved from similar evils.

Society then may proceed in the career of improvement, independently of first principles; it may be rendered happy or unhappy in the name of God, of the Prince, or of the Laws: experience will settle which of these three motives produce the most durable good, or an evil of most easy correction. Moreover it is of little consequence in politics, whether the notion of justice or injustice comes from the senses, or from some interior revelation. The laws must be good; and experience will soon pronounce on their advantages and disadvantages; these become manifest to the public, and every one must at length acknowledge them. It is not so in medicine, while the evil produced by the circumstances that modify and destroy our organs, are attributed to diseases, as if diseases were separate and real beings; and the reason of the mischief is, that empirical medicine never corrects itself; experience is lost upon it, and it goes on with a satisfied conscience, sacrificing other victims. A just conception of disease, therefore, is the first object of medicine, nor can this be acquired without explaining in what manner this conception is formed; that is to say, without probing to the bottom the real meaning of the words vital properties, vital forces, vital laws, for the purpose of understanding the words putrid fevers, malignant fevers, &c.&c.

It is necessary, therefore, that the physician should always have to present to his mind, the substance of the organs, and that he should never forget that the abstract ideas of the science he pursues, have come to him by means of the senses, and that he cannot safely proceed to study man, by means of any a priori notions.

The object of this book, is to put this truth in a clear light, and to guard medicine from the dangers that threaten her by means of a philosophical sect essentially invading.—Hence the necessity imposed on us, to present to young physicians liable to be seduced by false systems, a true notion of Psychology,* which advances toward them with her banner unfurled, and already anticipates an easy conquest.

Let us examine what is meant by force or power. It is necessary to dwell upon this. What then is it, but the induction drawn by an observer of something which acts upon or within a body, producing therein some alteration? The observer is naturally carried on to suppose that the body is moved by something acting on it, as he himself is accustomed to act in certain cases on certain other bodies: no doubt there is a tendency to this conclusion. It is impossible not to admit that we are driven to it by analogy; that is to say, we are compelled to judge of what we do not know, by that which we believe we do know: but it is here, and precisely here, that the fact stops. The man whose judgment governs his imagination, restrains himself, and laments that he is compelled to remain in ignorance of first causes. For him, the word power, force, is but a formula; the sign of a perception which he has received from some phenomenon, and he makes use of it only to search for others which his senses may equally seize hold of.

It is not so with a man whose imagination governs his judgment; a man of a poetical tendency; a Platonician, ancient or modern: equally credulous and presumptuous, he cannot support the idea of ignorance; and he passes from vague conjecture, to the most perfect conviction: he does more, he hastens to realize his induction; he personifies it; he makes it act as if it were an animated, living being; in short, like a man; then he frames his romance, of which this induction is the hero; and he is angry at those who refuse to pay it homage.

Such is the fanaticism of opinion: it differs in intensity according to the character of the person in whom it is developed, but it is at the bottom always the same. All authors of this description, whether in medicine, philosophy, or any other branch of knowledge, may profess toleration, but they are not

---

*The doctrine of an immaterial soul, or principle distinct from matter, but some how or other connected with the human body, and presiding over its intellectual functions.—*Transl.*

capable of it; they cannot be: they are too much attached to the fiction which has so agreeably occupied them; to their poetic prose, and to the incredible efforts which useless researches have given rise to; and looking at the picture for effect, they cannot support the idea that they have been occupied by chimerical reveries: they forgive a brother romancer, although the portrait of his idol may be different from theirs; but they never forgive a strict reasoner who pays them no deference, and passes by the temple of Ontology without bending the knee.

A figurative style suits marvellously the picturesque, and the fictions in which poetry deals: let it, if you please, be the style of idyls, or even of the epic; but it ought not to be the style of philosophy, which it in no wise suits. Frequent experience since Plato, has taught us this: hence, young students cannot understand this figurative philosophy: they regard it with astonishment, and accuse themselves in secret of a want of intellect. There are always some, who by dint of listening, or of reading, succeed in figuring to their imaginations, some of those fantastic beings which this style pourtrays; these, necessarily few in number, adopt the language of their teacher, and become violent in proportion as they were humble admirers of his sublime talent. As soon as these new adepts become unintelligible to their friends, and their conviction is carried so far as to make them smile with pity, and shrug up their shoulders at the names of Locke and Condillac—so soon as Cabanis is in their eyes nothing but an Atheist, happy that he escaped the severest punishment—so soon as Voltaire, Rousseau and Montesquieu, appear to them but sorry philosophers—that the works of Volney excite their indignation—and that the dryness of Destut de Tracy revolts them—their education is finished: they have no longer any occasion to study, or to consult the monuments of French literary glory, unless to criticize them, for they can find nothing of instruction in them; they are far above these legislators of reflection and of taste: what they cannot find in the classics of their own school, they are sure to find in their own consciousness; when discarding the senses, they withdraw within themselves, shut their eyes, avoid all noise, and listen to their own contemplations. When they have arrived at this high degree of perfection, their features become composed, they assume an expression of pride, and, they feel an inward conviction that their intelligence is infinitely greater than that of the persons who tell them with some surprise, "I do not understand you."

The moment, however, seems to have arrived, when we may tear away the veil which renders their masters impenetrable. We hope in this work to make known the secret of their apparent superiority; and the cause of that singular stupor which they have produced in the literary world.

It is to physicians that we shall offer the explanation of these mysteries; for it is their cause that we are now pleading; it belongs to the medico-physiologists to determine, what there is really appreciable in the causes of instinctive and intellectual phenomena. We address ourselves to physicians, because he who has studied nothing more than the regular and healthy physiology of the human being, does not possess facts enough for the solution of these problems. Man is only half understood, if he is observed only in health: sickness constitutes part of his moral, as well as of his physical existence. We must not, therefore, be surprised at the reveries of an Ontologist, who is a stranger to the physiology both of health and of disease; or who is content with a superficial knowledge of authors, whom he is unable to comprehend. Such is the case with the Kanto-Platonicians, and nothing is more strange than the pretension which they set up now-a-days to give laws to our science, especially at a moment when it is undergoing a stormy revolution, the nature of which they cannot understand. On all sides they find discussions of which they know not the true motive; truth and error, sincerity and dissimulation, honorable disinterestedness, and vile speculation imitating her language, are afloat, not in the whole medical world, but in the capital of France—in all the saloons—in all the academies; and the Kanto-Platonicians are at a loss to discover their own tenets: they know not what medicine is, and yet they dare calumniate and despise it: they proclaim that the science of man, such as they conceive it to be, has alone any pretensions to certainty: without having passed even ten years of their life in studying man as physicians, or knowing him, considered in his organs, living and dead, they think that the external observation of the grown man, is sufficient to explain all the phenomena of the embryo, the infant, the diseased, the deformed, and the dead, submitted to anatomical analysis. The first observation is for them the only true one, because it is theirs; the other is a vain and gross hypothesis, calculated for common understandings. It is of consequence to show them where the truth really lies; in particular, to make them understand that a victory over a few deserters, or some speculators, who sacrifice to them a science which they do not understand, is immeasurably distant from a victory over medicine.

We will not do so much injustice to the French youth, as to believe they can be entirely led astray by the bloated language of the Kanto-Platonicians—the fund of good sense which distinguishes them, will doubtless preserve them now, as it has done formerly. But they may be confounded by the clattering of words which assail their ears on every side, and the schools of medicine will be surprised to hear, that this senseless jargon is to be introduced into the midst of the medical faculty, while so much opposition is to be made to the fruitful and intelligible doctrine of the Physiological School. We shall endeavor to explain this enigma, and make them feel the dignity of the science they cultivate; and we shall prove undoubtedly, to every man who has consecrated the most valuable years of his life to anatomical, physiological, and pathological investigations, that the science which he has so laboriously acquired, neither is, nor ought to be, tributary to metaphysics, from which it can draw nothing useful; and that so far from receiving its laws from this science of words, ought to supply them to metaphysics which, like a ungrateful child, despises and denies its parent.

Following this great truth, we must collect the phenomena of instinct and intelligence around the excited nervous system, and give them an important place among the generating causes of irritation. We have not hesitated to adopt as the base of our work, the article Irritation, which we published in the Encyclopedie progressive, and which the public has favorably received. But the theory of irritation will receive in the following pages, a fuller development than suited the plan of that work: so that this is in reality a new treatise on Irritation, which we now offer our brothren. Since, of the four forms of Irritation, that of the nerves is more particularly developed in this book, as its importance required, and which we have hitherto refused to insist on, until time had matured our ideas,—we thought we could do nothing better than add to it by way of proof, a description of a correspondent malady. We have chosen Insanity, as being the disorder in which nervous irritation plays the most important part. This subject suited us better, as affording new strength to the arguments which we oppose to the ambitious pretentions of the Psychologist.

In truth, our design in this work is, to unveil that mystery, under whose protection bad taste threatens to spread itself over the whole science of man, physical and moral; to contribute by a new effort, to the progress of physiological medicine, and to mark the causes which have prevented that progress from being more rapid; in fine, to pursue the science which we love, and to whose glory we have consecrated the greater part of our life, from being subjected to a disgraceful subordination.

4.2

Psycho-Analysis and the Concept of Health

Heinz Hartmann

Perhaps it would be true to say that we attach less importance in analytical circles to differentiating between healthy and pathological behaviour than is often done outside those circles. But the concepts of 'health' and 'illness' always exert a 'latent' influence, so to say, on our analytical habits of thought and it cannot but serve a useful purpose to clarify the implications of these terms. Moreover, it would be a mistake to suppose that the subject possesses no more than a theoretical interest, that it lacks any practical significance. For, when all is said and done, it often depends upon the analytical concept of health whether we recommend a course of analytical treatment—so that the matter is important as a factor in our judgement of the indications present—or what changes we should like to see effected in a patient, or when we may consider that an analysis is ripe for termination. Differences of outlook in this sphere must ultimately lead to corresponding differences in our therapeutic technique, as was clearly foreseen by Ernest Jones[1] many years ago.

While psycho-analysis was still in its infancy, it seemed a relatively simple matter to define mental health and mental illness. At that period we became acquainted for the first time with the conflicts which give rise to neuroses and believed that we had thereby acquired the right to differentiate between health and illness. Subsequently the discovery was made that conflicts such as those we had come to regard as pathogenic could be shown to exist also in healthy people; it became apparent that the choice between health and illness was determined rather by temporal and quantitative factors. To a greater extent than any theoretical considerations our therapeutic experience has compelled us to recognize this truth. It has been found that our efforts have met with very variable success and we are not always able to accept the familiar explanations of the responsibility for this state of affairs. We are finally forced to the conclusion that the quantitative factor of the strength of the instincts and a

[1]'The Attitude of the Psycho-Analytic Physician towards Current Conflicts' (1913), *Papers on Psycho-Analysis,* Third Edition.

quantitative factor residing in the ego-function have here acquired, side by side with other factors of course, an importance of their own. Moreover, mechanisms are evidently not as such pathogenic but only in virtue of their topographical value in space and their dynamic value in action, if I may so express myself. The process of modifying the original analytical conception of health has been advanced a stage further by the contributions to the psychology of the ego which have now been in the forefront of psycho-analytical interest for nearly twenty years. But the more we begin to understand the ego and its manoeuvres and achievements in dealing with the external world, the more do we tend to make these functions of adaptation, etc. the touchstone of the concept of health.

However, a psycho-analytical definition of health presents certain difficulties which we shall now proceed to examine. As is well known, it is never at any time an easy matter to say what we really mean by 'health' and 'illness' and perhaps the difficulty of differentiating between them is even greater when we are concerned with the so-called 'psychological illnesses' than it is with physical maladies. Health is certainly not a purely statistical average. If it were we should have to look upon the exceptional achievements of single individuals as pathological, which would be contrary to the ordinary usage of speech; and besides this, a majority of people exhibit characteristics which are generally regarded as pathological (the example most frequently given being caries of the teeth). 'Abnormal' then, in the sense of a deviation from the average, is not synonymous with 'pathological'.

In the conceptions of health most widely prevalent, subjective valuations play a considerable part, whether explicitly or implicitly, and that is the chief reason why such conceptions, especially when they relate to mental health and mental illness, may vary considerably at different periods and among different peoples. Here judgement is influenced by a subjective factor depending on cultural and social conditions and even personal values. Within a uniform society these judgements will exhibit a far-reaching similarity, but that does not deprive them in the least of their subjective character. 'Health' is generally one expression of the idea of vital perfection; and this in itself implies the subjectivity of the judgements concerning it. A logical analysis of the concept of health (I shall barely touch upon the problem here) would have to denote especial attention to the valuations embodied in the different conceptions of health.

But these are not the only difficulties inherent in a psycho-analytical definition of health. So long as we make freedom from symptoms, for instance, the criterion of mental health, it is comparatively easy in practice to arrive at a decision. Even by this standard there exists no absolutely objective basis for our judgement; for a simple answer is not readily forthcoming to the question whether a given psychical manifestation is in the nature of a symptom or whether on the contrary it is to be regarded as an 'achievement'. It is often a difficult matter to decide whether the pedantry or ambition of an individual or the nature of his object-choice are symptoms in a neurotic sense or character-traits possessing a positive value for health. Nevertheless this standard does provide us, if not with a basis for objective judgement, at all events with a consensus of opinion which is usually sufficient for all practical purposes. But health as it is understood in psycho-analysis is something which means far more than this. In our view, freedom from symptoms is not enough for health; and we cherish higher expectations of the therapeutic effects of psycho-analysis. But over and above this, psycho-analysis has witnessed the development of a number of theoretical conceptions of health which often lay down very severe standards. We have accordingly to ask ourselves what health signifies in a psycho-analytical sense.

By way of preamble we would remark that man's relation to health and illness itself often presents features of a distinctly neurotic order. When these problems are very much in the foreground one is sometimes actually tempted to speak of a 'health-neurosis'. This idea is made the basis of a paper recently published by Melitta Schmideberg.[2] A conspicuous characteristic in certain well-marked types is their conviction that they themselves enjoy superior health, accompanied by a compulsive urge to detect in others deviations, mainly of a neurotic or psychotic kind, from their ideal of health. In certain circumstances such people are capable of fulfilling a useful function in society by very reason of their particular form of neurosis, which may mark them out for the rôle of eternal sick-nurse to their fellow-men. In the simplest form of this behaviour the operative mechanism is commonly projection; by constantly seeing others as patients in need of one's help one avoids recognition of one's own neurosis. In the same way Freud once expressed the opinion that many analysts probably learn to absolve themselves from personal compliance with the obligations of analysis by extracting it from others. We know too that a like tendency to overestimate the neurotic and psychotic reactions of one's fellow-men belongs to the growing-pains of many analysts. It is a common feature of 'health-neuroses' that those afflicted by them cannot allow themselves to suffer or to feel ill or depressed.[3] But a healthy person must have the capacity to suffer and to be depressed. Our clinical experience has taught us the consequences of glossing over illness and suffering, of being unable to admit to oneself the possibility of illness and suffering. It is even probable that a limited amount of suffering and illness forms an integral part of the scheme of health, as it were, or rather that health is only reached by indirect ways. We know that successful adaptation can lead to maladaptation—the development of the super-ego is a case in point and many other examples could be cited.

[2] "'After the Analysis . . .' ", *Psychoanalytic Quarterly*, Vol. VII, 1938. Cf. too the observation made by Glover in the ensuing discussion, quoted on p.141.

[3] Cf. Schmideberg, *op. cit.*

But conversely, maladaptation may become successful adaptation. Typical conflicts are a part and parcel of 'normal' development and disturbances in adaptation are included in its scope. We discover a similar state of affairs in relation to the therapeutic process of analysis. Here health clearly includes pathological reactions as a means towards its attainment.

But we must return to the concept of health and ask ourselves once more what criteria we possess in analysis for gauging mental health and illness. I have already mentioned that we do not identify health with freedom from symptoms. And we still find ourselves on ground which is comparatively accessible, from an empirical though not, of course, from a prognostic point of view, if we take into consideration the extent to which this immunity from symptoms is durable and capable of withstanding shocks. But the wider implications which the term health assumes for us and what analysis aims at in this sense cannot readily be reduced to a scientific formula. At the same time we find a number of useful theoretical formulations concerning the attributes of that state of health to which we are anxious to bring our patients with the help of the methods available to analysis. Of these the most general is Freud's 'Where id was, there shall ego be'[4]; or there is Nunberg's 'the energies of the id become more mobile, the super-ego more tolerant, the ego becomes more free from anxiety and its synthetic function is restored.'[5] But the distance between such necessarily schematic formulations and the measurement of actual states of mental health, of the actual degree of mental health enjoyed by a given individual, is far greater than one would like to suppose. It is not at all a simple matter to bring these theoretical conceptions of health into line with what we in actual fact call 'healthy'. Moreover, one gains an impression that individual conceptions of health differ widely among analysts themselves, varying with the aims which each has set for himself on the basis of his views concerning human development, and also of course with his philosophy, political sympathies, etc. Perhaps for the time being it will be advisable to proceed with caution before attempting to arrive at a precise theoretical formulation of the concept of health—otherwise we shall be in danger of allowing our standards of health to become dependent on our moral preoccupations and other subjective aspirations. It is clearly essential to proceed on purely empirical lines, i.e. to examine from the point of view of their structure and development the personalities of those who are actually considered healthy instead of allowing our theoretical speculations to dictate to us what we 'ought' to regard as healthy. This is precisely the attitude that psychoanalysis adopts towards the normative disciplines. It does not ask whether these norms are justified but concentrates on a totally different problem, namely that of the genesis and structure of behaviour which has, in fact, for

[4]*New Introductory Lectures*, 1933, p. 106.

[5]*Allgemeine Neurosenlehre*, 1932, S. 312.

whatever reason, been assigned a place in a scale of positive and negative values. And besides, theoretical standards of health are usually too narrow in so far as they underestimate the great diversity of types which in practice pass as healthy. Needless to say analysis itself possesses criteria intended to serve as a purely practical guide, such as the tests so frequently applied of a capacity for achievement or enjoyment.

But we propose here to examine in greater detail those theoretical schemes for the classification of mental health and illness which one finds contained, either expressly or by implication, in psycho-analytical literature; and for this purpose we may ask ourselves what conceptions of health have in fact been advanced and not whether certain conceptions 'ought' to be advanced. These descriptions of a healthy or 'biologically adjusted' individual, if we confine ourselves entirely to their broadest general outlines, reveal a pronounced development in two directions. In neither direction, it need scarcely be said, is it merely a question of some subjective factor, some personal predilection achieving expression; they are the results of a rich harvest of clinical experience, and of much valuable experience of the analytical process of cure. These two directions emphasize as the goal of development and health on the one hand rational behaviour and on the other hand instinctual life. This twofold orientation already commands our interest because it reflects the twofold origin of psycho-analysis in the history of thought—the rationalism of the age of enlightenment and the irrationalism of the romantics. The circumstance that these two aspects are emphasized in Freud's work certainly reflects a genuine insight into the dualism which does in fact inform the problem. Now the analytical conceptions of health which have developed on the basis of Freud's suggestions often proceed to assign undue prominence to one of these standpoints at the expense of the other.

When one makes the mistake in analysis of contrasting the id as the biological part of the personality with the ego as its non-biological component, one naturally encourages the tendency to make 'life' and 'mind' into absolutes. When in addition all biological values are acknowledged as supreme, one has approached dangerously near to that malady of the times whose nature it is to worship instinct and pour scorn on reason. To be sure, these tendencies, which lead to a glorification of instinctual man and which at the present time have widely assumed a highly aggressive and political complexion, play a less conspicuous part in the literature pertaining to psycho-analysis or subject to its influence than they do elsewhere.

At the other end of the scale we find the ideal of a rational attitude, and the 'perfectly rational' man is here held up as a model of health and as an ideal figure generally. This conception of mental health deserves closer consideration. That some connection exists between reason and successful adaptation seems clear enough, but it is apparently not such a simple one as is assumed in many psycho-analytical writings. We should not take it for granted that recognition of reality is the equivalent of adaptation to reality. The most rational attitude does not necessarily constitute an optimum for the purposes of adaptation. When we say that an idea or system of ideas is 'in accordance with reality', this may mean that the theoretical content of the system is true, but it can also signify that the translation of these ideas into action results in conduct appropriate to the occasion. A correct view of reality is not the sole criterion of whether a particular action is in accordance with reality. We must also reflect that a healthy ego should be able to make use of the system of rational control and at the same time take into account the fact of the irrational nature of other mental activities. (This is a part of its co-ordinating function). The rational must incorporate the irrational as an element in its design. Moreover, we shall have to admit that the advance of the 'rational attitude' is not an even one along a single front, as it were. One often has the impression that a partial progression in this respect may entail a partial regression in other directions. It is evidently very much the same with the process of civilization as a whole. Technical progress may very well be accompanied by mental regression or may actually bring it about by way of mass methods.[6] Here I can only present these ideas in brief outline but I have developed them at greater length elsewhere. They show us the need to revise those analytical conceptions which maintain that the individual who is most rational (in the ordinary sense of the word) is also psychologically the most completely healthy.

Another fundamental criterion of mental health available to psychology has a somewhat less general character, one more firmly rooted in the structural conceptions of analysis: I refer to the criterion of freedom. By freedom is meant not the philosophical problem of free will but rather freedom from anxiety and affects, or freedom to perform a task. The credit for introducing this criterion into analysis belongs to Wälder.[7] I believe that at the root of this conception there lies a well-founded idea; yet I would rather have avoided the term freedom because it is so equivocal in meaning and has been so heavily overtasked by successive philosophers. In the present context it means no more than control exercised by means of the conscious and preconscious ego and might well be replaced by that description. The mobility or plasticity of the ego is certainly one of the pre-requisites of mental health, whereas a rigid ego may interfere with the process of adaptation. But we would add that a healthy ego is not only and at all times plastic. Important as is this quality, it seems to be subordinated to another of the ego's functions. A clinical example will make this clear. We are all familiar with the obsessional neurotic's fear of losing his self-control—a factor which makes it so very difficult for him to associate freely. The phenomenon which I am thinking of is even more clearly marked in those persons who, for fear of losing their ego, are unable to achieve orgasm. These pathological manifestations teach us that a healthy ego must evidently be in a position to allow some of its most essential functions, including its 'freedom', to be put out of action occasionally, so that it may abandon itself to 'compulsion' (central control). This brings us to the problem, hitherto almost entirely neglected, of a biological hierarchy of the ego's functions and to the notion of the integration of opposites, which we have already met in connection with the problem of rational conduct. I believe that these considerations relative to the mobility of the ego and the automatic disconnecting of vital ego-functions have enabled us to make very considerable progress towards discovering an important condition of mental health. The threads which lead us from this point to the concept of ego-strength are clearly visible. But I do not now wish to discuss this well-worn theme, although one would have to deal with it at considerable length if a systematic exposition of our subject were intended, which is not the case.

I shall now develop this critical exposition of analytical conceptions of health in a direction which will enable us to penetrate more deeply into the realm of ego-theory. For obvious reasons psycho-analysis has hitherto been concerned principally with situations in which the ego finds itself in conflict with the id and the super-ego and, more recently, with the external world. Now one sometimes meets with the idea that the contrast between a conflict-ridden and a peaceful development can automatically be correlated with that afforded by mental health and mental illness. This is a quite mistaken view: conflicts are a part and parcel of human development, for which they provide the necessary stimulus. Nor does the distinction between healthy and pathological reactions correspond to that between behaviour originating or not originating in defence. Nevertheless it is by no means an uncommon thing to discover passages in psycho-analytical literature in which it is maintained that whatever is prompted by the needs of defence, or else results from unsuccessful defence, must somehow be accounted as pathological. Yet it is perfectly clear that a measure which is successful in relation to defensive needs may be a failure from the standpoint of positive achievement, and *vice versâ*. We are really concerned here with two distinct approaches to the classification of the same facts and not with two different sets of facts. This consideration does not invalidate our experience that pathological function offers the most fruitful approach to the problems of mental conflict. Similarly we first became familiar with the mechanisms of defence in their pathogenic aspect and it is only now that we are gradually coming to recognize the part they play in normal development. It would seem that we cannot adequately assess the positive or negative value which such processes possess for mental health so long as we only think of the problems of mental conflict and fail to consider these matters from the standpoint of adaptation as well.

Now if we examine these situations more attentively, we very often make the interesting discovery that the shortest way to reality is not always the most

---

[6]Karl Mannheim, *Mensch und Gesellschaft im Zeitalter des Umbaus*, Leyden, 1935.

[7]'The Problem of Freedom in Psycho-Analysis and the Problem of Reality-Testing', this Journal, Vol. XVII, 1936.

promising from the standpoint of adaptation. It would seem that we often learn to find our bearings in relation to reality by devious ways, and that it is inevitable and not merely 'accidental' that this should be the case. There is evidently a typical sequence here, withdrawal from reality leading to an increased mastery over it. (In its essential features this pattern is already realized in the process of our thinking; the same remark applies to the activity of imagination, the avoidance of unsatisfactory situations, etc.) The theory of the neuroses has always presented the mechanism of turning away from reality solely in terms of pathological processes: but an approach from the standpoint of the problems of adaptation teaches us that such mechanisms have a positive value for health.[8]

In this connection a further problem has a claim upon our interest: I allude to the way in which we use the terms 'regression' and 'regressive' within the analytical system of criteria for measuring mental health. We are generally accustomed to think of regressive behaviour as the antithesis of conduct adapted to reality. We are all familiar with the part which regression plays in pathogenesis and for that very reason I shall not need to consider that aspect of the problem. But in actual fact it would seem that we have to distinguish between progressive and regressive forms of adaptation. We shall have no difficulty in defining a progressive adaptation: it means an adaptation in the direction of development. But we also find instances of successful adaptation achieved by way of regression. These comprise many examples of the activity of the imagination; a further illustration is afforded by artistic activity as well as by those symbolic devices for facilitating thought which are found even in science, where it is most strictly rational.

We do not readily perceive at a first glance why it is so comparatively often the case that adaptation can only be achieved in these regressive *détours*. Probably the true position is that in his ego, especially as expressed in rational thought and action, in its synthetic and differentiating function,[9] man is equipped with a very highly differentiated organ of adaptation but that this highly differentiated organ is evidently by itself incapable of guaranteeing an optimum of adaptation. A system of regulation operating at the highest level of development is not sufficient to maintain a stable equilibrium; a more primitive system is needed to supplement it.

The objections which we felt obliged to raise against the definitions of mental health and illness last mentioned (in connection with the problems of defence, regression, etc.) may be summarized as follows: these conceptions of health approach the problem too exclusively from the angle of the neuroses or rather they are formulated in terms of contrast with the neuroses. Mechanisms, developmental stages, modes of reaction, with which we have become

[8] Cf. also Anna Freud, *The Ego and the Mechanisms of Defence*, 1937.

[9] Cf. also Fuchs, 'Zum Stand der heutigen Biologie', *Imago*, Bd. XXII, 1936.

familiar for the part they play in the development of the neuroses, are automatically relegated to the realm of the pathological—health is characterized as a condition in which these elements are absent. But the contrast thus established with the neuroses can have no meaning so long as we fail to appreciate how much of these mechanisms, developmental stages and modes of reaction is active in healthy individuals or in the development of those who later become so, i.e. so long as an analytical 'normal psychology' is still very largely non-existent. This is one of the reasons why it is precisely the analysis of conduct adapted to reality which is to-day considered of such importance.

I should add that the arbitrary nature of such definitions of mental health and illness is very much less evident in the literature of psychoanalysis itself than in many of its applications to social conditions, artistic activity, scientific production, etc. Where ethical, aesthetic, and political valuations enter very clearly into play and proceed to make use of the concept of health for their special purposes, a considerably wider latitude is allowed to such arbitrary judgement. By skilful conjuring with these kinds of standards it becomes easy enough to prove that those who do not share our political or general outlook on life are neurotic or psychotic or that social conditions to which we are for some reason opposed are to be acounted as pathological. I believe that we are all clear in our own minds that such judgements—whether we personally share them or not—have no right to speak in the name of psycho-analytical science.

It will now have become quite obvious to us where many of the conceptions of health and illness discussed in this paper stand most in need of amplification, namely in the direction of the subject's relations with and adaptation to reality. I do not mean to suggest that in these attempts to formulate a definition, to arrive at a theoretical concept of health, the factor of adaptation has been neglected; this is very far from being the case. But in the form in which it is expressed the concept of adaptation itself is in many respects too ill-defined—and, as we have already remarked, 'conduct adapted to reality' has hitherto offered little opportunity for a psycho-analytical approach.

It is obvious that what we designate as health or illness is intimately bound up with the individual's adaptation to reality (or, in the terms of an oft repeated formula, with his sense of self-preservation). I have recently made an attempt to probe more deeply into the problems which confront psycho-analysis at this juncture.[10] Here I shall confine myself to a few suggestions which may seem worth considering in framing a definition of health. The individual's adjustment to reality may be opposed to that of the race. Now it is true that we are accustomed, from the standpoint of our therapeutic aims, to allow a substantial margin of priority to the claims of individual adaptation over those of the race. But if we are to insist that some connection exists

[10] 'Ich-Psychologie und Anpassungsproblem', *Internationale Zeitschrift für Psychoanalyse und Imago*, Bd. XXIV, 1939.

between mental health and adaptation, we are bound to admit in the light of our previous remarks that the concept of health may bear inconsistent meanings according to whether we think of it in relation to the individual or to the community. Moreover, we shall deem it expedient to distinguish between the state of being adapted and the process by which it is achieved. And lastly we must point out that adaptation is only capable of definition in relation to something else, with reference to specific environmental settings. The actual state of equilibrium achieved in a given individual tells us nothing of his capacity for adaptation so long as we have not investigated his relations with the external world. Thus an unhampered 'capacity for achievement and 'enjoyment', simply considered in isolation, has nothing decisive to tell us concerning the capacity for adapting oneself to reality. On the other hand disturbances in one's capacity for achievement and enjoyment (for the sake of simplicity we will keep to these familiar criteria) are not to be evaluated simply as a sign of failure in adaptation. This really goes without saying and I only mention it because it is occasionally overlooked when attempts are made to formulate a definition. As an indispensable factor in assessing an individual's powers of adaptation we would single out his relation to a 'typical average environment'. We must take account of all these aspects of the concept of adaptation if we are to establish criteria of health based on adaptation or the capacity for it. We would insist that the processes of adaptation are always appropriate only to a limited range of environmental conditions; and that successful efforts at adaptation towards specific external situations may in indirect ways lead at the same time to inhibitions in adaptation affecting the organism.

Freud[11] recently characterized this state of affairs by quoting Goethe's 'Reason becomes unreason, beneficence a torment'. Conversely, when viewed from this angle, the proposition that the nature of the environment may be such that a pathological development of the psyche offers a more satisfactory solution than would a normal one loses its paradoxical character.

This necessarily condensed presentation must inevitably make the considerations here adumbrated appear somewhat arid; but I am convinced that no analyst would have any difficulty in illustrating them from his clinical experience. In this connection I should like to insist once more that we shall obviously be in a better position to correlate all these definitions with concrete, clinically manifest conditions and thus to apply the concept of health in an unequivocal and trustworthy manner, when we have been able to advance further in the sphere of analytical 'normal psychology', in the analysis of adapted behaviour. I believe that a more attentive examination of the phenomena of adaptation may also help us to escape from the opposition

[11]'Analysis Terminable and Interminable', this Journal, Vol. XVIII, 1937.

between 'biological' and 'sociological' conceptions of mental development which plays a certain part in analysis but is fundamentally sterile. It is only when we consider the social phenomena of adaptation in their biological aspect that we can really start 'getting psychology rightfully placed in the hierarchy of science, namely as one of the biological sciences'.[12]

It is important that we should clearly realize both that there exists a close connection between adaptation and synthesis, and the extent of this. An 'organization of the organism', the specific representative of which in the mental sphere we bring into relation with the synthetic function (and also with the differentiating function which has, however, been less fully explored), is a pre-requisite of successful adaptation; on the other hand its efficacy is doubtless dependent on the measure of adaptation achieved. A process when viewed 'from within' may often present itself as a disturbance of mental harmony; when viewed 'from without' we should have to characterize the same process as a disturbance of adaptation. So, too, instinctual conflicts are very frequently bound up with a disturbed relation to the environment. It is also significant in this connection that the same process of defence quite commonly serves the twofold purpose of acquiring mastery over the instincts and of reaching an accommodation with the external world.

By thus seeking to make adaptation, and especially synthesis, the basis of our concept of health, we seem to have arrived at an 'evolutionary' concept of health. And in point of fact this does represent a psycho-analytical contribution to the concept of mental health which should not be underestimated. But on the other hand a conception which relates the degree of mental health to the degree of development actually attained (compare the factor of rational control and, on the instinctual plane, the attainment of the genital stage as a pre-requisite of health) suffers from certain limitations, at least as regards the ego, to which I have briefly alluded.

I shall here conclude this necessarily schematic and fragmentary presentation. I have endeavoured to explain and discuss a number of standpoints which psycho-analysis has in fact adopted towards the concept of health, either expressly or by implication. In a one-sided fashion I proceeded to single out for almost exclusive attention those conditions of mental health which are seen to be related to the ego. I purposely restricted myself in this way. It seemed to me that there were good reasons why the psychology of the id had failed to provide us with a key to the problems of mental health. Moreover, by conducting my survey from the standpoint of the ego I found myself in a position to discuss certain problems of ego-theory which are decidedly no less important than the question of our criteria of health. The contribution that I myself have been able to make towards the further development and criticism

[12]Ernest Jones, 'Psycho-Analysis and the Instincts' (1935), *Papers on Psycho-Analysis*, Fourth Edition.

of these views certainly does not as yet enable us to formulate a concept of mental health in simple, unequivocal, definitive terms. But I believe that it will have helped us to discern quite clearly in which direction these prolegomena to a future analytical theory of health must be developed.

4.3

The Concept of Health in Psychiatry

F. C. Redlich

Introduction

The concept of health is important for all clinical specialties including psychiatry, but the subject seldom receives much serious thought. The word "health" is used loosely in everyday psychiatric practice and in the literature, and this looseness reflects our ignorance. The lack of a completely satisfactory and universally accepted theory of behavior may be an important factor in this ignorance, and a certain tendency for us psychiatrists to surround ourselves with a vague secrecy about therapeutic procedures, goals, and criteria increases the problem. Yet, as Lewis (52) pointed out, a concept of health would be of great importance for the assessment of therapeutic procedures. If psychiatrists could agree on such a concept, there probably would be more consensus on therapeutic effectiveness and aims. In this chapter an attempt will be made to deal with the concept of health or normality from both theoretical and practical viewpoints, adding new thoughts to a previous paper on the subject (64).

The concept of health is defined by the World Health Organization as "... a state of complete physical, mental, and social well-being and not merely the absence of disease or infirmity." Lewis pointed out that this proposition could hardly be more comprehensive and more meaningless.

Undoubtedly, the word *normal* has a number of denotations and connotations, and there are various major approaches toward an operational definition. It is used by epidemiologists and psychologists in a statistical sense denoting average, but to psychiatrists, who, like most physicians, are not used to thinking in terms of mathematical samples, the word hardly has such a meaning. The predominant psychiatric approach is clinical—*i.e.*, health is the absence of disease. The presence of disease can be established by certain techniques, and health is established when findings of disease are not detected. Yet, as the field of psychiatry is the field of behavior disorders—a concept more inclusive than that of disease—a broadening and modification of the health concept for psychiatry may be necessary. As many statements about health in the fields of psychiatry and organic medicine are value judgments, we must scrutinize such normative propositions.

The Statistical Approach

King (39) differentiated clearly the statistical term "average" from "normal." Average is that which results from mathematical computation based upon more than one sample—*i.e.*, a specimen mean; normal is that which functions in accordance with its inherent design—i.e., a pattern norm. No serious student of behavior should argue against describing variations of behavior in terms of frequencies. Actually, there are few good quantitative and taxonomic data in our field. Exceptions to this are data on intelligence, data collected in the field of child development, and the important taxonomic contribution on human sex behavior by Kinsey (40, 41) and his associates. Less commonly considered by psychiatrists are the data gathered by sociologists, ecologists (*e.g.*, the work by Faris and Dunham [20]), and social psychologists on occupation, education, ecological distribution, and attitudes and opinions toward a great variety of institutions and endeavors.

In contrast to the large body of data on general epidemiology, the epidemiological findings of psychiatric disorders are quite limited. In a critical review, Lemkau, Tietze, and Cooper (51) and, more recently, Lemkau (50) point to our lack of reliable and valid data on the incidence and prevalence of mental disorders. Actually, most work, such as that done by Malzberg (57) and by Dayton (13), has been limited to certified disease. With the exception of a rather focused approach, as in the excellent monograph by Fraser (21), who examined psychiatrically the population in a light engineering plant in England, and Bremer (6), who studied a fishing village in Norway, no data of an unselected *total* population have been published. There are a number of good studies covering primarily the hospitalized mental patient, such as the work by Brugger (8) in Germany, Sjögren (78), Ødegaard (62), and Stromgren (81) in the Scandinavian countries; there are also untranslated Japanese papers which may yield interesting information (Suwa [83]).

As a matter fact, we know nothing of the distribution in the total population of those behavior variables in which psychiatrists are particularly interested, such as anxiety, depression, hallucinations (omitting entirely the more inferentially derived processes of identification, repression, projection, etc.). Actually, a statistical concept of total mental health would be very complex because so many variables are involved. Our inability to isolate and quantify these variables meaningfully and the major difficulty in reaching a population which is not in therapeutic contact with psychiatrists are contributing factors in our ignorance. All workers in the field have experienced great difficulty in obtaining such information if the subject is not motivated to trade information for therapeutic help. Undoubtedly John Dollard (14) is right when he considers psychotherapy to be a window on human behavior.

In gathering information, Kinsey has again done better than anyone else, and it would be of interest if our profession could learn some of his techniques and extend them to fields other than sexual behavior. In attempts to gather data in various explorations and experiments, members of the Yale Department of Psychiatry and many others were startled by their findings when they examined persons who were not psychiatric patients. Freedman *et al.* (22) in studies on pregnant women, Eron (19) with students, and Redlich (68) with unselected control subjects found rich pathological material. Such experiences dramatize how little we know about the frequency distribution of traits, acts, and events which we call pathological. This ignorance makes difficult the selection of control subjects in research on psychoneurosis, and the inability to find proper controls for many of our investigations often leads to dubious inferences as to the relationship between social and personality variables. Yet the recent epidemiological research by Clausen (11), Goldhamer (27), Gruenberg (28), Hollingshead and Redlich (33,34,35), the Leightons (47, 48, 49), Lindemann (54), Rennie (70), Roberts and Myers (71) in this country, by Lewis (52) of the Occupational Psychiatric Unit at Maudsley Hospital in England and Muramatsu (60) in Japan lends new hope that some of these problems can be overcome.

It is obvious that the statistical norm and the clinical norm are not the same. There are diseases such as caries, athlete's foot, or, in certain areas, malaria or endemic syphilis which are extremely frequent (or "normal") in the statistical sense and yet abnormal in the individual from a clinical viewpoint. Such differentiations may be applied to many of Kinsey's findings—*e.g.*, that 40 percent of married middle-aged men masturbate, since such an activity cannot be considered clinically healthy. The issue becomes more complex, and even confused, since in contrast to the above examples we find instances in which statistical and clinical observations are positively and strongly correlated.

In the laboratory sphere of medicine, the statistical mode is usually identical with optimal function, as in the count of blood cells or in various chemical titers of plasma substances. In the behavioral field, we find the most severe forms of certain disorder categories, such as idiocy, criminal insanity, etc., infrequently. The same, of course, is true for the most desirable traits, such as creative intelligence at the genius level, "saintliness," etc. The most frequent form of behavior is that which is considered conformity behavior. Nevertheless, conformity is not an adequate measure of normal behavior, because nonconformity is often highly valued. To be sure, there is some correlation between conformity and statistical average, but there is a complex relationship between extremes of behavior and social evaluation.

We feel that the statistical approach, by establishing frequency distributions, is important even if it has little immediate and apparent relevance for the clinician, who can see little use in knowing the position of his patient on a frequency distrubution curve. It is an approach indispensable to research, and although in most instances we are still unable to count or to measure variables of human behavior, future research will increasingly determine the significant items that can be quantified statistically and those that cannot. It is the premature attempt to quantify which has brought some discredit to otherwise valuable and honest techniques. There is excellent reason to expect that these techniques will provide for psychiatry, as they have for medicine, important cues about the etiology for diseases.

The Clinical Approach

In clinical medicine, the terms "normal" and "healthy" are used interchangeably. Although the fundamental proposition of the World Health Organization asserts that health is more than the absence of disease, from a clinical viewpoint it is sufficient to equate health with absence of disease provided the term disease is used very broadly. As long as we are dealing with obvious cases, there is little doubt as to who is healthy and who is ill, but as soon as we pass into the lighter "shades of gray," doubt arises and we are unable to draw a clear line of demarcation.

Internists use three methods to determine whether a person is healthy or ill. (1) They obtain a history of subjective symptoms and of the informant's observations. (2) They note certain objective physical signs. (3) They use laboratory methods. Working from these three sets of data, they try to establish the existence and type of illness or the absence of illness. Certain aspects of these processes seem especially relevant for a discussion of normality.

In the process of establishing the presence of disease, the physician relies strongly on objective signs and tests and tends to minimize the environmental conditions in which they occur. More recently, with the development of comprehensive medicine, which recognizes the patient's experience and environment as well as his biological state, this viewpoint has been under attack; essentially, however, physicians by training and viewpoint are not too much concerned with psychological and social factors, although it is obvious that the consequences of disease will vary greatly with psychological and environmental variables. A definite orientation toward the environment and toward possible consequences of disease is really carried out only by a few individuals, as illustrated in Chapter IV of this volume, or in certain specialties such as occupational medicine and psychiatry.

There is one more consideration which bears mention at this time. If health is defined as the absence of disease, the condition of health implies not maximal but minimal performance. In the treatment and diagnosis of a patient with muscular weakness in his legs, the physician will be concerned with the patient's ability to walk, not with his ability to establish a new sprint record. Disease implies a mimimum standard of performance which the patient cannot meet.

In the broadest sense, illness may be considered as an impairment of the forces of life. The organism cannot adjust to certain adverse internal and external stresses it has to meet; manifestations of such inability to adapt are the signs and symptoms of trauma and illness. This viewpoint was expressed by Bernard (4) and recently by Romano (74) and Engel (17) and by Smith (79) as one of the cardinal criteria in the context of mental health and illness. In very general terms the concept of adaptation does enlighten us as to what is normal and abnormal.

Clearly, considerations of normality in the field of organic medicine are complex enough; yet they are much more complex in the field of behavior disorders. Whereas a precise proposition as to what constitutes most organic illnesses is possible, even if difficult, a precise definition of a particular mental disease is even more difficult and often not possible. There are a number of behavior disorders, such as the organic and toxic infectious psychoses and, to a certain degree, the so-called psychosomatic diseases and the functional psychoses, which are quite comparable to the diseases of organic medicine. There are others, like the neuroses, which bear only a remote resemblance to these conditions. Such disorders are not true disease merely because they are labeled with a word ending in "osis" or because physicians usually diagnose or treat such conditions or even because prevalent attitudes of the public tend to define them as disease. (The way the public defines a disorder [Koos (42)] is of great importance, however, from the viewpoint of subsequent intervention.)

The neuroses are more a dys-ease than a disease; they are manifestly difficulties in interpersonal relations. The differences and similarities of such behavior disorders and diseases in the more narrow sense of the word and the implications of these differences and similarities are beyond the scope of this contribution, but they make it necesary to extend the concept of mental health beyond the concept of physical health. The disorders which present the greatest difficulties in this respect are character neuroses (in the more narrow sense) and the antisocial reactions.

When Sigmund Freud began to scrutinize the behavior of abnormal persons and was able to show similar or identical phenomena in himself, his associates, and the more grossly disturbed, he began to tear down the rigid wall between the normal and the abnormal.[1] Psychiatrists who followed his thinking began to abandon the island of nuclear psychiatric disease and thus were engulfed in the boundless seas of human problems rather than in problems of diagnosis and treatment only. Absolute judgment became difficult, and for a time increased knowledge added further complications. The clearest statement that the concept of mental disorder is broader than the concept of other illnesses

[1] Freud also felt that absolute normality, like complete happiness, is impossible and that conflict is always present in human beings.

has come from Sullivan (82). He defines mental disorders as inadequate interpersonal relations, extending from forgetting the name of a person from whom one is about to request a favor to the chronic psychosis.

The methods of psychiatry which purport to establish differences between normal and abnormal are in many respects patterned after the methods of medicine; after all, psychiatry is a branch of medicine. These methods may also be divided into (1) eliciting the history of subjective symptoms; (2) obtaining objective signs, and (3) using laboratory techniques. Yet is it quite obvious that elicitation of subjective symptoms is more important in psychiatry than in internal medicine and that obtaining objective signs is more difficult and limited. The use of laboratory methods, for instance, is still in its infancy, and, although the testing methods of clinical psychology have made much progress, they can hardly be compared in validity and reliability to the laboratory methods of organic medicine.

The information the physician has to use in the course of diagnosis in psychiatry is both complex and diffuse. Although suffering may be considered one of the basic symptoms of all illnesses, the symptom of suffering itself is not pathological. Actually, as Hartmann mentioned, the lack of a capacity to suffer is pathological. Hallucinations are often considered a definite sign of mental disorders, yet hallucinations may occur in normal people. Although in biological medicine we are able to measure the degree of many signs, frequently permitting us to state when disease begins and health ends, we are not able to do this in a comparable manner in the sphere of psychiatric symptomatology. Particularly when dealing with psychoneurosis, we don't know how to measure anxiety, compulsive traits, aggression, depression, etc., and clear judgments as to what is normal or abnormal, based on reliable and valid scrutiny of signs and symptoms, are often not possible.

Yet, if any valid statements as to normality or abnormality can be made, they have to be restricted to a scrutiny of the single act, as Kubie pointed out, and not to a judgment of total behavior. Any extrapolation to total behavior has to be done with great caution.

There are three points which need to be considered before any act may even tentatively be labeled normal or abnormal. The first is motivation. The difference between a washing compulsion and "normal" washing depends not merely on the frequency but on the conscious and unconscious motivation of the act.

The second point involves consideration of the context in which the act occurs. A man promenading in swimming trunks on a New England main street in January may be considered "abnormal," but the same act on a beach in summer will not call for such a judgment.

The third point has to do with the question—by whom is the judgment made? Is it made by experts—*e.g.*, psychiatrists, who can claim a more thorough acquaintance with abnormal behavior—or by the general public? If there is agreement between expert and public, there will be little occasion to challenge expert judgment. If judgments are discrepant, they will be challenged either by fellow scientists or by the public. If the expert opinion is too much removed from the public's notions, it will be met with incredulity, ridicule, and criticism. As we do not possess a universal, rigorous science of man, many propositions on normality of behavior have a palpably low degree of validity and reliability and are apt to be challenged by a startled public, especially if scientific evidence for them is not particularly strong or runs counter to prevalent public opinion (Ruesch and Bateson [75]). An illustrative example of such an event is given in expert testimony in the court-martial in Wouk's *Caine Mutiny* (87).

> Greenwald resumed, "Doctor, did you note any peculiar habit Commander Gueeg had? Something he did with his hands?"
>
> "Do you mean rolling the marbles?"
>
> "Yes, did he do that in your presence?"
>
> "Not for the first week or so. Then he told me about it and I recommended that he resume the habit if it made him more comfortable. And he did so."
>
> "Describe the habit, please."
>
> "Well, it's an incesant rolling or rattling of two marbles in his hand—either hand."
>
> "Did he say why de did it?"
>
> "His hands tremble. He does it to steady his hands and conceal the trembling."
>
> "Why do his hands tremble?"
>
> "The inner tension. It's one of the surface symptoms."
>
> "Does the rolling of balls have significance in the Freudian analysis?"
>
> Bird glanced at the court uneasily. "Well, you go into technical jargon there."
>
> "Please make it as non-technical as possible."
>
> "Well, without analysis of the person you can only guess at the symbolism. It might be suppressed masturbation. It might be fondling poisonous pellets of feces. It all depends on...."
>
> "Feces?"
>
> "In the infantile world excrement is a deadly poison and therefore an instrument of vengeance. It would then be an expression of rage and hostility against the world."
>
> The court members were exchanging half-amused, half-horrified side glances. Challee protested again about the waste of court time, and Blakely again overruled him. The president was squinting at the Freudian doctor as though he were some unbelievable freak.
>
> "Doctor," Greenwald went on, "you have testified that the commander is a disturbed, not an adjusted, person."
>
> "Yes."
>
> "In laymen's terms, then, he's sick."
>
> Bird smiled. "I remember agreeing to the rough resemblance of the terms *disturbed* and *sick*. But by those terms an awful lot of people are sick...."

"But this trial only has Commander Queeg's sickness at issue. If he's sick, how could your board have given him a clean bill of health?"

"You're playing on words, I'm afraid. We found no disability."

"Could this sickness, greatly intensified, disable him?"

"Very greatly intensified, yes."

Greenwald said with sudden sharpness, "Isn't there another possibility, Doctor?"

"What do you mean?"

"Suppose the requirements of command were many times as severe as you believe them to be—wouldn't even this mild sickness disable Queeg?"

"That's absurdly hypothetical, because. . . ."

"Is it? Have you ever had sea duty, Doctor?"

"No."

"Have you ever *been* to sea?"

"No." Bird was losing his self-possessed look.

"How long have you been in the Navy?"

"Five months—no, six, I guess, now. . . ."

"Have you had any dealing with ships' captains before this case?"

"No."

"On what do you base your estimate of the stresses of command?"

"Well, my general knowledge. . . ."

"Do you think command requires a highly gifted, exceptional person?"

"Well, no. . . ."

"It doesn't?"

"Not highly gifted, no. Adequate responses, fairly good intelligence, and sufficient training and experience, but. . . ."

"Is that enough equipment for, say, a skilled psychiatrist?"

"Well, not exactly—that is, it's a different field. . . ."

"In other words, it takes more ability to be a psychiatrist than the captain of a naval vessel?" The lawyer looked toward Blakely.

"It takes—that is, different abilities are required. You're making the invidious comparison, not I."

"Doctor, you have admitted Commander Queeg is sick, which is more than Dr. Lundeen did. The only remaining question is, *how* sick. You don't think he's sick enough to be disabled for command. I suggest that since evidently you don't know much about the requirements of command, you may be wrong in your conclusion."

"I repudiate your suggestion." Bird looked like an insulted boy. His voice quivered. "You've deliberately substituted the word *sick*, which is a loose, a polarized word, for the correct . . ."

"Pardon me, what kind of word?"

"Polarized—loaded, invidious—I never said sick. My grasp of the requirements of command is adequate or I would have disqualified myself from serving on the board . . ."

"Maybe you should have."

Challee shouted. "The witness is being badgered."

"I withdraw my last statement. No more questions." Greenwald strode to his seat.

In defining normality, most psychiatrists and behavioral scientists, including psychoanalysts, have been satisfied with listing certain traits, capacities, and relationships which they consider normal. Jones (37) lists as criteria the intricate relationships between strivings for happiness and effectiveness and sensitive social relations. Glover (26) describes normality as characterized by freedom from symptoms, being unhampered by conflict, and having the capacity to love other than oneself. A plea for a balanced and integrated approach is made by Hacker (31), who finds any single or simple criterion unacceptalbe and defines normality as as successful integration of the personality. Hartmann (32) stresses the importance of balance of instinctual and ego forces. Menninger (58) writes, in a much quoted statement: "Let us define mental health as the adjustment of human beings to the word and to each other with a maximum of effectiveness and happiness. Not just efficiency, or just contentment, or the grace of obeying the rules of the game cheerfully. It is all of these together. It is the ability to maintain an even temper, an alert intelligence, socially considerate behavior, and a happy disposition. This, I think is a healthy mind."

Fromm (24) states in *Escape from Freedom*: "The term normal or healthy can be defined in two ways. Firstly, from the standpoint of functioning society one can call a person normal or healthy if he is able to fulfill the social role he is to take in that given society—if he is able to participate in the reproduction of society. Secondly, from the standpoint of the individual, we look upon health or normalcy as the optimum of growth and happiness of the individual."[2]

In the author's opinion, Waelder's (84) incisive statement on overdetermination and his principle of multiple functions lends itself to an analogy with regard to the concept of normality. According to Waelder, behavior is simultaneously serving the demands of the id, ego, and superego. Using this premise as a starting point for an integrative approach, behavior will approximate normality if it simultaneously gratifies and does not frustrate instinctual needs, leads to success rather than to failure, and produces social praise rather than punishment. Obviously, the conditions of satiation, mastery, and esteem will rarely and possibly never be fully met in life, but marked deviations from such an ideal may point to various degrees of abnormality. Appraisal of gratification, achievement, and social approval will depend on integrated and inter-

[2]Fromm gives a universalistic definition of mental health in *The Sane Society* (see p. 69): "Mental health is characterized by the ability to love and to create, by the emeregence from incestuous ties to clan and soil, by a sense of identify based on one's experience of self as the subject and agent of one's powers, by the grasp of reality inside and outside of ourselves; this is, by the development of objectivity and reason." Fromm states that such a concept essentially coincides with the norms postulated by the great spiritual teachers of the human race.

related judgment of individual and society. In most of our psychiatric patients, we will be able to discern some dysfunction in all three spheres; in the antisocial character, the dysfunction will be primarily, though never exclusively, in the deviation from social and ethical standards; in the neurotic, the dysfunction will be expressed more in frustration and failure and self-punishment.

Health and Unconscious Processes

Kubie (46) has attempted a penetrating analysis of what is normal and what is neurotic, aiming at the difference which, according to him, lies in the relative mixture of conscious, preconscious, and unconscious forces which determine a single act. He defines the goal of psychotherapy as one of extending the areas in the personality in which conscious processes play predominant roles and of shrinking the areas of the personality in which unconscious processes play a predominant role.

Kubie's hypothesis is an incisive attempt to define normal and abnormal within the framework of analytic theory and deserves careful attention and criticism. His bold attempt seems to paraphrase the old therapeutic dictum of psychoanalysis, "Where the id was, ego shall be," into "Where unconscious forces were, conscious forces shall be." In stating his hypothesis he limits mental illness to essential differences between normal and neurotic. He does not consider abnormal behavior determined by organic causes or the problem of mental deficiency. He advocates a quantitative approach in separating the mixtures of forces on which he bases his judment as to normality, but he is aware that we do not possess such an instrument.

In a previous paper I raised the question whether Kubie's viewpoint does not imply value judgments. Kubie does not feel that this is so; yet it seems to me that the assumption that rational acts, determined by conscious and deliberate forces, are healthier than those determined by irrational, unconscious, and uncontrolled forces implies such a judgment—as do all definitions of health. Judgments of this sort are not based on universally accepted facts, however; their acceptance depends to a certain degree on historical period, culture, subculture, and finally on the specific context in which the judgments are made. Kubie's accent on the motivation of the single act is an important and new idea, although it is difficult to say what constitutes a single act. Every act can be judged only in the context of other acts (and perhaps of total behavior) and cannot be viewed in terms of normal and abnormal without knowledge of motivation. However, there is no doubt that in most instances unconscious motivation implies rigidity, repetitiveness, insatiability and consciousness implies flexibility and capacity to learn.

To focus on this is the principal merit of Kubie's thinking about this problem. But does all unconscious motivation imply ridigity, repetitiveness, insatiability? Would strong emotions, as they arise in states of emergency, or powerful affects—such as love, passion, ecstasy, and much creative behavior, in which unconscious and preconscious vectors are strong—be abnormal? Aren't defensive mechanisms which are clearly unconscious at times also adaptive (as Hartmann pointed out)—as, for example, the utilization of identification and projection in empathy and in the appreciation of art or the mechanism of denial in unavoidable great danger such as approaching death? The point I wish to make is that the consequence of such behavior—whether it leads to satiation, mastery, or enchanced self-esteem—and not just its unconscious motivation, also determines whether it is normal or abnormal. Certainly, by Kubie's criteria alone, at least in its earlier formulation, we would have to consider the behavior of lovers, children, and artists invariably abnormal.

In a later paper (45) which is his most thorough statement, Kubie responds to various criticisms and elaborates on his earlier formulation. He repeats that he is fully aware of the present limitations of discussing quantitatively forces of psychological motivation, but that such an assumption, preceding availability of actual methods, is heuristically valuable. He states now quite convincingly that his ideas do not imply that "the well analyzed initiate is entitled to look down on the rest of the world with an assumption that he has full insight into his every motivation at every moment." But does this eliminate the assumption that the conscious-preconscious alliance is always preferable to the preconscious-unconscious alliance?

The most important innovation is that his present hypothesis clearly and definitely includes the importance of preconscious forces in such clusters of motivating forces. Since he assumes, following Freud and Kris (44), that preconscious forces determine creative processes in art and science, this is an important addition and clarification. Yet the main problem, in my opinion, remains untouched—*i.e.*, clear differentiation between the preconscious and unconscious forces and any mixture of such forces and their bearing on what is pathological and what is healthy.

The solution to the problem may lie in further differentiation of conscious, preconscious, and unconscious forces into those which are destructive, insatiable, and untamable, and those which are capable of satiation, sublimation, and neutralization. Actually, Kubie recognizes this when he writes that not all hidden depths of the personality are malevolent. The differentiation into benevolent and malevolent unconscious forces, and with this an exploration into the nature of repression, intersystemic and intrasystemic conflict, and adjusted and maladjusted behavior, is a task for future research which may well throw light on the essential difference between healthy and neurotic processes.

Actually, Kubie's ideas on mental health and my critical responses to them have converged considerably, as can be seen from Kubie's chapter on "Social Forces and the Neurotic Process" in this volume. In expressing his theories that the balance of unconscious, preconscious, and conscious forces determine the normality or abnormality of each act, Kubie has most recently made a definite and incisive effort to differentiate these processes and now stresses criterion of flexibility as particularly important. A number of authors—*e.g.*, Hartmann (32), Jahoda (36), Smith (79), and myself—fully agree that flexibility and the capacity to learn and adjust are elements of the normal. To refine these criteria to fit a great many—and possibly all—situations, acts, and total behavior would be a valuable research approach.

The Normative Approach

Most propositions about normal and abnormal behavior contain normative elements. We concur with Reider that the question as to normal or abnormal usually turns out to be a question about good or bad. Some of the most quoted statements, such as the one by Menninger, are definitely value statements. It is by no means clear whether some of these statements refer to an ideal (usually unattainable) adjustment or to the modal range in which people have managed to work out a fairly livable adjustment (Kraines [43]). It is obvious that normality, in the sense of freedom from mental disorder, is not identical with conformity to social norms. Certainly, conformity even to those social norms which may be considered dominant is not identical with clinical normality.

Cultural influences (as well as cultural judgments) in the area of mental disorders are as yet difficult to isolate and evaluate. In a society like ours, some of the most severe neurotics may be conformists and some of the most radical nonconformists may be relatively healthy. Patients with mental disorder are not necessarily morally weak or depraved and some of them have exhibited in their suffering and in the solutions of their problems the highest virtues.

Psychiatrists, in their practice as expert witnesses in courts of law, are attempting to differentiate crime and mental illness. Courts of law will exculpate a criminal for reasons of insanity only if definite evidence can be stated that his motivation and mode of communication are radically different from those of other persons, making his behavior unpredictable and nullifying his responsibility. Only in very severe cases, involving clear-cut and usually lasting disorder rather than temporary disorders or neuroses, will the insanity plea be accepted.

Lewis presents another argument differentiating abnormal from asocial or antisocial behavior, to the effect that, even in those societies in which suicide is socially and ethically acceptable, it may be a clinically abnormal act if carried out by a psychotic patient.

If one accepts this differentiation, we are then faced with the fact that, even if severe mental disorder proves to be universal in countries with higher and more complex civilizations (we still lack good scientific evidence for this), knowledge of social system and culture contributes relatively little to the understanding of the psychoses. On the other hand, our understanding of the neuroses is greatly enhanced by a knowledge of the culture and the subculture in which they occur. Behavioral scientists have barely begun to carry out such anthropologically oriented research (see Benedict and Jacks [3] and Caudill [10] for references) or explore differences in symptomology, treatability, and attitudes of the different social classes (Faris and Dunham [20], Ruesch, *et al.* [75], Clausen and Kohn [11], Hollingshead, Redlich, *et al.* [33, 34, 35].) Many value statements in the field of mental health have been made by middle-class psychiatrists and were addressed to and understood by middle-class people only (Davis [12], Redlich, *et al.* [66, 67]). We found only two social scientists, Smith and Jahoda, who appear to favor a transcultural concept of mental health over cultural relativism. Medical authors are more inclined to use a universal concept of mental health. However, whether differences in culture will produce not only different attitudes but also true differences in type and incidence of neurosis has not yet been established.

An Operational Approach to the Normality Concept

Although we do not know in clear scientific terms what normality is, we usually know quite well who should be treated by psychiatrists. Psychiatrists have some general guidelines for this, and they are usually able to decide whether or not a specific patient should receive treatment. I feel that the problem as to who should be treated, though not identical with the problem of normality, is an important practical problem on which social psychiatry can throw some light. Gruenberg (28), concerned primarily, in his chapter on mental health, with problems of prevention, points to three groups representing degrees of psychological disability: dangerous or dependent persons requiring institutional care, persons requiring outpatient care, and cases where psychiatric advice by nonpsychiatric personnel who have responsibility for a particular person is sufficient. Gruenberg's concept of failure of self-realization as an expression of mental illness seems to be a particularly important idea. His viewpoint has a certain similarity to the statements in the following paragraphs.

Who should be treated is not identical with the question of who acquiesces to treatment or of who is being treated; both questions, however, are of significance in the exploration of who should be treated, as judged by psychiatrists and by society. The question as to who *should be* treated is related in principle to other problems of selection and decision, such as who should be or should not be drafted into the Armed Forces, who should be admitted to higher educational institutions, who should be promoted for certain positions, etc. For many of these assessments we have commonsense and technical procedures, which essentially tell us, or pretend to tell us, who is or might be a problem or who might do particularly well in the Armed Service, in school, in jobs. Although psychiatrists have shown some interest in such problems, their central question remains and should remain: who should and could be treated?

The problem of normality, as the author sees it, can be put in form of the questions "normal for what?" and "normal for whom?" A moderately inadequate person working in a position of little responsibility in an industrial plant may be a very small problem to anyone except himself. The situation is entirely different if the man with "problems" is an important executive. It is different if psychiatric help is, for geographic, cultural, and psychological reasons, unavailable or if such help can be readily obtained and is considered beneficial in problems of this sort. Actually, only if the latter is the case should we speak of "psychiatric" problems. Otherwise, it would be more appropriate just to speak of "problems." To what extent such problems can be tolerated by the people who suffer from them or whether professional groups—*e.g.*, physicians, teachers, lawyers, ministers, welfare personnel, psychiatrists, etc.—who encounter them are ready to tackle them is another matter. The self-perception of the person with the problem and the role assignment of all actors involved will determine subsequent labeling (normal or abnormal with reference to certain tasks) and subsequent action.

Essentially, I propose to examine the interaction between psychiatrist, patient, and the society in which they function. In doing this there will be focus on the establishment of contact between psychiatrist and patient, on some of the social agreements implied in the treatment process, and on the termination and goals of treatment. It is hoped that these processes will be outlined with particular reference to norms, mores, laws, and social institutions which govern the conduct of the actors involved.

As a preliminary, I shall propose tentatively a dichotomy of the "abnormal" persons into a "severely abnormal" group and a "moderately abnormal" group. It is evident that the first group will not be rigidly delineated from the second group either by symptoms or etiology and course and that the second group will blend equally into the so-called "normal" population. Sometimes a severe disorder may be camouflaged by a seemingly normal surface and the more severe conditions may rapidly or slowly develop out of the mild conditions. Recognition of such phenomena usually will require high diagnostic skill from the expert and often enough challenges the expert beyond his present capacities. Yet I feel that the severe group, which includes all the psychotics and the severe neurotics, can more often be clearly recognized not only by the expert but by lay persons with whom these abnormal persons are in contact. Recognition of the moderately disturbed group is usually much more difficult and in most instances requires the most skillful professional judgment. I propose the above dichotomy because I think that it will aid us in our scrutiny of the social interactions between psychiatrist, patient, and society. Such a scrutiny involves not only an observation of social consequences of mental illness but an attempt to understand action in terms of social theory.

The first point of inquiry is concerned with the contact between psychiatrist and patient. How does one become a patient? There is considerable clinical experience in this area, but little systematic knowledge.

The relationship between psychiatrist and patient is defined by folkways, mores, and laws; these are different in the two groups of severe and moderate disorders. One of the more striking differences is the degree of urgency for treatment, which is usually greater in the case of the severe illness as compared with the mild disorder; sometimes a situation is found in which there is acute danger for the life and safety of the patient or those who are in contact with him. Intervention is often demanded so urgently that treatment and usually hospitalization is mandatory. As Parsons (63) pointed out, delay or avoidance of treatment is contrary to the expectations of the sick role. The contact between psychiatrist and the severely ill patient is at times brought about forcibly. Cooperation from the patient in such a process is thought to be desirable but not necessary. There is the assumption that such a step is necessary both from the patient's and from society's point of view, even if patients are not capable of, or willing to, recognize it.

The mandate of society to the psychiatrist in those cases is clear: to segregate, detain, and treat the patient and prevent his discharge until it is safe for him and society. In furthering such a mandate, society will, if necessary, deprive the patient of his most important citizen's rights and force him into a relationship of care and treatment. This is done by strong social pressures, by family, friends, and professional persons, or, in most instances, particularly in the lower socioeconomic group, by enacted laws. In the severe cases, psychiatric help is, theoretically at least, available to all who need it. When psychiatrists and psychiatric facilities do not exist, as in certain geographic areas, the lack of psychiatric help is felt as seriously as the lack of other medical personnel, facilities, and supplies. Ultimately, it is not the individual but society that decides upon intervention; the psychiatrist behaves according to the customs and enacted laws of his culture.

In the moderate disturbance and in the near-normal case, for which we have no name, there is no such urgency or such degree of obligation to submit to treatment. The agreement between patient and psychiatrist is voluntary and informal except for the general rules which apply to all relationships with medical practitioners. In comparison with treatment of the severe disorders, the treatment of the moderate group is considered less essential by society and to a certain extent still has the characteristics of a "luxury" for the upper classes who can afford and appreciate it. However, there is change too, both in a broader appreciation and in greater availability of such treatment to the less privileged classes (67).

In most instances, the contact will be established and maintained only if the patient wishes the contact, appreciates it, and expresses his cooperation through very definite effort of a personal or, if means are available, of a financial nature. Whereas in the severe case the psychiatrist is usually a hospital psychiatrist, in the moderate case the contact takes place in a clinic or a private office. In the last decades there has been an increasing trend in psychiatry toward this type of practice, with a definite change in interest, orientation, and training. The attitude of society toward this new type of psychiatry, essentially a discipline concerned with the understanding and aiding of interpersonal relations, has not yet been clarified. Though there is increasing demand for this kind of psychiatry, society has not caught up with the professional development, which in itself seems to be in a state of constant flux.

This new type of treatment, dynamic psychotherapy and psychoanalysis, is unthinkable without motivation for treatment on the part of the patient, although to a certain extent it is up to the psychiatrist to modify and reinforce existing motivations. Consequently, the dynamic psychotherapies are restricted to those with whom psychiatrists can communicate and, in the overwhelming number of cases, to those who can pay for such communication. In practice, this has meant restriction to the upper level of socioeconomic status and to those who accept, at least in part, the premises of psychodynamic theory. Actually, socioeconomic restrictions seem to be almost as important in determining the type of therapeutic intervention in psychiatry as are diagnostic-therapeutic indications.

Obviously, the ends or goals of the therapeutic processes in the case of severe disorder are different from those in the case of the moderate disorder. In the severe disorder the aim is stopping the pathological process, whereas the aim of psychoanalysis and to a somewhat lesser degree of dynamic psychotherapy is a profound change of personality. Particularly after a successful psychoanalysis, basic changes occur in the balance of ego, superego, and id forces, resulting in a different control and gratification of drive, accompanied by alterations in values and mastery of reality according to one's capacities. Incentive for a change must come from the patient, who must diligently and seriously work toward it, often for long periods of time.

In this approach good communication and similarity in certain basic values are essential. Psychoanalysis has little resemblance to most forms of medical treatment; its methods are educational and its goals prescribe a new pattern of living and a reorientation in many basic values. Another aspect of such analytic treatment is its interminability. The paucity of criteria for indicating the time to end analysis is admitted only with reluctance and concern; Freud (23) devoted his last opus on therapy to this problem. As change in basic structure of personality is its aim, therapy cannot stop with the cessation of symptoms; the process may last as long as life and only practical limitations call for a halt; even diminishing returns may be a form of resistance. The concept of health thus becomes an ideal which is never completely reached.

This discussion of the difference between the severely abnormal and the moderately abnormal patient was based on the application of social theory to clinical experience, not on a systematic investigation. Before these propositions become truly convincing, they will have to rest on solid evidence of well-designed research—evidence that will explain what a case is, its incidence and prevalence, how people become patients, how they change with and without specific intervention, and how treatment is terminated. We expect that conclusions from such research will provide us with more fundamental knowledge about normality.

In summary, we do not possess any general definition of normality and mental health from either a statistical or a clinical viewpoint. Actually, at this time clinicians can barely agree on satisfactory criteria. There is agreement only about extremes, not about the areas of transition or the "cut-off point." Sound epidemiological research on normality is in its infancy. In this chapter an attempt is made to investigate who should be treated psychiatrically rather than to consider the more complex problem of normality. Empirical research into the psychological and social elements of interaction of psychiatrists, patients, and their social environment will contribute to the solution of the problem of mental health; however, it is obvious that criteria of capacity for treatment and of mental illness are not identical. In any case, meaningful propositions on normality can be best made within a specific cultural context, notwithstanding some general propositions denying cultural relativism.

At present, it is true, the no-man's land between mental illness and mental health is ill-defined. Nevertheless, it seems justifiable to divide illness and health into two categories—the first roughly coinciding with psychosis and severe neurosis, the second including mild and transitory mental disturbances.

4.4

Mental Health and Mental Illness: Some Problems of Definition and Concept Formation

Ruth Macklin

1. **Introduction.** In recent years there has been considerable discussion and controversy concerning the concepts of mental health and mental illness. The controversy has centered around the problem of providing criteria for an adequate conception of mental health and illness, as well as difficulties in specifying a clear and workable system for the classification, understanding, and treatment of psychological and emotional disorders. In this paper I shall examine a cluster of these complex and important issues, focusing on attempts to define 'mental health' and 'mental illness'; diverse factors influencing the ascription of the predicates 'is mentally ill'; and 'is mentally healthy'; and some specific problems concerning these concepts as they appear in various theories of psychopathology. The approach here will be in the nature of a survey, directed at the specification of a number of problems—conceptual, methodological, and pragmatic—as they arise in various attempts to define and to provide criteria for applying the concepts of mental health and mental illness.

Closely related to the above-noted issues—indeed, an integral part of them—is a concern which has engendered much discussion and controversy among professionals in the past decade: the appropriateness of the "medical model," or health-disease conception of psychological disorders and emotional problems. The question arises as to whether or not the medical model of physical health and disease is the appropriate, correct, or most useful model for classifying, understanding, and treating the various emotional difficulties and behavior disorders which persons manifest. Space does not permit a detailed examination here of this controversial and interesting issue, but some remarks will be addressed to the problem in the final section of the paper.

In the words of one recent writer, "There is hardly a term in current psychological thought as vague, elusive, and ambiguous as the term 'mental health' " ([5], p. 3). There appears to be increasing recognition—even on the part of those who are not unhappy with the health-disease model—that some conceptual clarification is needed. Nevertheless, one psychologist claims that

> The definition of mental illness is not especially difficult, though a number of problems need to be considered in certain peripheral areas of breakdown in normal human behavior. Ordinarily, we think of mental illness as an unusually persistent pattern of behavior over which the individual has little or no voluntary control; it differentiates him from his fellows; it incapacitates him; it interferes with his normal participation in life. ([1], p. 37)

It is immediately obvious that this conception of mental illness is too broad, since it fails to distinguish mental illness from physical illness—a task which most writers in this area consider crucial. It should be noted that attempts to provide an acceptable definition of these concepts and a systematic set of criteria for their application have implications beyond the concerns of psychological or psychiatric theory. There are consequences, as well, for the direction of social and institutional practices such as therapy, civil commitment proceedings, legal and judicial concerns with the "criminally insane" and other social issues concerned with antisocial and deviant behavior. In addition, given a situation where need exceeds availability of psychotherapeutic time and personnel (both inside and outside hospital and institutional settings), it seems important to have a precise conception according to which comparative judgments ("is sicker than," "is more healthy than") can be made. Such judgments—if made according to some systematic and uncontroversial professional conception of health and illness—would facilitate decision-making problems in the area of assigning priorities for private, out-patient, and inpatient treatment of persons afflicted with psychological disorders of various sorts. So there seem to be crucial practical concerns, as well as more narrowly theoretical issues, which could benefit from greater clarification and systematization in this domain.

A word should be said at this point about the enterprise of defining. The difficulties of attempting to provide a definition of a term in natural language or a set of necessary and sufficient conditions for its application are well-known, and there is much philosophical literature on the subject. The generally acknowledged "open texture" of terms in natural languages (and even in scientific theories), in addition to multiple and possibly conflicting criteria of application, have led some philosophers to give up all attempts to provide such definitions. But psychologists and psychiatrists do not seem to have given up, even if their efforts are bent towards abandoning old conceptions or models in favor of new ones ([11], [16]). In addition, the pragmatic necessity for the enterprise in the area of mental illness and psychotherapy is dictated by the need to identify persons for treatment and to decide when they are "well," and to have some more precise criteria for commitment to and release from mental hospitals. The existing state of affairs is that in general, "mental illness is regarded usually as a residual category for deviant behavior having no clearly specified label" ([10], p. 26). So a partial justification for the inquiry conducted here—the objections of some philosophers and psychiatrists notwithstanding—lies in the stated needs and attempts on the part of many theorists and clinicians at further clarification and provision of a set of criteria for an adequate conception of mental health and mental illness.

One chief difficulty lies in the vagueness and ambiguity of the concept of mental illness as construed even by professional groups presumably committed to similar theoretical orientations and diagnostic procedures. In one recent study, the authors write:

> One need only glance at the diagnostic manual of the American Psychiatric Association to learn what an elastic concept mental illness is. It ranges from the massive functional inhibition characteristic of one form of catatonic schizophrenia to those seemingly slight aberrancies associated with an unstable personality, but which are so close to conduct in which we all engage as to define the entire continuum involved.... And, because of the unavoidably ambiguous generalities in which the American Psychiatric Association describes its diagnostic categories, the diagnostician has the ability to shoehorn into the mentally diseased class almost any person he wishes, for whatever reason, to put there. ([6], p. 80)

The authors point out that different norms of adjustment are employed by different users of the term 'mental illness', and that "usually the use of the phrase 'mental illness' effectively masks the actual norms being applied" ([6], p. 80). The acuteness of the situation is evidenced by the recognition that the group in question here is the American Psychiatric Association, whose members we might expect, presystematically, to share a body of norms and a roughly similar theoretical background. That this is not the case is readily apparent, and the above-noted authors claim that "the usual reason for variance in diagnosis is a variance in the theoretical orientation of the diagnosticians" ([6], p. 80, n. 18). So if such variation exists even within a circumscribed group of professionals, it is not surprising that a great deal of confusion and inconsistency obtains in the entire field of mental health workers, including clinical psychologists, social psychologists, social workers, and psychiatric nurses, as well as medically trained psychiatrists and psychoanalysts. When we consider the further fact that at least some professionals in all these groups (psychiatrists included) explicitly reject the medical model and the attendant notion of "disease entities," the hope for unanimity or even some widespread agreement on the definition of 'mental illness' becomes slim indeed.

In the light of these and other difficulties (a number of which will be discussed in the subsequent sections), Karl Menninger favors a "nonspecific, essentially unitary concept of mental illness" ([11], p. 87). In a brief historical review, Menninger notes that two systems of classification developed—the specific entity concept of mental illness and the unitary concept, the former of which prevailed in American Psychiatry. He writes:

> In the minds of many young doctors and in the minds of vast numbers of laymen, mental illness and particularly schizophrenia is a definite, specific, evil thing which invades the unsuspecting like a fungus or a tapeworm. The word schizophrenia becomes a damning designation.... A name implies a concept; and if this concept is unsound, the diagnosis can ruin the treatment; the very naming it can damage the patient whom we essay to help. ([11], p. 88)

In formulating his unitary concept of mental illness, Menninger emphasizes the degree of disorganization of the ego and its course or trend of development; his system is based largely on the theoretical concept of the ego—its failures and attempts at survival and optimal adaptation under stress. He holds that there are no *natural* mental disease entities, but that "an ordering of clinical phenomena on the basis of the economics of adaptation does justice to the essential unity of sickness and health; at the same time it leaves room for recognizing the latent potentials of every individual" ([11], p. 89).

While Menninger departs from the official psychiatric nosology, still he retains the conception of psychological disorders as instances of illness—a fact which marks him as an adherent of the medical model. Other psychiatrists and many psychologists argue for a more radical departure from the traditional schema, holding that we need to drop the notions of health and illness altogether in forming a conception of emotional problems and behavior disorders. Limitations of space in this paper preclude a detailed study of these increasing efforts to abandon the medical model, but a thorough account must include an examination of the arguments for and against the model, as well as a study of alternative approaches currently in practice (e.g. behavior modification therapy, existential psychiatry, and others).

In the next four sections I shall examine some problems related to definition and concept formation, as falling under the following categories: attempts to define 'mental health' in terms of the notion of mental illness; attempts to define 'mental health' and 'mental illness' in terms of normality and abnormality; obstacles to a clear conception of health or illness arising within or between specific theories of psychopathology; and, finally, problems with the conception of psychological disorders and malfunctioning as "disease" or "illness." There is an additional set of problems of a pragmatic sort: the identification of specific cases as instances of mental illness; conflicts between lay and professional definitions; the fact that different groups within society operate on the basis of different conceptions of mental health and illness; and the surprising fact that "the basic decision about illness is usually made by community members and *not professional personnel.* ... Community persons are brought to the hospital on the basis of lay definitions, and once they arrive, their appearance alone is usually regarded as sufficient evidence of 'illness'" ([10], p. 27). Although these practical issues are interesting and relevant to the conceptual and theoretical concerns of this paper, unfortunately space does not permit an examination of them here.

Before proceeding to examine the problems falling under the categories cited above, one general point needs to be noted. There is an ambiguity in the terms 'sick' and 'healthy' as they are employed in contexts of physical as well as mental health and illness. Marie Jahoda characterizes this ambiguity as follows. The concept of mental health can be defined "as a *relatively constant and enduring function of personality*, leading to predictable differences in behavior and feelings depending on the stresses and strains of the situation in which a person finds himself; or as a *momentary function of personality and situation*" ([5], p. 8). According to the first conception, individuals will be classified as more or less healthy. On the second conception, actions will be classified as more or less healthy. There is an analogue in the context of physical health, as Jahoda notes: according to the first conception, a strong man with a bad cold is healthy; according to the second conception, he is sick. Other examples can be given to illustrate the distinction, and the point is an important one in avoiding sources of error that are often overlooked. Jahoda claims that "much of the confusion in the area of mental health stems from the failure to establish whether one is talking about mental health as an enduring attribute of a person or a momentary attribute of functioning" ([5], p. 8). One area in which the relevance and importance of this distinction is crucial is that of the legal defense of persons charged with a criminal offense on grounds of insanity, temporary insanity, and the like. Still further implications exist for the selection of criteria according to which persons are committed to and released from mental hospitals. We now turn to an examination of some specific conceptual and theoretical problems in the area of mental health and illness.

2. **Attempts to define 'health' in terms of 'disease'.** The concept of disease is itself problematic, in somatic medicine as well as in the realm of psychological disorders. Two preliminary considerations will be noted briefly before examining specific problems in attempts to define the notion of health in terms of disease. Firstly, within the accepted framework of the medical model itself, there may be some difficulty in specifying relevant similarities in degree and kind between acknowledged cases of physical disease and putative instances of mental illness. This is the familiar problem of extending a concept from its standard or accepted usage to cover a new range of cases—a task first faced by Freud and others who were engaged in the process of noting affinities between the traditional cases of physical disease and the new cases (e.g. hysteria) which were being subsumed under a new, broadened concept of illness. But the familiarity of the enterprise of extending a concept does not

render the issue any the less problematic (see the discussion in section 5 below, pp. 361–363).

Secondly, if one chooses to abandon or to circumvent the medical model, there is still the problem of specifying a different set of criteria from those which proceed by analogy with physical disease. While there are some guidelines according to which we can classify mental illness or psychological disorders—antisocial or socially deviant behavior, malfunctioning behavior, self-destructive behavior, and the like—these guidelines are extremely rough and may result in a category that is too *broad* to specify what we want presystematically to count as mental illness or personality disorder (cf. Albee's definition cited above, p. 341). For example, an attempt along these lines may fail to distinguish between the mentally ill and the criminal. Or, it may result in classes of individuals—who by other psychological criteria would be considered "healthy," or "normal"—being classed as psychologically aberrant or emotionally disturbed, e.g. recluses, civil disobedients, radical revolutionaries, etc. On the other side of the coin, appeal to a specific theory of psychopathology might result in a definition of 'mental illness' that is too *narrow* to cover the range of cases which ought to be included under the category.

It should be noted, in this connection, that even among theorists and practitioners operating within the medical model, the current emphasis is on behavior disorders rather than on internal states of illness or on mental disease entities. In an influential and widely used textbook for students and practitioners of psychiatry, the authors write:

> In older texts and in current lay parlance, psychiatry is often defined as the science dealing with mental diseases and illnesses of the mind or psyche. Since these are terms reminiscent of the metaphysical concepts of soul and spirit, we prefer to speak of behavior disorder. Behavior refers to objective data that are accessible to observation, plausible inference, hypothesis-making, and experimentation. The term disorder, although vague, is descriptive of malfunctioning of behavior without specifying etiology or underlying mechanisms. Only some of the behavior disorders are caused by diseases of the brain or are accompanied by somatic reactions. Whereas many cerebral diseases produce a behavior disorder, and while we believe that cerebral processes must be related fundamentally to behavior, *medically* recognizable diseases of the brain cannot, for the most part, be demonstrated in behavior disorders. ([13], p. 2)

This position appears eminently sound, both in its emphasis on behavior and also in its presupposition that brain processes and other neurophysiological events underlie molar behavior. Behaviorists and other opponents of the medical model would do well to note the former point, while tough-minded philosophers who reject Cartesian dualism or other forms of "mentalism" (especially proponents of the neural identity thesis or modern materialism) should recognize the physicalist assumptions of at least some contemporary scientifically oriented psychiatrists. The fact that *medically* recognizable diseases of the brain cannot be demonstrated in most behavior disorders at the present time is no barrier to future progress in discovering such correlations and developing systematic psychophysical laws.

Turning now to the relationship between mental health and mental illness, we find that there is some disagreement on the matter. One writer points out the obvious fact that "consensus regarding positive mental health (or even mental abnormality) is far from unanimous" ([14], p. 3). He concludes, from an examination of several different conceptions, that the "criterion for mental health thus is simply the absence of mental illness" ([14], pp. 3–4). This view might be considered the standard conception, even among professionals in the field, as reflected in the words of Kenneth E. Appel, the 1954 president of the American Psychiatric Association: "mental illness is the opposite side of the coin of mental health" ([1], p. 38).

On the other hand, theorists such as Marie Jahoda, who are concerned to provide a workable *positive* conception of mental health, explicitly reject any attempt to define 'mental health' as 'the absence of mental illness or disease'. She notes that at present "knowledge about deviations, illness, and malfunctioning far exceeds knowledge of healthy functioning" ([5], p. 6), and it is apparent that the emphasis in this area has been on the study of disease and malfunctioning with the result that the health-disease model has prevailed, influencing theoretical developments and providing a framework according to which treatment and therapy have proceeded. In Jahoda's view, the assumption that health and illness are different only in degree needs to be tested. She is, herself, a proponent of the view that 'mental health' and 'mental illness' are *not* correlative terms, each denoting a state of the organism to be understood in terms of the absence of the other. She claims that a definition of psychological health as the absence of mental disease

> is based on the assumption that health is the opposite of disease, or that health and disease form the extreme poles of a continuum. What if this assumption should turn out to be unjustified and misleading? Some psychiatrists now speak of different health potentials in seemingly equally sick patients, as if they were dealing with two qualitatively different continua.... ([5], p. 14)

Jahoda believes that this issue requires a good deal of further research, especially since there is difficulty in clearly circumscribing the notion of mental disease itself. So it would seem to be more fruitful to concentrate on "the concept of mental health in its more positive connotation, noting, however, that the absence of disease may constitute a necessary, but not a sufficient criterion for mental health" ([5], p. 15).

Among the theorists whose conceptions of mental health are not formulated in terms of the absence of disease are a number of self-realization or self-actualization theorists, as well as proponents of existential psychiatry. Rollo May, for one, claims that the carryover of concepts from physical to psychological science is often unsuitable, as in the term 'health'.

> In the common popular meaning, physical health means the absence of infection and organic damage. In psychological therapy the term should mean something very different: "health" refers to dynamic processes; a person is healthy psychologically and emotionally to the extent that he can use all his capacities in day-to-day living. ([9], p. 167)

May stresses the *active* role of the individual in relating to himself and to others in his environment—a view which supports a conception of mental health as being something different from or over and above the mere absence of illness or disease.

Jahoda cites a number of theorists who oppose the traditional view ([5], pp. 73–75), one of whom holds that the category of positive health "applies when there is evidence that the individual fully utilizes a capacity or is working in that direction" ([5], p. 74). We shall return later in another connection to a brief examination of self-realization and self-actualization theories of psychopathology. The point to note in the present context is that the notion of *positive* mental health appears to be embedded in some theoretical conceptions while it is absent from others. To this extent, we might expect divergent views to be held on the relationship between mental health and illness by adherents of different theoretical systems in psychology and psychiatry. Jahoda points out that the relation between mental health and mental disease is still exceedingly complex, despite recent efforts at clarification, and that this relation remains one of the most urgent areas for future research.

3. **Problems with attempts to define 'mental health' and 'mental illness' in terms of normality and abnormality.** In this category, a number of problematic issues can be delineated. Redlich and Freedman point out, 'The concepts of normality and abnormality are more complex in psychiatry than in general medicine, and some people have suggested abandoning the concepts of normal and abnormal behavior entirely because simple concepts of health and disease do not apply" ([13], p. 112). One of the sources of difficulty with these concepts is the familiar issue of cultural relativism. We now turn to an examination of that issue.

A. Cultural Relativism. Jahoda notes that the evidence presented by cultural anthropologists is sufficient to demonstrate the vast range of what can be regarded as normal. Cultural anthropologists "have convincingly demonstrated a great variety of social norms and institutions in different cultures in different parts of the world; and that in different cultures different forms of behavior are regarded as normal" ([5], p. 15). It should be added that even within our own culture, the different norms and standards of behavior vary greatly among different age groups, socio-economic classes, and sub-groups of the population including religious, racial, and ethnic minorities. Thus, what may be considered "normal" sexual behavior for a twenty-eight year old divorcée who is a professional woman living in New York City will be considered "abnormal" for her fourteen year old sister living in Hudson, Ohio. Similarly, what is "normal" behavior for a black youth living in a crime-infested ghetto will be considered abnormal for a white, upper-middle class boy from Scarsdale.

Similar problems arise if we try to focus on the concept of abnormality as a criterion of mental *disease*. Again, Jahoda claims that anthropological studies throw doubt on the use of some symptoms for the diagnosis of mental disease:

> According to Ruth Benedict (1934), the Kwakiutl Indians of British Columbia engage in behavior that is, by our standards, paranoid and megalomaniacal. Their view of the world is similar to a delusion of grandeur in our culture. ([5], p. 12)

Other examples are given to support the view that "whereas identical observable symptoms are regarded in one culture as achievement, in another they are regarded as severe debility" ([5], p. 12). It is not clear, however, that the only conclusion to be drawn is that varying customs and accepted behavior in different cultures necessarily preclude a universally applicable conception of mental illness. Rather, it seems that in the absence of an overall psychological theory, or a well-developed personality theory that is acceptable to most, if not all, professionals and scientists in the field, no set of criteria can be agreed upon for making cross-cultural judgments of mental illness. The belief that a comprehensive psychological theory will be forthcoming someday may reflect an optimistic expression of faith in the progress and development of the science of psychology and related fields, but abundant evidence from the historical development of other sciences shows that such faith may not be wholly unwarranted. It is not unreasonable to hope that a more comprehensive and well-developed science of psychology (normal as well as abnormal) will provide us with a systematic approach to cultural and individual differences among people, enabling competent professionals to specify a workable set of parameters for formulating clear, univocal concepts of mental health and mental illness.

Redlich and Freedman address the issue of cultural relativism, claiming that abnormality depends on the cultural values of defining persons. They note that there is no agreement on what is normal drinking, that prostitution is accepted in some cultures but not in others, and that "there are remarkable differences in aggression, sexuality, and dependency needs in the different social classes of a single culture..." ([13], p. 114). They point out that despite the denial of relativism on the part of some social scientists, it is only extreme forms of behavior such as indiscriminate murder, cannibalism, or absolute disregard for property that are almost universally rejected. Severe behavior disorders are likely to be considered abnormal, no matter what the cultural setting. The authors write:

> In actual practice, psychiatrists use a composite approach; they diagnose behavior as clearly abnormal when it is seriously disabling, frustrating, deviates from established cultural norms, hence occurs relatively rarely; however, in borderline cases such an approach does not work well....
>
> Only gross deviations are clearly recognized and agreed upon in all civilized societies; borderlines of normal and abnormal behavior are fuzzy and overlapping. Cultural relativism with respect to milder disorders is the rule. The judgments of psychiatrists cannot in reality be far removed from those of the common man of the societies and cultures in which psychiatrists and patients live. At present we cannot make precise statements about normal and abnormal.... ([13], pp. 114–115)

Problems of cultural relativism constitute only a partial barrier to providing a clear and uncontroversial conception of normality and abnormality. Another set of difficulties lies in the way in which the terms 'normality' and 'abnormality' are to be construed, an inquiry to which we turn next.

B. Normality and abnormality as normative and as statistical concepts. It should be noted at the outset that if 'mental health' and 'mental illness' are not properly to be viewed as correlative terms (see section 2 above), then even *given* some acceptable account of normality and abnormality, we may be faced with the task of specifying an independent set of parameters for assessing types and degrees of mental health and mental illness. But apart from this, another set of problems emerges relating to the fact that normality is sometimes construed as a normative concept and sometimes as a statistical one. Jahoda rejects the attempt to provide a criterion for mental health based on normality on a number of grounds. One such ground is that of the problems presented by cultural relativity, as discussed above, and the second reason is as follows.

Noting that normality can be viewed either as a statistical frequency concept or as a normative idea of how people ought to function, Jahoda points out that a coincidence of statistical and normative correctness is, at best, fortuitous.

> To believe that the two connotations always coincide leads to the assertion that whatever exists in the majority of cases is right by virtue of its existence. The failure to keep the two connotations of normality separate leads straight back into an extreme cultural relativism according to which the storm trooper, for

> example, must be considered as the prototype of integrative adjustment in Nazi culture. ([5], pp. 15–16)

The issue is now identified as the old problem in philosophical ethics: the is-ought gap. Although I am not concerned to argue here about whether there is or is not, or should or should not be such a gap, it seems that the significance of the distinction for the problem of defining 'mental health' in terms of some conception of normality is clear. As Jahoda correctly points out, "insofar as normality is used in the normative sense, it is a synonym for mental health, and the problems of concept definition are, of course, identical" ([5], p. 16).

Another difficulty with 'normality' as construed in the normative sense is that the concept tends to function as an "ideal type," so that the actual behavior of persons is, at best, an approximation to some optimal conditions. The problem is, then, that according to some psychological theoretical frameworks it may be extraordinarily difficult or even impossible to draw the line between normality and abnormality (and, consequently, following Jahoda's insight, impossible to draw the line between mental illness and mental health). This issue will be brought up again in connection with a problem to be discussed below: considerations *within* certain theories which preclude the possibility of a precise definition of mental health and illness. Let it suffice to note at this point that an attempt to define 'mental health' in terms of a normative conception of normality appears to lead either to circularity (as Jahoda claims), or else directly back to cultural relativism. We shall next examine the frequency concept of normality to see if it fares any better.

The most obvious difficulty with a statistical frequency concept of normality is that a majority of people may do many things we hesitate to call mentally healthy. Thus, "psychological health may, but need not be, the status of the majority of people" ([5], p. 16). That this is so might be illustrated by considering the case of physical illness and health. No one would be likely to urge a definition of 'physical health' based on statistical considerations, for it might turn out that a majority of the population is suffering from some form or other of physical ailment or disease (whether temporary or enduring). As Livermore, Malmquist, and Meehl point out in this connection:

> From a biological viewpoint, it is not inconsistent to assert that a sizable proportion—conceivably a majority—of persons in a given population are abnormal or aberrant. Thus if an epidemiologist found that 60% of the persons in a society were afflicted with plague or avitaminosis, he would (quite correctly) reject an argument that "Since most of them have it, they are okay, i.e. not pathological and not in need of treatment." It is admittedly easier to defend this nonstatistical, biological-fitness approach in the domain of physical disease, but its application in the domain of behavior is fraught with difficulties. ([6], pp. 78–79, n. 11)

It is true, of course, that there are much more systematic and comprehensive biological and physiological theories on the basis of which the concept of physical or bodily health may be constructed in medicine than now exist in the realm of psychological or psychiatric theory. But the inadequacy of a statistical conception of normality for physical health provides an instructive comparison for present purposes. It may be objected here that the example just given presupposes the applicability of the medical model and a conception of mental health based on the analogue of physical health. Although this is so, the reasons for questioning the adequacy of the frequency concept of normality for defining 'mental health' do not depend on the analogy with physical health.

An additional difficulty with the statistical approach is noted by Redlich and Freedman. This difficulty constitutes a methodological problem rather than an objection in principle, but presents obstacles nevertheless.

> Few exact data... are available on the frequency and distribution of behavior traits. Such an approach presupposes that behavior is quantifiable and measurable, but obviously many forms of behavior are not.... Few data... exist on the prevalence and the incidence of psychiatric symptoms, such as anxiety, hallucinations, phobias, and so forth. ([13], p. 113)

The authors acknowledge that there are some good examples of the statistical approach in the data supplied by Kinsey et al. on sexual behavior, in the area of socio-economic data, and in the broad investigations of intelligence. However, the need for assessing the *relevance* of various sorts of behavioral data for the task of defining 'mental health' and 'mental illness' points to still another problem inherent in the statistical approach to normality and abnormality. This is the selection of a reference population—a procedure that involves nonstatistical considerations. Jahoda notes that "the choice of population inevitably contains, at least implicitly, a nonstatistical concept of health" ([5], p. 17), a factor which indicates the inadequacy of an attempt to define 'mental health' and 'mental illness' on the basis of a purely statistical concept of normality.

Moreover, even when the relevant reference population has been delineated, equal weight would not be given to all measurable psychological functions in developing a set of norms against which to evaluate the mental health status of individuals. "We thus find again that some, at least tacit, nonstatistical considerations must precede the application of the statistical approach" ([5], pp. 17–18). This is borne out once again by the example of physical health and disease where purely statistical considerations are insufficient for formulating a conception of health. In the domain of mental health, the most that a statistical approach can achieve is a specification of which behaviors and traits are "abnormal" in the general population. But we still require some nonstatistical parameters for deciding which "abnormalities" are to count as illness and which "normalities" should be construed as healthy. The selection of such parameters would appear to depend partly on considerations which are contingent upon the progress and development of a comprehensive psychological theory, and also on a range of value questions which, although relevant and important, cannot be gone into here (in this connection, see [3] and [8]). The above-noted difficulties with both the normative and statistical concepts of normality point to their inadequacy (at least if taken singly) as a basis for defining 'mental health' and 'mental illness'. Redlich and Freedman identify one further approach to normality which will be discussed briefly in the next section: the clinical approach.

C. The clinical approach. It was noted in subsection **B** above that when construed in the normative sense, the concept of normality tends to function as an "ideal type" according to whatever theory is being employed. This is not the case, however, in the clinical approach, as Redlich and Freedman point out: "In general terms, clinical normality is not ideal performance but minimal performance, just above the level of pathological performance for a given individual" ([13], p. 113). But now the problem is to identify such "levels of performance," a task which is not only clinically difficult but also depends on some theoretical assumptions on the part of the clinician. Indeed, according to Redlich and Freedman:

> The clinical approach defines as abnormal anything that does not function according to its design. This approach is useful in somatic illness, including brain disease, but it is less helpful in behavior disorders, because all too often we do not know what design or function a certain behavior pattern serves. ([13], p. 113)

Some criteria for normality which have been employed in the clinical approach are adaptation, maturity, "average expectable environment," and "predominance of conscious and preconscious motivations over unconscious motivation of behavioral acts" ([13], p. 113). But Redlich and Freedman find the concept of adaptation, "which is supposed to explain just about everything, only of very limited use in differentiating normal and abnormal behavior" ([13], p. 113); the conscious-unconscious criterion fails to apply to many forms of abnormal behavior determined by brain disease and ignores the fact that in many types of normal and socially desirable behavior, unconscious and preconscious motivations occur ([13], pp. 113–114). The criteria of "average expectable environment" and maturity are viewed more favorably, but the authors fail to note that 'maturity' and 'immaturity' are themselves value laden terms, depending for their application not only on the theoretical orientation of the clinician but also on a set of cultural and subcultural norms espoused by him.

One final problem in connection with the clinical approach lies in the unwitting conflation of a number of different criteria on the part of professionals. These criteria may encompass those already cited here, in addition to the personal, subjective conceptions of the psychiatrist or clinical psychologist. The situation has been described as follows:

> It is especially tempting to the psychiatrist or clinical psychologist, given his usual clinical orientation, to slip unconsciously from the idea of "sickness," where treatment of a so-called "patient" is the model, to an application that justifies at most a statistical or ideological or psychological-adjustment usage of the word "norm." Probably the most pernicious error is committed by those who classify as "sick" behavior that is aberrant in *neither* a statistical sense *nor* in terms of any defensible biological or medical criterion, but solely on the basis of the clinician's personal ideology of mental health and interpersonal relationships. Examples might be the current psychiatric stereotype of what a good mother or a health family must be like, or the rejection as "perverse" of forms of sexual behavior that are not biologically harmful, are found in many infrahuman mammals and in diverse human cultures, and have a high statistical frequency in our own society. ([6], p. 79, n. 11)

This situation not only complicates the process of diagnosing mental illness in individual persons, but also, if widespread or typical, precludes the use of the clinical approach as an effective means of defining 'normality' and 'abnormality'.

4. Obstacles to a clear conception arising within or between specific theories of psychopathology. This section will be devoted to an examination of some of the difficulties posed by different theories or theoretical conceptions—difficulties that stand in the way of a clear and precise concept of mental health or mental illness. The inquiry will be divided into two main areas: problems *within* theories (intratheoretical); and disparity or conflict *between* or *among* theories (intertheoretical).

A. Intratheoretical Problems. While it is likely that many different theories or theoretical systems contain tacit assumptions or explicit premises which create difficulties for attempts to provide criteria for the concepts of mental health and illness, we shall limit our inquiry here to two of these: Freudian and neo-Freudian psycho-analytic theories; and self-realization or self-actualization theories. It was noted above in connection with normality construed as a normative concept that according to some psychological theoretical frameworks it may be extraordinarily difficult or even impossible to draw the line between sickness and health. One such theory is the classical Freudian account, and one writer points out that if a psychiatrist is trained in the more orthodox psychoanalytic notions,

> his belief system makes it impossible to determine the "sickness" or "wellness' of the patient, since the classical theories assume that all people have unconscious drives which interfere with optimal functioning, and no clear practical criteria are provided for judging the "sick" from the "well." ([10], p. 27)

We shall not raise questions here about the nature of the theoretical entities to which Freudian theory is committed, nor about the testability of many propositions embedded in that theory. Although such questions are legitimate and interesting, they have been examined at great length by philosophers, psychologists, and psychiatrists alike, and are peripheral to the concerns of this paper. The question here is whether, *given* an initial acceptance of the Freudian notion of the Unconscious and all that it entails, a distinction can be made between healthy and unhealthy behavior. Jahoda seconds the view cited just above, noting that it has not been demonstrated that there are any human beings who are free from unconscious conflicts.

> If it is reasonable to assume that such conflicts are universal, we are all sick in different degrees. Actually, the difference between anyone and a psychotic may lie in the way he handles his conflicts and in the appearance or lack of certain symptoms. If this is so, mental disease must inevitably be inferred from behavior. But, apart from extremes, there is no agreement on the types of behavior which it is reasonable to call "sick." ([5], p. 13)

So according to this objection, the theory itself precludes any workable, clear distinction between instances of mental health and cases of mental illness. The most we can hope for, according to this theoretical framework, is the provision of *comparative* judgments of health and illness—a conclusion which would be welcomed by many Freudians and non-Freudians alike on this issue.

But this is not the end of the Freudian story. As Joseph Margolis contends, it appears that Freud himself employed a "mixed model that shows clear affinities with the models that obtain in physical medicine and at the same time with the models of happiness and well-being that obtain in the ethical domain" ([7], pp. 81–82). This further complicates the issue since the "mixed model" is really a combination of two different models, each having its own set of parameters along which health and disease, good and poor functioning, desirable and undesirable traits and behavior are identified. Margolis specifies further just how Freud's development of psychoanalytic medicine runs along two converging lines:

> In one, as in the studies of hysteria, Freud was extending case by case the medical concept of illness, by working out striking and undeniable affinities between physical illnesses and counterpart cases, for which the aetiology would have have had to be radically different. And, in the other, Freud inevitably assimilated the

> concept of mental health to concepts of happiness—in particular, to his genital ideal. The result is that, *given* some version of this (or another such) ideal, deviation from the ideal tends to be viewed in terms of malady and disease, even though there are no strong analogical affinities between the pattern in question and clear-cut models of physical illness. Hence, patterns as significantly different as hysteria and homosexuality tend both to be assimilated to the concepts of health and disease. ([7], pp. 75–76)

There is little doubt that Margolis's analysis here is correct. Indeed, on the Freudian account, the failure of an individual to pass successfully through the three developmental stages of sexuality in infancy and childhood (the oral phase, the anal phase, and the phallic phase) can lead to such diverse patterns of adult "illness" as those represented in the neuroses and those constituting the character disorders. In any case, successful passage (without "fixation," "regression," "arrest") through the early developmental stages is a necessary condition (although not sufficient) for the "healthy" adult, achieving or approximating the "genital ideal." The adult genital character is the *mature* individual; failure to attain the ideal results in varying degrees of "immaturity." Thus on the Freudian account, the concept of the "genital (ideal) character," which denotes the mature individual, is intimately bound up with the descriptive-explanatory theory of infant-childhood development. The interlacing of descriptive and normative components in this account, while not in itself pernicious, must be made explicit if there is to be any progress in providing criteria for the concepts of health and illness.

One need not, of course, accept the specific Freudian precepts concerning the developmental stages in infancy and childhood and the related notions of fixation at one level or another, regression to a previous stage, etc. Indeed, the refusal to accept this particular framework may result in different judgments as to the mental health or illness of a person who fails to live up to the "genital ideal." The fact that there are other ideals of health, happiness, and well-being which may be and are, in fact, postulated by different theorists leads not only to the presence of multiple criteria, but also to possibly conflicting ones. Even if we allow the legitimacy of a "mixed model" such as Freud's, it must be acknowledged that there exist multiple and possibly conflicting norms of health, happiness, and well-being. Consequently, deviation from one such norm might count as mental illness, while the same person might be termed mentally healthy according to some different set of norms whose ideal he fulfills or closely approximates.

We turn next to a brief look at some problems inherent in another set of influential theories: the self-realization or self-actualization theories. Mention was made earlier of these theories in discussing the failure of attempts to define 'mental health' in terms of the absence of disease or illness. The concepts of self-realization and self-actualization play a dual role in a number of psychopathological theories (notably, those of Karen Horney, Erich Fromm, Kurt Goldstein, and Abraham H. Maslow), functioning as a characterization of the healthy individual and also specifying the goal of psychotherapy (for a more detailed account, see [3]). Redlich and Freedman note that

> in highly individualized cultures, self-actualization or self-realization is seen as the goal of certain psychotherapies. The goal of realizing one's human potential is encountered in Buddhism, particularly in the practices of Zen Buddhism, which fascinated and stimulated Karen Horney, Erich Fromm, and Alan Watts... The behavioral changes... should be defined in rationally and operationally verifiable terms. There is no place in psychiatry for mystical, irrational, or suprarational approaches. ([13], p. 270)

Leaving aside the methodological issues connected with the goals and practice of psychotherapy, we may note that even in its role as characterizing the healthy person (a positive conception of mental health), the concept of self-realization is problematic. The difficulty is an old one in philosophy, harking back to Aristotelian notions of potentiality and essence. Indeed, Fromm cites Aristotle in his account of "activity" as "the exercise of the functions and capacities peculiar to man" and his emphasis on "the full development of our powers within the limitations set by the laws of our existence." ([3], p. 58)

Kurt Goldstein "speaks of a 'drive' that enables and impels the organism to actualize in further activities, according to its nature," emphasizing that "optimal self-actualization also means health" ([3], pp. 58–59). Karen Horney refers to "the real self as that central inner force common to all human beings and yet unique in each, which is the deep source of growth" ([3], p. 58). What all these theories— and others of this type—have in common is their emphasis on man's "inner nature" which he seeks to fulfill, his "potentialities" which need to be "actualized," and the "inner self" which develops and unfolds successfully through "self-realization." Both as goals of psychotherapy and as characterizations of positive mental health, these concepts are problematic. The assumptions about man's nature or essence cannot be accepted uncritically, and the difficulties of formulating a testable concept of man's "potentiality" (as a generic trait) are well-known. To the extent that a concept of mental health adopted by these theories rests on the foregoing assumptions, we cannot expect much in the way of criteria that meet the requirements of empirical testability and confirmability. Such theories may achieve a high degree of methodological adequacy in cases where a sensitive and insightful therapist can assess the specific "potentialities" or "natural inclinations" of a particular patient. But as attempts to provide a basis for constructing a clear and workable *concept* of mental health, the self-realization theories fail to satisfy the demands of conceptual clarity and empirical testability.

B. Intertheoretical Problems. A set of problems which naturally arise from the proliferation of theories in this area relates to the likelihood of multiple—possibly even conflicting—criteria for mental health and mental illness. Especially among theories which are couched in terms of some normative ideal of health, happiness, or well-being, we may expect that deviations from the ideal might be construed as "sick" on one theory, while no decision might be forthcoming according to another. This raises the question of whether deviation from some *normative ideal* should properly be counted as sickness or illness, on the model of physical disease. In any case, an obvious consequence of the present situation is that the *general* concepts of mental health and mental illness can only be understood in terms of some *specific* theory of psychopathology.

Enough has been said in the preceding section to indicate the divergence between the concepts of health and illness as conceived by classical Freudian theorists, on the one hand, and self-realization theorists, on the other. Both conceptions are embedded in the theoretical systems themselves and professional judgments concerning the health or illness of particular individuals may vary depending on which system the diagnostician espouses. The number of different theories is legion, and no attempt will be made here to survey them. Instead, a few general points will be noted.

Following Freud's tripartite division of the psyche into id, ego, and superego, much emphasis was placed by psychoanalytically oriented practitioners on the relationship among these and the relation of all of them to unconscious processes. Recent developments in the area known as ego psychology have tried to correct what some theorists held to be a bias in Freudian theory, attempting to replace the "one-sided emphasis on unconscious processes with a stronger acknowledgment of the importance of *conscious* experiences" ([3], p. xiii). It is apparent that with different norms of well-functioning and different emphases even in theories which accept many of the basic Freudian precepts, there is a broad scope of conceptions concerning what is to count as healthy or sick behavior.

Marie Jahoda favors a "multiple criterion" approach to problems of mental health. The value of this approach to the concepts of health and illness is that it has the requisite breadth and flexibility to comprehend a wide variety of human behavior without being so general as to become empty. Commenting on various criteria adopted by different theorists who propound different concepts of positive mental health and also on the various ways of using a multiple criterion, Jahoda writes:

> There is no incompatibility between the idea of diverse types of health and the use of such a criterion.... At the present state of our knowledge it may well be best to combine the idea of various types of health with the use of a multiple

> criterion for each. The former will prevent over-generalizations; the latter will permit us to do justice to the complexity of human functioning. ([5], p. 73)

It is evident that the work of providing criteria for the concepts of mental health and illness, as well as the task of evaluating proposed definitions needs to be done by theorists and practitioners in the fields of psychiatry and psychology. The task is partly conceptual and partly empirical, involving policy decisions as well as theoretical considerations. In this and the preceding sections, I have tried to specify a number of the problems which exist in this area and to note some of the issues that need clarification and careful scrutiny.

Finally, one large problem should be noted—a problem which might best be viewed as one that encompasses and gives rise to most of those already discussed. This is the absence of an overall scientific theory on which to base conceptions of mental health and illness, well-functioning and maladaptive behavior. It should be noted, however, that in this regard the concepts of health and disease face a number of similar problems in the domain of somatic medicine (i.e. the concepts are vague, there are multiple criteria for their application—criteria which may conflict occasionally, etc.). There is no general, well-integrated theory of the sort that exists in, say, physics, interconnecting the well-developed fields in medicine of physiology, anatomy, pathology, neurology, immunology, etc., with current developments in the biological sciences. The absence of bridging laws between these branches of medical and biological science, as well as the divergent theoretical and methodological approaches of experimental biologists, on the one hand, and medical scientists oriented towards pathology, on the other, all contribute to the present lack of systematization in the total field of biological science. So the absence of well-confirmed fundamental laws, from which other laws are derivable, and the absence of a systematic, general theory result in the situation that within medicine itself, there are no clear or precise formulations of the basic concepts of health and disease, and no set of necessary and sufficient conditions for their application.

These facts concerning the present stage of scientific development of somatic medicine may offer little consolation to the theorist in psychology or psychiatry who is looking to provide a clear, workable concept of mental health or mental illness. But it would seem that the clarity and precision of the basic concepts in this field—as in any other—go hand in hand with the related theoretical developments of formulating general laws, providing systematic interconnections among the various branches of the field, and relating all of these to existing, well-confirmed theories in the other sciences. The science of psychology is a long way from this goal, but there do not seem to be any good arguments that have been offered to show that the goal is unattainable, *in principle*. Some writers have attempted an operational reformulation of some of the basic psychoanalytic concepts [4], [15], and while the merits of such endeavors need to be assessed critically, these efforts point to the attempt to render more precise and testable concepts which have been found fruitful in psychotherapeutic practice. Moreover, it is not the case that all existing psychological and psychiatric theories should be viewed as competing with one another, or in some sense mutually incompatible. Rather, we might reasonably expect that with the further development of the science of psychology, bridging laws (perhaps of a very complex sort) will be formulated and theories at various levels (e.g. macro-behavior, physiological psychology, etc.) will be systematically integrated.

To show that the views expressed here do not reflect a philosopher's unwarranted optimism about the methods and goals of this field, it is appropriate to cite once again the views of Drs. Redlich and Freedman.

> As a technology based on the behavioral and biological sciences, psychiatry takes a deterministic point of view. This does not mean that all phenomena in our field can be explained, or that there is no uncertainty. It merely commits us to a scientific search for reliable and significant relationships. We assume causation—by which we mean that a *range* of similar antecedents in *both* the organism and environment produces a similar *set* of consequences. In general, we follow the procedures of basic sciences and attempt to determine the limits within which a range of antecedents has a high probability of producing similar results....
>
> The principles and basic methods of studying normal and abnormal behavior in individuals and in populations, in clinical practice, as well as under experimental conditions, are the same as in other naturalistic sciences. ([13], pp. 79–80)

To the extent that individual practitioners in the field—whether clinicians or theorists—depart from the above-noted principles and methods, psychiatry and psychology are not to be faulted, any more than physics is impugned by poor methodology or unsound theoretical conclusions on the part of some of its practitioners.

5. Problems with the conception of psychological disorders as "disease" or "illness." A number of arguments have been put forth by some influential psychologists and psychiatrists who hold that the conceptualization of psychological disorders in terms of illness represents an adherence to a mistaken model—the medical model of health and disease. These criticisms of the continued use of the medical model rest partly on conceptual and theoretical grounds and partly on pragmatic considerations relating to the consequences for the individual and society of adhering to this model. There is, however, a good deal of confusion surrounding these issues—confusion which stems largely from a tendency to conflate epistemological, conceptual, and pragmatic problems and attempts at solution to such problems. I shall concentrate on only a few of these issues here, specifically, those which relate most directly to the concerns of definition and concept formation.

The most outspoken opponent of the medical model is Dr. Thomas Szasz, a psychiatrist who holds the M.D. degree. Szasz claims that

> ... although the notion of mental illness made good *historical* sense—stemming as it does from the historical identity of medicine and psychiatry—it made no *rational* sense. Although mental illness might have been a useful concept in the nineteenth century, today it is scientifically worthless and socially harmful. ([16], p.ix)

Thus he argues that it is inappropriate or logically mistaken to construe emotional problems and psychological disorders as a species of illness, on an analogy with bodily disease. On Szasz's view, there exists a "*major logical and procedural error in the evolution of modern psychiatry*" ([16], p. 26). One "error" lay in decreeing that some malingerers be called "hysterics," which led to obscuring the similarities and differences between organic neurological diseases and phenomena that only looked like them ([16], p. 26). But it does not follow from the fact that hysteria (and other psychological disorders) are called "illness" that the similarities and differences between organic and nonorganic illness cannot be duly noted and treated accordingly. Indeed, the very introduction of the notion of *mental* illness to cover phenomena such as hysteria marks a decision to treat a class of seeming bodily disorders as different in relevant respects from organic neurological disease. The labelling itself need not involve a failure to attend to the relevant similarities and differences for the purpose of diagnosis, explanation, or treatment.

In general, the precise nature of Szasz's objection to construing psychological disorders as illnesses is not always clear. Sometimes he writes as though the reclassification and introduction of a set of "new rules of the medical game" consist in a sort of logical or conceptual error:

> During [the past sixty or seventy years] a vast number of occurrences were reclassified as "illnesses." We have thus come to regard phobias, delinquencies, divorce, homicide, addiction, and so on almost without limit as psychiatric illnesses. This is a colossal and costly mistake. ([16], p. 43)

In answer to the question, "from what point of view is it a mistake to classify nonillnesses as illnesses?" Szasz replies that "it is a mistake from the point of view of science and intellectual integrity." This would seem to imply that a proper scientific conception and a generally accepted classificatory schema preclude treating psychological disorders as illnesses. But there is no compelling evidence—either from Szasz's own account, or revealed in our inquiry in the preceding sections—to show that it is indeed the case that a clear "error" or "mistake" is involved in this type of classification. The consequence of the medical model approach and resulting reclassifications, according to Szasz, has been that although "some members of suffering humanity were promoted... to higher social rank, this was attained at the cost of obscuring the logical character of the observed phenomena" ([16], p. 295).

It is evident from the passages just cited that at least sometimes Szasz construes the reclassification of psychological disorders as illnesses to be a sort of error or mistake (logical or conceptual). At other times, however, he writes as though the change is "merely linguistic" and a matter of choice or preference of one classificatory schema rather than another. Thus he holds that it is "a matter of scientific and social choice whether we prefer to emphasize the similarities and, hence, place hysteria in the category of illness, or whether we prefer to emphasize the differences and place hysteria in a category of nonillness" ([16], p. 29). This view construes the issue as one of scientific and practical utility, rather than conceptual or logical error, and is borne out by Szasz's subsequent discussion. In a later passage, he reiterates this same view:

> From the standpoint of our present analysis, the entire change in renaming certain illnesslike forms of behavior from "malingering" to "hysteria" (and "mental illness") can be understood as nothing but a linguistic change employed for the purpose of achieving a new type of action-orientedness in the listener. The verbal change... served to command those charged with dealing with "hysterics" to abandon their moral-condemnatory attitude toward them and to adopt instead a solicitous and benevolent attitude, such as befitted the physician vis-a-vis his patient. ([16], p. 132)

It appears from the above passages and others which could be cited, that Szasz's position is at the very least, unclear, and at worst, inconsistent, with regard to the question of what is wrong with classifying behavioral disorders and disabling psychological difficulties as forms of "illness." We now turn to a brief discussion of Szasz's own view of what properly constitutes illness and some criticisms of his charge against those who have been engaged in reclassifying certain nonbodily disorders as forms of illness.

It is at least an implicit assumption of Szasz's—one which he sometimes makes explicit—that the only proper candidates for the notion of disease are those which refer to genuine *bodily* (organic or functional) ailments or involve a physical lesion. We need to examine this assumption in order to evaluate Szasz's contention that it is a mistake or error to construe nonbodily disorders as illness. The issue then becomes, on what grounds does Szasz reject mental "illnesses" as instances of some sort of disease, and are those grounds justifiable? He writes:

> The adjectives "mental," "emotional," and "neurotic" are simply devices to codify—and at the same time obscure—the differences between two classes of disabilities or "problems" in meeting life. One category consists of bodily diseases—say, leprosy, tuberculosis, or cancer—which, by rendering imperfect

> the functioning of the human body as a machine, produce difficulties in social adaptation. In contrast to the first, the second category is characterized by difficulties in social adaptation not attributable to malfunctioning machinery but "caused" rather by the purposes the machine was made to serve... ([16], pp. 41–42)

This view sets up two mutually exclusive categories of disability, such that an instance of the one category can never be construed as falling also under the second category. An antireductionist bias is evident in Szasz's remarks here and elsewhere, and it is legitimate to ask whether a clear distinction can be made between "the functioning of the human body as a machine" and "the purposes the machine was made to serve."

Moreover, it is certainly true, as Szasz contends ([16], pp. 79 ff.), that Freud continued to seek organic or physico-chemical *causes* of the psychological disorders and malfunctioning which he observed in his patients. But the question remains, *even if* Freud was mistaken in his continued search for neurological or some other physical bases for these behavioral disorders, does it follow that such disorders cannot properly be construed as forms of disease or illness nonetheless? Szasz's position seems to be that the absence of identifiable or probable physiological causes disqualifies a disorder or disability from the category of disease. Consequently, construing nonorganically based behavioral and personality disorders as diseases turns out to be *both* a logical and a scientific error. It is a logical error because the two categories of problems in facing life are mutually exclusive; and it is a scientific mistake because it erroneously presupposes an organic or neurological cause for every psychological, social, or ethical problem resulting from the malfunctioning of persons. Szasz wishes, therefore, to eliminate the entire notion of mental illness, claiming that "mental illness is a myth. Psychiatrists are not concerned with mental illnesses and their treatments. In actual practice they deal with personal, social, and ethical problems in living" ([16], p. 296).

Whereas Szasz chooses to *close* the concept of disease or illness, requiring as a necessary condition that there be a known or probable physiological basis, another view of the matter holds that the labors of Freud and others resulted in a legitimate *extension* of the then existing concept of disease or illness. The strategy in replying to Szasz's position would thus consist in the following two-stage argument: (1) showing that Freud and his followers were not making a logical or conceptual *mistake* in treating psychological disorders as illnesses, but were rather engaged in the enterprise of extending or widening the concept of disease or illness; (2) showing that such extension in this case is *legitimate*, that is, can be justified by noting relevant and important similarities between cases of mental illness and cases of physical illness. I shall take the question, "Is it *ever* legitimate to extend or enlarge a concept?" as admitting of an uncontroversial affirmative answer. Accordingly, one reply to Szasz is given in the words of Joseph Margolis:

> Szasz is absolutely right in holding that Freud reclassified types of suffering. But what he fails to see is that this is a perfectly legitimate (and even necessary) maneuver. In fact, this enlargement of the concept of illness does not obscure the differences between physical and mental illness—and the differences themselves are quite gradual, as psychosomatic disorder and hysterical conversion attest. On the contrary, these differences are preserved and respected in the very idea of an *enlargement* of the concept of illness. ([7], p. 73)

This passage serves not only to make the point about the legitimacy of enlarging the concept of illness to cover cases of mental or psychological illness, it also emphasizes that there is no clear and obvious line—as Szasz appears to think there is—between physical and mental illness, or between the "two categories" of problems in facing life. Indeed, it is apparent that Margolis has drawn this line in a different place from Szasz. While Szasz considers hysteria a nonbodily illness (hence, not an "illness" at all) on the grounds that it has no organic or neurological *causes*, Margolis construes hysterical conversion and other psychosomatic ailments at least as borderline cases, presumably on the grounds that such disorders are manifested in terms of observable and clear-cut bodily *symptoms* and *malfunctioning*. So it appears that there may be some genuine dispute as to the selection of criteria for an adequate or uncontroversial characterization of *physical* or *bodily* illness itself.

Once it is acknowledged that there are good reasons for construing Freud's maneuver as one of extending a concept rather than as a sort of logical or conceptual error, we may proceed to the second stage of the argument in reply to Szasz: the justification of the extension of the concept of illness to cover psychological problems and personality disorders. Margolis suggests the following, in answer to the question "Should mental 'disorders' be allowed, in a medical sense, to count as diseases or illnesses?"

> If I were to describe a condition in which a patient suffers great pain in walking and is quickly overcome by fatigue, a condition which lasts for several years, and we were to find that there is an organic cause for this pattern, we should be strongly inclined to regard what we have before us as a *physical illness.* Now, if we have the same sort of pattern but are unable to find any organic cause, and begin to suspect that, in some inexplained way, the condition is due to the emotional or psychical life of the patient, we may have a reason for insisting that the pattern is still a *pattern of illness.* ([7], p. 74)

The reasonableness of this conclusion—Szasz's view notwithstanding—is shown by observing the affinities between the new cases and the standard ones. It should be noted, further, that the existence of unexplained phenomena and the absence at present of psycho-physical laws (covering normal as well as abnormal behavior) do not in themselves compel theoretical conclusions and conceptual decisions of the sort that Szasz is prone to make.

There is a line of argument different from that employed by Margolis which can serve to show the relevant similarities between cases of physical disease and cases of putative mental illness. Whereas Margolis's method is a case by case approach, proceeding by comparison of new (mental) cases to old (physical) instances of disease and noting the affinities between them, the alternative method distinguishes general *categories* of behavioral symptoms and demonstrates that these categories are common both to bodily diseases and to disorders commonly construed as mental illness. David Ausubel uses this approach in arguing that "the plausibility of subsuming abnormal behavioral reactions to stress under the general rubric of disease is further enhanced by the fact that these reactions include the same three principal categories of symptoms found in physical illness" ([2], p. 262). Ausubel characterizes these categories as manifestations of impaired functioning, adaptive compensation, and defensive overreaction, and cites examples of both physical and mental diseases falling under each category, noting the relevant similarities between them. He concludes that there is no inherent contradiction in regarding mental symptoms *both* as expressions of "problems in living" (Szasz's preferred locution) *and* as manifestations of illness. "The latter situation results when individuals are for various reasons unable to cope with such problems, and react with seriously distorted or maladaptive behavior" ([2], p. 265). So according to some opponents of Szasz, the position is taken that in order to qualify as a genuine manifestation of disease, a symptom need not reflect a physical lesion.

We may conclude from the inquiry in this section that there appears to be no compelling reason to adopt Szasz's view that mental illness if a "myth" and that personality disorders and psychological problems are inappropriately viewed as illness and properly to be construed as "problems in living." In sum, there appear to be no logical or conceptual reasons why such difficulties cannot or should not be subsumed under the category of "illness." Moreover, whatever is gained in terms of social utility by viewing these problems as "problems in living" is not precluded by viewing them *also* as manifestations of disease, as Ausubel suggests. So whatever merits Szasz's position may have in terms of pragmatic consequences, these same results can be achieved if we retain the concept of mental *illness* along with the present classificatory schema.

By way of summary and conclusion, it would be well to note where the rejection of Szasz's antimedical model position leads us. Most of the problems discussed in this paper can be seen to re-emerge upon consideration of a brief quotation from Ausubel's paper. Arguing specifically against Szasz's contention that to qualify as a genuine manifestation of disease a given symptom must be caused by a physical lesion, Ausubel writes:

> Adoption of such a criterion would be arbitrary and inconsistent both with medical and lay connotations of the term "disease," which in current usage is

> generally regarded as including any marked deviation, physical, mental, or behavioral, from normally desirable standards of structural and functional integrity. ([2], p. 259)

While this statement may appear sufficiently general to escape controversy, upon closer analysis a range of familiar problems can be identified in connection with the phrase 'normally desirable standards'. The immediate difficulty concerns whether the phrase is to be construed descriptively or normatively, but even if this question is decided, further problems remain.

Construed descriptively, 'normally desirable standards' denotes those standards which people (the issue of just *which* people will be put aside for the moment) actually desire for themselves or others. The question of whether or not this is an adequate account of the general notion of desirability has been raised at least since John Stuart Mill wrote, in his essay *Utilitarianism*:

> The only proof capable of being given that an object is visible, is that people actually see it. The only proof that a sound is audible, is that people hear it: and so of the other sources of our experience. In like manner, I apprehend, the sole evidence it is possible to produce that anything is desirable, is that people do actually desire it. ([12], p. 221)

Critical views contend that the notion of desirability is properly to be explicated in terms of what *ought* to be desired, or what it is *rational* to desire, and that Mill's purely descriptive account fails to capture the normative force of the term 'desirable'.

Construed normatively (in terms of which standards ought to be adopted or are worthy of being maintained), the phrase generates a number of problems noted in detail above—chief among which is the cultural relativity of values. The questions "desirable *for* whom?" "desirable *according to* whom?" and "desirable for what ends or aims or purposes?" all need to be answered satisfactorily before Ausubel's general statement can serve to provide even a rough and ready criterion for the notions of mental health and illness. Moreover, it may emerge that there is no set of "normally desirable standards" that will be accepted without controversy by all individuals or groups because of the differing ideologies and value systems and differing background experiences in a society as large and diverse as ours (not to mention those of other societies and cultures).

It may be, however, that we need to emphasize the further phrase: "... of structural and functional integrity" in analyzing Ausubel's statement. On this view, the appeal to "normally desirable standards of structural and functional integrity" presupposes some general theory which provides an account of an integrated, well-functioning system. Such an account is given, for the most part, in biological (anatomical and physiological) theories so that the notion of physical disease, although not without a number of problems, can be specified without engendering a great deal of controversy. With regard to mental health and illness, however, not only is there no generally accepted psychological or personality theory that can be presupposed, but the search for criteria of application for the basic concepts is itself an attempt to fill out such a theory and provide the very parameters which enable us to judge that a personality system possesses "structural and functional integrity."

In the words of Redlich and Freedman, "a completely acceptable super-theory on which psychiatry can generally rest its work does not exist" ([13], p. 79). But these authors would be quick to note that progress in the behavioral and biological sciences has been rapid and steadily advancing in recent years. So whatever pessimism may accrue to the observations made in this study about the concepts of mental health and mental illness as currently understood and employed by professionals and laymen alike, a measure of optimism exists in the belief that fruitful and systematic developments will continue to be forthcoming in the experimental, theoretical, and clinical areas of psychology and psychiatry.

REFERENCES

[1] Albee, G. "Definition of Mental Illness and Mental Health Manpower Trends." *Psychopathology Today*. Edited by William S. Sahakian. Itasca, Ill.: F. E. Peacock Publishers, 1970.

[2] Ausubel, D. P. "Personality Disorder *Is* Disease." *Mental Illness and Social Processes*. Edited by Thomas J. Scheff. New York: Harper and Row, 1967.

[3] Buhler, C. *Values in Psychotherapy*. New York: The Free Press of Glencoe, 1962.

[4] Ellis, A. "An Operational Reformulation of Some of the Basic Principles of Psychoanalysis." *Minnesota Studies in the Philosophy of Science*. vol. 1. Edited by Herbert Feigl and Michael Scriven. Minneapolis: University of Minnesota Press, 1956.

[5] Jahoda, M., *Current Concepts of Positive Mental Health*. New York: Basic Books, 1958.

[6] Livermore, J. M.; Malmquist, C. P.; and Meehl, P. E. "On the Justifications for Civil Commitment." *University of Pennsylvania Law Review* 117 (1968): 75–96.

[7] Margolis, J. *Psychotherapy and Morality*. New York: Random House, 1966.

[8] Masserman, J. H., ed. *Psychoanalysis and Human Values*. New York: Grune and Stratton, 1960.

[9] May, R. "The Work and Training of the Psychological Therapist." *Psychology, Psychiatry, and the Public Interest*. Edited by Maurice H. Krout. Minneapolis: University of Minnesota Press, 1956.

[10] Mechanic, D. "Some Factors in Identifying and Defining Mental Illness." *Mental Illness and Social Processes*. Edited by Thomas J. Scheff. New York: Harper and Row, 1967.

[11] Menninger, K. "Unitary Concept of Mental Illness." *Psychopathology Today*. Edited by William S. Sahakian. Itasca, Ill.: F. E. Peacock Publishers, 1970.

[12] Mill, J. S. "Utilitarianism." *Essential Works of John Stuart Mill*. New York: Bantam Books, 1961.

[13] Redlich, F. C. and Freedman, D. X. *The Theory and Practice of Psychiatry*. New York: Basic Books, 1966.
[14] Sahakian, W. S., ed. *Psychopathology Today*, Itasca, Ill.: F. E. Peacock Publishers, 1970.
[15] Skinner, B. F. *Science and Human Behavior*. New York: Macmillan Company, 1953.
[16] Szasz, T. S. *The Myth of Mental Illness*. New York: Harper and Row, 1961.

4.5

Hidden Conceptual Models in Clinical Psychiatry

Aaron Lazare, M.D.

Many physicians find it difficult to understand how a psychiatrist selects the clinical data that he considers relevant, how he formulates a case and how he chooses the treatment he prescribes. In the psychiatrically ill patient, is it the symptom complex, the "unconscious conflict" or the abnormality in family interactions that contains the key to clinical decision making? How is it that one psychiatrist will emphasize electroconvulsive therapy or tricyclic antidepressants, another individual therapy, and a third family therapy for apparently similar patients? Why is it apparently easier to formulate and implement a treatment plan for a patient suffering from a medical illness such as congestive heart failure?

One major reason for the difficulty in understanding psychiatric thinking is that several different conceptual models are implicitly used in the clinical formulation but rarely identified as such. The four most common models are the medical, the psychologic, the behavioral, and the social. When a patient is treated, the kind of history obtained, the meaning assigned to certain historical facts, and the treatment modalities most often chosen depend on what model or combination of models is employed. These points are illustrated by four case histories of the same middle-aged depressed female patient. Each history is formulated in terms of one of the four conceptual models.

CASE HISTORY—MEDICAL MODEL

Mrs. J., a 53-year-old widow, gave a history of a depressive syndrome. During the past few months she had lost 9.1 kg in weight, had early morning awakening, and had a diurnal variation in mood manifested by feeling better as the day went on. She described herself as feeling hopeless, helpless, and worthless. There was some retardation of speech. She denied suicidal intent and presented no evidence of delusions or paranoid ideation. Twenty-three years previously a similar episode of depression had remitted spontaneously. The patient had a sister who was hospitalized for a depressive illness that responded positively to electroconvulsive treatments.

CASE HISTORY—PSYCHOLOGIC MODEL

Mrs. J., a 53-year-old widow, had been depressed for a few months after the death of her husband. Although the marriage seemed happy at times, there were many stormy periods in their relation. There had been no visible signs of grief since his death. Since the funeral, she had been depressed and had lost interest in her surroundings. For no apparent reason she blamed herself for minor events of the past. Sometimes she criticized herself for traits that characterized her husband more than herself. She had had a similar reaction after the death of her mother 23 years previously, when she and her mother had lived together. From the family history, it could be inferred that the relation was characterized by hostile dependency. Six months after her mother's death, the patient married. She seemed intelligent and motivated for treatment, and had considered psychotherapy in the past to gain a better understanding of herself.

CASE HISTORY—BEHAVIORAL MODEL

Mrs. J., a 53-year-old widow gave a history of depressive behaviors of anorexia, insomnia, feelings of hoplessness, helplessness, and worthlessness. These behaviors had begun shortly after the death of her husband. Throughout the marriage, he had been a continuous source of reinforcement to the patient. This quality of the husband's interaction with his wife had been evident since the marriage, at a time when the patient was still depressed after her mother's death. The family stated that the husband had always ignored the patient's demands and pleas of helplessness while responding actively to the more positive aspects of her personality. After his death, she began to complain to her children about her loss of appetite and her sense of helplessness. They responded to these complaints with frequent visits and telephone calls, but the depressive behavior only worsened.

CASE HISTORY—SOCIAL MODEL

Mrs. J., a 53-year-old widow, had been depressed during the past few months since the death of her husband. He had been the major figure in her life, and his loss has left her feeling lonely, and isolated. After his death, she moved to a small apartment, which was some distance from her old neighborhood. Although she was satisfied with her new quarters, she found the community strange. Furthermore, she did not have access to public transportation, which would have enabled her to visit her old friends, children, and grandchildren. Since her husband's death, old strains between the patient and her children had been aggravated.

These four histories could each have been elicited from the same patient by four different clinicians, each employing a different conceptual model in formulating the case. This use by psychiatrists of different conceptual models often bewilders the nonpsychiatrist, who sees patients with similar symptoms diagnosed and treated differently. The psychiatrist himself, by using one model to the exclusion of others, unnecessarily limits his treatment options.

This paper will first describe the four most frequently employed conceptual models for the diagnosis of psychiatric illness by reference to the histories cited above. It will then attempt to show how in everyday practice the decision to use one or a combination of models is implicitly determined by the interplay of physician, patient and clinical situation. By making explicit the implicit, the decision-making process in clinical psychiatry can become more rational, a broader range of treatment modalities should be made available, and the communication between physicians should be enhanced.

FOUR MAJOR MODELS

The Medical Model

The medical model views psychiatric illnesses as diseases like any others. For each disease, it is supposed that there eventually will be found a specific cause related to the functional anatomy of the brain.[1] The physician using the medical model concerns himself with etiology, pathogenesis, signs and symptoms, differential diagnosis, treatment and prognosis. Knowing the syndrome or disease determines the treatment. Although he addresses his patients with proper medical respect, he keeps his distance so as to maintain objectivity.

Consider the case history according to the medical model. The psychiatrist, in eliciting the history of the symptom picture, observes a group of symptoms consistent with the cluster of endogenous depression.[2,3] The current syndrome, the earlier episode of depression, and the family history make the diagnosis of manic-depressive illness (depressed type) the most probable. The patient's relation with her family, her ambivalence toward her husband and her motivation to understand her illness are interesting, are perhaps even relevant, but not central to the recognition of the illness. Antidepressant medications or electroconvulsive treatments will be the treatment of choice. The patient will be told that she is suffering from a depression, a psychiatric illness, which is not uncommon in her age group. The illness is time limited and, with proper treatment, has a favorable prognosis.

The Psychologic Model

According to the psychologic model, the developmental impasse, the early deprivation, the distortions in early relations, and the confused communication between parent and child lead to the adult neuroses and vulnerabilities to certain stresses. As a result of these psychologic determinants, we see patients who distort reality, who are prone to depression, who avoid heterosexuality, or who fear success. The social setting may be changed, psychotropic drugs may be given, but the abnormality remains because the personality is abnormal.

Therapy consists of clarifying the psychologic meaning of events, feelings, and behaviors. The patient is taught how to experience appropriate feelings and how to bear "unbearable" feelings.[4] Forgotten events may be remembered, re-experienced, and then put into perspective so that the patient can be freed to see current situations as they really are. As a result, growth and maturity are enhanced.

Most important to the therapeutic situation is the doctor-patient relation. It is the therapeutic alliance between the two that will enable the patient to remember what she has not wanted to remember and to abandon familiar but pathologic ways of coping. It is through the vehicle of the therapeutic relation—by experiencing these feelings toward the therapist—that the patient will recreate some of his previous pathologic relations to important others and have the opportunity for a "corrective emotional experience."[5]

Returning to the case history—the psychiatrist, using the psychologic model, first takes note of the problems in the marital relation. He pays special attention to the absence of grief,[6] which has psychologic meaning and is related to her ambivalent feelings toward her husband. A similar reaction after her mother's death suggests the possibility of a psychologic connection between her feelings toward both husband and mother. This is reinforced by the history that she married only six months after the death of her mother. The patient's criticism of herself in terms that she had used to criticize her husband suggests Freud's concept of introjection of the lost object.[7] Since the primary modality of treatment is psychotherapy, it is a favorable sign that she is motivated to gain a better understanding of herself.

The Behavioral Model

According to the behavioral model, both neurosis and psychosis are examples of abnormal behavior that has been learned as a result of aversive events and are maintained either because they lead to positive effects or because they avoid deleterious ones. The overt symptoms are the ones that require treatment since they themselves are the problem and not secondary manifestations of disease or unconscious conflict. The typical therapeutic course includes: (1) determining the behavior to be modified; (2) establishing the conditions under which the behavior occurs; (3) determining the factors responsible for the persistence of the behavior; (4) selecting a set of treatment conditions; and (5) arranging a schedule of retraining. The conditions that precede the behavior may be modified by such technics as desensitization, reciprocal inhibition, and conditioned avoidance. The conditions that result from the behavior may be modified by positive reinforcement, negative reinforcement, aversive conditioning, and extinction.[8]

Considering the case history according to the behavioral model, the psychiatrist first identifies the pathologic behaviors of anorexia, insomnia, and feelings of helplessness. He then determines the empirical relation between the depressive behaviors and the antecedent and consequent environmental events that precipitate and maintain the depression.[9] The death of the husband, considering the history of the marriage, is interpreted as a sudden withholding of positive reinforcement of adaptive behavior. The attention received from family members inadvertently reinforces the depressive behaviors.

Treatment consists of reinforcing adaptive behaviors incompatible with depression and extinguishing depressive behaviors. The psychiatrist may accomplish these therapeutic goals by teaching the family to respond positively to the adaptive behavior instead of the depressive behavior[10] or by purposefully encouraging the patient to express feelings incompatible with depression.[11]

The Social Model

The social view of psychiatric illness focuses on the way in which the individual functions in social system. Symptoms are traced not to conflicts within the mind, not to manifestations of psychiatric disease, but to the "relationship of the individual to his manner of functioning in social situations—i.e., in the type and quality of his 'connectedness' to the groups which make up his life space."[12] Symptoms may therefore be regarded as an index of social disorder[13,-15] Accordingly, when a socially disruptive event occurs such as a daughter's leaving the home, a wife's death, a geographic displacement by urban renewal, a war, or an economic depression, the resultant symptoms are seen as stemming from the social disorder.

Treatment consists of reogranizing the patient's relation to the social system or reorganizing the social system. If others do not seem to care, how can she get them to care? If the patient's behavior is irrational, how can she learn to stop acting irrationally, or how can her family better tolerate the behavior? If the therapist wants to restructure the "nuclear" social system, he may see the patient with her family. If the therapist wants to affect the broader social system, he may attempt to influence major social issues such as housing or education.

The psychiatrist, using the social model to study the case, notices that the patient's social matrix has been altered in two ways. In the first place, she has permanently lost the one person to whom she has been closest. Secondly, by moving, she has placed herself in a situation where she has lost access to those with whom she had previously related. In individual or group therapy one could temporarily substitute a transitional social system. Simultaneously, the therapist would attempt to re-establish a social field in which she could be comfortable after discharge. To this end, he might encourage her to move to a home where she could have better access to family and old friends. He might work with the family to repair any estrangement. He might suggest a return to work. Continued individual or group therapy might help her acquire social skills that she might never have developed in the marital situation.

CHOICE OF CONCEPTUAL MODEL

The psychiatrist implicitly uses one or a combination of conceptual models in evaluating and treating the patient by the process referred to as clinical judgment. He may make the selection according to the results of outcome studies. He may select the conceptual model on practical grounds: "This is the only available treatment; let's make the best of it." Sometimes he decides on ideologic grounds. In this section, I will attempt to describe some of the variables that determine the choice of conceptual model in clinical practice.

Ideology of the Therapist

Studies of the attitudes of psychiatrists toward the understanding of mental illness have concluded that several ideologies exist. Ideology here refers to a coherent system of ideas subscribed to by a subgroup of the profession as a whole. Armor and Klerman point out that ideologic factions are most likely to occur when the codified knowledge base is markedly incomplete or ambiguous about the means to be used to attain a professional goal.[16] This is precisely the position of psychiatry today.

Studies of psychiatric ideologies describe three basic orientations: medical (somatotherapeutic, directive-organic): psychologic (psychotherapeutic, analytic-psychologic); and social (sociotherapeutic).[16-20] These studies do not explore the behavioral orientation, which, in contrast to the other three, has received its greatest impetus from psychologists. Of the ideologies described above, it must be remembered that only a small number of psychiatrists can be rigidly classified into a single ideology. More commonly, the psychiatrist is committed in various degrees to one or more ideologies.

Diagnosis and the Effectiveness of Somatic Treatment

Other things being equal, particular psychiatric syndromes are more apt to be viewed by one model in preference to another. The schizophrenic and manic-depressive psychoses are apt to be conceptualized primarily as medical illness. This is supported by the mounting evidence of genetic transmission of the schizophrenias[21] and some of the depressive illnesses[22] and by the clear-cut efficacy of phenothiazines for the treatment of schizophrenia, lithium for the treatment of manic-depressive illness, and the tricyclics, monoamine oxidase inhibitors, and electroconvulsive therapy for the treatment of the endogenous depressions. In current practice, social treatments, especially in inpatient settings, are combined with the medical approaches described above. The zeal for psychotherapeutic intervention in these syndromes has certainly lessened over the past decade, although that approach continues to enjoy considerable support.

The neuroses are more apt to be treated by the psychotherapeutic approach, although some psychiarists maintain a medical model of neurotic behavior.[23] For these disorders, syndromes are less clearly separable, there is no definite evidence of genetic transmission, and medication has less specific effects. Furthermore, the efficacy of psychotherapy in these disorders is gaining support from clinical research.[24,25]

Clinical phenomena currently thought by many psychiatrists to be more a social disorder than a psychologic or medical illness are drug abuse and many forms of violence. From the social perspective, changes in society, rather than massive psychotherapy programs or breakthroughs in psychopharmacology, will be necessary to effect change in these problems.

Social Class and Other Attributes of the Patient

A number of studies have demonstrated the importance of the patient's social class in the application of psychotherapy.[26-29] Patients of the middle and upper social classes are more apt to be accepted for, and to continue in, psychotherapy. Patients of the lower and lower-middle class, in contrast, have a poorer chance of being accepted for therapy and drop out of treatment at higher rates.[30] Other patient characteristics that determine the use of psychotherapy include responsibility, verbal intelligence, psychologic mindedness, the capacity for forming a close personal relation, young adult age, history of effective adaptation before the current difficulty, likeability, and attractiveness.[31] In addition, patients treated by psychotherapy are apt to continue in treatment when their expectations are congruent with those of the therapist.[32]

Such a patient population, presenting as they often do as relatively healthly people who want help in achieving personal fulfillment (greater psychologic strength, more satisfactory relationships, comfort with their sexual identity, etc.), may be rejected by the medical psychiatrist as "not mentally ill."

Although a psychotherapeutically oriented psychiatrist may attempt to explain and understand most or all of pathologic and normal behavior by psychoanalytic theory, he is likely not to take patients into treatment if they want medication or advice, if they have had previous psychiatric hospitalization, if they are authoritarian in personality, if they are vulnerable to psychosis, if they are psychotic or older, or if they present a multitude of somatic complaints.[31]

Available Services

The available treatment resources are an important determinant of the choice of model. Psychotherapy clinics, especially when not overcrowded, attempt to apply psychotherapy in understanding of patients. Walk-in and emergency clinics, in responding to large numbers of patients, approach the patient from social and medical perspectives that usually require less time from the psychiatrist but are effective for many clinical conditions.

There are many psychiatric hospitals that specialize in the application of electroconvulsive treatments. These facilities, in their application of the medical model, frequently overdiagnose syndromes as responsive to this form of therapy. In similar fashion, psychiatric hospitals that specialize in social (family therapy, therapeutic communities) or psychologic technics (intensive individual psychotherapy) may regard medical treatments such as electroconvulsive treatments and psychotropic drugs as offering "only" symptomatic relief even when it is likely that such a treatment will produce marked clinical remission.

Immediacy of the Social Situation

Where the social cause is obvious, pressing, and immediate, first consideration is usually given to a social treatment. If a child is apathetic and withdrawn as a result of a continuous psychologic and physical assault at the hands of his parents, the child must initially be treated by a change in his social situation. Either the parents must change their behavior, or they must be separated from the child. If a soldier becomes psychotic in combat, the initial treatment must be his removal from the front line. Psychologic attempts at treatment during a social crisis are usually unsatisfactory.

DISCUSSION

The various conceptual models in clinical psychiatry may lead some to draw a comparison to the Tower of Babel, where confusion reigned because many languages were spoken. To the contrary, I believe the current positions of the medical, psychologic, behavioral and social models attest to the vitality of psychiatry as it attempts to understand the complex problems of abnormal behavior.

The medical model, after giving psychiatry its classification of mental illness in the late 19th century, has provided the conceptual foundations for (1) the development and use of the antipsychotic and antidepressant medications, (2) studies of the genetic transmission of mental illness, and (3) metabolic studies of psychiatric illness, especially the depressions.[33,34] The most important events in all the above three areas have occurred since 1950.

The psychologic model has exerted considerable influence not only on American psychiatry but also on everyday thinking. Its derivative, psychotherapy, has become a commonly accepted treatment of choice, especially for the neuroses and personality disorders. Advocates of the psychologic model, especially since World War II, have been able to translate the clinical insights derived from classical psychoanalysis and more recent developments of ego psychology into concepts that residents in nearly all training centers in the United States can use in the understanding of most psychiatric patients.

The behavioral model, resting on theoretical foundations from the early 20th century, began its period of rapid growth in the late 1950's. Its derivative, behavior therapy, has enjoyed considerable interest in the clinical field during the relatively brief period of its existence. Behavior therapists are hopeful of offering several possible advantages to other forms of treatment, including shorter duration of treatment and applicability to a broad range of patients.

The social model, like the medical, psychologic and behavioral, was reawakened in the 1950's. Since that time the psychiatric ward has been viewed as a social system,[35,36] the relation between social class and mental illness has been established,[26] and federal legislation to provide psychiatric care for catchment areas in the community has been enacted.[37] During these years, various treatment modalities have succeeded as treatment for the mentally ill patient with minimal separation from his social milieu.

It is unfortunate that the conceptual models have remained so separate from each other. To the degree that this occurs, communications between professionals are impaired, progress requiring a broad focus is slowed, and treatment options are unnecessarily limited. There are several forces, however, that are forging the various models into a multidimensional framework:

1. Mounting evidence for the effectiveness of particular treatment does in time overwhelm partisan advocacy of a theoretical position. For example, the success of lithium in the prevention of recurrences of manic-depressive illness has led to its more widespread use in preference to wholly psychodynamic approaches.
2. Over the last two decades, the almost monolithic influence exercised by psychoanalysis on American psychiatry has waned as evidenced by appointments of chairmen of academic departments of psychiatry with more eclectic interests and a greater competence in basic research.
3. Psychiatric residents, moved by the concern for the large number of patients excluded from psychiatric consideration by the limited use of models, have insisted on broader grounding in a wide variety of treatment approaches.
4. Theoretical bridges between models point the direction toward a unified theory of human behavior. For example, attempts have been made to demonstrate how behavioral technics are involved in dynamic psychotherapy,[38,39] how the psychoanalytic approach to symptom formation can be understood as a social process,[15] and how medical problems related to the autonomic nervous system can be approached by means of behavioral technics.[40]

Conceptual Problems

Despite these favorable trends, serious conceptual difficulties remain. Whereas human beings are simultaneously biologic organisms, psychologic selves, behaving animals, and members of social systems, we lack a comprehensive set of general "laws" that include the models described here as medical, psychologic, behavioral and social. Failing that, we must come to terms with the following observations:

1. No model offers a complete explanation for the phenomena to which it addresses itself. Each model by its very definition ignores a universe of phenomena that are important in the patient's life and function. In limited cases, nevertheless, a single conceptual model will suffice to explain the disorder and provide treatment. The hallucination of a patient suffering from bromidism may indeed reflect prior personal experience, but the patient can be restored to health by detoxification with no attention paid to the psychologic content of his hallucinations.
2. Any two conceptual models may offer alternative explanations for the

same behavioral events. For example, the psychodynamic psychiatrist may argue that the relief of phobias obtained by "reciprocal inhibition" is in fact a "transference cure"—that is, it is the relation between the therapist and patient, rather than the technics of relaxation and desensitization to fear, that accounts for the beneficial outcome. Contrariwise, the behaviorist may contend that the psychotherapist is employing reinforcement methods rather than psychodynamic principles in shaping the behavior of his patient.

3. In applying more than one conceptual model in treating a given patient, we must recognize the possibility of apparent contradictions. In other words, pieces borrowed from more than one theory for simultaneous use in a given case may be orthogonal to one another. As a result, we give our patient mixed messages. For example, a schizophrenic patient may simultaneously be given medication (which implies a biologic basis for his disorder), be offered psychotherapy (which implies that past experience accounts for present dysfunction), be a member of a therapeutic community (which implies that he must control the behavior that distresses others), and be subject to a "token economy" in which healthy behavior is rewarded by tokens that bring special privileges.

Comparable Dilemmas in Medicine

The importance of attention to each of the levels at which the patient functions is as important in other areas of medicine as it is in psychiatry. The patient with chronic rheumatoid arthritis suffers from a biologic disorder for which a number of nonspecific pharmacologic remedies exist. Whether the patient ends bedridden with ankylosed limbs may depend on how faithful he is in carrying out the prescribed exercises. This in turn will depend on his motivation, his relations to his physician and family, and the availability of facilities for physical therapy in the community. Disagreement between physicians about treatment is not unique to psychiatry. The patient with a bleeding peptic ulcer who consults a surgeon is more likely to have a gastrectomy than the one who consults an internist; a carcinoma of the breast will be treated by simple mastectomy in one hospital and by radical mastectomy in another.

The conceptual problems described in this paper reflect limitations in our understanding of human behavior. In good clinical practice, a psychiatrist will employ several conceptual models with the knowledge that all reflect some aspect of truth but all are incomplete versions of truth. The test of clinical skill is the assemblage of an appropriate mix for a particular case. To accomplish this best, the clinician should be explicit about the models that he employs in assessing a case and about the principles upon which he bases his treatment.

REFERENCES

1. Slater E, Roth M: Clinical Psychiatry. Third edition. Baltimore, Williams and Wilkins Company, 1969
2. Kiloh LG, Garside RF: The independence of neurotic depression and endogenous depression. Br J Psychiatry 109:451-463, 1963
3. Rosenthal SH, Gudeman JE: The endogenous depressive pattern: an empirical investigation. Arch Gen Psychiatry 16:241-249, 1967.
4. Semrad EV: Teaching Psychotherapy of Psychotic Patients: Supervision of beginning residents in the "clinical approach." New York, Grune and Stratton, 1969
5. Alexander F, French TM: Psychoanalytic Therapy: Principles and application. New York, Ronald Press Company, 1946
6 Deutsch H: Absence of grief. Psychoanal Q 6:12-22, 1937
7. Freud S: Mourning and melancholia (1917), Collected Papers, Vol. 4. New York, Basic Books, Inc., 1959, pp 152–170
8. Urban HB, Ford DH: Behavior therapy, Comprehensive Textbook of Psychiatry. Edited by AM Freedman, HI Kaplan. Baltimore, Williams and Wilkins Company, 1967, pp 1217–1224
9. Liberman RP, Raskin DE: Depression: a behavioral formulation. Arch Gen Psychiatry 24:515–523, 1971
10. Liberman R: Behavioral approaches to family and couple therapy. Am J Orthopsychiatry 40:106–118, 1970
11. Lazarus AA: Learning theory and the treatment of depression. Behav Res Ther 6:83–89, 1968
12. Thomas CS, Bergen BJ: Social psychiatric view of psychological misfunction and role of psychiatry in social change. Arch Gen Psychiatry 12:539–544, 1965
13. Weiss RJ, Bergen BJ: Social supports and the reduction of psychiatric disability. Psychiatry 31:107–115, 1968
14. Coleman JV: Social factors influencing the development and containment of psychiatric symptoms. Mental Illness and Social Processes. Edited by TJ Scheff. New York,Harper and Row, 1967, pp 158–168
15. *Idem*: Adaptive integration of psychiatric symptoms in ego regulation. Arch Gen Psychiatry 24:17–21, 1971
16. Armor DJ, Klerman GL: Psychiatric treatment orientations and professional ideology. J Health Soc Behav 9:243–255, 1968
17. Sharaf MR, Levinson DJ: Patterns of ideology and role definition among psychatric residents. The patient and the Mental Hospital. Edited by M Greenblatt, DJ Levinson, RH Williams. Glencoe, Illinois, Free Press, 1957, pp 263–285
18. Gilbert DC, Levinson DJ: Ideology, personality, and institutional policy in the mental hospital. J Abnorm Soc Psychol 53:263–271, 1956
19. MacIver J, Redlich FC: Patterns of psychiatric practice. Am J Psychiatry 115:692–697, 1959
20. Ehrlich D, Sabshin M: A study of sociotherapeutically oriented psychiatrists. Am J Orthopsychiatry 34:469–480, 1964
21. Wender PH: The role of genetics in the etiology of the schizophrenias. Am J Orthopsychiatry 39:447–458, 19699

22. Winokur G, Clayton PJ, Reich T: Manic Depressive Illness. St. Louis, CV Mosby Company, 1969
23. Feighner JP, Robins E, Guze SB, et al.: Diagnostic criteria for use in psychiatric research. Arch Gen Psychiatry 26:57–63, 1972
24. Truax CB, Carkhuff RR: Toward Effective Counseling and Psychotherapy: Training and practice. Chicago. Aldine-Atherton, Inc, 1967
25. Meltzoff J, Kornreich M: Research in Psychotherapy. Chicago. Aldine-Atherton, Inc. 1970
26. Hollingshead AB, Redlich FC: Social Class and Mental Illness: A community study. New York, John Wiley and Sons, 1958
27. Lief HI, Lief VF, Warren CO, et al: Low dropout rate in a psychiatric clinic: special reference to psychotherapy and social class. Arch Gen Psychiatry 5:200–211, 1961
28. Schaffer L, Myers JK: Psychotherapy and social stratification: an empirical study of of practice in a psychiatric outpatient clinic. Psychiatry 17:83–93, 1954
29. Myers JK, Schaffer L: Social stratification and psychiatric practice: a study of an out-patient clinic. Am Sociol Rev 19:307–310, 1954
30. Overall B, Aronson H: Expectations of psychotherapy in patients of lower socioeconomic class. Am J Orthopsychiatry 33:421–430, 1963
31. Levinson DJ, Merrifield J, Berg K: Becoming a patient. Arch Gen Psychiatry 17:385–406, 1967
32. Heine RW, Trosman H: Initial expectations of the doctor-patient interaction as a factor in continuance in psychotherapy. Psychiatry 23:275–278, 1960
33. Schildkraut JJ: The catecholamine hypothesis of affective disorders: a review of supporting evidence. Am J Psychiatry 122:509–522, 1965
34. Schildkraut JJ, Kety SS: Biogenic amines and emotion. Science 156:21–30, 1967
35. Caudill WA: The Psychiatric Hospital as a Small Society. Cambridge, Harvard University Press. 1958
36. Stanton AH, Schwartz MS: The Mental Hospital: A study of institutional participation in psychiatric illness and treatment. New York, Basic Books, 1954
37. Caplan G, Caplan RB: Development of community psychiatry concepts, Comprehensive Textbook of Psychiatry. Edited by AM Freedman, HI Kaplan. Baltimore, Williams and Wilkins Company, 1967, pp 1499–1516
38. Marmor J: Dynamic psychotherapy and behavior therapy: are they irreconcilable? Arch Gen Psychiatry 24:22–28, 1971
39. Marks IM, Gelder MG: Common ground between behaviour therapy and psychodynamic methods. Br J Med Psychol 39:11–23, 1966
40. Miller NE: Learning of visceral and glandular responses. Science 163:434–445, 1969

4.6

Disease and Mental Disease

Antony Flew

One main outcome of Part I should be a realisation of the dependence of the derivative notions of mental health and mental disease upon the prior notions of (physical) health and (physical) disease. If this dependence were merely historical and etymological it would be of little present concern. To urge that the true and proper meaning of all expressions as now employed must be determined by either the ultimate etymology or the original English senses of the words involved is unsound and tiresome. But it is both correct and important to insist that, if a large part of the point of applying the descriptions 'mental health' and 'mental disease' is to imply that most if not quite all which is involved in (physical) health and (physical) disease is involved in these further cases also, then any attempt to elucidate the former should begin from some preliminary examination of the latter.

This modest methodological claim may appear trite and obvious. But triteness and obviousness are essentially relative to time and place and person. For it is most remarkable how little attention seems to be paid in the now abundant literature on the nature and criteria of mental health and mental disease to the similarities and dissimilarities between these and their physical analogues. Indeed the present essay will, I believe, be sufficiently justified if it succeeds in persuading some future contributors to this literature to proceed in this now obviously sound way.

* * * *

The more immediately astonishing thing about the statements at the beginning of the chapter on 'Mental Disorder and Criminal Responsibility' is the conclusion that the collapse of all attempts to develop a suitably objective distinction between mental health and mental disease must clear the way for assertions that all behaviour of some particular disfavoured sort is in fact a symptom of mental disorder. But, as has been hinted already, we should also be more profoundly astonished that Lady Wootton is prepared to suggest that such an attempt must be unsuccessful, notwithstanding that extraordinarily little direct attention has been paid to the crucial physical paradigm. Certainly she more than most others does notice its importance from time to time. But what, while she is considering and rejecting a series of suggested definitions of 'mental health' or 'mental disease', she significantly does not do is to ask herself how mental health or mental disease, so defined, would relate, or fail to relate, to ordinary health or regular disease.

Let us therefore at very long last raise the neglected fundamental questions, 'What is health?' and 'What is disease?' The Compact Edition of *The Oxford English Dictionary* suggests that Plato was right to pick out the idea of function as central. Health, it tells us, is 'Soundness of body; that condition in which its functions are duly and efficiently discharged'. Disease in the relevant sense is, correspondingly 'A condition of the body, or of some part or organ of the body, in which its functions are disturbed or deranged; a morbid physical condition; a departure from the state of health especially when caused by a structural change.'

A first objection is that this is in two respects too broad. It would include both those malfunctionings due to some congenital defect and those caused by wounds. But although doctors might hesitate to pass a man who is in consequence of some genetic defect blind as without qualification fit, his blindness could scarcely be rated as a disease. Similarly a person whose digestive processes have been deranged by bullet wounds in the stomach will be very seriously ill. He will not be diseased. The Royal Commission on the Law relating to Mental Illness and Mental Deficiency was taking account of the first of these two distinctions when it recommended the use of 'mental disorder' as the generic expression, with 'mental illness' and 'mental deficiency' as species labels.[38] The Commission found no corresponding merit in any mental analogue of the distinction between wounds and diseases.

A second objection is that these definitions fail to allow for the possibility that the malfunctioning may be delayed. For a condition may be said to be diseased in as much as either it is now resulting in, or if not suitably treated it will later result in, malfunctioning. (Here death is of course the limiting case of malfunctioning.) This possibility of delayed action is very practical. It is what gives point to programmes for regular physical check-ups on apparently fit and well people. To us its theoretical interest lies in the opening it makes for expert knowledge, not merely of the causes and cures of diseases, but also of whether a given condition is or is not diseased. Yet so long as disease is defined in terms of malfunctioning, and malfunctioning is something which it is in principle possible for the layman himself to recognise, the possibility of some delay in its actual manifestation makes no change in the nature of the expertise involved.

What would present new problems would be if the effects in the delayed action cases were of some radically different kind, and such that the patient himself could only recognise the threatened malfunctioning as really being such after some special course of self-transforming training. It is one thing—and very disturbing—for my doctor to tell me that, although I now both feel perfectly well and can do all the things which I can normally do, I am nevertheless the victim of a condition which will if untreated become both painful and incapacitating. It is quite another thing—and to the unregenerate natural man wholly undisturbing—to be told by some Platonic para-medical adviser that my present state, and that into which this will develop if I do not forthwith submit myself to his ministrations, are both such as I would, if only I were a quite different and much better person, utterly deplore. For in that second case I remain, such is my actual present so scandalous condition, complacently content.

The third objection is more fundamental. Although the idea of function is surely in some way central, Plato and the dictionary are both wrong in attending to actuality rather than potentiality. The tongue of a Trappist is not diseased merely because during a penitential fast it is employed neither in tasting nor talking. My rose bushes are not diseased simply because they are not taking in water which is not there. It will be time to begin asking questions about disease if when the Trappist eventually tries to exercise his tongue he finds that he cannot, and if when the bushes are inundated by a cloudburst still no water enters the system.

A fourth and still more important point comes out when those two examples are compared further. In so far as both show that what matters here is potentiality rather than actuality, they are the same. But in other respects they are crucially different. Suppose that water is supplied to my rose bushes, and that none is then absorbed. That will constitute a sufficient reason for inferring that there must be something organically wrong, although what is organically wrong will not necessarily be a disease. Contrast with this the case of the fasting Trappist. He is a person and not a plant. So the fact that he does not eat when food is provided is no more sufficient to show that there is something organically wrong than is the fact that he refrains from making passes at the pretty girls. In his case, but not in that of the plants, there is room for questions about what he can do if he wants and what he could do if he tried. Indeed it is essential to the description of this particular example that there actually is a gap between what he is doing and what he could be doing if he chose. For anyone who suggests that a dumb eunuch is fitted for a Trappist vocation is altogether failing to grasp what monasticism is about.

The fourth point, which applies to people and not to plants, is different from the third, which applies to both equally. The fundamental facts which give purchase to such questions about people are universally familiar and practically inescapable. Yet it seems to be difficult to describe these facts in a theoretically neutral way. The unfortunate consequence of failure is that the resulting theoretically loaded and thus legitimately controversial descriptions provoke those who cannot accept the overload to attempt to ignore or to minimise the facts themselves.

The facts which I therefore want at this stage merely to indicate and not to theorise about are: that in the happy bloom of youth and health our bodies are partly, although still only partly, subject to our wills; and that there is a fundamental difference between for instance the claim that I moved my arm and the claim that my arm moved (although I did not move it).[39] Let us, in order to save words later, distinguish movements of the former sort as movings, while reserving the word 'motions' for movements of the second kind. And let us also, again for future reference, notice the dangerous possibilities of that favourite word 'behaviour'; which bridges—and which may therefore blur—this basic distinction between voluntary movings and mere motions. For these possibilities may be even more important than the fact that to employ this word as it is employed by behavioural scientists is to assimilate into a single category both what people say and what they do—two things which it is for many purposes necessary to be ready to contrast.

Now it is just not on to attempt to deny the subsistence of a difference: between on the one hand the case of—say—my liver, which however hard I try I cannot move at all except by shifting my whole torso; and on the other hand my little fingers, which I can wiggle around whenever and however the fancy takes me. But if in referring to such familiar differences I characterise the equally familiar possibilities of control as manifestations of the freedom of the will, then this affirmation may not be similarly uncontroversial. For, whether rightly or not, the word 'freewill' and the expression 'the freedom of the will' are often so construed as to imply some measure of indeterminism and radical unpredictability. Even if human beings and their affairs do happen in fact to be as believers in the freedom of the will in this philosophically libertarian sense believe that they are, that this is so is certainly not as immediately obvious and undeniable as the facts which I am trying to indicate.

Once these fundamental truths have been brought into the centre of attention we are ready to recognise a fifth point about the notion of (physical) disease in its primary employment. This primary application is surely to people and their organs, rather than to the brutes and theirs, much less to the plants and theirs. But to say of disease in a person that it is 'A condition of the body, or of some part or organ of the body, in which its functions are disturbed or deranged' is to challenge the question whether these functions do or do not include besides mere motions some movings or abstentions from movings.

The response to this gets us to the heart of the matter. For the concept of capability, of what we can or cannot do if we try, is central to the notion of (physical) health—at least in its primary application to human beings. For a man to be fit is not for him to do, but only to be able to do, whatever it is which he is fit to do. Certainly, to be fit to do what a sick or otherwise unfit man cannot do, does in fact always require the actual or potential proper functioning of organs which never are subject to the will. Nevertheless the criterion of the fit man's fitness is: not the propriety of these actual or hypothetical motions; but rather his capacities for not necessarily proper movings and not movings. So, if a definition of 'disease' in terms of the disturbance or derangement of functions is to be retained, we shall have to take it that the function of whatever is normally subject to our wills precisely is to be in this normal way thus subject.

To illustrate this fifth point, consider malingering. The malingerer is the man who 'reports sick' when he believes that he is not. He pretends to be suffering from some disease, or to be otherwise unfit, in order to be excused from duties which he does not want to fulfil. His pretences, and the response of the authorities if they are persuaded that the malingerer genuinely is 'sick', are intelligible only in so far as what he is pretending to would involve some relevant incapacity. His supposed disease, that is to say, or other disorder, must be such as, whether immediately or later, to render the patient either incapable of doing at all, or at least incapable of doing so well, something which otherwise he could have been required to do, or could have been required to do better. No authority concerned to prevent the avoidance of the duties which it imposes can afford to allow that disease excuses, except in so far as the irregularities involved are relevantly incapacitating.

The sixth point about the dictionary definition is that in referring to disturbances or derangements of functions it is appealing to some sort of norm determining how things ideally ought to be. In thus picking out a normative element in the meanings of the words 'health' and 'disease' this definition is obviously right. But whereas it is easy to notice that this element is present, and to appreciate the consequence that medicine must be an essentially impure science, it is harder to explicate the nature and the content of the norms involved. One first sure thing is that disease is not, any more than is delinquency, something 'that is abnormal, by its infrequency of occurrence'.[40] For a disease, just like some forms of delinquency in some milieux, could be endemic and universal. As recently as the last century there used in fact to be even in Europe areas in which the entire population suffered from malaria. I am told too (by both Hungarians and Rumanians) that in the old, unregenerate, pre-conquest days Hungarian chauvinists would advise travellers: 'Where everybody steals, that's Rumania.'

Another sure thing, and one much more worth remarking, is that at least as regards disease the norms involved seem to be comfortably undisputatious. Where there is agreement about the clinical facts we do not expect doctors, even from very different cultural backgrounds and of quite opposite ideological persuasions, to disagree more than very occasionally as to whether a patient is or is not physically diseased. This comparative undisputatiousness in practice is a good reason for hesitating over the suggestion that these particular norms are to a significant extent culturally conditioned.

Such suggestions have been made in the seemingly somewhat sketchy literature. Thus Dr Lester King, in an essay on 'What is Disease?', gives the answer: 'Disease is the aggregate of those conditions which, judged by the prevailing culture, are deemed painful or disabling, and which at the same time deviate from either the statistical norm or from some idealized status.'[41]

But what actually is painful, and what actually is in some way disabling, does not depend on what the prevailing or any other culture may happen to believe. Where therefore there are differences on these counts someone has to be wrong on a point of fact. What does provide room for cross-cultural value conflicts is: not the question of what is a pain and what is a disability; but the secondary issue of which pains and which disabilities to be disturbed about, and which to take as tolerably normal. This scope is widened by the fact that the capacity to do one thing can often be bought only at the price of an incapacity to do something else. That massive build for instance which gave you your chance to be anchorman in the tug-or-war team must make it impossible for you to go to the bottom as a world-class caver.

To support his contention that the application of the concept of disease is culturally conditioned King refers to the artificial deformation of the daughters' feet in aristocratic families in traditional China. The example is inept, yet for that very reason it can be instructive. It would not surely be correct to describe the condition of the girl's feet—whether before or after the binding treatment—as diseased. Certainly that treatment made them unfit for either labour in the fields or table-tennis contests. Unfitness however can result from congenital defect or from mutilation as well as from disease. We have, without prejudice to any disputes about the ideals involved, to insist that this is not an instance of causing or curing disease. It is rather a matter of artificial deformation—or reformation. Certainly there can be, and indeed have been, cross-cultural conflicts about the practice of foot-binding; just as there have been, and indeed still are, about the categorically similar cases of male and female circumcision. But these disagreements are not, I submit, about whether the untreated are or are not as such diseased. They are about whether such treatments are proper, and whether their results constitute mutilations.

To all this the notion of disease becomes relevant only in so far as it may be argued that if such treatments promote health then they cannot be illicit, and their results cannot properly be abused as mutilations or deformations. This may be a plausible contention as regards male circumcision. But supporters of female circumcision and foot-binding were—or are—much more likely to refer not to general health but to adaptation for a particular social role. Here we certainly do find dramatic cases in which fitness for one way of life must be unfitness for another: for what fits a woman well for her prescribed role in traditional Kikuyu society necessarily unfits her to serve as an emancipated playmate for Mr Hefner's young men; while what fits a child to become an instrument of 'conspicuous waste' inevitably unsuits the adult for the heavier tasks required to realise the thoughts of Chairman Mao.

These dramatic cases illustrate how fitness for one role may preclude fitness for another. They are not however cases of health as opposed to disease. There seems to be no parallel example in which what doctors of one culture rate as a physical disease is by their fellow doctors of some opposed ideology accounted perfectly healthy. Indeed it is this comparative undisputatiousness of the norms of physical disease which constitutes one, but only one, main reason why so many moralists have been eager in one way or another to incorporate delinquency into the same category. For how very convenient it would be if only conflicts over whether or not someone is at fault could, like questions as to whether his physical condition is diseased, safely be left to expert adjudication. If only too those who have been at fault could always be handed over to medical or quasi-medical experts in the secure knowledge that their treatment would be for their own as well as for the public good. 'We know', Boethius consolingly assures us, 'that in the case of the soul health means goodness and sickness means wickedness. And thus the protector of the good and scourge of the wicked is none other than God, the soul's guide and physician. He looks out from the watch-tower of Providence, sees what suits each person, and applies to him whatever He knows is suitable.'[42]

This undisputatiousness of the norms of disease, in so far as they are indeed undisputatious, depends upon certain fundamental facts about organisms. It is typical of organisms that they should be composed of non-redundant organs. It is this familiar and perhaps somehow necessary characteristic which enables both biologists and the Common Law to work on the presumption that any organ does have a function even when it is not at present known what that function is.[43] It is also a fact that given sufficient data biologists generally find little difficulty in agreeing on what the function or functions of any particular organ are, and whether these functions are in fact being discharged efficiently; and in harmony with the discharging by other organs in the organism of their functions. But there is and can be no similarly convenient consensus about whatever in the human organism is subject to the will; except of course in so far as, as has been suggested, the function here is taken to be precisely and only that of being thus for better or for worse subject to the will.

*

Further points about the concept of physical disease can best be brought out by commenting on another suggested definition. In an enumeration 'Of

Circumstances influencing Sensibility' in *An Introduction to the Principles of Morals and Legislation* Jeremy Bentham wrote: 'Health is the absence of disease, and consequently of all those kinds of pain which are among the symptoms of disease. A man may be said to be in a state of health when he is not conscious of any uneasy sensations, the primary seat of which can be anywhere in his body.' (VI, 7)

It is characteristic of Bentham, but wrong, to make 'uneasy sensations' the heart of the matter. For someone can be easily unaware that he has a disease. This possibility was dramatically actualised in a recent British case, much quoted in the press overseas. A man picked up the victim of a traffic accident, left lying by the wayside, and drove him to hospital. There the doctors spotted that the Good Samaritan himself was all unwittingly subject to a disease which would, had it not been treated forthwith, have been fatal within hours. I do not know whether this particular disease would finally have caused 'uneasy sensations'. But it certainly is possible for even a fatal disease to be totally or almost totally painless. Happily this seems to have been the case with David Hume's terminal illness, the 'wasting disease of the bowels'. The same surely applies even more decisively in many of the cases in which someone is so fortunate as to die quite unexpectedly 'peacefully, in his sleep'.

By contrast it is also perfectly possible for some physical condition involving neither wounding nor hereditary defect to give rise to very 'uneasy sensations' indeed, without its thereby qualifying as a disease. The most obvious illustrations here are pregnancy and the actual process of childbirth. A woman can feel very ill during pregnancy, and may be more or less incapacitated by her condition. Nor in this event will things be made easier for her by the fact that these misfortunes are among those, like seasickness, to which other people who do not suffer similarly are apt to be unsympathetic. Yet none of this apparently is sufficient to warrant the diagnosis 'disease' when the condition itself and the culminating performance are both so indisputably instances of biologically normal functioning.

The truth, as was with something less than an unshakeable conviction suggested in the previous Section 4, seems to be that the core notion, in so far as there is a core notion, is that of malfunctioning. But since, as is most commonly insisted in discussions of the theologian's Problem of Evil,[44] the biological function of pain is to compel attention to some threatened or actual malfunctioning in or damage to the organism, it is usual for both wounds and diseases to be at some if not in all stages painful. However the system is of course not perfectly complete and effective. Just as there are some dangerous substances which we find attractively sweet-smelling, so there are some diseased conditions which are not signalled by any 'uneasy sensations'.

Even if we do not ourselves share Bentham's commitment to develop a comprehensive ethical and psychological Utilitarian theory, we may still be led astray by two pairs of more particular pulls. First Bentham's account of disease does in an appealingly simple way meet what earlier seemed to be two of the essential requirements. For if disease necessarily and not merely normally involved uneasy bodily sensations, then this would surely be sufficient reason to insist that it must always be presumptively and in itself bad for the sufferer. Suppose too—a little generously—that the reference to 'the primary seat' being 'anywhere in his body' is construed as excluded sensations produced directly and artificially by chastisement or other rough treatment, whether inflicted by others or by the patient himself. Then presumably the patient is now, even if earlier he could have avoided getting into this condition, a victim of the disease, which he cannot escape immediately and at will.

But this first pair of requirements is satisfied equally by our own insistence upon malfunctionings rather than painful sensations. Take the second first. Either the malfunctioning is confined to organs not normally subject directly to the will, and/or it causes, or partly or wholly consists in, incapacities. This sufficiently guarantees that the patient who has actually got the disease cannot get rid of it immediately and at will; and hence that he must be to that extent, and in this respect, a victim. The rather awkward temporal qualifications are needed to provide for the fact that many patients could at some earlier stage have avoided getting into their present condition. For instance: both syphilis and gonorrhoea are by the exercise of a little timely prudence nowadays very largely avoidable; albeit often only at the price of using a sometimes unacceptable old-fashioned oral prophylactic—saying 'No', and meaning it. But such earlier avoidability is no more a reason for saying that the patients could now change their condition at once and at will, than their admitted present need of medical help is a reason for saying that they never had a chance of not getting themselves into this state.

The first requirement is that disease must be presumptively and in itself bad for the sufferer. This too can be satisfied by an account in terms primarily of malfunctioning. For in so far as the malfunctionings either cause, or partly or wholly consist in, incapacities; then they must surely be rated as, presumptively and in themselves, bad for the people concerned. Yet, as before, the various qualifications are essential. My disease must be presumptively and in itself bad for me; and it can be, notwithstanding that the fact that I am thus incapacitated may be a blessing for others. The illness which has the torture specialist of the political police lying helpless in his bed is presumptively and in itself bad for him; but it is certainly a fine thing for his intended subjects, and probably good absolutely. Again your tuberculosis must still be allowed to be presumptively and in itself bad for you; even though it is entirely to the fact that you have this disease that you owe your exemption from military conscription, and all which that may involve. It must be: since clearly it would be better still for you if you could both retain that exemption and recover your health; and since, equally clearly, your qualified satisfaction with your diseased condition can be made intelligible to the mean sensual man only by reference to particular present circumstances.

*

Of the second pair of pulls, which might mislead someone to accept Bentham's erroneous account of the nature of disease, the first is that that account carries the consequences that everyone must be his own best expert on whether he is himself diseased. The second is that, if Bentham is right, it is the seemingly negative notion of disease, and not the apparently positive concept of health, which—in J. L. Austin's memorably inelegant phrase—is the one 'to wear the trousers; commonly enough the "negative" (looking) word marks the (positive) abnormality, while the "positive" word... merely serves to rule out the suggestion of that abnormality'.[45]

Such attractions are not of course attractions for everybody.

4.7

The Concept of Disease and its Implications for Psychiatry

R. E. Kendell

It has often been suggested in recent years that there is no such thing as mental illness; that the conditions psychiatrists spend their time trying to treat ought not, properly speaking, to be regarded as illness at all, or even to be the concern of physicians. Szasz is the best-known exponent of this viewpoint, and the core of his argument is essentially this: that as prolonged search has never demonstrated any consistent physical abnormality in those regarded as mentally ill, and as their 'illness' consists simply in behaving in ways that alarm or affront other people, or in believing things which other people do not believe, there is not justification for labelling them as ill,and to do so is to use the word illness in a purely metaphorical sense (Szasz, 1960). Schneider had previously been led by the same reasoning to the conclusion that neurotic illness and personality disorders were 'abnormal varieties of sane mental life' rather than disease, but he took care to exempt schizophrenia and cyclothymia by assuming that both would in time prove to possess an organic basis (Schneider, 1950). The argument Eysenck puts forward in the first edition of his textbook, though written from the quite different standpoint of academic psychology, is a similar one. After observing that 'the term psychiatry does not denote any meaningful grouping of problems or subjects of study' he went on to suggest that the traditional subject-matter of psychiatry should be divided into a small medical part 'dealing with the effects of tumours, lesions, infections and other physical conditions' and a much larger behavioural part 'dealing with disorders of behaviour acquired through the ordinary processes of learning', thereby implying that most of what doctors regarded as mental illness was really learnt behaviour rather than disease, and therefore much better understood, and dealt with, by psychologists than by physicians (Eysenck, 1960). A third line of attack is provided by R. D. Laing, and a fourth is exemplified by the sociologist Scheff. Laing argues that schizophrenia, far from being a disease or a form of insanity, is really the only sane or rational way adolescents have of coping with the intolerable emotional pressures placed on them by society and their families (Laing, 1967). Scheff has developed the somewhat similar argument that what psychiatrists call mental illness is largely a response to the shock of being labelled and treated as insane and the expectations this produces; in other words that schizophrenia is created by the people and institutions that purport to treat it (Scheff, 1963).

Psychiatrists have generally reacted to these various assaults with indignation or disdain. They have either ignored their critics, or told them, with varying degrees of candour, that they don't know what they are talking about, or suggested, with varying degrees of subtlety, that they are motivated by professional jealousy, a taste for publicity, or emotional difficulties of their own. Perhaps there is some truth in these retaliatory jibes. But what matters is the strength of the critics' arguments, not their motives. They come from a variety of backgrounds—psychology, sociology and psychiatry itself—and although they disagree with one another almost as vehemently as they do with orthodox psychiatry, they have one central argument in common—that what psychiatrists regard as mental illnesses are not illnesses at all. The purpose of this essay is to examine this proposition.

THE NEED FOR A DEFINITION OF ILLNESS

To question the existence of mental illness, or to assert that the word illness in such a context is no more than a misleading metaphor, assumes that one already has a clear idea of what illness is. It is equally meaningless to assert either that something is, or that it is not, illness unless one has a clearly defined concept of illness to start with. Unfortunately, although medicine has adequate working definitions for most individual illnesses, it does not possess an agreed definition or an explicit concept of illness in general (Engle and Davis, 1963). So before we can begin to decide whether mental illnesses are legitimately so called we have first to agree on an adequate definition of illness; to decide if you like what is the defining characteristic or the hallmark of disease.

Most doctors never give a moment's thought to the precise meaning of terms like illness and disease, nor do they need to. They simply treat the patients who consult them as best they can, diagnose individual diseases whenever they can, and try to relieve their patients' suffering even if they can't. At times they are well aware that they are dealing with matters other than illness—childbirth and the circumcision of infants are traditional examples, and family planning a more recent innovation—but rarely do they pause to consider what is the essential difference between the two. The practical nature of medicine is not conducive to theorizing. But there are some situations in which this unthinking empiricism is inadequate. Psychiatrists are only too well aware of this, since they are often required to express opinions about the presence or absence of illness in the courts, and to defend these opinions to hard-headed lawyers, but they have not been conspicuously successful in finding a solution.

An American writer has recently pointed out that when doctors disagree whether a particular condition is a disease or not it is almost invariably the case that those who regard the subject of the condition as ill also regard some medical procedure—either treatment or investigation—as necessary, while those who do not regard the subject as ill do not regard either as warranted. This gives rise to the suspicion that, whether or not they realize it, doctors do not have a clearly formulated concept of illness, and that the answer they give to the question 'Is this a disease?' is really a covert answer to the quite different question 'Should this person be under medical care?' (Linder, 1965). This rather cynical judgement is not entirely justified, if only because doctors do perceive that some of their activities, such as the delivery of babies and the circumcision of infants, are not the treatment of illness, despite the fact that the technology and expertise involved are the same in both. But it is undoubtedly extremely difficult to pin down the essential element distinguishing illness from non-illness, or, to put it another way, to produce a definition of disease which neatly covers all the individual diseases we currently recognize, and excludes other phenomena.

CHANGING CONCEPTS OF DISEASE

The main reason why this is so is that, for historical reasons, the defining characteristics of individual diseases are very diverse. To most of the schools of medicine of the ancient world symptoms and signs were themselves diseases. Fever, joint pains and skin rashes were all separate diseases to be studied individually. The idea of disease as a syndrome, a constellation of related symptoms with a characteristic prognosis, originated with Sydenham in the seventeenth century, though the Hippocratic school had had the germ of the idea long before. However, the popularization of post-mortem dissection of the body in the latter half of the eighteenth century by Morgagni and Bichat slowly converted disease from a syndrome observed at the bedside to a characteristic morbid anatomy observed in the cadaver, and thereafter new concepts followed one another in rapid succession, mainly in response to the introduction of new types of observational technology. The development of powerful microscopes in the middle of the nineteenth century enabled individual cells to be examined for the first time, and the consequent detection of cellular pathology led Virchow and his contemporaries to assume that cellular derangements were the basis of all disease. This concept was in turn displaced by the discovery of bacteria by Koch and Pasteur, and currently new techniques like electrophoresis, chromosome analysis and electron microscopy are producing further concepts of disease expressed in terms of deranged biophysical structures, genes and molecules.

Each of these waves of technology has added new diseases, and from each stage some have survived. A few, like senile pruritus and proctalgia fugax, are still individual symptoms. Others, like migraine and most psychiatric diseases, are clinical syndromes—Sydenham's constellation of symptoms. Mitral stenosis and hydronephrosis are based on morbid anatomy, and tumours of all kinds on histopathology. Tuberculosis and syphilis are based on bacteriology and the concept of the aetiological agent, prophyria on biochemistry, myasthenia gravis on physiological dysfunction, Down's syndrome on chromosomal architecture, and so on. In fact the diseases we currently recognize are rather like the furniture in an old house, in which each generation has acquired a few new pieces of its own but has never disposed of those it inherited from its predecessors, so that amongst the inflatable plastic settees and glass coffee tables are still scattered a few old Tudor stools, Jacobean dressers and Regency commodes, and a great deal of Victoriana.

A logician would have started by defining what he meant by disease as a whole and then produced individual diseases by sub-dividing the territory whose boundaries he had thus defined. Medicine, being essentially practical and opportunist, proceeded the other way and started with individual diseases. As a result, many of these overlap with one another, and the outer perimeter between disease and health is based on different criteria in different places. Hence the difficulty in producing a satisfactory definition.

Historically it seems likely that the concept of disease originated as an explanation for the onset of suffering and incapacity in the absence of obvious injury, and that the concept of health was a later development, implying the absence of disease. Naturally enough, therefore, attempts have often been made to define illness in terms of suffering and incapacity, or at least in terms of a complaint of some sort. But this immediately leads to difficulties. Many people whom we regard as ill neither complain nor suffer, either because they experience no symptoms, or because they ignore what in others would be cause for complaint, or simply because they drop dead without warning. A man with a cancer growing silently in his lung, or someone with anginal pain which he dismisses as a touch of wind, would both be regarded by both doctors and laymen as ill and urgently in need of treatment, yet neither complains, or even suffers to any significant extent. The same is true of the typhoid carrier harbouring salmonellae in his gall bladder. Other people, whom we call hypochondriacs or hysterics, complain incessantly, and insist that they suffer, without either their doctors or anyone else being convinced that they are genuinely ill.

Partly because of such problems, attempts have sometimes been made to define illness in terms of the need for treatment rather than the presence of a complaint; in other words to make the situation to which Linder was drawing attention overt rather than covert. Kräupl Taylor, for instance, recently suggested that disease, or patienthood, should have 'as its sufficient and necessary condition the experience of therapeutic concern by a person for himself and/or the arousal of therapeutic concern for him in his social environment' (Kräupl Taylor, 1971). A criterion of this kind is certainly capable of embracing people whom doctors, or society as a whole, regard as in need of treatment as well as those who complain or suffer personally, but in doing so it creates worse problems than it solves. Equating illness with a complaint allows the individual to be sole arbiter of whether he is ill or not, and is unsatisfactory because some people who should be complaining don't do so, and others who complain so repeatedly don't seem to have adequate reasons for doing so. Equating illness with 'therapeutic concern' implies that no one can be ill until he has been recognized as such, and also gives doctors, and society, free rein to label all deviants as ill, thus opening the door to all the inconsistencies and abuses that Szasz has so vividly conjured up.

The fact is that any definition of disease which boils down to 'what people complain of', or 'what doctors treat', or some combination of the two, is almost worse than no definition at all. It is free to expand or contract with changes in social attitudes and therapeutic optimism and is at the mercy of idiosyncratic decisions by doctors or patients. If one wished to compare the incidence of disease in two different cultures, or in a single population at two different times, whose criteria of suffering or therapeutic concern would one use? And if the incidence of disease turned out to be different in the two, would this be because one was healthier than the other, or simply because their attitudes to illness were different?

DISEASE AS A LESION

During the last century the development first of morbid anatomy and then of histology produced widespread evidence that illness was accompanied by structural damage to the body, at either a gross or a microscopic level. It was only a short step from this observation to the assumption that these lesions constituted the illness, and that illness always involved structural damage. Subsequently, as knowledge of physiology and biochemistry grew in the first half of this century, this concept was expanded to include biochemical and physiological abnormalities, without relinquishing the basic assumption that illness necessarily involved a demonstrable physical abnormality of some sort.

In this milieu it was almost inevitable that the presence of an identifiable lesion should come to be regarded as the essential attribute of disease, and this concept of illness held sway for over a hundred years. Such a standpoint certainly has many advantages. It provides an objective and usually reliable criterion which is not at the mercy of changing social attitudes and therapeutic fashions, and also embodies at least a partial explanation of the patient's symptoms or disabilities. On close examination, however, it has several shortcomings. In the first place, conditions whose physical basis is still unknown cannot legitimately be regarded as diseases. Trigeminal neuralgia, senile pruritus and dystonia musculorum deformans must all be discarded. Twenty years ago the same would have been true of migraine and narcolepsy, and sixty years ago most forms of epilepsy, Parkinson's disease, chorea, Bornholm disease and pellagra would all have failed to qualify. Indeed, to insist on the presence of a demonstrable lesion implies that most of the great scourges of mankind have only become diseases during the last hundred and fifty years. A further difficulty is that no distinction is drawn between what is trivial and what is crippling. A child with spina bifida and an oligophrenic imbecile both suffer from congenital diseases—the first by virtue of an anatomical defect acquired early in embryonic development, the second because of the absence of the enzyme needed to convert phenylalanine to tyrosine. But children with fused second and third toes have a similar congenital defect to those with spina bifida, and those with albinism also lack an enzyme involved in tyrosine metabolism, yet despite the presence of these lesions we do not normally wish to regard them as ill.

There is a third problem as well. The concept of an abnormality or a lesion is quite straightforward so long as one is concerned with deviation from a standard pattern. But as soon as we begin to recognize that there is no single set pattern of either structure or function, that even in health human beings and their constituent tissues and organs vary considerably in size, shape, chemical composition and functional efficiency, it becomes much less obvious what constitutes a lesion; where normal variation ends and abnormality begins. Is, for instance, hypertension a disease, and if so what is the level beyond which the blood pressure is abnormal? And at what point does a raised blood sugar level, or a prolonged response to a carbohydrate load, become the disease diabetes?

It was in fact the example of hypertension which finally discredited the nineteenth-century assumption that there was always a qualitative distinction between sickness and health (Oldham, Pickering, Frazer Roberts and Sowry, 1960). The demonstration by Pickering and his colleagues twenty years ago that such a major cause of death and disability as this was a graded characteristic, dependent, like height and intelligence, on polygenic inheritance and shading insensibly into normality, was greeted with shock and disbelief by most of their contemporaries, and the prolonged resistance to their findings showed how deeply rooted the assumptions of Koch and Virchow had become.

The resistance finally crumbled not only because Pickering's evidence was strong but because at the same time advances in other fields were also discrediting another of the major assumptions of the old concept—the assumption that every illness had a single cause, both necessary and sufficient. As the focus of medical research widened from an exclusive concern with individual patients to embrace the study of disease in populations, it slowly became apparent that a host of interacting factors, both internal and environmental, all contributed to the development of disease; and as knowledge increased the decision to regard one of these as 'the cause' and the rest merely as 'precipitating or exacerbating factors' appeared increasingly arbitrary. This was true not only of degenerative diseases like arteriosclerosis but even of classical illnesses like tuberculosis. Although tuberculosis cannot develop in the absence of the Mycobacterium tuberculi, the presence of the organism is insufficient to produce the illness. It is ubiquitous in many populations, yet only a minority develop the disease. Genetic studies reveal differences in concordance between MZ and DZ twins, and epidemiological studies show that these constitutional differences are matched by a host of environmental factors—dietary, climatic, occupational and social—all exerting a powerful influence on the liability of individuals exposed to the tubercle bacillus to develop the disease.

A STATISTICAL CONCEPT OF DISEASE

By 1960 the 'lesion' concept of disease, and its associated assumptions of a single cause and a qualitative difference between sickness and health had been discredited beyond redemption, but nothing had yet been put in its place. It was clear, though, that its successor would have to be based on a statistical model of the relationship between normality and abnormality. Lord Cohen (1943) had anticipated this in an essay in which he defined illness simply as 'deviation from the normal... by way of excess or defect', and indeed Broussais and Magendie had had the germ of a quantitative concept of disease a hundred years before. But Cohen never developed his suggestion any further, and as it stands his definition is inadequate because it fails to distinguish between deviations from the norm which are harmful, like hypertension, those which are neutral, like great height, and those which are positively beneficial, like superior intelligence. Scadding was the first to recognize the need for a criterion distinguishing between disease and other deviations from the norm that were not matters for medical concern, and suggested that the crucial issue was whether or not the abnormality placed the individual at a 'biological disadvantage' (Scadding, 1967). Although he was primarily concerned with defining individual diseases, his definition of *a* disease has clear implications for the corresponding global concept. He defines illness not by its antecedents—the aetiological agent or the lesion producing the overt manifestations—but by its consequences. In itself this is not new; previous attempts to define illness as a condition producing suffering or as meriting medical intervention had done the same but, as we have seen, had proved inadequate. The concept of 'biological disadvantage' differs from these, however, in being more fundamental and less obviously an epiphenomenon, and in being immune to the idiosyncratic personal judgements of patients or doctors which had proved the undoing of its predecessors.

I should like to examine Scadding's definition in detail. He defines a disease as 'the sum of the abnormal phenomena displayed by a group of living organisms in association with a specified common characteristic or set of characteristics by which they differ from the norm for their species in such a way as to place them at a biological disadvantage'. Differing from the norm for the species is Cohen's 'excess or defect' set out in more explicitly statistical terms and carrying with it several fundamental implications—that deviation in either direction, too much or too little, is equally capable of producing disease; that the boundary between health and disease may need to be an arbitrary one, like the boundary between mental subnormality and normal intelligence; and that the majority are debarred from being regarded as ill. The 'specified common characteristic or set of characteristics' is the defining characteristic of the disease in question. Its presence is essential for establishing the presence of that disease, and it is worth noting that the wording allows it to be either monothetic (a single trait) or polythetic (a set of traits no one of which is mandatory).

THE 'BIOLOGICAL DISADVANTAGE' CRITERION

Scadding avoided elaborating on what he meant by 'biological disadvantage'. Presumably, though, it must embrace both increased mortality and reduced fertility. Whether it should embrace other impairments as well is less obvious, and the consequences need considering carefully before deciding.

Despite this uncertainty, Scadding's definition does not founder on the shoals which were the undoing of its predecessors. Diseases like hypertension and diabetes which are or may be purely quantitative deviations from normality present no problem. Nor do conditions like dystonia musculorum deformans in which no consistent lesion has yet been identified and whose aetiology remains unknown. Provided that it can be established that a biological disadvantage is involved, their status as diseases is secure. The definition is also independent of whether the affected invididual complains or suffers; and it provides a clear indication of which conditions should and which should not merit medical attention, without being influenced by whether or not they currently do so. It also successfully discards lesions, like congenitally fused toes, whose ill-effects are trivial, and provides a clear cut answer to the problem posed by conditions like the sickle cell trait which are disadvantageous in some environments but harmless, or positively beneficial, in others. Despite the presence of a qualitative deviation—an abnormal haemoglobin molecule—it is only to be regarded as a disease in environments in which its presence is a real disadvantage. By the same token, albinism would rank as a disease in Delhi or Khartoum, but probably not in Newfoundland. The 'lesion' concept of disease ignored the environment, except as a source of pathogens, but the biological disadvantage criterion gives environmental influences a powerful role, rightly so in an age in which all disease is increasingly seen as the result of a complex interaction between the individual and his environment, rather than as arising *de novo* within him, or attacking him from without.

My interpretation of 'biological disadvantage'—restricting it to conditions which reduce fertility or shorten life—means that some conditions, like post-herpetic neuralgia and psoriasis, fail to qualify as illnesses despite the fact that they cause considerable suffering, are accompanied by well-defined lesions, and are capable of being relieved by medical means, and on all these counts it seems unreasonable not to regard them as diseases. This is admittedly rather disconcerting, but the problem is that if the meaning of the phrase is broadened to take account of conditions of this kind there is a danger that it will lose all sharpness of meaning, and that as a result anyone with a complaint, or whom doctors think they can treat, will once more be accepted uncritically as ill. [It is also advisable, if one is trying to show that mental illnesses fulil the same criteria as other illnesses and finds oneself presented with a choice of criteria, to use the stricter of the two.]

Despite these doubts about precisely how to define 'biological disadvantage', Scadding's definition is better matched to the ethos of contemporary medicine and to current attitudes to the nature of disease than any of its predecessors, and also more successful in embracing conditions that by common consent are diseases and excluding those that are not. It could still be argued that it and all the other definitions I have discussed are equally inadequate, in which case assertions about the existence or non-existence of mental illness would remain untestable. But if any definition is to be accepted it must surely be this one, or some modification of it.

Having reached this decision I can now come back to my starting point and pose my original question once more. Do mental illnesses possess the essential attributes of illness or not? Do they, by reducing either fertility or life expectancy, produce a significant biological disadvantage?

THE FERTILITY OF THE MENTALLY ILL

In purely biological terms fertility is all-important. It is this that determines which species flourish and expand and which die out, and which genotypes within a species become dominant and which remain rare. The fertility of the mentally ill has been the subject of over a dozen studies in the last fifty years, and these indicate that psychotics as a whole marry less often than other people, remain childless more often even when they do marry, and have fewer children than other people in or out of wedlock. To some extent these findings are an artificial consequence of confining the mentally ill in asylums, but this is only a partial explanation. Dahlberg (1933) found that the fertility of psychotic women was less than that of other women of the same age even before admission to hospital, and the studies of Macsorley (1964) and Stevens (1969), carried out since the introduction of 'open door' policies, confirm that despite their increased opportunities for marrying and reproducing those with psychotic illnesses still have fewer children than other people. As Sir Aubrey Lewis concluded in his Galton Lecture seventeen years ago, the evidence 'points towards the personal characteristics of the patients rather than their enforced residence in a mental hospital as the main reason for their low marriage rate and low fertility,' (Lewis, 1958). This reduction in the fertility of psychotics as a whole is largely due to the low fertility of schizophrenics; it is open to doubt whether the fertility of manic-depressives is significantly below that of the general population. Although six studies in the last forty years have all suggested that it is reduced, Essen-Möller's classical study in Munich did not (Essen-Möller, 1935), nor did the more recent investigations by Hopkinson (1963) and Stevens (1969).

The condition which stands out above all others in its implications for fertility is homosexuality. Although there have been few formal studies of the fertility of male or female homosexuals, it can hardly be doubted that it is drastically reduced in both. In simple biological terms their lack of interest in forms of sexual activity capable of resulting in conception puts homosexuals, and other sexual deviants like transsexuals, at a quite daunting negative selection advantage. Whether neurotic illnesses and personality disorders are associated with any significant reduction in fertility is still uncertain, mainly because the question has rarely been considered. There are suggestions that the fertility of criminal psychopaths is below that of the general population (Rosenthal, 1970). There is also some evidence that the sexual activity of neurotics is reduced (Slater, 1945; Eysenck, 1971), and one might expect this to result in a reduction in fertility.

Rosenthal was recently driven to the unwelcome* conclusion that fertility is reduced 'in at least four major types of disorders—schizophrenia, manic-depressive psychosis, psychopathy and homosexuality'. Some might wish to dispute the evidence relating to manic-depressive illness and psychopathy, but it would be hard to do so in the case of schizophrenia or homosexuality.

THE MORTALITY OF THE MENTALLY ILL

Although fertility may be all-important biologically, death is a more obvious, and to the individual a more important consequence of disease. It also has a greater biological significance in social animals like man, whose offspring are dependent on their parents for a high proportion of their life span, than in species whose young can fend for themselves from birth. The studies of Alström (1942), Ødegaard (1951) and Malzberg (1953) indicate that the risk of death for patients newly admitted to public mental hospitals is, or

*Unwelcome because it forces geneticists to postulate either a very high spontaneous mutation rate or else some compensatory advantage in gene-carrying relatives in order to explain the high incidence of these conditions.

was until recently, between four and ten times that of the general population, but this high mortality might well be due in part to physical ill-health contributing to the decision to seek hospital admission, or even to infections or other harmful influences encountered in hospital. Larsson and Sjögren (1954), in a meticulous study of the population of two Swedish islands, showed that over a forty-five year period schizophrenics, and to a lesser extent manic-depressives also, had a mortality considerably higher than that of the general Swedish population, but they were unable to match the two for the many variables liable to influence mortality.

More recently, studies have been done of the mortality of patients reported to psychiatric case registers. These provide data on outpatient populations with neurotic illnesses and personality disorders, and also allow accurate matching of observed mortality rates with those of the catchment area population. Innes and Millar (1970) studied the mortality over a five-year period of a cohort of 2,000 patients reported to the N.E. Scotland Psychiatric Case Register. Even though they assumed that all untraced patients were still alive, they found that the overall mortality of their cohort was twice the expected rate. Organic psychoses accounted for much of this increase, but all age groups and all diagnostic groups except male character disorders had a mortality above expectation. Even in neurotic illness the mortality was twice the expected rate. A similar study based on the Monroe County register in the United States produced almost identical findings (Babigian and Odoroff, 1969). Even after careful matching for age, sex and marital and socio-economic status, the mortality of the patient group was three times that of the general population, and all diagnostic groups, including neurotic illnesses and character disorders, shared this increased risk. Although the suicide rate was increased tenfold in the register population, suicide was not an important cause of this increased mortality. Indeed, there was no single cause; instead there was a fairly uniform increase in mortality from all major causes of death, including neoplasms, cerebrovascular disease and coronary artery disease. It is possible that this increased mortality is due to intercurrent physical illness increasing the likelihood of psychiatric referral, or even to psychiatric symptoms developing secondarily in the presence of physical illness, but these findings do suggest that a wide range of mental illness may be associated with a significantly increased risk of death.

There have been surprisingly few studies of the mortality associated with individual conditions. Rosenthal quotes three studies of manic-depressive illness all indicating that after the onset of the illness mortality is increased about 1½ fold and life expectancy decreased by about 15 per cent. There is also evidence from numerous sources that at least 15 per cent of manic-depressives die prematurely by suicide (Sainsbury, 1968), and without treatment the mortality would be considerably higher—from exhaustion and accidents of diverse kinds in mania, and from inanition and suicide in depression. The picture is less clear where schizophrenia is concerned, mainly because of the distorting effects of prolonged institutional care. The schizophrenic inmates of the great asylums certainly died prematurely, mainly from tuberculosis and other infections, but the institutions themselves may have been partly responsible for this rather than the disease. However, if schizophrenics were simply to be ignored and provided neither with sanctuaries where they could be fed and clothed nor with modern chemotherapy there is little doubt that comparatively few would survive to old age. Many would die of exposure, the indirect effects of malnutrition, or plain starvation, and others would die in accidents of various kinds, or by suicide. The asylums of the nineteenth century were, after all, built primarily for the protection of the insane and only secondarily for the protection of society. Finally, there is the evidence that several types of drug dependence, including alcohol and heroin—and also nicotine dependence in its common form, cigarette smoking—are all associated with a well-documented increase in mortality.

There is evidence, therefore, that schizophrenia and manic-depressive illness, together with some sexual disorders and various kinds of drug dependence, are associated with either a reduction in fertility or a reduction in life expectancy, or both, and for that reason are justifiably regarded as illnesses. The same may eventually prove to be true of some neurotic states and some types of personality disorder, but at present the evidence is not strong enough to justify firm conclusions in these areas.

At this point it will be worth while to recall the arguments of our critics. The various assertions that what psychiatrists regard as mental illnesses are nothing of the kind have all been based on the argument that no physical lesion has ever been demonstrated in these conditions, and that some kind of lesion is essential to establish the presence of disease. This argument is quite explicit in Szasz's case, and implicit in the reasoning of Eysenck, Laing and Scheff also. The arguments of these writers are therefore all based, wittingly or unwittingly, on a concept of disease which has been abandoned not just by psychiatry but by medicine as a whole. The position they are in is like that of Ishmael in *Moby Dick*, arguing that whales must be fish because they have fins and swim under water, unaware that the defining characteristics of fishes had been revised some time before.

BIOLOGICAL AND SOCIAL DISADVANTAGES

There are other arguments, however, which do require an answer. I have argued that mental illnesses are justifiably so-called because they are associated with reduced fertility and life expectancy, and that these two constitute a biological disadvantage. Scheff and other sociologists would argue that these handicaps may exist but are secondary consequences of the individual having been labelled as ill rather than being innate and inevitable.

They might argue, for example, that the main reason people labelled as schizophrenics have relatively few children is because they are regarded, both by others and by themselves, as lunatics and are less likely to marry and have children for this reason; and they die at an early age because we either lock them up in institutions where they catch tuberculosis, or shun them so that they eventually die of neglect or are driven to suicide.

Essentially the problem is to distinguish between a biological and a purely social disadvantage, and this is difficult because man is necessarily a social animal. His long post-natal immaturity and his use of language are both intimately linked to this fact, and our species has only achieved its present ascendency over others because of the ability of its members to assist one another to overcome both competing species and the physical hazards of the environment. If, therefore, an individual is discriminated against and shunned by his fellows, it could well be argued that that in itself places him at a substantial biological disadvantage, and not merely a social one. The argument could be buttressed by the evidence that other social species, like the rat and the chimpanzee, have also been observed to discriminate against deformed or diseased individuals, excluding them from the group and sharply reducing their chances of survival by doing so. The situation is further complicated by the fact that over the last two hundred years our dominance over our physical and biological environment has become so complete that cultural rather than purely biological forces are increasingly becoming the main determinants of natural selection. Which human genotypes become dominant, and how severe the negative selection pressures on others, are increasingly determined not so much by their inherent hardiness and adaptability as by cultural attitudes towards them. The increased survival chances of diabetics in the twentieth century and the reduced survival chances of Huguenots in the seventeenth century are both examples of this. There is another issue as well. It could legitimately be argued that because man is a social species what matters is the contribution the individual makes to the survival chances of the group rather than his own personal survival, and that a trait which is, biologically speaking, a disadvantage to him personally may be advantageous to his social group, or *vice versa*. If, for example, homosexuality could be shown to be associated with valuable aptitudes which others lacked, it might be positively advantageous to a community to have a proportion of homosexual members. Indeed, in an era of explosive population growth it might be beneficial to a community to have its fertility reduced. Clearly the complexities of the situation created by man's distortion of his original biological environment are almost endless. Yet somehow we have still to find a way of distinguishing between innate biological disadvantages and others attributable to cultural and social determinants of varying kinds.

The answer, I suggest, is that we must ignore the increasing importance of purely cultural factors in determining who lives and who dies; ignore the existence and fatal effects of social discrimination in other species, and also ignore the argument that it is the survival of the group rather than of the individual that matters. Despite all these complications we must still insist that for a characteristic to qualify as a biological disadvantage it must be shown to be harmful to the individual possessing it, and also to be innate and not simply one that leads to rejection by others. The criterion must be, would this individual still be at a disadvantage if his fellows did not recognize his distinguishing features but treated him as they treat one another? In the case of schizophrenia the argument hinges on whether the high mortality and low fertility associated with this condition are innate, or whether they would melt away if those whom we call schizophrenics were not merely treated like other people but not even recognized as deviant. Although the proponents of the labelling theory have demonstrated that recognition of deviance may often increase rather than reduce the handicaps associated with it, they are far from establishing that labelling is the primary problem. Indeed, the evidence from both twin and adoption studies for the genetic transmission of schizophrenia establishes beyond doubt that it is not.

CONCLUSIONS

I think, therefore, that my earlier conclusion is still justified: we have adequate evidence that schizophrenia and manic-depressive illness, and also some sexual disorders and some forms of drug dependence, carry with them an intrinsic biological disadvantage, and on these grounds are justifiably regarded as illness; but it is not yet clear whether the same is true of neurotic illness and the ill-defined territory of personality disorder.

What is the significance of this conclusion? First, it is an answer to the argument that there is no such thing as mental illness. At least part of the territory regarded by psychiatrists as mental illness fulfils the same criteria as those required for physical illness. But only part of it does so. Many of the conditions which psychiatrists have come to regard as illness, and hence as required treatment, do not qualify, or rather there is little evidence at present that they do. This does not necessarily mean that psychiatrists have no right to meddle in these areas, or that people who are anxious or depressed should be dissuaded from visiting their doctors. For one thing, childbirth and family planning provide precedents for the involvement of medicine beyond the boundaries of disease.

Even so, psychiatrists might be well advised to reconsider where their sphere of responsibility should end. A century ago they were concerned only with madness. But from that time onwards their concept of their proper role expanded steadily until the stage was reached, particularly in North America, at which some were claiming a mandate—and the ability—to treat anyone whose behaviour was annoying or alarming to other people. It is worth reflecting whether the many attempts we have recently witnessed to discredit the concept of mental illness might not be a reaction to the equally absurd claims we have made that all unhappiness and all undesirable behaviour are manifestations of mental illness.

The attempt to relieve suffering is medicine's oldest and noblest tradition, and I am not suggesting that psychiatrists should stop trying to help husbands and wives to live together in harmony, or aimless adolescents to find their feet. But if we are to venture into such areas let it be in full recognition of the fact that in doing so we may be straying outside our proper boundary, and that in the end it may turn out that other people can deal with such problems as well as or better than we can, and that in these areas their training and their concepts are more appropriate than ours. By all means let us insist that schizophrenia is an illness and that we are better equipped to understand and treat it than anyone else. But let us not try to do the same for all the woes of mankind.

REFERENCES

Alström, C. H. (1942) Mortality in mental hospitals. *Acta Psychiatrica et Neurologica Scandinavica*, Suppl. 24.

Babigian, H. M. & Odoroff, C. L. (1969) The mortality experience of a population with psychiatric illness. *American Journal of Psychiatry,* **126**, 470–80.

Cohen, H. (1943) *The Nature, Method and Purpose of Diagnosis.* Cambridge.

Dahlberg, G. (1933) Die Fruchtbarkeit der Geisteskranken, *Zeitschrift für die gesamte Neurologie und Psychiatrie*, **144**, 427.

Engle, R. L. & Davis, B. J. (1963) Medical diagnosis: past, present and future. I. Present concepts of the meaning and limitations of medical diagnosis. *Archives of Internal Medicine*, **112**, 512–19.

Essen-Möller, E. (1935) Untersuchungen über die Fruchtbarkeit gewisser Gruppen von Geisteskranken. *Acta Psychiatrica et Neurologica Scandinavica*, Suppl. 8.

Eysenck, H. J. (1960) Classification and the problem of diagnosis. In *Handbook of Abnormal Psychology* (ed. Eysenck). London.

——— (1971) Personality and sexual adjustment. *British Journal of Psychiatry*, **118**, 593–608.

Hopkinson, G. (1963) Celibacy and marital fertility in manic-depressive patients. *Acta Psychiatrica Scandinavica*, **39**, 473–6.

Innes, G. & Millar, W. M. (1970) Mortality among psychiatric patients. *Scottish Medical Journal*, **15**, 143–8.

Kräupl Taylor, F. (1971) A logical analysis of the medico-psychological concept of disease. *Psychological Medicine*, **1**, 356–64.

Laing, R. D. (1967) *The Politics of Experience.* Penguin Books.

Larsson, T. & Sjögren, T. (1954) A methodological, psychiatric and statistical study of a large Swedish rural population. *Acta Psychiatrica et Neurologica Scandinavica*, Suppl. 89.

Lewis, A. (1958) Fertility and mental illness. *Eugenics Review*, **50**, 91–106.

Linder, R. (1965) Diagnosis: description or prescription? A case study in the psychology of diagnosis. *Perceptual and Motor Skills*, **20**, 1081–92.

Macsorley, K. (1964) An investigation into the fertility rates of mentally ill patients. *Annals of Human Genetics*, **27**, 247–56.

Malzberg, B. (1953) Rates of discharge and rates of mortality among first admissions to the New York civil state hospitals. *Mental Hygiene*, **37**, 619–54.

Ødegaard, Ø. (1951) Mortality in Norwegian mental hospitals, 1926–41. *Acta Genetica*, **2**, 141–73.

Oldham, P. D., Pickering, G., Fraser Roberts, J. A. & Sowry, G. S. C. (1960) The nature of essential hypertension. *Lancet*, *i*, 1085–93.

Rosenthal, D. (1970) *Genetic Theory and Abnormal Behavior*. New York.

Sainsbury, P. (1968) Suicide and depression. In *Recent Developments in Affective Disorders* (ed. Coppen and Walk). London.

Scadding, J. G. (1967) Diagnosis: the clinician and the computer. *Lancet*, *ii*, 877–82.

Scheff, T. J. (1963) The role of the mentally ill and the dynamics of mental disorder: a research framework. *Sociometry*, **26**, 436–53.

Schneider, K. (1950) Systematic psychiatry. *American Journal of Psychiatry*, **107**, 334–5.

Slater, E. (1945) Neurosis and sexuality. *Journal of Neurology and Psychiatry*, **8**, 12–14.

Stevens, B. C. (1969) *Marriage and Fertility of Women Suffering from Schizophrenia or Affective Disorders* (Maudsley Monograph No. 19.) London.

Szasz, T. S. (1960) The myth of mental illness. *American Psychologist*, **15**, 113–8; or book of same title. London: Secker and Warburg, 1961.

4.8

The Concept of Mental Illness: Explanation or Justification?

Thomas S. Szasz

> Notable enough too, here as elsewhere, wilt though find the potency of Names; which indeed are but one kind of such custom-woven, wonder-hiding Garments. Witchcraft, and all manner of Specterwork, and Demonology, we have now renamed Madness, and Diseases of the Nerves. Seldom reflecting that still the new question comes upon us: What is Madness, What are Nerves?
>
> *Thomas Carlyle* (1795–1881)
> *Sartor Resartus* ([2], p. 280)

I

Why does the concept of 'mental illness' cause continuing difficulties, both philosophical and practical? There are, as I have tried to show for the past twenty years, several reasons for this [7, 11, 12, 14].

One reason is that 'mental illness' is a literalized metaphor; that is, although minds can be sick only in the sense in which remarks can be cutting, people treat mental diseases much as if they were trying to carve their steaks with cutting remarks [10].

Another reason is that although 'mental illness' names a role, it is used as if it named a condition; that is, it points to being a patient, but is used as if it pointed to being sick [7, 8].

A third reason is that although 'mental illness' is a prescriptive term, it is usually used as if it were a descriptive one; that is, its actual linguistic function is like that of the phrase 'Please close the door,' but it is widely used as if it were like that of the phrase 'The door is closed' ([8], pp. 49–67).

I have remarked on all three aspects of the problem of 'mental illness,' but have perhaps written more extensively about the first and second aspects of it than about the third. To be sure, these interpretations or misinterpretations of the term are, in actual usage, often combined—for example, literalized metaphor being used strategically as prescriptive-dispositional injunction. Nevertheless, it has seemed to me that I might best fulfill the task assigned to me for this occasion by concentrating on the third aspect of the problem of mental illness—namely, on its use as prescription concealed as description, as justification disguised as explanation.

II

Typically, an explanation refers to an event, whereas a justification refers to an act. The difference between these terms is much the same as that between things and persons.

For example, we might ask 'How did lightning kill Jones?' We might then be told that it did so by causing him to have ventricular fibrillation and cerebral anoxia.

We might also ask 'Why did lightning kill Jones?' We might then be told that it was because he continued to play golf during a thunderstorm instead of going back to the clubhouse for a drink, as did his friend Smith. It is important to keep in mind that this sort of statement is an assertion about Jones, the victim, not about lightning or some other aspect of the 'cause' of his death.

Our question about why lightning killed Jones may, however, elicit another type of reply, and it is essential that we consider it also. If our interlocutor is a devoutly religious person, or a very mystical one, he might tell us that lightning killed Jones because it was 'God's will' (or something of that sort). What is important about this answer is that it purports to 'explain' an event by assimilating it to the model we use for explaining an action. By imagining God as some sort of superman, death caused by lightning is pictured as God 'taking' a life. This sort of account pleases and satisfies many people because it fulfills the deeply felt human need for legitimizing, or illegitimizing, not only those things that people do to one another but also those that happen to them.

Suppose, however, that Jones was killed not by lightning but by Smith. We might then reasonably ask both how and why Smith acted as he did. The 'how' question seeks to elicit an explanation of Smith's method for causing Jones' death—for example, did he shoot him, poison him or stab him? What, then, does the 'why' question seek? The usual answer is that it seeks an account of Smith's motives or reasons for killing Jones. But this, as I shall now show, is only partly true. Actually, in asking this sort of question about Smith, people usually want to know several things, among which the most obvious and important are: (1) Smith's avowed aim or reason for his act; (2) his 'real' reason;

(3) the authorities' official account of the reason; (4) the psychiatrist's expert opinion about the reason; (5) the defense attorney's claim about the reason; and (6) the jury's judgment about the reason.

Each of the above reasons is, strictly speaking, a claim or a conjecture; none is an explanation or a cause, in the sense in which these latter terms are understood and used in natural science. Nevertheless, when confronted with this sort of situation, most people feel, as it were 'instinctively,' that one or another of the reasons listed is 'true,' and that the others are 'false.' In fact, they may all be 'true,' in the sense that each represents the sincere conviction of the speaker; or they may all be false, in the sense that Smith acted for reasons, perhaps known only to himself, other than any of those articulated in the several conjectures. Let me illustrate this with a simple example.

Suppose that a person observing patrons ordering food in a restaurant is asked why one of the customers, named Smith, ordered hamburger rather than lobster. The observer would, of course, first ask Smith, who might explain that he did so because he prefers hamburger to lobster. The observer himself might conjecture that it was because hamburger is cheaper. Who really knows why Smith chose as he did? In the sense in which we can know the chemical composition of hamburger or lobster, no one can know why anyone orders one or the other. The only honest answer to this sort of 'why' question is to give an account of the reason for the act *as* claim or conjecture, and to acknowledge frankly the *identity of the claimant or conjecturer.*

III

Since being a claimant seems to me to be central to the genesis and phenomenology of the things we call mental illnesses, and since being a claimant is obviously quite peripheral to the genesis and phenomenology of the things we call bodily illnesses, I find it astonishing that this plain fact and basic distinction has been so neglected, not only by psychiatrists but also by philosophers. To illustrate this point, let us consider the situation in which a bodily disease may be discovered and diagnosed without any prior claims of illness by or about the 'patient.' On a routine medical examination for admission to college or entrance into the armed forces it is discovered, on the basis of tests of the subject's urine or blood, that he has diabetes or latent syphilis or leukemia. The subject does not claim that he is ill. No one (prior to the examination) has claimed that he is ill. In short, his illness is diagnosed completely independently of any such claims.

Is it possible to discover mental illness in a person in a similar situation and in a similar way? Clearly, it is not. The diagnosis of mental illness depends wholly on what the subject says about himself, or what others say about him. Moreover, the things that are reported to medical authorities in such contexts are in the nature of claims, some of which may be verifiable by others, but some of which may, by their very nature, not be. I do not see how we can confront the problem of the meaning of 'mental illness' without coming to grips with these typical 'psychiatric claims'—that is, with the sorts of assertions that have historically led, and that often continue to lead, to the diagnosis of mental illness.

In the case of an examination for the draft, the subject may tell the doctor that he wets the bed or that he is a homosexual. These are claims. The assertion about bedwetting is a claim that the subject may be able to verify. The claim about homosexuality may also be verifiable (for example, by a previous arrest for it), or it may be just as unverifiable as the claim of heterosexuality (which the subject would not be expected to verify). In the absence of such claims, mental illness cannot be diagnosed. This, it seems to me, is its most essential characteristic.

Let us pursue this matter of claims a bit further by inspecting some of the historical claims that have given rise to diagnoses of mental illness. These claims have, in the main, been of two types: namely, having pains in the absence of lesions legitimizing them, and not having pleasures in the presence of laws legitimizing them. In traditional psychiatry, claimants of the first type have been classified as suffering from such 'mental diseases' as hysteria, hypochondriasis, and neurasthenia, whereas claimants of the second type have been classified as exhibiting such 'mental symptoms' as frigidity and impotence.

Why do we categorize persons exhibiting such behaviors as sick? Because their alleged diseases are similar to diabetes, or because we want to justify calling the claimants 'patients?' As I have remarked elsewhere, the difference between holy water and ordinary water lies not in the water, but in the priests; similarly, the difference between the claims of so-called mental patients and the claims of other people lies not in the claims but in the medical profession [12, 14]. Thus a woman who is sexually unresponsive to her husband (or other men) is frigid, and frigidity is a paradigmatic symptom of a mental illness. But an orthodox Jew who is alimentarily unresponsive to a ham sandwich (or other pork products) is not said to exhibit any 'symptoms' of any 'mental illness.'

I shall now try to amplify these observations by considering an actual historical paradigm of a mental illness.

IV

Except for what used to be called 'madness' and is now called 'psychosis,' the single most important mental illness, from an historical point of view, is hysteria. This is why I chose it as my model in *The Myth of Mental Illness* [7]. Here

I want to consider briefly—but in sufficient detail to illustrate my argument concerning the role of claims and justifications in the very definition of mental illness—a book on hysteria written in 1917 by the great French neuropsychiatrist Joseph Babinski (1857–1932).

Hysteria, asserts Babinski, quoting with approval Ernest Laségue, 'has never been defined and never will be' ([1], p. 17). Why? Not, as it might seem, because hysteria is not a disease but is nevertheless defined as one, but because the term has been used too loosely. The remedy Babinski recommends is, therefore, to distinguish among the various things that have been placed in this category in the past, to retain some, and to reject others:

> ... it was impossible in former times to define the conditions comprised under this title. Nowadays, it is different. The isolation of the group of phenomena which may be called indifferently hysterical or pithiatic is an accomplished fact. They possess characteristics which belong only to themselves, which are absent in all other morbid states, and which therefore constitute the elements of the definition of hysteria, which I have set forth as follows ([1], p. 17):

I hope the reader is now waiting breathlessly to hear, at last, a 'definition' of hysteria. Babinski is going to tell us what hysteria *is*, just as if it were an object or an event. He is going to 'explain' it, not 'justify' it. Or so he claims:

> Hysteria is a pathological state manifested by disorders which it is possible to reproduce exactly by suggestion in certain subjects and which can be made to disappear by the influence of persuasion (counter-suggestion) alone ([1], p. 17).

Here, then, is one of the leaders of turn-of-the-century French neuropsychiatry 'explaining' hysteria by calling it 'a pathological state manifested by disorders...'—a 'definition' that is, in fact, a justification for his particular way of labeling certain kinds of actors.

Actually, Babinski defines hysteria as acting: he tells us—as I would paraphrase it—that there are two kinds of actors, legitimate and illegitimate. Legitimate actors perform on the stage. Producers and directors ask them to play this role or that, and to cease playing them. We do not call the director's communications 'suggestion' and 'counter-suggestion;' nor do we call the actors' performances 'pathological states.'

Illegitimate actors perform off stage. Psychiatrists ask them to play this role or that, and to cease playing them. We call the psychiatrists' communications 'suggestion' and 'counter-suggestion,' and the players' performances 'pathological states.'

I submit it is as simple as that. Stage actors are legitimate performers off-stage actors are hysterics. Or, we might put it differently, as follows. Some people act sick and doctors accept their act as legitimate: they are the bodily or medically sick patients. Other people act sick and doctors do not accept their act as legitimate: they are the mentally or psychiatrically sick patients. *Mutatis mutandis*, children born to married women are legitimate; those born to unmarried women are illegitimate. In the latter case, we recognize, however, that the 'illegitimacy' of the child is actually a moral judgment about the mother; whereas in the former case we believe that the 'illegitimacy' of the act is a 'symptom' of a medical disease in the actor.

Indeed, Babinski is so naive about his medicalizing of conduct that he candidly admits that he is identifying a disease characterized by the fact that a person can be talked out of having it. He writes:

> There might even be some advantage of abandoning the use of the term hysteria, which in its etymological sense is in no way suitable for any of the phenomena under consideration.... I have proposed the substitution of the term 'pithiatism', from [the Greek for] 'I persuade' and 'curable,' which expresses one of the fundamental characteristics of these symptoms, viz., the possibility of being cured by the influence of persuasion ([1], p. 17).

By 'cured,' Babinski here refers simply to one person telling another to stop doing something, and the latter complying. I could not imagine anything more unlike what is entailed in curing a real disease, such as syphilis.

Having justified hysteria—renamed 'pithiatism'—as an illness, and the 'pithiatic' patient as a sick person 'cured' by 'counter-suggestion,' Babinski has fulfilled his duty as psychiatric patriot: he has conquered an area of personal conduct for pathology. He is ready, next, to fulfill his duty as regular patriot: he must now protect France from pithiatism. With boundless pride he quotes a recommendation for which he was evidently partly responsible:

> ...on October 21, 1915, the [French] Neurological Society sent a recommendation to the Under Secretary of State for the Sanitary Service to the effect that '*no soldier at the present time, under any circumstances, with a psycho-neurosis should be brought before a medical board with a view to discharge from the army.*' (Italics in the original) ([1], p. 229).

On page 17, hysteria is a 'pathological state,' justifying its annexation to medicine; on page 229, it is a condition that under no circumstances justifies discharging the 'patient' from the army. In his recommendation concerning compensation for illness, Babinski reiterates a view that supports a policy quite inconsistent with viewing hysteria as an illness, but quite consistent with viewing it as an act (which may be called malingering, simulation, claiming to be ill, or playing patient):

> At a recent meeting of the representatives of the neurological centers (December 15, 1916) to discuss the subject of 'Discharges from the Army, Disabilities and Allowances in the Neuroses,' the questions with which we have dealt in this book were discussed from the point of view of a medical board, and the conclusions of

> a report drawn up by one of us were adopted to serve as the groundwork for the next edition of *The Ready Reckoner of Disabilities*. They are of interest to all medical officers, and may therefore be reproduced here. They are as follows: 1. For purely hysterical or pithiatic disorders: no discharge nor allowances ([1], p. 234).

Babinski's dilemma, his apparently complete obliviousness to it, and the consequent glaring inconsistencies in his claims about hysteria continue to be very relevant to the problems facing contemporary psychiatrists: like Babinski, they too would like to expand or contract the category of disease according to whether they seek their rewards from medical or military (or other) authorities.

As a medical patriot, Babinski saw his duty as declaring as many men as possible to be sick; whereas as a French patriot, he saw it as declaring as many men as possible to be fit for military service. He thus exemplifies the 'great' psychiatrists whom he imitated, and who in turn imitated him: he could conceive of no intellectual or moral duty other than serving Medicine or the State.

V

Babinski was, of course, neither the first nor the last to resort to the rhetoric of madness to conceal denigration as diagnosis. While I have been unable to trace this practice to its earliest origins, I have, in my search for these origins, found some remarkable examples of it. Here is one from the fourth century:

> Emperors Gratian, Valentinian, and Theodosius Augustuses: An Edict to the People of the City of Constantinople.
> It is Our will that all the people who are ruled by the administration of Our Clemency shall practice that religion which the divine Peter the Apostle transmitted to the Romans... We command that those persons who follow this rule shall embrace the name of Catholic Christians. The rest, however, whom we adjudge demented and insane, shall sustain the infamy of heretical dogmas, their meeting places shall not receive the name of churches, and they shall be smitten first by divine vengeance and secondly by the retribution of Our own initiative, which We shall assume in accordance with the divine judgment ([4], p. 440).

This prescription—ostensibly describing as 'demented and insane' those who reject the Catholic faith—was issued 'on the third day before the kalends of March, at Thessalonica, in the year of the fifth consulship of Gratian Augustus and the first consulship of Theodosius Augustus' (February 28, 380) ([4], p. 440). It forms a part of the *Codex Theodosianus*, or the *Theodosian Law Codes*, published in their final form in 438, and constituting then the essential body of Roman Law.

In keeping with this law, in the fourth century 'heretics' were categorized as 'demented and insane' by the priests, and persecuted 'in accordance with divine judgment.' *Mutatis mutandis*, in the twentieth century, 'heretics' are categorized as 'psychotic and schizophrenic' by psychiatrists, and persecuted 'in accordance with diagnostic judgment.'

Moving from the sublime to the ridiculous, or at least from the theological to the theatrical, here is an illustration from the recent literature of my contention that psychiatric diagnostic terms are sadly lacking in descriptive content. Peter Shaffer's play *Equus* was a great theatrical success in America, despite an attack on it by a Harvard psychiatrist. Sanford Gifford, the psychiatrist, characterized the play in the *New York Times* as a 'fictitious piece of psychopathology. The basic ingredient in the central character's syndrome is hysteria...' ([5], p. 11). He had some quite nasty things to say about the play which are fortunately not relevant to our present concerns.

I mention *Equus* and Gifford's attack on it because in September, 1975, the magazine *Frontiers of Psychiatry*, published by the Roche pharmaceutical company, devoted a whole issue to the psychiatric implications of the play. In it, there appeared the following remarkable footnote. (in small print):

> Since the American Psychiatric Association task force that is preparing the third edition of the *Diagnostic and Statistical Manual* has announced its intention to delete hysteria as a diagnostic term from Category VII, Hysterical Disorders, Roche Report informally questioned four psychiatrists (one, a specialist in diagnostic terms; another, a child analyst), three psychologists, and four social workers, all of whom had seen *Equus*, and asked them how they would diagnose the boy as he presented at the hospital. There were nine different opinions, ranging from 'adolescent episode' through 'transient psychosis' to 'schizophrenic break.' Two psychiatrists took the Fifth Amendment ([1], p. 6).

What should we make of this? We might use this incriminating poll to justify our contemp to psychiatry—which would be a good thing, so far as it went: but it would trap us into adopting the same sort of behavior toward psychiatrists that psychiatrists exhibit toward patients. Can we do better? I think so—by concluding that psychiatrists are, in fact, crypto-priests, and that their job is to bless and to damn. Holy water is holy not because of the kind of water it is, but because a priest has blessed it. A schizophrenic patient is schizophrenic not because of the sort of person he is but because a psychiatrist has damned him [12, 14].

Suppose that, in accordance with the 'diagnostic' manual of the *Theodosian Law Codes*, a person has been declared 'insane.' Clearly, that term did not, and was not intended to, describe his beliefs: such a person might have been a believer in many Roman gods, in one Jewish god, or in no god. But the theological diagnosticians of that age were not interested in classifying his *beliefs*; they were interested in classifying *him*. They were not interested in *understanding* his beliefs; they were interested in *justifying* their own condemnation and destruction of him.

Similarly, when a playwright now offers us a dramatic encounter between a modern madman and his mad-doctor, and when psychiatrists are asked to 'diagnose' the 'patient,' it is hardly surprising that they make nearly as many diagnoses as there are diagnosticians. After all, the diagnostic terms they are supposed to produce, in response to such a query, are all the synonyms of the ancient term 'insane:' they are all psychiatric terms of abuse, not descriptive terms referring to any actual human behavior.

Ironically, the real description of behavior in plays such as *Equus*—or *Hamlet*, or *King Lear*—is in the plays themselves. The work of art—the play, the performance—is, as it were, the 'science.' The psychiatric 'explanation' of such behavior thus not only lacks any genuine descriptive content, but is actually a distortion, and a vertiable destruction, of precisely the sorts of 'data' that constitute the raw materials of science. Indeed, the 'denaturing' or 'falsification' of the 'data' of direct observation and plain reporting is what psychiatry is all about. A few remarks about this process may be in order here.

VI

What is industrial alcohol? It is 'denatured' alcohol—that is, pure alcohol made unfit for human consumption.

I submit that 'mental illness' stands in the same sort of relationship to human behavior as industrial alcohol stands to ethanol. Distilleries produce alcohol that is, more or less, chemically pure. It requires the active intervention of human beings to make this 'natural' product 'unnatural:' hence the apt name for it, 'denatured alcohol.' Similarly, human beings 'produce' behavior. They act. They speak. It requires the active intervention of human beings to make these 'natural' products 'unnatural:' hence the revealing names for such acts—'perversion,' 'delusion,' 'psychosis.'

Let us take a simple example. A man declares that he is Jesus. What shall we make of it?

First, we might take it for just what it is: a person asserting that he is the Savior.

Second, we might respond to it plainly, matching it against our own knowledge of the world: a person asserting a false identity; in short, a liar.

Third, we might respond to it psychiatrically, matching it against our knowledge of psychiatry: a person displaying a delusion; in short, a psychotic.

The question we must face is this: is the psychiatric account of such behavior a more abstract and 'scientific' description, or even explanation, of such behavior, or is it the distortion and redefinition of it? I have argued that it is, overwhelmingly, the latter. I thus hold that learning psychiatry is largely a matter of learning to see human behavior—perhaps even the whole world—through the distorting lenses of this fake science. People who learn this lesson—whether as professional psychiatrists or as laymen 'educated' in mental health—thus learn, first of all, that there are two kinds of behavior, and two kinds of people, in the world—mentally healthy and mentally sick. Having learned that lesson, they are ready to tackle the problem of 'understanding mental illness.'

This approach and perspective are exemplified by virtually every psychiatric publication. A recent article entitled 'Some Myths about "Mental Illness",' by Michael S. Moore, a professor of law at the University of Kansas is typical. One of Moore's conclusions, offered at the end of a long argument based on a mixture of a few assertions I have made and of many I have not, is this:

> No one merits society's condemnation or punishment unless they are morally blameworthy, and no one is blameworthy if he acts as he does because of his mental disease. Szasz's conclusion is reminiscent of the Erewhonian practice of punishing the ill, and evokes in most of us the same distaste ([3], p. 1495).

I should like to note that Moore actually packs two mistakes into a single sentence:

(1) By asserting that no one merits punishment who is not blameworthy, he implies that by treating 'mentally ill' people as 'mentally ill' we do not punish them; but by treating them as if they were not 'mentally ill' we do, *ipso facto*, punish them.

(2) He also asserts that some people act as they do *because* of their 'mental disease.'

I disagree with the second assertion. But that is not the point here. The point is that Moore adduces no evidence in support of the view that some people act as they do because of their mental illness, and others because of another 'cause.' What, one wonders, could that 'cause' be? Free will?

As to the second assertion, Moore surely must have heard, before Andrei Sakharov announced it in his Nobel lecture, that 'Worst of all is the hell that exists in the special psychiatric clinics' [6]. Yet Moore claims that by opposing involuntary psychiatric interventions I propose to 'punish the ill.' This is a typical instance of the breakdown of language between the adherents to psychiatric true belief and psychiatric agnostics. The true believers assert, with Moore, that:

> Since mental illness negates our assumptions of rationality, we do not hold the mentally ill responsible. It is not so much that we excuse them from a *prima facie* case of responsibility; rather, by being unable to regard them as fully rational beings, we cannot affirm the essential condition to viewing them as moral agents to begin with. In this the mentally ill join (to a decreasing degree) infants, wild beasts, plants, and stones—none of which are [*sic*] responsible because of the absence of any assumption of rationality ([3], p. 1496).

To which I reply: If this is not using language to dehumanize and destroy persons then I do not know what is. Moore here reasserts the proposition that some individuals who seem to be persons are, in fact, not; they ought to be classed with 'wild beasts, plants, and stones.'

There is, of course, nothing new about this idea. Nor is there anything new about the irreconcilable conflicts such 'religious' controversies generate. On this occasion, it must suffice to state, or restate, the terms of the controversy. The supporters of the concept of mental illness claim that 'madmen' are like plants and we should, in order to be 'good' to them, treat them as if they were plants. I say that 'madmen' are persons and that we should treat them as if they were.

VII

The view that 'mental illnesses' have to do with claiming and justifying, rather than with diseases and treatments, helps to explain why psychiatry has traditionally been linked to the law in ways quite unlike the rest of medicine. Like psychiatry, the law deals with conduct and with the justification of conduct.

Indeed, Anglo—American law is premised on, and displays, precisely the sort of understanding of human acts which I have sketched—and which is obscured by psychiatry; and it is aimed at resolving conflicting claims between persons fairly and consistently—a process which psychiatry renders unfair and capricious. In both civil and criminal trials, the arbiters assume that plaintiff and defendant, prosecuting attorney and defense attorney, each presents different claims and conjectures about why the protagonists in the judicial drama acted as they did. It is up to the jury to develop its own conjectures, whose consequences the court then imposes on the litigants. The jury, or court, does so not because it is more intelligent or more honest than the participants in the litigation, but because it is more neutral than they are, and because it has the authority and the power to do so.

Psychiatric 'expert' testimony distorts, and indeed destroys, this judicial arrangement in which facts are reasonably well demarcated from opinions. The reason for this is that in so far as the psychiatrist testifies about why a person acted as he did, he offers a conjecture which, however, is widely defined and accepted as a cause. This is epitomized by the belief—now authoritatively accepted as scientifically 'correct' or 'true'—that some people kill because they hate their victims, others because they want their money, and still others because they 'have schizophrenia.' Mental illness as a cause, and murder as a product of it, must thus be seen for what it is: not just a mistaken idea, but the manifestation of the judicial acceptance—and indeed acclaim—of the psychiatrist as scientist of the mind.

I maintain that it is precisely this acceptance of psychiatry as a legitimate science that is responsible for two closely interrelated phenomena: the corruption of the administration of justice in the courtroom; and the confusion of the nature of human behavior in the classroom. Each of these processes has, of course, consequences that extend far beyond the actual locations of these 'rooms.'

Suppose that astrology were accepted as a legitimate science, and that astrologers were allowed to testify in court the way psychiatrists now are. We might then have the spectacle of one set of astrologers testifying that, because of the constellation of planets on the night of a particular murder, the accused was not responsible for his act; while another set of astrologers, basing its 'expert opinion' on ostensibly the same 'data,' would testify that the accused was responsible for his act. If, despite this kind of astrological testimony, astrology would continue to enjoy the unqualified support of the scientific community, then astrological 'theories' would seriously interfere with our understanding of the nature of human behavior. Indeed, this is no idle analogizing. We saw this very thing happen with theological theories concerning witchcraft and their impact on both the popular and 'scientific' understanding of human behavior [9].

The fact, then, that psychiatry is an accepted field of science—it is taught in medical schools next to subjects such as biochemistry and physiology; it is supported by the government; and it is accepted in courts of law as if it had 'methods' similar to those of ballistics or toxicology—exercises a significant influence on the very 'observations' about which its practitioners supposedly possess 'expert' knowledge. The concept of 'mental illness' itself, as I tried to show elsewhere [7], embodies and epitomizes this fatal prejudgment—namely, that 'scientists' have identified a phenomenon which they, and we, must try to understand. But the term 'mental illness' does not identify any clearcut phenomenon or class of phenomena; instead, it is a piece of self-justificatory rhetoric that precludes our understanding of the very problems we are supposed to be trying to understand.

VIII

In actuality what determines whether a person's sanity is called into question is not what he, as an actor, does, but rather what the authorities, as his audience, think about it. As a rule, behavior deemed to be good or desirable is accepted without further justification, whereas behavior deemed to be bad or undesirable is not. Hence it is that people now turn to psychiatrists to explain why someone committed a bad deed, but do not turn to them to explain why someone committed a good deed. Thus, confronted with a person who destroys life, say by killing many people, the most natural thing to do now is to ask psychiatrists to 'explain' why he did so; and the most 'scientific' thing is to accept that he did so because of his 'mental illness.' However, confronted by a person who preserves life, say by discovering how to prevent or cure a disease, the most absurd thing to do would be to ask a psychiatrist to explain why he did so; and the most 'unscientific' thing would be to accept that he did so because of his 'mental illness.'

In other words, although we speak about medical diseases when we are confronted by deviations from biological norms, and about mental diseases when we are confronted by deviations from behavioral norms, only in the former case do we designate deviations from the norm as 'diseases' regardless of the direction the deviation takes. Thus, whether a person has too many white corpuscles or too few, he is said to have a disease. This is not true for behavioral 'abnormalities,' virtually all of which designate deviations from the norm in one particular direction—that is, toward the immoral or illegal. For example, psychiatrists consider persons who are more wicked than the norm 'sick' and call his disease 'psychopathy,' but they do not consider persons who are more virtuous than the norm sick and have no 'disease' corresponding to psychopathy to 'explain' their behavior. This discrepancy between our attitude toward 'explaining' good and bad deeds should alone suffice to show how pervasively we have confused justifications of human behavior with their explanations.

Although all this might be obvious to some, the fact remains that the whole history of institutional psychiatry is characterized by, and is the consequence of, the experts' insistence that what needs attending to is not the public or professional acceptance or rejection of acts, leading to their justification or nonjustification— but the actor's sanity or insanity [11]. By consistently asking the wrong questions—'wrong' in the sense that they are psychiatrically self-serving, rather than phenomenologically significant—psychiatrists, and all who have accepted their premises, could come up with nothing but wrong answers.

IX

The fact that the phrases found in textbooks of psychiatry are in the main justifications rather than explanations goes a long way toward accounting for the stubborn disjunctions between avowed claims and actual conduct so characteristic of the behavior of both mental patients and psychiatrists. For example, a person, likely to be diagnosed schizophrenic, may declare: I am the Messiah, God commands me to save the world, and to do so I must kill so-and-so.' The 'patient's' putative aim is to 'save the world,' to do good. However, his actual conduct, as judged by the recipients of his benevolence, is deemed to be 'dangerous' and 'harmful,' with consequences all too familiar.

The situation with respect to the psychiatrist is much the same, with the roles reversed. He declares: 'I am a doctor, my medical training and ethic command me that I help sick people, and to do so I must treat so-and-so for his schizophrenia.' The doctor's putative aim is to help the 'patient,' to treat him for his 'disease.' However, his actual conduct, as judged by the recipients of his benevolence, is deemed to be not treatment but torture, with consequences again all too familiar.

Such disjunctions between putative aims and actual performances cannot long stand unresolved. In the modern world they are resolved, at least in the areas I am here considering, by the simple expedient of substituting authority for evidence, power for compassion, force for reason. Thus, when the majority, the government, and science—through its duly appointed agents and agencies—declare, as they do in the case of mad-doctoring, that its actual performances are the same as, or closely approximate, its putative objectives, the disjunction between the 'doctor's' self-serving aims and his other-damaging acts is instantly resolved. Indeed, it is better than resolved: it is defined out of existence.

Similarly, when the majority, the government, and science—through their duly appointed agents and agencies—declare, as they do in the case of madness, that both its putative objectives and actual performances are the meaningless 'symptoms' of a medical disorder, the disturbing disjunction between the self-serving aims of the 'madman' and his other-damaging acts is again instantly resolved. And again it is better than resolved: it is defined out of existence. Henceforth, both of these disjunctions can be recognized and addressed only at the risk of insulting established professional beliefs and practices, and incurring the risks customarily accompanying such behavior.

In my opinion, herein lie the fundamental ideological, economic, and political sources of the difficulties that face the contemporary student of psychiatry. Countless psychiatric principles today are based on, or articulate, deliberate deceptions—such as calling people who reject medical help 'patients' and the buildings in which they are imprisoned 'hospitals.' And countless psychiatric practices today consist of nothing but crass coercions—such as the incarceration of innocent persons under psychiatric auspices called 'mental hospitalization.' These dramatic disjunctions between putative objectives and actual performances, pervasive of all institutional psychiatry, are now supported by both church and state, law and science. Accordingly, the psychiatric scholar's first task must be to re-assert, the evidence of his naked eyes and ears. For it is of little use to explain, justify, or modify policies that linguistically entail events as facts which are actually frauds, and that morally authenticate aims as medical and technical albeit actually they are moral and political.

X

In conclusion I should like to restate one of the central arguments that I have been making about psychiatry for the past twenty years or more, and that I have also made in this essay.

I do not assert, as some of my critics claim, that psychiatry is not a science because it deals with non-existent things, such as 'mental illnesses.' I assert that psychiatry is not a science because its practitioners are basically hostile to the ethic of truth-telling. Why should this be so? Assuredly not because psychiatrists are bad people; they are, on the whole, no better or worse than other people. Instead, it is because the ethic of truth-telling, as it is institutionalized in modern science, is not found outside of the narrow border of science. Politicians and priests, lawyers and theologians are all important and respectable members of society; but the crafts they practice are not based on truth-telling.

If, as I claim, truth-telling is the essential ethical-linguistic 'method' of science, what is the corresponding 'method' that characterizes such professions or groups as priests, politicians, and psychiatrists? It is the telling of literalized metaphors, strategic myths, and even of calculated mendacities—which are designed to advance not only the interests of the speaker but also those of his 'club.' Whatever else priests, politicians, and psychiatrists may say or do, they must, to remain in good standing, protect and promote the greater glory of God, the fatherland, and 'mental health.' This is why, strictly speaking, there can be no sciences of priesthood, politics, or psychiatry; there can be only criticisms of them.

BIBLIOGRAPHY

1. Babinski, J. and Froment, J.: 1918, *Hysteria or Pithiatism*, trans. by J. D. Rolleston, University of London Press, London.
2. Carlyle, T.: 1890, *Sartor Resartus*, Home Book Co., New York.
3. Moore, M. S.: 1975, 'Some Myths about "Mental Illness"', *Archives of General Psychiatry* **32**, 1483–1497.
4. Pharr, C.: 1952, *The Theodosian Code and Novels and the Sirmondian Constitutions*, Princeton University Press, Princeton.
5. Point of View: 1975, 'Playwright Peter Shaffer Raps American Normalcy, Conformity, Psychotherapy', *Roche Report: Frontiers of Psychiatry* **5**, 1–2, 5–11.
6. Sakharov, A.: 1975, 'Excerpts from the Nobel Lecture', *The New York Times*, Dec. 13, p. 6.
7. Szasz, T.S.: 1961, *The Myth of Mental Illness*, Hoeber-Harper, New York.
8. Szasz, T.S.: 1970, *Ideology and Insanity*, Doubleday Anchor, Garden City, New York.
9. Szasz, T.S.: 1970, *The Manufacture of Madness*, Harper and Row, New York.
10. Szasz, T.S.: 1970, 'Mental Illness as a Metaphor', *Nature* **242**, 305–307.
11. Szasz, T.S.: 1973, *The Age of Madness*, Doubleday Anchor, Garden City, New York.
12. Szasz, T.S.: 1973, *The Second Sin*, Doubleday Anchor, Garden City, New York.
13. Szasz, T.S.: 1974, *Ceremonial Chemistry*, Doubleday Anchor, Garden City, New York.
14. Szasz, T.S.: 1976, *Heresies*, Doubleday Anchor, Garden City, New York.

4.9

Szasz on Mental Illness

Baruch Brody

Dr. Szasz tells us that he will argue that the concept of mental illness causes continuing difficulties because it is a prescriptive concept being used as though it were a descriptive concept, a justificatory concept disguised as an explanatory concept. If his arguments were correct, then he would certainly have spotted a fundamental difficulty with the current use of that concept. I do not know whether or not Dr. Szasz's claim is ultimately correct; all that I shall try to show in my remarks is that Dr. Szasz's arguments for this claim fail.

Two preliminary points. First, by his own account of what he is trying to establish, the most that Dr. Szasz can hope to show is that there is something wrong with the current use of our concepts of mental illness, not that there is something inherently wrong with those concepts. That stronger thesis, which I believe Dr. Szasz holds, would require a different argument. Secondly, there is a confusion in Szasz's account of how the concepts of mental illness are misused. He sometimes says that they are mistakenly used as descriptive concepts, but on other occasions he says that they are mistakenly used as explanatory concepts. Now, in general, a description is not equivalent to an explanation. I may describe what has happened by saying that John killed Frank. That description provides us with no explanation of what has happened. It would seem, therefore, that descriptive concepts (concepts used in descriptions) are not necessarily identical with explanatory concepts (concepts used in explanations).

In light of these two points, it would probably be best to take Dr. Szasz's thesis to be: the current use of concepts of mental illness creates difficulties because it uses a prescriptive concept (one used to justify certain behavior towards people) as though it described or explained the behavior and state of the people in question.

I. MENTAL ILLNESS AND CLAIMANTS

In Sections II and III of his paper, Dr. Szasz sets out an argument that diagnoses of mental illness are necessarily claim-based diagnoses and are, therefore, an attempt to justify certain types of treatment rather than a description and explanation. I frankly do not see either why he accepts his premises or why he thinks that the conclusion follows from them.

Dr. Szasz usually seems to have the following in mind when he says that diagnoses of mental illness are necessarily claim-based: in order to carry through such diagnoses, it is necessary to consider either the claims that the person makes about himself and his own behavior or the claims that others make. This is unlike the case of bodily illness in which such claims *need* not be considered (of course, they may be helpful in suggesting diagnoses, but the crucial point is that they need not be considered).

This thesis seems wrong. Do we not, if necessary, advance diagnoses of people by considering their publicly observable behavioral patterns and without considering the claims that they and others make? (One case of this is when they advance no such claims.) Consider, for example, Dr. Szasz's own example:

> In the case of an examination for the draft, the subject may tell the doctor that he wets the bed or that he is a homosexual. These are claims. The assertion about bedwetting is a claim that the subject may be able to verify. The claim about homosexuality may also be verifiable... or it may be just as unverifiable as the claim of heterosexuality... In the absence of such claims, mental illness cannot be diagnosed ([1], p. 238).

The last part of this quotation is just wrong. Homosexuality and bedwetting are patterns of publicly observable behavior that can be noted and verified (and can serve as the basis for diagnoses) without any claims being advanced by anyone.

It is, of course, harder to advance diagnoses on the basis of facts that are not publicly observable, e.g., that someone fails to take pleasure in any form of sexual behavior. Here, the claims that these people make about their failures are of great help. Once more, however, there are behavioral indications of taking pleasure or failing to take pleasure, and if necessary, we can and do make diagnoses based upon these indications. Similarly, we cannot observe Smith's motives for killing Jones, and it is very helpful (in understanding Smith' behavior), to have his claims about his motives. If we do not have them, however, we can make do (often very well) by investigating the circumstances in question and Smith's own behavior.

In short, then, Szasz's assertion that diagnoses of mental illness cannot be advanced and confirmed without the claims of the person in question or others, is just false. In fact, our remarks so far have been far too generous to Szasz's thesis. We have seemed to grant that the claims made by people, while not necessary, are at least the best basis for such diagnoses. Whether this is or is not so depends on many factors, the veracity of those making the claims, their ability to avoid self-deception, etc. The truth of the matter is that such claims are at best viewed as just further behavioral evidence to be used in the making of diagnoses of mental illness, and they occupy no special status.

Sometimes, Dr. Szasz seems to have something else in mind when he talks about diagnosis as a claim-based activity. He sometimes is asserting that diagnoses are only conjectured; we cannot know, for example, Smith's motives, we can only make conjectures. We cannot know for sure whether a woman is frigid, we can only make conjectures. But if this is what he has in mind, that is not something that is special to the diagnosis of mental illness. Much of our diagnoses of bodily illness is equally conjectural.

Suppose, however, that the diagnosis of mental illness is a claim-based activity. Why should Szasz suppose that this entails that such diagnoses are prescriptive jusificatory claims masquerading as descriptive or explanatory claims? The closest that he comes is the following passage (where he emphasizes the conjectural element of such diagnoses):

> Each of the above reasons is, strictly speaking, a claim or a conjecture; none is an explanation or a cause in the sense in which the latter terms are understood and used in natural science. Nevertheless, when confronted with this sort of situation, most people feel, as it were 'instinctively,' that one or another of the reasons listed is 'true,' and that the others are 'false.' In fact, they may all be 'true,' in the sense that each represents the sincere conviction of the speaker; or they may all be false, in the sense that Smith acts for reasons, perhaps known only to himself, other than any of those articulated in the several conjectures... The only honest answer to this sort of 'why' question is to give an account of the reason for the act *as* claim or conjecture, and to acknowledge frankly the *identity of the claimant or conjecturer* ([1], p. 237).

I find this passage one mess of confusion: (a) each of the claims may be conjectures, but that does not prevent them from being conjectures of what is the explanation or cause of the behavior in question; (b) moreover, and most crucially, this does not mean that all of the conjectures are on an equal epistemological plateau. Some of them (perhaps the claim of the agent, perhaps the conjectures of others) may have the backing of much more behavioral evidence than the others, and may, therefore, be regarded as likely to be true, even if not certainly true; (c) the situation here is really no different than in the search for causes in the natural sciences. The search for causes is a conjectural search, that may never lead to certainty, but which does lead to hypotheses likely to be true.

What has gone wrong here? I think that Dr. Szasz has failed to understand the basic epistemological relation between people's behavior and our hypotheses about their mental life, both healthy and diseased. With a proper understanding of these relations, one can see the failure of Szasz's first major argument against the descriptive or explanatory content of the concept of mental illness.

II. MENTAL ILLNESS AND NON-NORMAL BEHAVIOR

At a number of points in his paper, Dr. Szasz argues for his thesis by appealing to the relation between our classifying a type of behavior as a form of mental illness and our evaluating that behavior. The following passage is typical:

> In other words, although we speak about medical diseases when we are confronted by deviations from biological norms, and about mental diseases when we are confronted by deviations from behavioral norms, only in the former case do we designate deviations from the norm as 'diseases' regardless of the direction the deviation takes. Thus, whether a person has too many white corpuscles or too few, he is said to have a disease. This is not true for behavioral 'abnormalities,' virtually all of which designate deviations from the norm in one particular direction—that is, toward the immoral or the illegal. For example, psychiatrists consider persons who are more wicked than the norm 'sick' and call his disease 'psychopathy,' but they do not consider persons who are more virtuous than the norm sick and have no 'disease' corresponding to psychopathy to 'explain' their behavior. This discrepancy between our attitude toward 'explaining' good and bad deeds should alone suffice to show how pervasively we have confused justifications of human behavior with their explanations ([1], p. 247).

I find in this argument, as in the last, difficulties both with the premises and the transition to the conclusion.

To begin with, it seems just false that only deviations from the norm in the direction of immoral or illegal behavior are considered diseased behavior patterns. The person who washes his hands two hundred times a day behaves in a pattern that we describe and/or explain by reference to concepts of mental illness although his behavior is neither immoral nor illegal. The person who is terrified of enclosed spaces and refuses to enter elevators behaves in a pattern that we describe and/or explain by reference to concepts of mental illness although his behavior is neither immoral nor illegal.

Secondly, it seems just false that any deviation from a biological norm is a bodily disease. People who are considerably taller than normal, people with unusually shaped noses, people with unusually brilliant red hair, are all people who deviate from biological norms but are not diseased. There are indeed, many types of deviations from biological norms that are physical assets rather than diseases. Examples that immediately come to mind are unusual strength, especially keen sight, etc.

These remarks raise, of course, a very fundamental problem about the concept of a disease. What type of deviation from the norm constitutes a disease? In fact, can there be a disease that is a norm? Is it a function of the survival disvalue of the deviation? Is it a function of some essentialist conception of a well-functioning human being? Is it a function of some social disvalue of the deviation? These questions arise for both mental and physical diseases, and I cannot now attempt to deal with them. All that I can say at this point is that Szasz's account, which is the premise of his argument, is clearly wrong.

Suppose, however, that there is some element of truth in Szasz's account, suppose that we only describe something as an illness if we disvalue it. Does that entail that concepts of mental illness are only justificatory of our responses to behavior and are not explanations and/or descriptions of it as well? I do not see why it is supposed to entail the conclusion. Szasz presumably has in mind the following: given that we have picked out as diseased only socially objectionable forms of behavior, we clearly are doing so to justify certain treatments of the people in question. Suppose that this is true; it still does not follow that the concepts in question cannot also be descriptive and/or explanative.

This leads me to my second major conclusion about Dr. Szasz's arguments. Much as he is wrong about the relation between mental illness and behavioral patterns, so he is confused about the relation between the prescriptive and the descriptive and/or explanative. These concepts are not mutually exclusive; there is no reason why a concept cannot have both descriptive and prescriptive content. Consider the familiar example of the concept of an apple. A good apple must satisfy certain descriptive criteria and yet calling something a good apple prescribes choosing it if one wants a good apple. There is no reason, similarly, why mental-illness concepts cannot be both descriptive and prescriptive.

At one point, Szasz sets forth the following argument for doubting that concepts of mental illness have any descriptive content:

> Similarly, when a playwright now offers us a dramatic encounter between a modern madman and his mad-doctor, and when psychiatrists are asked to 'diagnose' the 'patient,' it is hardly surprising that they make nearly as many diagnoses as there are diagnosticians. After all, the diagnostic terms they are supposed to produce, in response to such a query, are all the synonyms of the ancient term 'insane:' they are all psychiatric terms of abuse, not descriptions referring to any actual human behavior ([1], p. 243).

There is, I think, something of a point here. Psychiatric terms are not as well-defined as most medical terms; there certainly are few operational definitions of such terms. But, of course, none of this entails that they do not refer to any actual human behavior. It shows at best that their mode of reference is indirect, and one of the fundamental lessons of modern philosophy of science is that theoretical terms refer to observational data only in this indirect fashion. So nothing much follows from what is right in this last remark of Szasz's.

III. ON BABINSKI

In advancing his argument, Dr. Szasz devotes much space to Babinski's account of hysteria as illustrative of his thesis. I do not see what it is supposed to illustrate, but let me in any case point out a number of further confusions in Szasz's treatment of that case.

Babinski's definition of hysteria is clearly inadequate, for it fails to deal with Szasz's counter-example of the actor. Still, what follows? Our not treating the actor the way we treat the patient can be justified by the context surrounding that behavior, and that context also provides the descriptive difference between the actor and the patient. So unless we are not allowed to count contextual features, and all concepts of mental illness certainly must involve these features, we can provide adequate descriptive criteria for hysteria.

Szasz also finds it very revealing that Babinski defines hysteria as a disease that one can be talked out of. He writes:

> By 'cured,' Babinski here refers simply to one person telling another to stop doing something, and the latter complying. I could not imagine anything more unlike what is entailed in curing a real disease, such as syphilis ([1], p. 240).

There is no doubt that curing a case of hysteria is unlike curing a case of syphilis (as, no doubt, contracting a case of one is very unlike contracting a case of the other). But why is that supposed to be problematic? The crucial resemblance between the two cures is the modification of the condition of the patient so that the disease is no longer present. As long as the concept of the disease is satisfactory (and Szasz has yet to show anything wrong with it), the concept of a cure will be acceptable.

Finally, Dr. Szasz is extremely unhappy about Babinski's going on to argue against medical discharges based upon hysteria. How, he seems to ask, can Babinski really treat hysteria as a disease and yet argue against using it as a basis for discharging soldiers? A number of arguments actually come to mind: (1) the difficulty of telling real cases of hysteria from sham cases; (2) France's desperation required it to use diseased soldiers; (3) the disease may still allow soldiers to fight adequately. I do not say that Babinski was right. In fact, I do not know what led him to his conclusion. All that I want to claim is that Szasz has failed to establish an inconsistency in Babinski's approach to hysteria.

IV. CONCLUSION

Dr. Szasz may well be right. But if he wants to show that he is right, he will have to present more substantial and careful arguments than the ones that he does present.

REFERENCE

1. Szasz, Thomas S.: 1977, 'The Concept of Mental Illness: Explanation or Justification', in this volume, pp. 235–250.

Part 5

Contemporary Analysis of Disease and Health

Much of the current discussion about health and disease focuses on whether the criteria used to define these terms are discovered or invented. Earlier disputes about the ontological status of disease appear in current disputes as arguments over whether or not disease and health can be identified on the basis of certain physiological and psychological functions natural to human beings. Proponents of the biomedical mode of disease, as described by Fabrega, Veatch, and Boorse, believe that a set of functions necessary for human life can be described and specified. These functions are reflected in the purposive or teleological organization of the various parts of the human body. Any impairment of normal, natural function, for example, respiration, excretion, or digestion, under normal environmental circumstances ought to be considered a state of disease on the biomedical model.

Many writers, such as Margolis, Veatch, Fabrega, and Engel, have challenged the adequacy of analyzing disease as dysfunction and health as normal function. These authors argue that health and disease can be understood only in terms of a set of normative value judgments. Functional analysis, these authors maintain, is ultimately a matter of values and, thus, invention—not simply description. To know what normal function means, the social, cultural, and personal norms that are present for a particular person must be analyzed.

The biomedical model is criticized in these selections on a number of other grounds. Many of the authors note that the biomedical model is not useful in the study, diagnosis, and treatment of illness—understood as a subjective mental state. Others note that the biomedical model is more prescriptive than descriptive, leading researchers and clinicians to prefer biochemical therapies over social reforms or verbal interventions.

Much of the dispute among the views presented in this section centers around the role played by values in functional assessments. Part of the difficulty with resolving this issue is the vagueness that surrounds the term "value." This term may not be clearly understood by all the participants in current debates over the definition of health and disease. Since many types of values may enter into the analysis of health and disease in a variety of ways—as indicators of the scope of the concepts, as adjuncts to the causal analysis of function, as variables for determining therapy—greater specificity may be required if the role of values is, ultimately, to be properly understood.

5.1

The Concept of Illness Behavior

David Mechanic, Ph.D.

One of the principal tasks of the medical sciences is to understand and determine the conditions under which particular symptoms or disease entities arise either in individuals or among groups of individuals. Public health physicians have the further problem of effecting the arrival of "ill" persons at medical settings so that treatment can be effectively administered. Whether we concern ourselves with the necessary conditions for building adequate etiological theories or those for bringing treatment to persons most in need of such help, it is necessary that we understand the influence of a variety of norms, values, fears, and expected rewards and punishments on how a symptomatic person behaves.

Such considerations lead us to propose a concept of *illness behaviour*. By this term we refer to the ways in which given symptoms may be differentially perceived, evaluated, and acted (or not acted) upon by different kinds of persons. Whether by reason of earlier experiences with illness, differential training in respect to symptoms, or whatever, some persons will make light of symptoms, shrug them off, and avoid seeking medical care; others will respond to the slightest twinges of pain or discomfort by quickly seeking such medical care as is available. In short, the realm of illness behaviour falls logically and chronologically between two major traditional concerns of medical science: etiology and therapy. Variables affecting illness behavior come into play prior to medical scrutiny and treatment, but after etiological processes have been initiated. In this sense, illness behavior even determines whether diagnosis and treatment will begin at all.

We are here dealing with an area important for public health and medical sociology and it becomes a matter of both theoretical and practical concern to discover the sources and consequences of different illness behaviors. And if, in given populations, there are systematic differences in illness behavior, this fact has obvious implications for public health programs [5]§, estimated needs for medical care, medical economics, and our understanding of health and illness in general.

That the behavioral sciences can shed some light on such questions is indicated, for example, by the researches of Koos and Saunders. Koos [7] found that upper class persons more often reported themselves ill than lower class persons, and also that they were more likely to seek treatment when afflicted. Lower class persons, on the other hand, while having more actual symptoms, reported themselves to be less often ill, and were the least likely of all persons in the community studied to visit a physician. Similarly, Saunders [8], comparing the attitudes and behavior of Spanish and English-speaking populations in the Southwest, found many differences in the way the two populations responded to illness and used medical facilities. Whereas the "Anglos" preferred modern medical science and hospitalization for many illnesses, the Spanish-speaking people were more likely to rely on folk-medicine and family care and support.

The concept of the "social role of the sick person" as developed by Sigerist [9] and elaborated by Parsons [10], provides a convenient starting point in approaching illness behavior. According to Parsons' analysis, when a person's illness has been legitimized by medical sanction, or that of intimates and/or persons having influence over him, the person occupies a special role in society. During the time of the illness, he may be relieved of usual demands and obligations and his "sick role" takes priority over other social roles (e.g. occupational, familial etc.). Moreover, the person is expected to seek help in restoring his full energies and to co-operate in the treatment process. Persons may be motivated to adopt the sick role to obtain release from various kinds of responsibilities; but there are also others who fear the dependence of the sick role or who are suspicious of physicians and avoid seeking medical advice even when serious symptoms appear.

Whether a person does or does not assume the sick role when ill is dependent on a variety of group and personal factors. The person's age, sex, and position in his social group as well as the importance of his role for the group must be considered [1]. If a man's failure to appear at work—even for one day—results in hardship for his family, it is likely he will avoid consulting a physician and the possibility of being encouraged to assume the sick role unless his symptoms become so serious as to prevent him from working; if time and money are available and a short departure from usual roles impose no undue hardships, the person is more likely to seek medical advice, get into bed, and release himself from his usual role demands.

Another factor of importance is the person's learned behaviors for dealing with symptoms. These behaviors may be learned for ideological reasons as with the Christian Scientist or for practical reasons as with the members of lower income groups. What symptoms the person recognizes as important or worthy of attention and what he neglects or tends to ignore largely conditions when and for what reasons he might appear for medical diagnosis. This has often been a considerable problem for public health people as the evaluations by patient and physician of what constitutes serious symptoms and what necessitates treatment and attention may, indeed, be discrepant. One of the prime functions of public health programs is to teach populations to accept, and behave in accordance with, the definitions made by the medical profession.

In evaluating how best to bring about successful educational programs, two questions become apparent: (1) What are the factors affecting the appearance or nonappearance of persons for medical diagnosis? and (2) how can these people be reached most effectively by educational and information programs?

The latter problem is outside the scope of this paper, but Professor Volkart and I have explored the former problem to some extent in an investigation of 614 male students at a large University. These students were approximately of the same age, and lived and ate their meals in the same university dormitory. Because of school requirements, the academic demands made upon them were also substantially similar. Data were obtained by means of both a questionnaire and investigation of their medical records. Using a series of hypothetical questions concerning whether these students would seek advice from a physician if they had various symptoms, we were able to distinguish students with varied inclinations, to seek medical attention. Our concern then became threefold: (1) what is the relationship between the inclination to seek medical attention and the actual use of medical facilities as measured by the students' health records? (2) what social and personal factors are associated with the expressed inclination to seek medical advice? and (3) what diagnostic categories are most affected by differential inclinations to seek medical advice? As expected, we found that the actual frequency of visits made to a free University medical clinic was highly associated with a high inclination to seek medical help as measured by responses to a set of hypothetical medical conditions. The measure of inclination to seek medical advice, also, was significantly related to the person's religion, his social class position, his dependency on others, and the magnitude of stress he reported. More specifically, we found that while approximately 71 per cent of the Jews in the sample and 70 per cent of the Episcopalians expressed a high inclination to use medical facilities in various hypothetical situations, only 32 per cent of Christian Scientists and 42 per cent of Catholics did so. These differences persisted within social class groups indicating that class influences on religious affiliation could not explain all of the variance. Our findings suggested a theory of learned alternative channels for dealing with life stress situations, including illness. Symptoms presented to the physician by Jews and Episcopalians may be presented to priests, lay practitioners and druggists by members of other groups. The differences observed and the theory suggested are being investigated now with other populations.

These findings suggest the importance of further investigations of cultural and social response to *dis-ease.* Zborowski's classic study [11] of reactions to pain showed that Jewish, Italian, Irish and "old American" patients responded differently. While Jews and Italians responded emotionally tending to exaggerate their pain experience, Irish and "old Americans", in contrast, were more stoical. Response to pain and response to disease take place within an elaborate cultural context, in which the patient, his family, and the community respond in socially patterned ways. Zborowski reports how Jewish and Italian respondents related that their mother showed over-protective and over-concerned attitudes toward the child's health, participation in sports and the like, and that they were constantly warned of the advisability of avoiding colds, injuries, fights, and other threatening situations. While excessive concern in clinical situations may be regarded as hypochondriasis or even malingering, it is essential for the practicing physician to recognize that these patterns are often acquired in the child's training process and that the patient's prior training affects how and when he presents himself and his symptoms to his physician.

One of the main concerns of our research was the effects of "stress" on illness behavior. We found that persons who reported high "stress" as measured by frequency of loneliness and nervousness, were significantly more likely to use medical facilities than persons with lesser "stress'. While 60 per cent of our high stress respondents visited the health service three or more times during the period studied, only 38 per cent of the low stress persons visited this service frequently. Moreover, we found that stress was associated, also, with the inclination to use medical facilities expressed in various hypothetical situations. While 60 per cent of high stress persons expressed a high inclination to use medical facilities, only 43 per cent of the low stress persons did so. In the group with a high inclination to use medical facilities as measured by hypothetical situations, 73 per cent of persons under high stress made three or more visits during the period observed, while the same group only 46 per cent of low stress persons were such frequent visitors. In the group with low inclination to use medical facilities, 42 per cent of high stress persons visited three or more times, as compared with only 30 per cent of the low stress persons. Thus, stress was more likely to affect the act of using medical facilities among persons who already had a high inclination to use such facilities.

We suspected that the type of stress experienced by a person might be important in its effect on his illness behavior. This idea was based on the assumption that the physician's role is ideally suited to the needs of persons in interpersonal difficulty. The physician's role includes the technical skills and knowledge to deal with "illness"; and because it involves communication, interaction, and nurturance, it also meets the interpersonal needs of such persons. Interaction with a physician is suited, also, for persons in interpersonal difficulty in that it can be initiated with little difficulty, not requiring the complex and subtle cues and responses often necessary in other types of relationships. Also, the primary function of the physician is to aid and restore health, and this serves to insure that the patient will not be rejected openly or humiliated. Nor is he likely to be comdemned for his various symptoms and complaints—at least initially. In many ways, then, the doctor-patient relationship can serve as a temporary substitute for other kinds of insufficient or inadequate interpersonal relationships.

In our study, questionnaire data were obtained dealing with students' experiences, worries and difficulties during their freshman year. As expected, it was found that students having more interpersonal difficulties (worries about interpersonal matters, worries about dating, feelings of loneliness, etc.) were more likely to express a high inclination to use medical facilities than were persons with lesser interpersonal difficulties. It was further suggested that interpersonal stresses exerted greater effects on persons' expressed inclinations to use medical facilities than did non-interpersonal stresses of similar importance like worries about money, finding studies interesting, etc. These data support the interpretation that interpersonal stress is a significant factor affecting who will seek medical care and when. Aside from clear emergencies and acute illnesses, which scarcely permit alternatives, the maintenance of a doctor-patient relationship involves an interaction between certain services the physician offers and certain needs of the patient which may go beyond "traditional medicine" in its usual connotation.

In evaluating how various diagnostic categories were related to the inclination to seek medical aid as measured by hypothetical situations, we proposed the following rationale: a given illness may be regarded as having certain dimensions or characteristics, more or less perceptible to the sick person and possible to others in his social environment. In the context under study, four dimensions seemed of particular importance.

(1) The frequency with which the illness occurs in a given population, i.e., its commonality;
(2) The relative familiarity of the symptoms to the average member of the group;
(3) The relative predictability of the outcome of the illness; and
(4) The amount of threat and loss that is likely to result from the illness.

The first two dimensions refer to the problem of "illness recognition"; the last two to the problem of "illness danger". When a particular symptomatology is both easily recognizable and relatively devoid of probable danger, it is a routine illness; when a given symptomatology occurs more infrequently in the population, it is more difficult to identify, and when its mystery then casts the shadow of danger, there is likely to be a greater sense of concern.

The common cold, for example, as its name suggests, is both easily recognizable and relatively devoid of danger—at least initially. Hepatitis, on the other hand, is less often encountered by most persons and is more likely (and accurately) to be perceived as potentially dangerous.

The point to this approach to illness is that persons perceive symptoms differently. The definition of a symptom may greatly exaggerate its consequences as well as affect the behavior of the patient involved. We expected, therefore, that persons who expressed a high inclination to use medical facilities on our hypothetical questions would seek help under slight provocation; when their symptoms are common and familiar, or unusual and perplexing, they will probably seek medical diagnosis and treatment immediately. Persons with a low inclination to seek medical advice, on the other hand, are more likely to ignore "routine" illnesses and common aches and pains; only the more unusual or severe illnesses should bring them to medical attention.

In our analysis of diagnostic data, illnesses were classified on a matrix which permitted us to focus on illness "sites", irrespective of etiology, e.g., gastro-intestinal, skin; or on a given etiological category, irrespective of site, e.g., viral, traumatic; or the possible combinations of etiologies and sites, e.g., viral respiratory or, bacterial skin. Sixteen such diagnostic categories were used in the analysis of our data. These categories were classified as to whether or not they met the criteria of "routine illness" indicated (commonality, familiarity, predictability, and lack of threat). Our hypothesis concerning the relationship between inclination to seek medical attention and "routine" and "non-routine" illness was, then, tested and confirmed. Persons with a high tendency to seek medical aid were significantly more likely than low tendency persons to report to the health service for diagnoses of illnesses meeting the criteria of "routine illness" for our population. These categories included respiratory, viral, viral respiratory, bacterial, and bacterial respiratory categories. Those illnesses classified as "non-routine" (those less common in the population studied, less familiar, less predictable, and threatening illnesses), did not show such large or statistically significant relationships to the inclination to seek medical care. Included among these categories were allergic conditions, poisonings, unknown skin, etc. [2].

From the public health point of view, the results must be scrutinized with some caution. For a symptom viewed by a layman as not serious, may be of great medical consequence. For example, cancer is often not detected until fairly widespread in the organism, because the layman has not learned, as yet, to view the early signs of cancer as signs sufficient to merit medical consultation. Persons, of course, also sometimes visit the physician unnecessarily, thus, wasting valuable medical time. Physicians and others working on public health information programs have the difficult task of teaching laymen that some of the symptoms, often defined as minor, are important, indeed, and that early detection might greatly reduce the future consequences of the illness, while, at the same time, discouraging tendencies toward hypochondriasis.

These findings also have important implications from the point of view of medical research. The data demonstrate that there are differential visiting patterns for different categories of illness. Thus, clinic and hospital cases used for the study of some illnesses, especially the more "routine" ones, may represent highly select and biased cases from which generalization may not be possible to the larger group of persons in the general population having that illness. The observation, for example, that persons who are ill (with whatever diagnosis) are also under stress is inadequate for any assertion of causality. Individuals with similar medical conditions who are not under stress may not seek medical advice. For some illnesses, at least, appearance in medical statistics may be as much a result of patterns of illness behavior and situational events as it is of the symptoms experienced.

If precise understanding of medical etiology is to be developed, and if health programs are to operate at maximum effectiveness, it is essential that we have a deeper understanding of the concept of illness behavior. It is necessary that we learn a good deal more about the various attitudes, values, and social definitions applied to symptoms, and how these influence the adoption of patient roles. What is equally important is that this understanding be used constructively and effectively in medical practice; and that the person be regarded as a social being with hopes and fears and varied predispositions which are influenced by the groups within which he lives.

REFERENCES

1. Mechanic, David: Illness and social disability—Some problems in analysis, *Pacif. Sociol. Rev.* 2, 37–41, 1959.
2. Mechanic, David and Volkart, Edmund H.: Illness behavior and medical diagnosis, *J. Hlth. hum. Behavior*, 1, 86–94, 1960.
3. Mechanic, David and Volkart, Edmund, H.: Stress, illness behavior and the sick role, *Amer. Sociol. Rev.* 26, 51–58, 1961.
4. Mechanic, David and Volkart, Edmund, H.: *Interpersonal Worry and Doctor-Patient Relationship*, Paper read at the meetings of the American Sociological Association, St. Louis, Missouri, August 1961.
5. *Health Education Monographs*, Oakland, California Society of Public Health Educators.
6. Simmons, O. G.: *Social Status and Public Health*, Social Science Research Council Pamphlet 13, New York, 1958.

7. Koos, Earl: *The Health of Regionsville: What the People Thought and Did About it*, Columbia Univrsity Press, New York, 1954.
8. Saunders, Lyle: *Cultural Differences and Medical Care*, Russell Sage Foundation, New York, 1954.
9. Sigerist, Henry E.: The Special Position of the Sick, in *Henry E. Sigerist on the Sociology of Medicine*, M. I. Roemer (ed.) New York, M.D. Publications, 1960.
10. Parsons, Talcott: *The Social System*, Chapter X, The Free Press, Glencoe, 1951.
11. Zborowski, Mark: Cultural Components in Responses to Pain, *J. Soc. Issues*, **8**, 16–30, 1952.

5.2

Concepts of Disease: Logical Features and Social Implications

Horacio Fabrega, Jr., M.D.

INTRODUCTION

It is a truism that conceptualizations about disease have important social implications. Medicine, an institution of society, is defined in terms of its concern with disease. The very definition of disease, as we shall see, is a product of historically determined social happenings. Medical activities, thus, are rooted in socially structured categories. In addition, since definitions of disease seem to entail the phenomena of human suffering, consequences of medical activities bear directly or indirectly on the lives of members of society. So central and basic is a concern with disease in the minds of persons tied to medicine that, quite often, the meanings and logical properties of the term "disease" are taken for granted or left unexamined. Developments in contemporary society have brought into focus the organization and delivery of health services and challenged traditional medical orientations and goals. Problems involving the distribution and quality of medical care have been emphasized. Many of the issues that have been raised can be seen as reflections and even outcomes of the meanings of key medical terms, especially that of "disease." It will prove instructive to examine these issues by relating them analytically to concepts of disease. In order to accomplish this in a clear manner it will be necessary to review different approaches to the study of disease in society [1–8]. The essay, in summary, represents an attempt to provide a logical analysis of concepts of disease with the aim of clarifying their meanings and social implications. It is hoped that this analysis will clarify problematic aspects of medical care and education.

I. DISEASE AS A BIOLOGICAL DISCONTINUITY

In a biologistic perspective the term "disease" designates a medical concept whose meaning or intension involves an abnormality in function and/or structure of any part, process, or system of the body.[1] The range of application of the term or the class of things to which it applies—its extension—would include such things as appendicitis, elevated blood pressure, enlarged heart, or diabetes. In any particular instance of its use, the term might refer to one of these items. Part of the difficulty of discussing the meanings of disease stems from the fact that the term itself can function semantically and syntactically in a number of different ways. The term "disease" can be used as follows:

1. As an abstract general term, purporting to refer to each or any of the members of the class of "diseases" that includes hypertension, diabetes, etc. For example: (*a*) "Diseases found in this community tend to be more serious." (*b*) "Diseases due to bacteria have always plagued mankind." In each instance the term "diseases" functions as a general abstract term. However, the meaning context provided by each sentence differs, serving to narrow the focus of the term: (*a*) a subgroup of diseases that are serious, and (*b*) any and all diseases caused by bacteria.

2. With a singularizing modifier the term can purport to refer to exactly one thing. For example: "That disease has an abrupt onset"; or "the disease that he has." In these instances, the term together with the singularizing modifier function as an abstract singular term.

A different and independent manner of classifying the term follows:

1. As a denotative term, purporting to *refer* to things. For example: "The disease" had an abrupt onset. Here the abstract general term "disease" is conjoined with a singularizing modifier, "the," and forms a denotative term that refers to a specific disease.

2. As an attributive term, purporting to *apply* to things. For example: You could see that he was "diseased." In this instance, the term is used to qualify things.

Two particular features seem to contribute to ambiguity in attempts at specifying the meaning and logical features of the term "disease." The first is

---

[1]The delimitation of the body as the significant locus of events of illness, events having direct experiential consequences, was an obvious necessary prerequisite for developments that were in time to culminate in the specification of the biological substrates of disease. At least three aspects of medical experience probably contributed directly to the view of disease or illness as a manifestation of bodily processes having periodicity and precise identity. The first was the general ubiquity of crises we now term medical and surgical emergencies, crises that were capable of producing sudden change in bodily function, awareness, and level of consciousness. The second was the general prevalence of infectious agents, agents capable of producing bodily changes and illness experiences in sharply bounded segments of time. The third was the growing recognition that changes in the body's structure and function characterized individuals who were or had been sick. One might regard the view that disease represents a bodily or biological discontinuity as the initial crucial "paradigm" of medicine.

ambiguity as to whether it is being used as a general or singular term. Thus, in the statement "man must constantly guard against disease," the term appears to function singularly and refer to one specific quality or state, namely, "diseasehood." Here, then, the idea of an abstract *singular* property that people take on or acquire is suggested. Yet, as used in the statement the term may very well purport to refer to any of several diseases, and in this latter usage the term would be used as an abstract *general* term. Changing the term "disease" to "diseases" in the statement makes this latter usage clear. The second feature contributing to ambiguity stems from the experience of studying the manifestations and properties of various diseases. This leads to the tendency of using the term as if it referred to concrete objects having spatial and temporal extension. Strictly speaking, there is no object or concrete thing that is a disease, although there are tissues, hearts, livers, and respiratory passages that may demonstrate or reflect the manifestations and characteristics that we would attribute to disease. In summary, it would appear that in everyday discourse the term "disease" can contribute to ambiguity because it raises questions touching on the philosophical problem of universals, an aspect of what Quine refers to as the "ontological problem" [9]. On the one hand, the term suggests the existence of an abstract entity (i.e., quality, a property) that people take on or acquire. Conversely, the term as used can sometimes suggest the existence of concrete entities, or objects located in space and time.

The logical grammar and meaning of the "disease" term may be illustrated by focusing on diabetes. The following conventions and rules will prove useful:

1. D = the disease diabetes.
2. P_i = defining characteristics of D (e.g., P_1 = disorder of carbohydrate metabolism, P_2 = disturbance in normal insulin mechanism, P_3 = abnormality of the pancreas, etc.).
3. Q_j and R_i = indicators of D (e.g., elevated blood sugar, glycosuria, polyuria, ketonuria, retinitis, etc.). A set of indicators relevant to diabetes is used. Depending on the type of focus, subsets of these indicators are labeled as either Q_j or P_i.
4. X has D if and only if $P_1, P_2 \ldots P_m$ are true of X. A biconditional statement which specifies the analytic definition of D. Observe that the statement is true (by definition) in the two component forms of the biconditional, for example, if X had D, then he has $P_1 - P_m$; if X has $P_1 - P_m$, he has D.
5. If X has $Q_1 - Q_k$, then X has D. A conditional statement which if true specifies that the conjunction of $Q_1 - Q_k$ constitute a *sufficient condition* for X to have D. Note that asserting a true conditional statement of this form does not allow assigning a truth value to its converse (i.e., if X has D, it does not follow that he must show indicators $Q_1 - Q_k$).
6. If X has D, then X has $R_1 - R_j$. A conditional statement which if true specifies that the conjunction of $R_1 - R_j$ constitutes a necessary condition for the

induction that X has diabetes. Note again that the truth value of the converse of this conditional statement cannot be assigned (i.e., $R_1 - R_j$, need not constitute sufficient conditions for D).

7. It is to be emphasized that the indicators used in the logical forms of items 5 and 6 above are drawn from the same set, but in general are not the same (i.e., specific indicators $Q_1 - Q_k$ are not usually identical with specific indicators $R_1 - R_j$). Thus, if X has symptoms highly suggestive of diabetes together with an elevated fasting blood sugar and glycosuria, then we might be reasonably sure that he has diabetes. However, if X has diabetes he may or may not demonstrate all of these features. The aim of scientific medicine is to reach a state of affairs where these two sets of indicators are in fact identical: A state of affairs where the biconditional form could be applied, but this time including indicators instead of defining characteristics. If this were the case one could then speak of diseases as having indexical definitions [10]. In contrast to the analytic definition provided in item 4 above, this can be viewed as an empirical definition. There is reason to believe that indicators such as those obtained from a glucose tolerance test will come to serve this function in the case of diabetes.

In a biologistic framework, then, the defining characteristics of specific diseases refer to biological processes. The necessary and/or sufficient conditions that allow inferring the presence of diseases are expressed in information pertaining to such things as blood sugar levels, electrographic patterns, chest X-rays, or microscopic specimens of tissues. This information is interpreted by means of the empirically derived knowledge about human biological functioning. Indeed, the operations used to generate such information have meaning in terms of such knowledge. This particular framework for defining disease, then, quite obviously grows out of and is tied to historical developments associated with the Western scientific tradition. It should be noted that on occasions particular verbal reports or behaviors may serve as ("pathognomonic") indicators of a disease, as for example the report of the pain of myocardial infarction or dissecting aneurism, the reports of a migraine syndrome, or the history of sudden unconsciousness. In some instances these types of indicators are necessary and, in rare instances, sufficient for establishing the presence of disease. The application of sophisticated technology to human biological functioning has the effect of enabling physicians to slowly replace these reports by indicators that more directly and reliably reflect biological processes and changes.

Psychiatric "diseases" occupy an anomalous and ambiguous status when considered against a strictly biologistic framework. Their defining characteristics involve mentalistic concepts or entities (such as feelings, impulses, drives, ego strength, psychological defenses, etc.) as well as concepts referring to types of social relationships. Their indicators consist of inferences about these matters which are reached following standardized interviews or tests. In most instances, no direct information about the body's structure (i.e., X-rays, biopsies, palpation) or function (derived indirectly from blood, urine, or other bodily fluids) is used. If these latter considerations are viewed as criterial of a biologistic framework, then they would suggest that psychiatric diseases have little to do with biological happenings. However, since judgments about psychiatric diseases are reached in terms of representative formulations about human behavior generally (according to many, in terms of formulations about the way the mind functions) they can and are viewed by many as dealing with biological happenings, but at different levels or in terms of different organizing principles. One defense of this position would state that, in a procedural sense, reliance on verbal reports (referring to key "symptoms") as indicators of *any* disease represents activity that is equivalent to psychiatric diagnosing. In other words, the way medical information is used by physicians (i.e., laboratory reports, physical exam or interview data, psychological test data) can be described as being similar from an instrumental standpoint, regardless of the type of disease. This argument has as its conclusion a proposition to the effect that any examination and systematization of life processes can be said to be "biologistic." Ultimately, clarification of this issue leads to central problems in the sociology of knowledge and will not be pursued further here [11]. Suffice it to say that psychiatric diseases are somewhat problematic when considered against a strictly biologistic framework such as was illustrated earlier.

It should be clear that a consequence of applying or using this essentially biologistic framework regarding disease is that specific diseases can then be said to be *universal* or transcultural occurrences. That is, providing the norms physicians currently use in determining whether disease is present represent a reliable and valid framework from which to generalize, then indicators of biological function reflecting a deviation therefrom (as do Q_i and R_i above) constitute prima facie evidence of disease. There is no reason to doubt that man everywhere is biologically the same individual in most of the important respects that enable physicians to make judgments about disease. Certainly diet, climate, and level of activity have biological effects that are reflected in body chemistries, muscle mass, and even tissue appearance and function; however, scientifically based medical knowledge and experience is such that it enables physicians to confidently interpret biological indicators when they reflect abnormality despite the fact that such "abnormal" indicators may be typical of particular population groups. The use of verbal reports as indicators of disease is not problematic in most instances of disease evaluation. However, since these types of indicators are likely to reflect culturally structured categories as well as biological happenings, their utilization in medical evaluation pose problems of cross-cultural equivalence, limiting the extensional use of those disease terms that they characterize (see subsequent sections).[2]

II. DISEASE AS A BEHAVIORAL DISCONTINUITY

It should be stated that in a broader intellectual context, the idea of disease or illness does not logically entail an understanding of bodily function, nor does it require that the users of the concept regard the body's function as a salient consideration. It was mentioned that the defining characteristics of most psychiatric diseases refer to disturbed social relationships, to particular types of beliefs, and to morbid and disturbing feelings. These latter features can be seen as not logically presupposing or implying a particular understanding of bodily function. Inspection of the literature in social science and medicine indicates that it is possible and even common to conduct meaningful discourse about health and illness employing an orientation that bears little relation to bodily events and processes. As will be illustrated subsequently, a careful examination of how preliterate groups conceptualize and respond to illness will reveal that the domain of bodily function is quite often separated logically from that of illness. Supernatural and social concepts quite often suffice to explain "disease" [14, 15].

A number of behavioral scientists are today emphasizing that the social sciences are as basic or "required" for the education of the physician as are the concerns of other disciplines such as anatomy, biochemistry, physiology, or pharmacology. Implicit in these emphases appears to be the view that disease must be seen in behavioral terms. The central premise behind the argument that states that the biological sciences are crucial to medical education, of course, stems from the awareness that the empirically derived knowledge of these sciences enables detecting and controlling many of the consequences of altered biological states, and thereby specifies with some reliability the underlying processes and mechanisms of human functioning. Social scientists are emphasizing that since what patients seek medical advice and care for is expressed *behaviorally*, then it follows that behavioral science is equally relevant

---

[2]The manner in which the biologistic framework is used varies considerably and depends on the concerns and questions needing resolution. For example, epidemiologists readily diagnose diseases on the basis of one examination of a stool specimen. The presence of ova and parasites constitute necessary and sufficient conditions for the application of a disease label. The question of whether the person feels sick is not of salience to the problems under investigation, and consequently is not considered in the process of diagnosis [12, 13]. This epidemiological approach may be regarded as analogous to that of the physical anthropologist interested in typing blood group substances. At the other extreme of the continuum of medical evaluation stands the transaction between a physician and his client. In this instance, verbal reports are also critically vital parts of planning an evaluation since providing help for the patient is in salience. In this latter instance, however, the physician is also relying on alternative medical frameworks (see subsequent two sections).

to a rational understanding of medical problems or "disease." This argument is supported by an appeal to the following sets of issues. The first bears on the traditional concern of medicine with diagnosis and includes the following: (1) Not all patients present for evaluation and care with complaints referable to recognized biologically altered processes or states. (2) Some present with complaints that appear to be rooted in and defined by social and interpersonal factors. (3) Many persons with complaints clearly linked to biological and social factors do not present formally for scientific medical care but instead seek other types of help or none at all. Nevertheless, such persons may be equally in need of scientific care. (4) The manner in which persons perceive, organize, and express disability, *regardless of its origin*, is embedded in behavior, and the form of this behavior, which in many ways is the raw data of medical evaluation, is determined by social, psychological, and cultural factors as well as by biologic, ecologic, or genetic factors. And (5) decisions affecting what persons do vis-á-vis disability are determined by behaviorally relevant priorities that are also diverse as to source. The preceding issues, together, give substance to the conviction of social scientists that physicians, the practitioners of scientific medical care, need to be aware of the many competing factors that impinge on the decision to seek care as well as many factors that determine the expression of disability. With regard to the other traditional concern of medicine, namely treatment, social scientists emphasize the fact that the process of delivering and evaluating medical care involves the problem of specifying *unhealthful behaviors* and then planning for their modification or elimination. The behaviors in question, as already stated, are promoted, maintained, and structured by various factors having social, cultural, and psychological significance. According to these social scientists, then, a physician, in order to make rational and effective use of his knowledge about biological processes, must be aware of the behavioral dimensions and implications of his aims and actions. Stated succinctly, he needs to appreciate the extent to which disease processes link and interconnect with behavioral factors in order to effectively treat patients.

The preceding issues suggest an alternative framework for understanding or defining disease. It will prove instructive to develop a sociobehavioral framework of disease. In such a framework, disease will be construed in behavioral and sociological terms. The biological framework discussed earlier will not logically articulate with this new framework. However, it should be understood that both definitional frameworks can be applied to similar phenomena, and that a correspondence or relationship between the frameworks could be delineated. The nature of this relationship is problematic and constitutes an empirical matter. Leaving aside for the moment this issue of the relationship between frameworks of disease, let us examine issues bearing on a behavioral framework.

If it were possible to list in a relatively exhaustive manner the activities, tasks, responsibilities, and pursuits that occupied persons during the daily conduct of their lives, this would provide a basis for the construction of a grid which could be used to map their behavioral participation in life affairs. Proper framing of the "units" of this grid would allow them to serve as indicators of participation. Different theoretical schemes could be used to define "participation units." By systematically applying such a framework (i.e., coding or measuring a person's degree of participation in the various work units of this grid thru time) a *level* of participation could be obtained. This, in turn, would provide a basis for classifying and quantifying changes which could be studied both internally and with respect to external events or processes.

A requirement for a behavioral framework of disease, in other words, is a set of disease indicators which would refer to *behavioral units*. What would be needed, thus, is a list of categories that would enable mapping or evaluating how individuals behave. For example, a basic set of tasks and actions could be used and persons evaluated in terms of how they performed these activities: A_1 = performance of routine household tasks; A_2 = performance of strenuous physical activities; A_3 = consumption of foods, etc. Alternatively, how persons performed basic role duties and functions could be used as indicators: R_1 = role behaviors of family member (i.e., father, husband, etc.); R_2 = role behaviors tied to employment; R_3 = role behaviors tied to ethnic identity; R_4 = role behaviors involving religious affiliation, etc. Either or both of the preceding dimensions (i.e., tasks, actions, and role duties) might be selected for the purpose of developing indicators in a behavioristic framework. By systematically evaluating the types of patterned changes that occurred within and across individuals through time, a typology of disease states might be developed, disease states which in effect would represent behavioral entities.

An an illustration of a behavioral framework of disease, we will give attention to basic tasks and actions. Diseases defined on this basis might take the following form:

1. D_i = a disease construed in sociobehavioral terms.
2. X has D_i if and only if he shows $P_1 - P_j$ ($P_1 - P_j$ indicate defining characteristics).
3. Three types of diseases might be described: P_1 = the regular features of the way X behaves in response to social demands are curtailed; P_2 = the regular features of the way X behaves in response to social demands are quantitatively affected (i.e., the intensity and activity are either increased or diminished); P_3 = the regular features of the way X behaves in response to social demands are qualitatively affected.
4. Indicators of D_1 might include: Q_1 = verbalizes complaints of weakness and exhaustion; Q_2 = stays in bed a large proportion of time; Q_3 = does not go to work; Q_4 = food intake is significantly diminished, ... Q_n.
5. Indicators of D_2 might include either: (*a*) Q_1 = spends much time sitting, Q_2 = walks more slowly, appears less active, Q_3 = speaks less frequently and

more slowly, Q_4 = eats less frequently and smaller amounts, Q_5 = work output diminished... Q_n; or (*b*) Q_1 = prefers to stand and walk, Q_2 = walks faster, appears more active, Q_3 = speaks frequently and rapidly, Q_4 = eats more frequently and in larger amounts, Q_5 = work output increased... Q_n.

6. Indicators of D_3 might include: Q_1 = talks about irrelevancies, Q_2 = now violates social conventions, Q_3 = utters statements that disregard logical and/or empirical principles, Q_4 = cries frequently and appears sad, Q_5 = is argumentative, etc.

It should be evident that this definitional framework could be substantially refined so that each unit or category is made to refer to more specific behavioral sets. Thus D_1 above could be further subdivided as follows:

1. Defining characteristics: P_{11} = the regular features of the way *X* behaves are curtailed as a result of visible structural faults; P_{12} = the regular features of the way *X* behaves are curtailed but there are no visible structural faults.
2. Indicators: of D_{11}-same Q_1-Q_n as for D_1 + Q_n + 1, faulty or unmovable extremities; Q_n + 2, faulty extremities that can be moved only with much labor and verbalization about pain; of D_{12}-same Q_1-Q_n as for D_1 + Q_n + 1, verbalizes constant pain; Q_n + 2, reports feeling weak and having no energy, etc.

Further differentiation might yield, for D_{11}, P_{111} (faulty lower extremities), P_{112} (faulty upper extremities); and for D_{12}, P_{121} (there are associated problems in bowel function), P_{122} (there are associated problems with breathing), etc. By a procedure analogous to this one it should be possible to develop a branching classification scheme of sociobehavioral diseases, such that a "species" of disease located at the terminal loci of the branches are indicated by rather discrete and specific sets of behavioral elements. Careful analytic work might yield a refined scheme which would be exclusive and whose categories could approximate segments of the biologistic framework. However, despite the possibility that the two frameworks might bear a systematic relationship to each other, they would refer to different sorts of phenomena. That is, "disease" in one framework would refer to biological matters, in the other it would refer to behavioral matters. Any number of functions could be served by a behavioral framework. For example, were a society's medical care system to be structured on the basis of such a framework of disease, a framework of the latter type might serve as the basis for the allocation of discrete tasks to particular types of health personnel.

It is important to keep salient the following characteristic that a behavioral framework of disease would demonstrate: Disease entities wuld bear a systematic relationship with social categories and contexts. To clarify this point, let us review briefly considerations bearing on the biologistic framework. It should be evident that from the standpoint of studying the distribution of disease in human groups a biologistic framework enjoys an unusual advantage. This is that the framework for defining disease does not articulate logically with social categories. In other words, the study and evaluation of how disease relates to social categories (e.g., social class, ethnic identity, occupational groupings, etc.) can take place by means of concepts, variables, and relations that are logically independent of the unit that assigns medical meaning (or identity, or status) to the individual. Stated succinctly, the determination of whether and in what manner an individual is diseased does not affect the procedure that we may adopt to classify him socially; conversely, the concepts and methods used to locate an individual in a social system are logically distinguishable from and not affected methodologically by the status assigned to him by the biologistic framework. Given this logical separation between the two dimensions (societal and biomedical), it is then possible to empirically analyze the relationship that exists between them knowing that no systematic biases or errors will contaminate one's methods. Clearly, were we to use a behavioral disease framework and then attempt to analyze how disease conditions (or disease rates) are distributed in a social group, we are likely to observe that systematic relations obtain. Thus, keeping in mind the illustrative "behavioral indicators" introduced earlier, we can say that only persons who are family members can be evaluated in terms of performance of family role duties, and only persons whose work requires heavy physical exertion can be evaluated on this task-action indicator. Stated more directly, behavioral categories (from which behavioral indicators devolve) are distributed in patterned ways in a social system, and what is more this patterning between social and behavioral dimensions results from what we might term logical considerations. Thus, a factor explaining a particular distribution of a behavioral disease in a social group would be the analytic link that obtains between that group and certain types of behaviors. A different way of making clear the logical independence that exists between social categories and a biologistic framework is to point out that biologistic indicators can all be used systematically and equivalently to evaluate persons: That is, blood sugars, lung parenchyma, and blood pressure levels are parameters that apply equally to all individuals—all persons can be evaluated in terms of these traits. However, behavioral categories of the type herein considered are not equally relevant to all persons. Any distributions or patterns noted by the use of these indicators (e.g., disease rates) may reflect the association that behaviors have with social groupings.

III. DISEASE AS A PHENOMENOLOGICAL DISCONTINUITY

Clearly, specification of what is meant by an *understanding* of bodily function is a complex task. There are, quite obviously, not one but many such understandings, ranging from the perspective of the physician, through that of the chiropractor, to the understanding of some natives who view their corporal selves not as interrelated systems having diverse functions, but rather as the objectification of spiritual and supernatural events and decisions.

The understandings that persons claim to have about their body have rarely been the focus of intensive study. An individual's ideas about the body have been studied in relation to the phenomena of pain and as part of general psychologic studies [16–18]. The relationship that exists between the experience or sensation of the body and the understanding that subjects or groups have a bodily processes and functioning remains relatively unexplored. Cognitive anthropologists who rely on the methods of structural linguistics have documented with fidelity the contrasting meanings associated with domains having concrete and publicly shared referents. Richness of language terms brought to bear on a particular phenomenal domain generally tends to reflect the salience or relevance of that domain to members of the group [19, 20]. The body as an anatomical entity quite obviously "exposes" only a portion of its features to the inspection and hence recognition of the self and others. Much remains hidden "beneath the surface," so to speak. Nevertheless, the number of anatomical terms in use, their organization, and the importance that is attached to them, differ across cultural groups and tend to reflect the nature of the subsistence patterns and occupational roles that characterize the culture. Similarly, the degree of access that subjects have to the interior of the human body is a cultural trait that probably differs substantially across cultures.[3]

The language or knowledge about the body's functioning, together with the experiential precipitates of significant past events involving the body, will no doubt influence the role and importance that the body is given in general discourse and, more important, the natue of the "reality" that subjects will have about the body. Sensations and feelings that are linked to biologically altered states must be viewed as a function of these symbols and meanings that involve the body. If symbolic attributes of the body affect the sensations individuals have when the body is altered or stimulated, then a consideration of how the body is *experienced* will not necessarily provide a framework or common denominator that might serve to unify our thinking about illness and disease. This is to say that we cannot readily turn to a consideration of how the body is experienced as an end point or reference with which to conclude that diseases ultimately are composed of generally shared, specifiable, and discrete properties. It is likely that such bodily states as fractures, lacerations, and contusions that stem from observable and externally induced events will to a large extent be experienced similarly across individuals and groups. This is the case because, in addition to the stimulation of particular types of pain fibers,

[3]Such culturally determined factors as degree and form of intra- and intergroup violence, manner of disposing of deceased persons, as well as beliefs about illness and death are factors that are likely to affect whether persons have access to the interior of the human body [21].

touch receptors will also be stimulated, thus aiding in fixing the locality and the "sociality" of the sensation [22]. Clearly, the pattern and type of nerve stimulation is similar in these instances, and more important, the stimulation is linked to phenomenological "events" that share formal characteristics (e.g., discrete onset, traumatic cause, heightened anxiety, visible abnormality, etc.). It should be emphasized, however, that the study of pain, involving such issues as its quality, its localization, its spread and reference, and its relationship to bodily events is far from being rigorously understood [23]. Individuals who study the neurophysiology of emotion are frequently forced to rely on tautologies, in part because the mind-body dichotomy and our language demands it, in part because the bulk of the experimental subjects who furnish reports of pain are all members of related cultural and language communities, and last because of the obvious inability to precisely capture the essence of the sensation. The result is that there is no unambiguous manner of depicting pain, and thus one can expect to find much variability even in descriptions of bodily changes originating in the surfaces of the body and in areas richly innervated.

If one excludes these particular bodily events (generally speaking, traumatic bodily changes) one is left with a multitude of biologically altered states which will be *experienced* in a variegated (ultimately idiosyncratic) manner. Obviously, diverse interpretations to these experiences can be attached. Only a subset of these is likely to be viewed universally as evidence of illness or disease. Table 1 illustrates two sets of clinically relevant happenings that are likely to be judged as illness by different individuals or groups with varying degrees of uniformity. Items on the right of the table which, in general, constitute typical medical and surgical emergencies are likely to be regarded as evidence of abnormality or illness in a large proportion of instances. Clearly, the experiences of the subject of actor are likely to be minimal in affecting the judgment that an abnormality is present, although, of course, the general significance that the group will assign to that disturbance would depend on the repertoire of explanations available for dealing with personal crises. On the other hand, those abnormalities listed on the left of the table will likely be subject to considerable cultural masking or "distortion," with the designation of ilness or abnormality applied more variably. Items on the left (and the list could obviously be expanded) are likely to underlie the bulk of medical complaints that physicians practicing in industrialized nations are called upon to treat. It is these clinical manifestations that are the substance of medical practice, the manifestation that physicians would like patients to notice and seek prompt relief for. Since these manifestations will be judged by the actor (and by extension, his significant others) in terms of available existential symbols that link with the body, psychological factors will prove important in their interpretation and action consequences. Whether these manifestations are noticed or ignored, the manner in which they are defined (e.g., either as illness, tiredness, or part of the aging process), and last, the actual form that they will take are likely to be influenced by psychological facors. This is to say, although terms such as weakness or nausea may have straightforward clinical implications, it must be emphasized that they are rooted in differing phenomenologic complexes. For example, what causes nausea, and how it is conceptualized, experienced, and reported will differ according to meanings people attribute to their body, to their food, to vomiting, and whether they believe it is due to a poisoning or a punishment.

Preceding issues suggest that in certain ways it can be said that diseases, as defined in Western scientific clinical medicine, do not "exist" in preliterate settings. (For an elegant discussion of the theoretical issues that are involved see [24].) What do exist, instead, are signs, symptoms, and disabilities that are structured, interpreted, and acted upon in terms of the concepts and beliefs of the group. The results are a set of culturally patterned entities or folk illnesses to which are attached unique implications, action imperatives, and behavioral expectations [25, 26]. Anthropologists who study medical problems have shown that the criterial elements of such illnesses quite frequently are moral or ethical concerns. Treatment may, thus, entail propitiating the gods or counteracting malevolent forces by means of culturally prescribed rules. Native practitioners are consulted and their judgments regarding the type of ceremony that is required may result in the formation of alliances and/or rivalries that can have important consequences for members of the family of the "patient" or for suspected out-group competitors [27, 28]. The point that we wish to emphasize is how varied and unique is the nature of sickness and the phenomenological complexes that give it meaning and interpretation.

A third classification framework is suggested, and we could term it a phenomenological framework. The defining characteristics of a disease formulated within this framework would include changes in the *states-of-being* (e.g., feeling, thought, self-definition, impulses, etc.) which are (*a*) seen as discontinuous with everyday affairs, and (*b*) believed to be caused by socioculturally defined agents or circumstances. Indicators would represent statements of modified states cast in symbolic categories having multivalent meanings. These individualistic statements judged to constitute disease might contain references to disturbed feelings, bodily sensations, beliefs regarding how the body functions, self-derogatory convictions, imputations of moral guilt, etc., which together would designate an altered conception or identity about the *self*. Biological indicators and behavioral parameters, although theoretically related and perhaps empirically embodied in this changed identity, should be regarded as independent of the categorization process. The units rationalizing an inability to function productively and in conformance with the implicit and explicit rules of the group would thus refer to features of the person's identity. Diseases as formulated in this framework could be described as follows:

1. D_i = a particular disease construed in phenomenologic terms.
2. X has disease D_1 if and only if he has P_i.
3. P_i = defining characteristics. Two diseases will be illustrated: P_1 = disorder due to punishment by supernatural agencies for failing to comply with certain sociomoral norms; P_2 = disorder due to malevolent and conspiratorial actions of other person's harboring invidious feelings toward the patient.
4. Indicators: Q_{11}—malaise, weakness, and feverishness; Q_{12}—nausea and vomiting; Q_{13}—feelings and behaviors reflecting a sense of worthlessness and guilt; Q_{14}—religious preoccupations, etc.; Q_{21}—evidence of malaise, weakness and feverishness; Q_{22}—complaints of generalized aches and pains; Q_{23}—feelings and behaviors indicating suspiciousness and antagonism toward others.
5. In this framework, it is likely that no conjunction of *types* of bodily sensations and malfunctions would constitute a sufficient condition for a person to have a particular disease, although some of these types of indicators might be necessary. Important factors in determining disease would be the manner in which the self perceives or judges himself vis-à-vis others and the various institutions (i.e., the individual's felt relationship and identity).

This framework might appear to be inapplicable or unrelated to medical matters as these are observed in Western settings. Certainly it is the case that the most lucid illustration of this type of medical paradigm is observed in preliterate settings. However, there is a growing literature documenting the existence of analogous types of medical beliefs and convictions among residents of Western industrialized settings [29, 30]. It is not unlikely that many patients explain or rationalize a medical illness by means of folk and sociomoral symbols. A subset of psychiatric diseases, when viewed from the perspective of the person demonstrating symptoms (e.g., paranoia, depression, schizophrenia, etc.) clearly reflects this phenomenologic view of disease.

IV. SOCIAL IMPLICATIONS OF DISEASE DEFINITIONS

Three independent frameworks for describing disease have been reviewed. These frameworks can be seen as products of distinct symbolic traditions and sociohistorically determined orientations. It was suggested that each framework could be used exclusively, thus enabling the grouping and description of phenomena having medical import. Framework *A* represents what could be termed a biological approach to disease. Framework *B* draws from social science approaches to medicine and to some extent from psychiatry. Framework *C* derives from a consideration of the way actors in contrasting sociocultural units define and classify disease, although it has some influence in Western settings as well. At any point in time, a person or organism may b said to be normal or diseased in terms of any or all three frameworks. *Although independent and logically self-contained, the frameworks are alike in three principal respects.* First, the unit of categorization is a discrete point in space, namely a person or organism. Second, the frameworks suggest that disease is a qualitative state; that is, a particular instance of disease is described as if it were discontinuous or temporally bounded.[4] And third, implied is the view that disease is an undesirable state insofar as it constitutes a deviation and can be a source of human misery and suffering. These three properties, then, tie the previously described independent frameworks together. The fact that the frameworks share the three properties leads to their being easily confounded. Social processes and activities having medical import can thus be set in motion precisely because a measure of consensus between disease frameworks is allowed by the properties described. In large part because of its antiquity and conformance to commonsense notions about illness, behavior and how the body functions, the view of disease reflected by these shared properties and implied by the frameworks, namely that disease is an undesirable organism centered discontinuity, appears implicitly to be used by many patients and medical personnel. This view of disease will be termed "organismic."

Certainly it appears to be the case that the organization and functioning of the medical care system have heretofore been predicated on this traditional organismic view of disease. All persons appear to seek care when they or their immediate fellows reach a judgment that disease is present; this judgment is usually reached subsequent to an analysis that involves a comparison with norms or standards, an analysis that produces a decision that an undesired state or deviation exists. Facilities and personnel are separated in space and located in settings designed to emphasize their distinctness and separation from regular social happenings; treatment is episodic and focused on discrete problems; payment is tied to a specific service aimed to resolve this problem;

[4]The view that disease represents a stage that is bounded in time has interesting implications. For example, it might be possible to develop a model of how persons behave during the time that they are sick. This would require that an organism be seen as made up of component variables with different values of these variables constituting stages of the organism. An organism's movement in time (i.e., his trajectory or line of behavior) could thus be represented as a series of states that change, either continuously or in a discrete fashion. The nature of the variables to be included would naturally depend on the behavior that is to be modeled. If use of health services were to be modeled, then variables representing such things as economic level, personal significance of illness episode, degree of discomfort, value placed on medical care, etc., as well as baic demographic variables would have to be considered [31–33]. Each of the variables is associated with values (either quantitative or qualitative) that are relevant vis-à-vis use of health services. Clearly, at present our knowledge of human behavior in general, and specifically as it relates to use of health services, does not allow constructing models or "machines" that are state determined, i.e., that follow regular and reproducible courses [34]. In another context, the notion that disease is a stage that is bounded in time has been seized upon by social scientists who speak of the behaviors of persons who are sick as constituting "illness careers" [35]. In this instance, the vicissitudes of a person who is ill are being described in social and phenomenologic terms, and the influence that contacts with the medical care system (i.e., physicians, hospitals, etc.) have on his behavior (i.e., his career as a patient) is under close scrutiny.

and more generally the implicit and often explicit premise guiding the medical transaction is that there is an endpoint to the concern, to the "disease." Writings of social scientists dealing with the role of the person who is sick have emphasized the activities and responsibilities of the patient to work to get well, to cooperate with the physician's efforts to terminate the "state of illness" [36]. Woven into the fabric of medical care and practice, then, appears to be the view that disease is person centered, temporally bounded, and discontinuous. Medical care could be conceptualized analogically as if it represented health surveillance with physicians seen as supervisors, transactions as elements of a continuous monitoring process, and payment as rent or investment. If this were followed, many of the features of care delivery would be structured differently. An organismic view of disease tends to promote a discrete and segmental approach to medical care that seems to require the fee-for-service notion and a concentration on describably salient deviations.

Many of the present problems in health care and its delivery may be traced, at least in part, to problems stemming from the dominating influence of an organismic conception of disease.[5] As implied above, an episodic view of disease underscores the need for only episodic treatment and militates against the comprehensive and continuous evaluation that some patients require. When the disease "appears" as defined by a set of symptoms, the person may then seek help, have this discomfort validated, and pay for it on the basis of a completed service. The patient, of course, seeks help for what he judges or suspects is *a* discontinuity (i.e., a "disease") of some unspecified sort. However, the way in which medicine is practiced and medical care structured is premised not only on the proposition that diseases are biological entities but also that differences exist between diseases. Segmenting the body and its problems in terms of a biologistic framework has the effect of fragmenting services and can also relegate more general concerns to an ancillary status and blur the boundaries of physician responsibilities. The patient's felt discontinuity, which is often unitary and lodged in an alternative framework, may be left out of focus. These issues, when magnified and concentrated, account in part for the dilemmas surrounding the management of the "problem" patient. Patients may unwillingly attract this label by conflicts with the physician in the course of negotiating an illness diagnosis or by the sheer persistence of their needs [37–39]. Factors that seem to lead to many of these specific difficulties in patient management are similar to those already alluded to which involve differences in medical orientations. The "problem" patients tenaciously hold on to their conviction that they have a disease despite a medical workup that

---

[5]The assumption that a formulation about disease contributes in part to problems of medical care and practice in no way minimizes the contributions of other factors to these problems. Economic, transportation, and structural factors, for example, can obviously contribute to problems in medical care delivery independent of any conceptual issues.

failed to demonstrate a bodily abnormality. The problems *posed* by these patients can be seen as consequences of having what are essentially conflicting frameworks cloaked within an organismic view of disease. The individual, feeling disarticulated in a social or psychological sense, concludes that he is diseased, the intervening premise in his formulation being "dis ease = disease." The physician, relying on a different framework but on the same organismic conception of disease, cannot validate this label. A referral to a psychiatric clinic can often accomplish professional validation. Motivationally oriented psychiatrists, on the other hand, may view this type of patient as "displacing" or "converting" his psychological problems onto the body (as "somatizing"), or perhaps as the result of "cancer phobia." The emphasis here is often on the "anxiety" that is expressed in or as bodily preoccupations. Sometimes the label "somatic delusions" may be employed. The possibility that the "symptoms" of the patient may represent his naïve attempts to fuse contrasting frameworks is not entertained.[6] In these instances, then, the "existence" of a person-centered discontinuity is not at issue, but instead the framework that should be adopted to label it.

A great deal has been written about the impersonality of the physician, his alleged disinterest and detachment, and about his tendency not to "care" about his patient. Criticisms that are offered state that a physician, instead of seeing a person in distress, tends to see an isolated body or machine that is abnormal. Insofar as alleviating human suffering is currently viewed as a principal goal of medical activity, it seems to inescapably follow that physicians need to concern themselves instrumentally with this objective. It should be noted in passing that the conception that disease is or involves suffering often leads to the converse assertion—namely that suffering is or involves disease. However, the implications of this particular position are currently very far-reaching and cannot be discussed fully at this juncture. We will return later to related issues. However, given that the alleviation of human suffering in a broad sense is seen as a principal feature or object of medical transactions—the so-called ministerial function of the physician—the criticisms about the physician's alleged preoccupation with bodily centered happenings and his tendency to discount humanistic and social concerns appear to also reflect conflicts in the prevailing view of disease. If we view the language of scientific medicine (particularly the terms; propositions, and directives that follow from a biologistic conception) as a set of symbols to which attach dispositions,

---

[6]The validity of psychoanalytic theory is not being questioned. Quite obviously, the application of psychoanalysis to medical problems has led to significant insights regarding the mechanisms of disease. However, the use of psychoanalytic formulation in dealings with patients unaccustomed to this manner of conceptualizing phenomena that are believed to be implicated in the disease process requires great skill and tact. Working-class patients, for example, typically persist in formulating their medical problems using the language about the body, and it frequently is necessary to learn their perspective about the "disease" needing resolution before therapeutic gains can be made.

attitudes, and other behaviorally relevant prescriptions, then the formalistic and stereotypical aspects of the physician's demeanor which appear to underlie the criticisms referred to above seem understandable. An organismic view of disease, when biological issues are given salience, contains a picture or a "construction of reality" [40]. In this picture the individual who is ill and seeking help often appears as a changed organism. He may be treated as a potential "case," his body searched for abnormalities, and the totality of his humanness subordinated. What assumes importance now are his complaints, his pains, his physical limitations, and his habits as they may pertain to his medical (i.e., bodily) condition. His relatedness to the world is probed and dissected, not for its humanity but as part of a "medical history." The stripping down, the systematic reduction of the person, and his transformation into a set of diagnostic possibilities can be viewed as a necessary and perhaps desirable process that enables the precise thinking and rigorous inquiry that constitute a medical evaluation. Our intent here is not to judge the merits of this process but to point out that it conflicts with the processes expected by persons holding other frameworks (behavioral or phenomenological) that are formally comparable with the biologistic view. Stated more succinctly, the reciprocal expectations of physician and patient are mediated by an organismic view of disease, but the underlying frameworks that each participant follows differ, thus creating friction in the transaction. Criticisms about the physician's demeanor and mode of relating, then, can be traced to basic disagreements in the underlying and guiding frameworks that happen to be fused in and concealed by an organismic view. Since the various disease frameworks share formal properties, this allows for the illusion that expectations about conduct and behavior are shared when in fact they are not.

Inconsistent meanings about disease that are obscured by an organismic view, as well as features of this view itself, also account for problems of articulating other types of health services with consumers. The implementation of "preventive" programs are hindered by a consequence of the dominating influence of the organismic view, namely, the emphasis that diseases are discrete and recognizable discontinuities or deviations. A logical consequence, of course, is the lack of a concept of health that is different from that of "absence of disease." Here, in other words, the view that treatment is directed at disease, an undesirable state that somehow needs to be recognized in order to "exist," proves problematic. The definition of the patient as a person who seeks help for what he judges is a discontinuity beclouds the issue of whether, for example, an undetected instance of diabetes is actually a disease and whether treatment is required. These issues in turn underlie the confusion that medical students demonstrate when asked if the person with an asymptomatic or "silent" chest lesion "has a disease." Indeed the tendency to see disease as a changed state of the organism accounts in part for the disbelief that persons sometimes experience when, following a routine evaluation, they are told that they "need" an operation or treatment. The implicit premise behind the person's reaction seems to be that, if the body is diseased, one expects that he should "know" about it. The organismic view of disease appears to assume that social processes simply funnel or propel patients directly to physicians once they are aware that they "have" a disease; the social rootedness of disease, or more precisely, the fact that there are different frameworks contained within the prevailing organismic view, is lost sight of.

The issues discussed above are equally relevant when viewed from a different standpoint. The tendency of people to view disease as a separate and "altered" state that is person centered, a personal discontinuity so to speak, may account for some of the delays in seeking care and for problems in adhering to medical advice. This is the case because, as already mentioned, the organismic view suggests that only identified personal discontinuities require evaluation and attention. The organismic conception also implies that since disease represents an abnormality that is atypical, it may be distinct from the person. This, in turn, tends to militate against openness about and acknowledgment of the body's function, as well as its dynamic relation to everyday situations. In other words, acceptance of the body as a component of the self, a dimension that is subject to modification, change, and levels of functioning, might facilitate attending to its care. One could say that much of the mystery that persons attribute to the body, the tendency to compartmentalize and isolate it and to avoid responding to its needs, may be attributed to consequences of the traditional organismic view which ascribes to disease features of a discontinuity that is somehow apart from the person. Conversely, it should not be forgotten that the view that disease is somehow separate and atypical is an outgrowth of the mystery and fear with which individuals reflect upon the functioning of the body. Social meanings about disease and the body, in short, are intertwined; are products of historically structured traditions; and are frequently at variance with refined views of related phenomena made possible by subsequent intellectual developments. In a similar vein, the connotations of death and the multifaceted problems of "managing" patients with terminal illness can be viewed as both determinants and resultants of these implications of the traditional organismic view of disease.

It can be argued that a portion of the undesirable social and psychological consequences that individuals experience as a result of receiving medical care (i.e., having the label of disease applied to them) stem from the properties of the organismic view of disease. The implication of separation, discontinuity, and alteration that this view seems to attach to a disease concept can very often have the effect of promoting in the patient a feeling of being separate, different, and abnormal. The connotation that disease may represent a change in personal identity can promote social withdrawal and lead to new self-definitions that may prove deleterious to the individual regardless of whether the biological correlates of the disease actually interfere with function. Much has been written about the sick role, the set of behaviors and dispositions that are adopted by persons who are ill and that are sanctioned for him by others as a result of illness. In many instances, of course, such roles can be adaptive and actually necessary or inevitable. Diseases that are acute in onset, short lasting, and accompanied by much distress and disability no doubt require social redefinitions and informal contractual realignments in order to dampen their effects on established social equilibria and patterns. We suspect, however, that in a number of instances sick-role behaviors and dispositions can be activated even though they are inapplicable and, furthermore, that their sociopsychological correlates can prove to be harmful to individuals classified as diseased (and to their families). Disease classified as "psychiatric" is known to have such pernicious effects. To this must be added diseases such as tuberculosis, syphilis, and cancer. Indeed, such attributive forms as "diabetic," "asthmatic," and "epileptic" remind us that relatively common diseases can be associated with, if not the cause of, altered personal identities. The literature dealing with the discrediting and stigmatic effects of disease which describe the personal and social havoc that the disease label can produce should be consulted for further details [41]. The point we wish to emphasize is that some of the sociopsychologically undesirable consequences of receiving care stem from features implied by symbolic correlates of the traditional organismic view of disease.

V. MODIFICATIONS OF THE ORGANISMIC CONCEPTION: THE UNIFIED OR SYSTEMS VIEW OF DISEASE

It is, of course, inaccurate to imply that all physicians and students of disease generally hold to the conception that disease represents a person centered discontinuity. This is so for two reasons. In the first case, it is simplistic to assume that any one view of disease is shared by physicians or students of disease. What obtain, instead, are views and perspectives composed of elements that shift and fluctuate according to clinically relevant situations. Nevertheless, to the extent that orientations share general features, it is permissible to use the notion of a general view of disease. A more serious inaccuracy is promulgated if we assume that the disease concept as outlined in previous sections represents the important contemporary medical paradigm among medical researchers and educators. That this is not the case will be substantiated here by summarizing recent contributions that have had the effect of broadening earlier viewpoints about disease.

A somewhat different but nevertheless related view of disease is that delineate by human ecologists [42–44]. To begin with, they describe persons not as separate and self-sufficient units, but as fleeting nodal points in a broad and diversified field that includes other persons, animals, and the physical environment. In this framework, the group, the population, and the ecosystem are the analytic units. The exchange between populations and physical environments represent the significant processes; evolution represents the mechanism that controls or brings about change. To Dubos, for example, disease is not a discontinuous qualitative state that man simply enters into or passes through. Instead, disease is viewed as a term that we arbitrarily use to label what in actuality constitute temporary setbacks in the perpetual struggle between man and the forces of nature. Man and the human group are viewed as standing in an "open" relationship with nature, each an interdependent part of the other. This means that the biological and social levels of human activity are, in a literal sense, structurally and functionally interpenetrated with nature (i.e., with viruses, bacteria, waste products, climatological features and periodicities, etc.). Man is thus viewed as always "diseased"; the relevant question becomes in what particular way and to what extent at this moment in time. To other ecologists, disease is seen as an organic entity with a life of its own, subject to modifications, growths, and decrements through time (see Burnet's description of disease types and epidemics [45]). Clearly, in this framework the traditional view that man and his disease represent a significant focal point or unique biological disjunction in the course of human events is not in salience.

The ideas of Engel, Hinkle, and Wolff bear on the ecological perspective just described [46–49]. Engel's key articles to a large extent emphasize the unique psychological and experiential components of all conditions labeled as disease. He stresses the need for a *unified view of disease* and has lucidly described the arbitrariness and pernicious consequences of traditional definitions. In a fashion reminiscent of human ecologists, Engel argues that health and disease, rather than representing discrete "states" or conditions, need to be seen as phases of the continuously changing multilevel set of processes (e.g., cellular, chemical, physiological, behavioral) that at any one moment constitute human striving. Hinkle and Wolff, on the basis of their now classic longitudinal studies of individuals of varied ages and background, have described the manner in which illnesses cluster in individuals and in time. The ecologic perspective is clearly in evidence when they probe in depth a person's adjustment to his social environment, his work habits, his emotional responsivity, as well as his physical status through time, with the goal of arriving at a broadly grounded meaning of health and illness. The framework proposed by Howard and Scott [50] for the analysis of stress, insofar as it is multileveled, holistic, and concerns both the internal and external environments of man, can be seen as congruent with the ecological approach to disease. Significantly, Hinkle, Wolff, Engel, Scott, et al., although they concern themselves with phenomena that are obviously "medical," carefully avoid the concept of disease as traditionally employed. Instead, the organism's attempts at mastery, that is its attempts to successfully solve problems that are posed to it by its environments, receive analytic emphasis. Failure in mastery leads to excessive energy expenditure, and this in turn leads to a state of tension or stress which in the long run is deleterious to the organism.

Feinstein [51–53] has carefully reviewed the problems that exist in traditional medical classification schemes. Although adhering rather closely to biologistic considerations, he has managed to construct a powerful attack on the existing nosology. The differing interpretations, meanings, and implications of specific disease types and the problems that they can create for physicians are lucidly discussed. Diseases, or more precisely, the defining characteristics of various disease types, are shown to be by-products of differing emphases and criteria. Some diseases, for example, denote physiological system malfunction, others the microorganism that may be responsible, others refer to underlying structural changes, and still others to names of individuals who made critical observations. Since he develops his arguments in a historical context, he is able to demonstrate very convincingly how medical activities in general, whether diagnostic exercises, treatment plans or simply disease definitions, are by-products of existing scientific traditions that repeatedly change, often quite arbitrarily. The consequences of these changes for physicians and health planners are outlined. The essence of medicine is seen as clinical activity, efforts exended to organize medical data so as to promote effective treatment. He points out that much of the ambiguity and inconsistencies in clinical activity stem not from deficiencies of the clinician or the nature of the clinical enterprise, per se, but rather from an inadequate language for discussions about disease. The imperfect correlation between laboratory data and clinical data (what he terms "form-function dissociation") is linked to the way disease is conceptualized generally and to diagnostic classification in particular. A disease type is shown to be an abstraction; rather than being a "biological fact," disease is described as sets of clustered biological facts.

The view of health and illness developed in the writings that have been reviewed bears an obvious relationship to recent theoretical developments in the social and biological sciences. General-systems theory, a corpus of organized concepts and approaches to the evaluation of regularities in the empirical world, has recently been applied more directly to the study of medicine in society [54, 55]. An attempt has been made to depict the health-care delivery system as an abstracted system. When applied to the disease concept, these theoretical developments appear to strengthen the unified view which was described earlier. In this perspective, disease is not viewed as a discrete and discontinuous state that attaches to an organism in space and time. What obtain, instead, are systems in articulation—molecular systems within cells; biochemical energy-processing systems at the tissue level; homeostatically geared systems at the organ-physiologic level; biopsychologic and sociopsychologic systems at the level of the self; sociointerpersonal systems at the family and institutional level; etc. All levels of this complex hierarchically organized system are described as being implicated in the processual stream of life. It is important to emphasize that in a unified or systems view of disease, not only are the *manifestations* or expressions of what we term "disease" seen as interconnected and hierarchically organized (i.e., a segments of a whole). In addition, the *determinants* of disease are also conceptualized holistically. Disease is seen as a natural consequence of man's open relationship with his physical and social environment. Styles of coping are seen as rooted in patterns of neuromuscular and humoral integration, and difficulties in coping (i.e., stress, frustration, etc.) as expressed in altered biological processes that give rise to symptoms or signs of disordered function (i.e., "disease"). Thus, cause is multifactorial, processes interconnected, and manifestations multifaceted. What we can observe are systems showing different degrees of adaptation and equilibrium. A "symptom" or a "sign" of dysfunction, then, appears to be no less medical whether it occurs at the biochemical level, the psychological level, or the social level. Similarly, emphasis on processes that are interconnected means that temporal boundaries become less clear and relevant when applied to disease. In other words, where and when disease or health begins and ends becomes problematic, just as does the "location" of an individual, functionally speaking. For example it becomes no less correct to "locate" a disease in tissues or body fluids as opposed to, say, the relationships and motivations that contribute to the bodily alterations. General-systems theorists emphasize the linkage that exists between subsystems implicated in any disease process; the unit of organization to which attention and effort is to be directed is determined by the particular aims and goals of the practitioner or planner.

VI. DISEASE FRAMEWORKS AND ORGANIZATION OF HEALTH CARE

A theme implicit throughout this essay has been that conceptualizations about disease are mirrored by and reflected in social attitudes, values, and perspectives. Similarly, what is done about disease and how this is accomplished bears a systematic relationship to the way in which disease is defined. Specifically, insofar as conceptions of disease underlie and pattern medical practice and care, alternative conceptions present challenges to the underlying basis of the profession and institution of medicine. This underlying basis has been considered a mandate, and includes: (1) a fundamental definition of the role of the professional; (2) his ethics, or the norms of practice usually develop into a professional code; (3) the etiquette, or rules about the nature of the client; and (4) a perspective regarding the aim of medical treatment. The mandate of medicine is typically defined as curing disease and maintaining health or, more dramatically, dealing with life and death. In practice, through the view of disease we have termed the "organismic," attention seems to be narrowed to the treatment dimension of the mandate. This narrowed conception is mirrored by the location of the physician in individual, entrepreneurial roles which tie him to the daily demands of his patient population in response to its definition of disease. As was reviewed earlier, some of the problematic aspects of medical care and health-services delivery can be seen as stemming from ambiguities, inconsistencies, and current implications of an organismic view of disease. It must not be concluded that the problems that have been linked to an organismic view of disease cannot be resolved in such a way that the advantages of continuing to work with this view of disease are retained. The delineation of these problems, as has been done in past reviews, is an obvious first step toward their resolution. An important reason for striving to maintain an organismic view, it is to be emphasized, is that it does articulate with the rather basic expectations and conceptions of medical consumers. In Western settings and in preliterate settings, common sense notions about the body's function, disease, health, and treatment partake of the view that disease is person centered, temporally bounded, and undesirable.

We have seen that an apparent logical consequence of the unified or "systems" view of disease is the disappearance of the traditional concept of organism and discontinuity, as well as the notion of what is "medical." Stated differently, what arbitrarily we respond to or label as "medically" relevant and salient (e.g., a chest pain, diabetic acidosis, pneumonia, a fracture, etc.) are described as systems that are disequilibrated. However, they are subsystems of larger systems that also are involved in any disease process. An implication of this view might be that practitioners of medicine, at the very least, must become biological-systems experts; yet given the hierarchic, multi-leveled and mutually influencing nature of medical phenomena, it would apear that practitioners might need to also become social science experts. Clearly, a view of disease that emphasizes holism and interconnectedness or continuity between "systems" does away with the traditional organismic features that seem to be implicit in the organization of medical practice. Thus, on the one hand, the rigorous application of a unified conception of disease might lessen problems discussed earlier involving the delivery of care, problems stemming from symbolic correlates of an organismic conception. However, the reformulation of disease along the lines articulated by educators influenced by systems theory, although theoretically justified and consistent with accumulating knowledge about nature, contains far-reaching implications for medical care and practice since, as we have seen, medical services are currently anchored in an organismic view. The consequences of institutionalizing a unified view of disease would appear to affect every facet of medicine.

The system or unified conception of disease is associated with important medical research that has led to enhanced understanding and knowledge of man's attempts at adaptation. The utility of this framework for conceptualizing health and disease is, thus, unquestioned. What does appear to require examination are the implications of this view of disease for the organization of medical care and practice and for the division of medical labor. The application of general-systems theory to this facet of medicine would appear to raise questions regarding (1) composition, location, organization, and structure of treatment and/or prevention units; (2) the significance and role of persons administering medical care; (3) the nature of the information base required of such persons; (4) the actual process of diagnosis and administration of care; and (5) the linkage of the preceding with the remainder of society's institutions. The full implementation of a systems view of disease would require far-reaching changes precisely because its emphasis on hierarchy, holism, and interconnectedness seems to blur the boundary betwen types of problems or sufferings—about what disease is and where it is located. It thus appears to require that equal emphasis be given to all the components or levels that appear to be implicated in an instance of what it terms "disease" as well as to matters currently viewed as external to and separate from disease.

The way in which a particular conceptualization about disease can relate generally to social phenomena and, specifically, to the manner in which medical care and practice are organized and conducted, can be illustrated by considering in further detail the biologistic framework that was discussed at the beginning of this essay. It appears reasonable to believe that given sufficient time, it might be possible to begin to apply this biological framework in quantitative terms. The application of this particular framework of disease in such a fashion could yield a number or measure which could be assigned to individuals on the basis of a medical evaluation; such a measure would represent the amount of a "disease" (e.g., a disease score) that X has. Indeed, since what is being measured is a continuum underlying any disease process, it becomes more accurate to speak of diabeticity scores, hypertensive scores, etc. (For a very lucid analysis of issues related to the point being illustrated here, the reader is urged to consult [56].) For example, the various "biological" indicators that signal different diseases could each be quantified whenever possible, and on the basis of a suitable formula wherein indicators appear as variables, a number computed for each person (not patient). The following form is suggested:

$D = a_1 Q_1 + a_2 Q_2 + \ldots a_n Q_n;$
D = "amount" of diabetes;
a_1 = weighting constants ("how much" each indicator or variable contributes to D);
Q_i = an indicator of D specified in appropriate units.

The use of a biological framework in this fashion would avoid the suggestion that disease is a (qualitative) changed state. Thus, logical problems such as that of "determining" whether *X* has or does not have *D* are avoided; everyone has *D*, the question becomes how much of *D* and how is the *D* score lowered so as to promote certain desired ends (i.e., less malaise, less pain, longer life expectancy, etc.). If sufficient knowledge were available vis-à-vis the causes of *D*, its manifestations, its mechanism, and how to modify bodily processes and indicators reflecting or showing *D*, then treatment plans could also be specified in terms of formulas containing quantitative variables (i.e., how much and how long *X* needs to take of *A*, how much he needs to do of *B*, etc.). In the long run, the use of this framework in this fashion could lead to the conception that all individuals can be characterized by numbers (i.e., D_1, D_2, D_3, etc.), each of which reflects the status and levels of biological functioning (embodied conceptually as "disease scores") which in turn contribute to decrements of desired ends; correspondingly, to each individual would attach formulas or treatment plans. The orientations and values required to support such a view of disease and the social implications and consequences of adopting this conception and manner of evaluating disease would obviously be profound.

A state of human affairs wherein the preceding notions are actualized (i.e., put into practice and acted upon) would probably require a different type of medical consumer, as well as sharp differences in the way that medical care and practices are organized. For one thing, it would be important for persons to demonstrate some knowledge about the implications of these disease scores. The body's function would have to be made a relevant area of concern for people, and accurate information about biological matters would have to be made available and, more important, desirable. Motivation to maintain scores within acceptable ranges could become a domain of greater personal responsibility if individuals were systematically educated about individual differences in how their body functioned, about determinants of bodily changes, and about the short- and long-range implications of deviations in scores. Provided this was done early in life, systematically, by means of educationally sound procedures, and with optimal social values placed on this type of human activity, there is reason to expect that the enterprise could be successful.[7] The result might then be a population of persons who are

---

[7]The use of the word "optimal" in this sentence condenses what needs to be seen as a relatively complex set of notions. To conceptions about the body, its function, its fluids, and its emanations are attached a variety of values and prudential interests that are incorporated in and form an integral part of routine social prescriptions. Attitudes and orientations toward *disease* are reflected in these valuations and conceptions about the body. It would seem that openness toward and acceptance of the use of "disease scores" would logically demand particular types of meanings and values about the body. A social system which institutionalizes a biologistic conception of disease inthe manner outlined would likely require orientations and dispositions toward bodily affairs that are different from those currently reflected in what is termed acceptable discourse and behavior. These new orientations and dispositions would need to be reflected in any educational efforts aimed at changing the prevailing view of disease.

interested and informed about the body's function, about the wear and tear that it is subject to, and committed to the notion of their responsibility for its care. The management of disease could then become a highly technical, impersonal, and computerized affair. Regular evaluations would provide a profile of score values together with a printout containing a list of modifications in living habits that are required in order to reach particular desired ends. Short-term flare-ups of different "disease scores" might require some form of external supervision and surveillance by technicians or biological engineers skilled and trained in the methods of restoring "elevated scores." A variety of different types of technicians and engineers can be imagined, all regularly situated in specialized facilities that service bounded population segments. The management of chronic elevations, of course, would be systematically woven into routine daily habits and practices that all persons continually engage in.

Dealing with the emotional and psychological correlates of disease could be retained as a feature of the obligations of the "physician," a view highly consistent with the current position of many medical educators and theoreticians. However, this facet of what currently is viewed as a requirement of good *medical* care could be regarded as logically independent of concerns discussed above. For example, social and psychological difficulties that stem from or involve work situations, economic constraints, interpersonal relating, life-cycle adjustments, and the physical constraints and bodily abnormalities associated with disease-score changes could be defined a priori as distinctly separate realms of human activity and concern. "Human relationship experts" might be the title of personnel skilled and trained in helping others with these types of problems. The notion that these everyday living concerns (although problematic, painful, and disorganizing to human productivity and social equilibrium) constitute diseases would, of course, have to be eschewed. Disease, to repeat again, would be defined in terms of biological system malfunction and indicated by the type of information reviewed earlier. Insofar as brain changes are capable of effectuating social and psychological changes that mimic typical problems that might confront the human relationship experts, the latter personnel (or subtypes of these) would need to scan computer printouts of their clients in order to define those in need of more specialized forms of help.

One consequence of institutionalizing the above view is that it would separate out notions that today are viewed as indivisible, namely that disease invoves suffering, and suffering involves disease. A premise of the above program would be that score elevations can be associated with human suffering and in fact for this reason need to be closely regulated and monitored. The prevailing view of and orientation toward suffering, however, would be that it represented an affair different from that of disease and consequently that it needed to be dealt with differently. Specifically, "diseases" would be treated as strictly biologistic affairs, whereas the suffering traceable to "disease," together with other types of sufferings, would be seen as altogether different concerns. It needs to be emphasized that the values and traditions that link with and stem from "disease" as it is currently conceptualized and handled could hardly accommodate the separation of services as outlined. The form and expression of disease and its correlative problems, as well as approaches to their treatment, are outgrowths of historical and social contingencies. In brief, the type of problems tied to disease, the anticipations of consumers, and their satisfactions or dissatisfactions with medical care are embedded in formulations of disease that are anchored in social categories. New was of handling disease and its problems such as those touched on here would for this reason require quite different social contexts.

SUMMARY

This essay has involved an examination of alternative conceptualiations about disease. Three frameworks that assigned different meanings to the term "disease" have been presented. Each framework defines disease using alternative types of indicators. The frameworks are associated with different intellectual, social, and cultural traditions. The formal characteristics that these frameworks have in common were reviewed. The organismic view of disease is the name given to the distillates of the three frameworks. The premises that organize and structure medical care and practice were seen as reflecting an organismic conception. Some of the problems involving health care were related to an organismic conception per se and to the conflicts that it can create insofar as it can mask basic disagreements in underlying frameworks. The unified or systems view of disease that is salient among many medical researchers was reviewed. Some of the problems for medical care posed by this view of disease were mentioned. The potential consequences of institutionalizing an alternate disease conception were illustrated by using a strictly biologistic view. The object of the essay has been to systematically analyze how frameworks used to define disease relate to social phenomena and how they influence what man does and can do about disease.

REFERENCES

1. R. M. Dreger, J. Gen. Psychol., **78**:41, 1968.
2. R. L. Engle and B. J. Davis. Arch. Intern. Med. (Chicago), **112**: 512, 1963.
3. R. L. Engle, Arch. Intern. Med. (Chicago), **112**:520, 1963.
4. ———. Arch. Intern. Med. (Chicago), **112**:530, 1963.
5. B. MacMahon and T. F. Pough. Epidemiology: principles and methods. Boston: Little, Brown, 1970.

6. I. M. Moriyama. J. Chronic Dis., **11**:462, 1960.
7. H. A. Tyroler. *In*: M. R. Greenlick (ed.). Proceedings of the conference on conceptual issues in the analysis of medical care utilization behavior, p. 33. Washington, D.C.: Department of Health, Education, and Welfare, Public Health Service, Health Services an Mental Health Administration, 1968.
8. D. F. Sullivan. Conceptual problems in developing an index of health. Public Health Service Pub. No. 1000, Serv. 2, No. 17. Washington, D.C.: National Center for Health Statistics, U.S. Government Printing Office, 1966.
9. W. V. Quine. From a logical point of view. 2d ed. New York: Harper & Row, 1969.
10. H. S. Leonard. Principles of reasoning: an introduction to logic, methodology and the theory of signs. New York: Dover, 1967.
11. H. Fabrega and P. Manning. Theoretical perspectives on deviance. Ed. J. Douglas. New York: Basic, in press.
12. A. A. Buck, R. I. Anderson, T. T. Sasaki, and K. Kawata. Health and disease in Chad: epidemiology, culture, and environment in five villages. Baltimore: The Johns Hopkins Press, 1970.
13. A. A. Buck, R. I. Anderson, T. T. Sasaki, and K. Kawata. Health and disease in four Peruvian villages: contrasts in epidemiology. Baltimore: The Johns Hopkins Press, 1968.
14. L. R. Schwartz. J. Health Soc. Behav., **10**:201, 1969.
15. H. Fabrega. Yale J. Biol. Med., **43**:385, 1971.
16. T. S. Szasz. Pain and pleasure: a study of bodily feelings. New York: Basic, 1957.
17. P. Schilder. The image and appearance of the human body. New York: Wiley, 1950.
18. S. Wapner and H. Werner (eds.). The body percept. New York: Random House, 1965.
19. F. G. Lounsbury. Language, **32**:158, 1956.
20. W. H. Goodenough. Cultural anthropology and linguistics, p. 167. Georgetown Univ. Monogr. Ser. Lang. Linguis. 9. Washington, D.C.: Georgetown Univ. Press, 1957.
21. K. J. Franklin. Southwest. J. Anthrop., **19**:54, 1963.
22. G. L. Engel. Signs and Symptoms. Ed. C. M. MacBryde and R. S. Blacklow. 5th ed. Philadelphia: Lippincott, 1970.
23. B. B. Wolff and S. Langley. Amer. Anthrop., **70**:494, 1968.
24. P. Winch. The idea of a social science. London: Routledge & Kegan Paul, 1958.
25. A. Rubel. Ethnology, **3**:268, 1964.
26. H. Fabrega. Ethnology, **9**:25, 1971.
27. ______. Milbank Mem. Fund Quart., **48**:391, 1970.
28. ______. Behav. Sci., **15**:471, 1970.
29. S. H. King. Perceptions of illness and medical practice. New York: Russell Sage Foundation, 1962.
30. A. Rubel. Amer. Anthrop., **62**:795, 1960.
31. R. Andersen. A behavioral model of families' use of health services. Res. Ser. 25. Chicago: Center for Health Administration Studies, Graduate School of Business, Univ. Chicago, 1968.
32. I. M. Rosenstock. Milbank Mem. Fund Quart., **44**:94, 1966.
33. H. Fabrega and R. E. Roberts. Medical care, in press.

34. W. R. Ashby. An introduction to cybernetics. New York: Wiley, 1963.
35. E. Goffman. Psychiat., 22:133. 1959.
36. T. Parsons. Amer. J. Orthopsychiat., **21**:452, 1951.
37. M. Balint. The doctor, his patient, and the illness. New York: International Universities Press, 1957.
38. H. Fabrega, R. J. Moore, and J. R. Strawn. J. Health Soc. Behav., **10**:334, 1969.
39. O. Von Mering and L. W. Earley. Hum. Organ., **25**:20, 1966.
40. P. L. Berger and T. Luckmann. The social construction of reality: a treatise in the sociology of knowledge. New York: Doubleday, 1967.
41. E. Goffman. Stigma: notes on the management of spoiled identity. Englewood Cliffs, N.J.: Prentice-Hall, 1963.
42. R. Dubos. Man adapting. New Haven, Conn.: Yale Univ. Press, 1965.
43. F. L. Dunn. Man the hunter. Ed. R. B. Lee and I. Devore. Chicago: Aldine, 1968.
44. J. E. Gordon. Amer. J. Med. Sci., **235**:337, 1958.
45. M. Burnet. Natural history of infectious disease. Cambridge, Mass.: Cambridge Univ. Press, 1966.
46. G. L. Engel. Perspect. Biol. Med., **3**:459, 1960.
47. L. E. Hinkle, H. Whitney, E. W. Lehman, J. Dunn, B. Benjamin, R. King, A. Plakun, and B. Flehinger. Science, **161**:238, 1968.
48. L. E. Hinkle. Psychosom. Med., **23**:289, 1961.
49. H. G. Wolff. Psychosom. Med., **24**:25, 1962.
50. A. Howard and R. A. Scott. Behav. Sci., **10**:141, 1965.
51. A. Feinstein. Clinical judgement. Baltimore: Williams & Wilkins, 1967.
52. ______. Annals Intern. Med., **69**:807, 1968.
53. ______. Annals Intern. Med., **69**:1037, 1968.
54. D. D. Rutstein and M. Eden. Engineering and living systems: interfaces and opportunities. Cambridge, Mass.: M.I.T. Press, 1970.
55. A. Sheldon, F. Baker, and C. P. McLaughlin (eds.). Systems and medical care. Cambridge, Mass.: M.I.T. Press, 1970.
56. S. Israel and G. Teeling-Smith. Social and economic administration, no. 1, p. 43. London, 1967.

5.3

The Medical Model: Its Nature & Problems

Robert M. Veatch

With few exceptions addiction to morphine and heroin should be regarded as a manifestation of a morbid state.

British Rolleston Committee, 1926

Addiction should be regarded as an expression of mental disorder, rather than a form of criminal behavior.

Brain Committee, 1961

...the addict should be regarded as a sick person...and not as a criminal, provided he does not resort to criminal acts.

Brain Committee, 1965

...according to the prevalent understanding of the words, crime is not *a disease. Neither is it an illness, although I think it* should *be!*

Karl Menninger, 1968

Ultimate policy conrol of the programs as well as day-by-day supervision must be securely lodged in medical *rather than political, probation, parole, or police hands.*

Consumers Union Report on Licit and Illicit Drugs, 1972

In sociological parlance, a model is a complex, integrated system of meaning used to view, interpret, and understand a part of reality; and one of the most deeply rooted such systems in our rationalistic and scientifically oriented Western society is the medical model. A pervasive and complex instrument for interpreting a wide range of behavior, the medical model has served well as a means of organizing our attitudes and actions toward a variety of human abnormalities. In fact, it has served so well that attempts are continually being made to expand its boundaries to include forms of abnormal behavior which had previously been interpreted within other models.

Today an entire series of behaviors are doubtful candidates for the category of illness, that is, for interpretation in the medical model: narcotic addiction, mental deviancy, unwanted pregnancy, alcoholism, homosexuality, unwanted folds in the facial skin, and virtually all criminal behavior. At least some members of our society view all or some of these conditions as most meaningfully understood in the medical model, as part of the health-illness complex in some sense or another. Some generations ago, other forms of abnormality were in a similar position as dubious illnesses: tuberculosis, leprosy, epilepsy, psychosis from lead poisoning. The fact that we have a history of expanding the medical model to include an ever widening circle of forms of human variant behavior previously interpreted as resulting from moral, religious, or political aberration is sometimes used as an argument from precedent, i.e., with further enlightenment (i.e., scientific understanding) we shall see how the presently ambiguous variant behaviors also fit into the medical model.

What, then, is the nature of the medical model, its basic elements, and its implications for society? Before outlining what I see as the basic characteristics of the medical model, however, we must first examine the nature of illness as one among many forms of socially constructed deviancy. Having done this, we can then consider what I see as four essential characteristics of the medical model. Finally, we shall conclude by exploring the implication of the medical and other models for marginal forms of deviancy.

I. ILLNESS AS A SOCIALLY CONSTRUCTED DEVIANCY

A. The Social Construction of Deviancy

In the past two decades the sociology of medicine and the sociology of knowledge have together made great progress in gaining insight into the human interpretation of human behavior. Individuals who are ill, according to our ordinary understanding, are in possession of biological attributes seen as abnormal in some sense. While we are all familiar with concepts of psychogenic and psychosomatic illness, the man on the street normally conceives of illness as a biological aberration. Beginning, however, with Parsons' work in the 1950s, it became apparent that the process of being labelled as ill was much more complex. Illness is a socially assigned category given meaning from society to society by social interpretation and evaluation of the biologically abnormal characteristics. Thus Freidson argues that two kinds of imputed deviance figure in the notion of illness: biological and social.[1]

It is clear that biological aberation alone is not enough to make a person ill. The seven-foot tall basketball player is hardly ill. He is admittedly grossly abnormal—and rewarded for it. Thus some kinds of biological aberration are

[1]Eliot Freidson, *Profession of Medicine* (New York: Dodd, Mead, 1971), p. 211.

deviant (both socially and biologically), yet positively evaluated. Still other kinds of biological deviance are not positively evaluated, but are not negatively valued either—sporadic dense pigmentation of the skin called "freckles," for instance. In the sociology of deviance, normally the term deviance is limited to *negatively* evaluated deviance. However, it is possible to possess a negatively evaluated attribute which is clearly biological in nature and still not have the condition interpreted in the medical model. In a racist society, for instance, which evaluates generally distributed black pigmentation negatively, possessors of that biological characteristic will encounter discrimination but are not considered sick.

All forms of deviancy have in common the fact that they are necessarily social constructions. Freidson argues, "Human, and therefore social, *evaluation of what is normal, proper, or desirable is as inherent in the notion of illness as it is in notions of morality*."[2] We should not lose sight of the fact that all understandings of reality are socio-cultural constructions. Working with perceptual raw data, which are nothing more than an endless series of impressions, human beings, as members of social groups construct categories and systems of meaning and value which make sense out of an otherwise meaningless stream of existence.[3] This is true even for such fundamental systems of meaning as the Western scientific world view. But it is more obviously true for the socially constructed patterns by which types of deviancy are evaluated and for the establishment of roles which organize the life of the deviant.

To claim that all understandings of reality are socio-cultural is emphatically not the same as saying that all meanings and values are culturally relative. It is simpy to say that *understandings* and *systems* of meaning which are used by human beings to interpret experience are necessarily products of a culture. Certainly language is a critical element in interpretation and understanding of experience, and language is a cultural construction. Likewise world views, underlying systems of meaning and value, are the products of a culture. But in making this claim we are purposely leaving open the question of whether there may be "in reality" values and meanings upon which our socio-culturally constructed systems of understanding are based, and which could give rise to meaningful debate about whether or not such social constructions are "constructed properly."[4]

---

[2]*Ibid.*, p. 208. Italics in the original.

[3]See Peter L. Berger and Thomas Luckmann, *The Social Construction of Reality* (Garden City, N.Y.: Doubleday, 1966).

[4]In fact, it is our position that there are "absolute and objective" values and meanings upon which one may properly or improperly construct a socio-cultural understanding, but to argue this point, just as to argue the point of whether or not there are in fact real physical objects in reality to which our natural scientific sense impressions should correspond, is to lead into the realm of metaphysics and theology. I have made such arguments elsewhere (*Hastings Center Studies* 1 [Number 1, 1973], pp. 50–65), but would claim that the present discussion is independent of these debates about the nature of the transcendent. For a similar position see Peter L. Berger, "Appendix II. Sociological and Theological Perspectives," in *The Sacred Canopy* (Garden City, N.Y.: Doubleday, 1967), pp. 179–88.

To have one's body invaded by bacterial organisms which produce fever, nausea, and vomiting is not the same as being sick. Animals quite ordinarily may have the former characteristics, but it is not until social interpretation is given to those characteristics that the affected one is "sick." To be sick is to have aberrant characteristics of a certain sort which society as a whole evaluates as being bad and for which that society assigns the sick role.[5] According to the Parsonian formulation, the sick role includes two exemptions from normal responsibilities and two obligations or new responsibilities.[6] First, the person in the sick role is exempt from normal social responsibilities. Second, the person in the sick role is exempt from responsibility for his condition and cannot be expected to get well by an act of decision or will; he cannot be expected to "pull himself together." The third characteristic of the sick role is that it is itself undesirable. There is an obligation to want to get well.[7] Finally, one in the sick role has an obligation to "seek technically competent help."

No matter how unusual, "unnatural," or even death-inducing a set of characteristics may afflict him, the individual is not "sick," and thus exhibiting

[5] Of course, it may be, at least for a holder of the view that real values and meanings exist in the transcendent world of objectivity, that some individuals have characteristics which ought to be seen and treated by a society and yet are not—or, on the other hand, are seen and treated by society as sick but ought not to be. The fact is however that one really is sick in the sense of living the sick role if and only if the social judgment is made by society or some portion of it.

[6] Talcott Parsons, *The Social System* (New York: The Free Press, 1951), pp. 428–79. This chapter is probably the most significant in (and the origin of) contemporary sociology of medicine. It grows out of an earlier field study of medical practice conducted by Parsons. It is important to realize that not only sociology of medicine, but some important categories in theoretical sociology, especially the sociology of the professions and the sociology of deviance, grow out of this medical context. We would suspect that the use of the medical model as the paradigm for study of these more general issues has generated the expansionist tendencies for the medical model, the sick role and related theoretical constructs, the use of the model to cover all legitimated, nonculpable forms of deviancy, and the transfer of the obligation to seek technically competent help to the obligation to use medial personnel. Other sociological interpretations of illness as a form of legitimated deviancy can be found in David Mechanic, *Medical Sociology* (New York: The Free Press, 1968); Robert N. Wilson, *The Sociology of Health* (New York: Random House, 1970); Stanley H. King, "Social psychological Factors in Illness," in Howard E. Freeman, Sol Levine, and Leo G. Reeder (eds.), *Handbook of Medical Sociology* (Englewood Cliffs, N.J.: Prentice-Hall, 1963), pp. 99–121, especially p. 112; and Robert N. Wilson, "Patient-Pratitioner Relationships," in *ibid.*, pp. 273–95, especially pp. 276–77.

In addition there are now several examples in the literature of authors who begin with the notion of illness as socially constructed deviancy and build this into a critical commentary on the incorporation of major forms of deviancy into the medical model. These include Erving Goffman, *Asylums* (Garden City, N.Y.: Doubleday, 1961); Thomas Szasz, *The Myth of Mental Illness* (New York: Harper & Row, 1961), and *The Manufacture of Madness* (New York: Harper & Row, 1970).

[7] There is some disagreement about whether the person in the sick role has an obligation to "want" to get well or only to "try" to get well. Normally desires or wants are not obligated. Robert N. Wilson in *The Sociology of Health* (New York: Random House, 1970), p. 17, claims simply that there is "an obligation to 'get well' and to cooperate with others to this end." If, however, the sick role is by social definition undesirable, probably Parsons' formulation of the obligation to "want to get well" is appropriate. Parsons in "Definitions of Health and Illness in the Light of American Values and Social Structure," in E. G. Jaco (ed.), *Patients, Physicians and Illness* (New York: The Free Press, 1958), p. 176, says the sick person has an "obligation to try to 'get well.'"

behavior interpreted in the medical model, until a social judgment is made. Among other things, that social judgment must include a negative evaluation. That is true for *any* class of deviant behavior no matter what its origin.[8]

This critical point should not be lost throughout the remainder of this discussion. Even organic sickness in the most narrow and traditional sense as interpreted in the medical model necessarily contains a socially bestowed negative evaluation. Sedgwick and others are thus on the right track in attacking Szasz, Leifer, Goffman, and other critics of treating mental illness in the medical model, when they base their argument on the assumption that mental illness differs from organic illness. These critics claim that while organic illness refers to biological conditions which are objective and exist independent of any human value judgments, mental illness is a social, value-laden category.[9] I shall later disagree with Sedgwick's conclusion that because organic and mental illness share in common a socially constructed negative evaluation which is in either case a value judgment, mental deviaiton should, therefore, be classified as an illness. That shall be argued later, but at this level Sedgwick is certainly correct and reflects sound thinking in the sociology of knowledge and the sociology of medicine. If one refuses to place mental deviation in the same "illness" category as organic illness, it must be done on grounds other than that the former involves social value judgments and the latter supposedly does not.

B. The Differentiation of Social Deviancies

Having identified all illness as a type within the broader category of social deviance, it is now important to differentiate it from other types and to trace the history of what differentiation and the study of it. Nowadays it is a commonplace to recognize that in an earlier age deviancies were not well differentiated. The ill person, the criminal, the possessed, the religiously inspired were not well separated into different roles. Likewise the functionaries with special roles were not differentiated. In many societies, the medical practitioner, law enforcer, psychologist, and priest were combined in one role, that of the medicine man-priest. One of the primary characteristics of "higher" civilization, however, according to this school of functional analysis, is the differentiation of different functionary roles.

Talcott Parsons again has provided the definitive analysis of the differentiation of the medical model from other major forms of deviancy which he saw

---

[8]Classifying illness as one among many types of socially defined deviant behavior which are disapproved does not mean that blame is imputed. The literature distinguishes between "legitimated and "nonlegitimated" forms of social deviancy.

[9]See the article by Peter Sedgwick in this volume.

as important conceptual models in societies.[10] Parsons differentiated deviances on two major axes.[11] First, he separated those deviancies which involve disturbances in commitments to norms and values (giving rise to the deviancies of crime and sin respectively) from those deviancies attributed to "the exigencies of the situation in which the person must act" (deviancies of disloyalty and illness). The second axis of differentiation separates those deviancies of the person as a whole from those which involve only a problem of accepting particular obligations. Disturbances of particular obligations (disloyalty and crime) are differentiated from disturbances of the total person (immorality and illness). When these two variables are crossed as the major axes of differentiation, illness is thus separated from immorality in being situational rather than normative in focus; from disloyalty by being a disturbance of the total person rather than of particular obligations; and from crime or illegality on both of the axes.

In less sophisticated analyses, the polarity is erroneously reduced to the extremes of crime and illness. For example, the title of an important study, formulating policy for two major relevant professional groups on the subject of drug addiction, poses the question—"Drug Addiction: Crime or Disease?"[12] It is little wonder that the authors had difficulty reaching a conclusion. Once again the origins of the study suggest that the *Sitz im Leben* may be important for the understanding of the theoretical categories for classifying negatively evaluated deviancies and the unique interests and perspectives of the professional groups in the debate. The study was conducted by the professional associations representing the cadres of experts in the two models posed as alternatives for interpretation of drug addiction: the American Bar Association and the American Medical Association. One wonders what the alternative models would have been if the study had been sponsored by associations of priests, behavioral psychologists, or sociologists.

For understanding the medical model and the disputes currently arising about doubtful illnesses such as narcotic addiction, it is crucial to realize the nature of the primary axes of major differentiations of types of deviancy. At the level of the Parsonian differentiation, if a deviance is to be seen as situational (rather than normative) and total (rather than particular), the only category

---

[10]Talcott Parsons, "Definitions of Health and Illness in the Light of American Values and Social Structure," pp. 165–87.

[11]*Ibid.*, p. 173.

[12]*Drug Addiction: Crime or Disease?* Interim and Final Reports of the Joint Committee of the American Bar Association and the American Medical Association on Narcotic Drugs (Bloomington: Indiana University Press, 1961). In a newly published volume, Anthony Flew, *Crime or Disease?* (New York: Macmillan, 1973), creates the same polarization for the opposite motive in a discussion of the nature of mental disorder. He finds the removal of responsibility implied in the "disease" model a threat to individual dignity and is thus critical of its application to criminal behavior.

available is "illness." Since one of the primary motives (functions) for classifying a doubtful illness as illness is to gain these characteristics, it may be that we are in need of more than one category with such characteristics, and that only failure to carry the analysis far enough has left but one appropriate category, that of illness. Much of the difficulty about classifying doubtful illnesses may rest here.

The task of model differentiation has been carried somewhat further by the work of Siegler and Osmond. Working with a series of questionable forms of negatively evaluated deviancies (schizophrenia, alcoholism, drug addiction) they have constructed a series of models of interpretation now numbering eight: the medical, moral, psychoanalytic, social, family interactional, impaired, psychedelic, and conspiratorial models.[13]

The classification of marijuana use may well rest at this level of debate. If it is the case that marijuana is relatively harmless to the physical health of the self and to others, it is still possible to argue that it is wrong to use it—on the grounds that it would lead to a life style which is incompatible with the value system of those doing the disapproving. On the other hand, proponents of marijuana's legitimacy would simply reply by arguing that its use is consistent with a better set of values. Independent of whether a deviancy is included in the medical model, one must still deal with the social value judgment that the deviancy is evaluated negatively rather than positively. Thus it would be possible to have a deviancy which clearly fit the characteristics of the medical model and to still reject that this medical deviancy is negatively evaluated. For the use of drugs or any other deviant behvior to be a medical problem, the behavior must first of all be considered bad.

II. THE CHARACTERISTICS OF THE MEDICAL MODEL

Having argued that the medical model is a systematic mode of interpretation of a type of social deviance and that it, therefore, incorporates negative evaluations of the deviancy, we must now move on to specify the characteristics of the medical model—those elements which differentiate this model from other models of interpretation of deviancy. It is our thesis that a negatively evaluated deviancy will be perceived as fitting the medical model to the extent it conforms to these characteristics.

---

[13]Mariam Siegler and Humphry Osmond, "Models of Madness," *British Journal of Psychiatry* 112 1966), 1193–1203; "Models of Drug Addiction," *International Journal of Addictions*, 3 (No. 1, 1968), 3–24; and "The Impaired Model of Schizophrenia" *Schizophrenia* 1 (No. 3, 1969), 192–202; and Miriam Siegler, Humphry Osmond, and S. Newell, "Models of Alcoholism," *Quarterly Journal of the Study of Alcoholism* 29 (No. 3, 1968), 571–91. Unfortunately, the authors in this series do not devote much attention to the theoretical distinctions responsible for the differentiation of their interesting list of models.

We have identified four characteristics which seem to be essential. A deviancy will be placed within the medical model if it is seen as (a) non-voluntary and (b) organic, if (c) the class of relevant, technically-competent experts is physicians, and if (d) it falls below some socially defined minimal standard of acceptability. A negatively evaluated deviancy will be perceived as fitting the medical model to the extent that it conforms to these characteristics. Every example of negatively evaluated deviancy which is a doubtful illness and therefore only ambiguously included in the medical model can be shown, we believe, to be questioned on at least one of these grounds.

A. Non-Voluntariness

Probably the most central characteristic of the medical model is incorporated in the second exemption from the sick role. As Parsons defined it, the person in the sick role is exempt from responsibility for his condition. A sinner or criminal or morally irresponsible person would be seen as deficient in character to the extent that he has brought on his condition; the person in the sick role is not. More significantly, one in the sick role is not expected to use will power or self control to overcome his condition. This is a crucial dimension of the medical model and one of the reasons for its attractiveness. The other major candidates for models of interpretation—especially the criminal, moral, and sinner models—normally suggest deficiency of the will of the deviant person. In the Parsonian major axes of differentiation, all of the other forms of deviancy are probably voluntary forms of deviancy. The one exception would be some interpretations of the sinner role, especially in a Calvinistic form of double predestination where, logically at least, the sinner is predestined to his sinner role by the decree of God and, therefore, is not responsible for his condition. Needless to say, the doctrine of double predestination is not very viable in contemporary society, and if an individual is to be considered non-culpable for his actions, another model of interpretation must be found.[14]

It seems clear that one of the primary functions of the medical model is to remove culpability. The attempt to place narcotic addiction, violence associated with rage, and larceny and assault by children into the medical model is in large part a move to remove blame by removing attribution of voluntary control of the action. We think there is sound empirical and moral reason for efforts to remove culpability from many forms of deviance. Nevertheless, there are serious problems in using the medical model to do this.

---

[14]We shall sometimes use the term non-culpable in place of non-voluntaristic. Technically, however, an important difference should be noted. A deviancy such as marijuana smoking may be viewed as voluntary and yet non-culpable if one simply challenges the negative evaluation. Culpability thus implies simultaneously willful control and negative evaluation.

First, we believe it is reductionistic to force all forms of blameless deviance into the medical model. We have already seen that there are forms of non-culpable religious deviance for which the individual is in no way to be blamed. There are, at least at the theoretical level, many other types of non-voluntary deviancy which should not be forced into the medical model. This will be discussed more fully in the next section.

Second, increasing scientific study of biology and medicine has jeopardized the notion of blamelessness for even some of the human conditions most traditionally classified in the medical model. Certainly a heart attack is partially preventable, and an individual who fails to watch diet, exercise, and standards for physical examination may be seen as blameworthy if he has a coronary. Exposure to bacteria may be willful, through failure to observe sanitary and innoculation precautions known or thought to be effective. A parent may be blamed and feel guilty if his child suffers an attack of a preventable disease. The elaborate precautions taken by parents of the previous generation to avoid contact with children with polio suggests the extremes to which traditional illnesses can be culpable. Even cancer is now subject to the norms of the "seven danger signals." Genetic counseling and screening is moving rapidly to make even genetic disease a culpable event albeit culpable at the parental level. This suggests that the notion of non-responsibility in the sick role is in jeopardy although the assumption that one cannot get well by an act of the will alone certainly remains central to all of these illnesses. The medical model may be less functional for the removal of culpability in the future than it has been in the past.

Third, the *utility* of attributing non-culpability is most recently being challenged. Over the past century there has been increasing enlightenment about the implausibility and injustic in assigning blame to individuals who are quite possibly acting in a non-voluntary manner. The medical model served this purpose well. Very recently, however, the virtue of culpability is being rediscovered, especially by radical groups of mental patients, minors, political radicals, and advocates of alternative life styles. They recognize that to place an individual in the medical model is to remove blame, but to remove blame is to remove responsibility, and to remove responsibility is to challenge the dignity of the individual and the validity of the values he claims to be acting upon. Removing culpability by means of the assumption that the act is non-voluntary is thus not without its price. Those who place great significance on the values of diversity, autonomy, and individual freedom and dignity will accordingly be very cautious in assigning a deviant behavior to the medical model.[15]

This, of course, is a discussion of the functional status of the medial model in removing culpability. In the end, assigning a deviancy to the medical model

[15]See Goffman, *Asylums*, pp. 153–54.

or to models which imply voluntarism (and, therefore, praiseworthiness and blameworthiness for actions) depends at least in part on the ontological status of the concept of individual free will. The question of whether there really is such a thing as free will is one of the classic debates in philosophy and probably will not be resolved definitively in the near future. Those who opt (or are determined) for the deterministic interpretation of man's nature will be more inclined to the medical model, while those who are determined (or opt) for a position more supportive of the free will position will be more cautious.

It is important to realize, however, that Western society in general and the United States in particular is heavily committed to the voluntarist tradition. The victories of the political voluntarists combine with the victories of the Arminian and anti-predestinarian theological forces to make American society probably the most heavily committed to voluntaryism of any society in history. This reality is manifested even in the Skinnerian claim that we must *choose* to use the correct conditioning techniques for the correct ends if our society is to survive in an age beyond freedom and dignity. Such an extreme commitment to voluntarism probably predisposes us to abandon the medical model in its classical form as scientific and technological breakthroughs rationalize and routinize illness. We may well be coming to the day when all illness will be divided into two classes: those blameworthy at the individual level when some individual preventive actions could have been taken and were not, and those blameworthy at the national level where the National Institutes of Health will be blamed for failure to develop scientific explanation and cure. This possible trend toward the decline of the medical model as an interpretation of deviance stands directly in opposition to Parsons' suggestion that American value predispositions to "activism," "instrumentalism," and "worldliness" lead us to place selectively high emphasis on the health-illnes complex.[16]

I have argued that many questionable forms of deviancy may be brought into the medical model in order to remove culpability and imputation of blame by removing the attribution of voluntary choice. There are good functional and philosophical reasons, I believe, for continuing to hold that many of these forms of deviancy (narcotic addiction, alcoholism, other erratic behavior) really are based on an element of voluntary choice. Probably the man in the street is really not convinced that the alcoholic, the addict, the "criminal," are really acting from some drive or determining force independent of voluntary control. So long as that belief remains, it will be impossible to incorporate these deviancies into the medical model in any complete way. Let us now turn, however, to those deviancies which are assumed, according to the belief system of the society, to be non-voluntary.

---

[16]Parsons, "Health and Illness," pp. 178ff.

B. Organicity

1. *Sub-System Theories of Determinism.* In order to differentiate different types of non-voluntary, negatively evaluated deviancy, it is perhaps most helpful to use a standard classification of the total realm of human behavior. The division of behavior into organic, psychological, social, and cultural sub-systems is helpful in clarifying and codifying different levels of action.[17] The cultural sub-system includes the systems of symbol, value, belief, and meaning. It can in turn be differentiated into the language system, the basic philosophical assumptions organizing conceptions of reality with a system of belief and meaning (philosophy and theology), and the basic values of the culture. The social system encompasses the basic institutions of the society which include the economic, the familial, the political, and the religious forms of organization. Both the cultural and the social sub-systems are clearly super-personal in character. On the other hand the psychological and organic sub-systems are more often seen as intra-individual. This internal-external dichotomy is particularly important, but the somatic-psychological dichotomy, sometimes represented in the body-soul duality in the history of philosophy, is also crucial.

A total realm of human action may be interpreted with any one of these sub-systems as the primary reference point. In fact, reductionistic philosophies specifically expressing deterministic or non-voluntary causation have focussed on each. Somatic (organic, biochemical, or physical) determinisms have been contemplated by every college philosophy student. But the psychological deterministic theory of Skinnerian behaviorism is also well known. Social sub-system determinisms are less clearly represented; but the emergence of the social sciences, they also have had their impact. Their view is best illustrated by the notion that a ghetto child involved in a crime is not guilty of willful wrong-doing, but is determined by racial, economic, and political factors to a role in life which forces him into his particular act. Cultural level determinisms are probably best illustrated by variants of predestination theories in which divine forces control man's every action, but also include sophisticated linguistic theories dealing with the ways in which language organizes behavior and in turn controls the individual.

It is clear that a total explanation of the universe can originate from any one of these sub-systems. Taken exclusively, any one of these theories of causation is reductionistic. In the end, the only theory which adequately accounts for man's total experience is one which works simultaneously with several causation theories as well as a doctrine of free will.

---

[17] Talcott Parsons, et al. (eds.), *Theories of Society: Foundation of Modern Sociological Theory* (New York: The Free Press, 1961).

2. *Stages of Sub-system Analysis* The notion of organicity as an essential element of the medical model becomes even more confusing when we realize that there are many different points of analysis. Every human action is organically related in the sense that a heavy dose of barbiturate (from a blow dart if necessary) will probably modify every conceivable human behavior. While clearcut traditional diseases are conceived of as somatic, all of the doubtful illnesses also are related in some way to a somatic component. I shall propose four different stages for sub-system analysis: the deviant behavior itself, the response (treatment), he proximal cause, and the ultimate cause.

a. *Behavioral Stage.* Taking narcotic addiciton as our model, we shall see that the confusion about organicity (and, therefore, about the appropriateness of the medical model) begins at the level of the deviant behavior itself. What is the behavior (symptom) which arouses our interest in narcotic addiction? On the one hand, there are clearly organic symptoms experienced by the addict in withdrawal—nausea, vomiting, dilated pupils, diarrhea, elevated heart rate and blood pressure—which are negatively evaluated. In this dimension narcotic addiction is not very different from invasion of an influenza virus. Yet narcotic addiction also produces psychological symptoms—euphoria, craving, feelings of dependency. perhaps the social and cultural impact arouses the most interest, however. The narcotic addict's symptoms, albeit derivitively, include social impact which is economic and political and a life style (e.g. that of the stereotype opium den) which probably are the major worries of the public. Thus even at the behavioral level there is confusion about the sub-system classification. It appears, however, that some addicts, maintained on maintenance heroin, survive and behave quite normally. William Halsted, one of the four founders of Johns Hopkins School of Medicine and a practicing physician, continued to function effectively for roughly half a century as an addict.

b. *Response Stage.* At another state, that of response to the deviant behavior, narcotic addiction may also be classified as organic.[18] The addict may be maintained on maintenance doses or brought down on gradually declining doses of narcotics. He may have his behavior blocked by blocking agents such as N-allylnormorphine, or he may be conditioned away from his addiction using succinylcholine. The same may be said for alcoholism and nicotinism. But other forms of response are possible to these doubtful illnesses, including jail, social and psychological manipulation, preaching, moral exhortation, and peer group pressure. On the other hand, clearly nonsomatic forms of social deviancy can be controlled by the use of organic agents as a response, especially if one includes conditioning agents. I believe that organicity of the

---

[18]Treatment is a term which probably could be applied to this level, but in some contexts implies a medical model metaphor. This is possibly not always true—crops are treated with insecticide—but we prefer to use the more neutral term "response."

response, like organicity of the deviant behavior itself, should not be sufficient to classify the behavior within the medical model. A problem is created here because if the response is organic (a drug, a surgical procedure, or a physiologically acting device) it may require an "organicity expert" (a physician) to administer the response. This necessarily brings the deviancy closer to the medical model, but physicians will be among the first to reject their functioning as societal control agents for types of deviant actors whom physicians classify as other than ill. The most dramatic example of the situation requiring an "organicity expert" for response, although the situation cannot be adequately interpreted in organic categories alone, is probably the abortion chosen because of, say, high parity and low socio-economic status. The condition which is to be controlled (the pregnancy) and the method of response (dilation and currettage, saline injection, or hysterectomy) are clearly organic in every conceivable way. Yet, it is only with the greatest effort (and then probably for pragmatic political purposes and not very effectively) that abortion for socio-economic reasons is forced into the medical model.

c. *Proximal Cause Stage.* The contrast between an abortion for socio--economic reasons and one for "medical" reasons such as a cancerous uterus indicates the third stage of sub-system analysis. In the abortion for the cancerous uterus the cause of the "problem" is also organic. In narcotic addition the cause of the deviant behavior may also be seen as organic. There certainly are organic changes in the body when one is addicted.

On the other hand, other theories of addiction deal with immediate causes of the behavior which are more psychological The notion of "needle addiction" probably suggests a psychological causation model. We need to distinguish between the immediate causes of addiction, which are at least partially organic in character, from earlier causes. Let us use the terms proximal and ultimate causes.[19]

d. *Ultimate Cause Stage.* Even if the proximal or immediate cause of addictive behavior is organic, which it may well be, it is still an open question whether the earlier or "ultimate" cause is organic. There are at least three addiction theories proposed today.[20] The psychological theories are based on the belief that there are "addiction prone personalities." Through childhood or other personality structuring, the individual acquires a behavioral pattern which is served by addiction; the appropriate response would require restructuring of

[19]Ultimate is clearly a relative word. The Western notion of causation often implies an infinite regress. I, however, shall consider a cause ultimate at the level of the individual to be organic if the first entry into the human organism in the causation chain is organic.

The British Rolleston Committee documented its use of the distinction between organic and non-organic causation models when it defined drug addiction as the use of a drug for purposes other than the relief of symptoms of an organic disease.

[20]Edward M. Brecher and the Editors of Consumer Reports, *Licit and Illicit Drugs* (Boston: Little, Brown and Company, 1972), pp. 67–68, offers a brief summary.

the psychological make-up of the addict. Sociological theories place causation in the surrounding environment of the addict. Racial, economic, and political conditions, according to this view, predispose the individual to addiction. A third theory of causation is biochemical. While holders of all theories are willing to concede that the proximal cause of addiction has a biochemical component, holders of the biochemical causation theory place organic chemical factors in a much more central place. One version of the theory holds that the morphine molecule causes physical changes which are permanently coded in the nervous system of the individual, perhaps changes in the receptor site. This, however, from our perspective would still not be an ultimate biochemical causation theory. If, however, one were to argue that there are anatomical or biochemical predisposing factors which lead certain individuals to addiction—say by the presence of aberrant enzymes or biochemical ratios—then organic causation would be ultimate in the sense in which we are using the term. There are analogous causation theories for homosexuality and schizophrenia. Narcotic addiction is organic at the level of ultimate cause only according to the biochemical causation theory.

The confusion over the placing of narcotic addiction into the medical model on the dimension of organicity is thus seen. It is only ambiguously organic at each of the four stages of analysis: behavior, response, proximal, and ultimate cause. No wonder there is doubt about the appropriateness of the medical model.

3. *Organicity in Other Doubtful Diseases.* Other "illnesses" also raise confusion about the dimension of organicity. A heart attack, for instance, is clearly organic or somatic at the level of the behavioral symptom which is the origin of concern. Likewise, the treatment may be primarily organic, as is the proximal cause. But at the stage of the ultimate cause, there is more doubt. Certainly social factors predispose to heart attack. The sedentary life or poor social patterns may increase risk, but then more narrowly organic factors might do so also.

Cystic fibrosis may be the prototypical organic disease. Its symptoms are somatic, as is the intervention with vasodilators and respiratory aids. The genetic origin, which is not clearly understood and not diagnosable prenatally, leads us to believe that the causation is somatic and little can be done to modify the disease process. At all four stages, it is plausible to believe that the somatic component dominates.

In contrast, alcoholism seems to be heavily somatic in its symptomatology, but the response may be organic (as in succinylcholine "therapy") or social (as with Alcoholics Anonymous). The immediate cause of the behavior of the alcoholic is clearly organic, and we know precisely what the chemical is; but an organic theory of an ultimate cause must share a place with psychological, social, and cultural level causal theories. Alcoholism's organic proximal cause, behavior, and possible treatment do not make alcoholism as clearly an organic disease as is the case of cystic fibrosis.

Homosexuality lends itself to organic interpretation primarily at the causal level with research on andosterone/estrogen ratios suggesting abnormal balances in homosexuals. Treatment, however, has tended to be psychological. It appears that the more clearly the deviance is associated with organicity at the four stages we have identified, the more neatly it fits the medical model.

The relationship between organicity and non-voluntariness is important. There is quite clearly an association between a belief in organicity and non-voluntariness. If behavior is "in the chemistry," we are convinced it is not in the control of the will. For the most part this association tends to be borne out, but there are enough instances where behavior which is clearly non-organic at all four stages is non-culpable and, on the other hand, instances of behavior which is organic yet culpable, that the correlation is not perfect. When these inconsistencies arise, the appropriateness of the medical model is questioned.

The World Health Organization's definition of health as "complete physical mental, and social well-being, and not merely the absence of disease or infirmity" is an innovative definition in which an attempt is made to stretch the concept of health and illness beyond the organic metaphorically to the non-organic. Whether or not this reforming definition will lead to a change in the meaning of the term is not to be decided here. The reason for this move, however, is apparent. Proponents of this definition are attempting to gain the virtue of nonculpability for non-organic forms of negatively evaluated deviancy as well as to mobilize the imperatives which have been associated with health and illness, i.e., the right to health and the obligation to give its attainment high priority. I believe there are great dangers in this expansionistic conception of health. Rather it seems preferable to make clear the missing categories—namely, non-culpable deviancy cause psychologically, socially, and culturally, for example, by the lack of various forms of psychological, social, and cultural welfare. The case can then be made that such psychological, social, or cultural support, too, is fundamental to man's existence, at least as fundamental as health in the somatic sense.

If it is the case that deviancies can be meaningfully differentiated as organic and non-organic as well as voluntary and nonvoluntary, then we must disagree with Sedgwick in the conclusion he draws in his argument against Szasz, Laing, Goffman, and others. Earlier I indicated that Sedgwick was correct in his claim that both organic and mental deviancies require social evaluations. Merely establishing, however, that the two phenomena are not to be differentiated on *this* dimension does not establish the positive argument that therefore "mental illness *is* illness." Against Sedgwick, I would argue that even though they are the same in both being negatively evaluated social deviancies, they differ in that one is organic while the other is in the psychological realm. This, we shall argue, has important practical as well as theoretical implications.

Thus far, I have focussed on the primarily analytical argument, claiming that the medical model, at least in its original and pure form, applies to non-voluntary and organic deviations from the norms established by a society. Let us now turn to the practical implications. By far the most important practical consequence of the limitation of the medical model refers to the professional cadre who will become involved depending upon the model employed. Before taking up that point in the next section of the paper, however, I wish to consider a quesion growing out of the alternative role models implied in the different sub-systems.

In a theoretical discussion of types of roles, Lemert distinguishes between primary and secondary deviant roles.[21] This distinction, also reflected in Parsons' axis of differentiation between total and partial deviance, is between roles which totally reorganize one's life and roles which permit one to continue in other roles with minimal impact. Freidson applies this distinction to the medical model and argues that there are really different types of deviant roles in the health-illness complex.[22] Minor medical difficulties, of which the cold is the type case, produce only a primary role. The individual with a cold does not normally fully adopt the sick role with its new exemptions and responsibilities. On the other hand, the person with a major disease such as polio clearly adopts all of the characteristics of the role. The sick role, or at least the patient role, is thus a secondary role, while minor forms of deviancy in the medical model (a cold, a cut finger, a headache) generate only a new primary role actor.

Now the question arises if there is a precisely parallel pattern in deviancies which, according to our philosophy of causation, are best understood as non-organic. There is no theoretical reason why that would be the case. There may well be something uniquely associated with organicity which would lead to the development of a secondary deviant role. The notions of contagion, the need for rest for bodily repair, the effectiveness of special technical instruments and procedures for "healing" the sick person may generate pressures to remove the (organically) sick individual from his normal roles in favor of the sick role which are far greater than for the non-organically caused deviancy. People interpreted as being psychologically deviant may be more likely to continue in their normal primary roles. Those with deviancies thought to be socially caused are quickly put in the criminal role, but the role implies voluntary deviance in the social realm. The concept of non-voluntary socially determined deviancy is a newer concept and one for which virtually no one is

[21] Edwin Lemert, *Social Pathology* (New York: McGraw-Hill, 1964).

[22] Freidson, *Profession of Medicine*, p. 231–34.

assigned a secondary role. To collapse the different sub-systems may well have a serious impact on the development of primary and secondary deviant roles.

C. The Physican as the Technically Competent Expert

The third characteristic of the medical model is that the technically competent expert is the physician (often supported by a cadre of associates and assistants). The sick role includes an obligation to seek technically competent help appropriate to the need of the sickness. Parsons goes on specifically to state that the technically competent expert is "in the most usual case" the physician. This seems to be one of the most clearly established characteristics of the medical model. One of the important ideological implications of the sick role as Parsons states it is that in addition to removing the sick one from the realm of responsible actors it places him under the control of the medical professional.

The physician has authority; he gives "doctor's orders." More than this, the medical professional has first claim to jurisdiction in labelling of illness.[23] When a case is unambiguously within the medical model, it may well be appropriate for the medical professional to have the primary responsibility for labelling of a specific illness. Thus, when one has a small growth on the skin and wants to know whether it is cancer, a boil, or a normal bump, it is appropriate to turn to a physician. That, it seems to us, is where the authority must stop. It is not appropriate, for instance, for the medical professional to carry out the social evaluation of the badness or the goodness of the cancer (granted that the naming and diagnosing function of the physician must include telling the "seriousness" of the medical condition, the prognosis under various alternatives).

All too often, however, doubtful or ambiguous illnesses are placed into the medical model for the purpose of determining whether or not they are indeed illnesses rather than other forms of deviancy. This is fundamentally different from approaching a physician to determine whether or not a lump is a cancer. Let us grant that the experts in any form of deviancy, if they exist at all, have authority to diagnose the presence of deviancies which are clearly within their realm. But that does not mean that they have authority to arbitrate a dispute about whether an identified but marginal deviancy is within their model.

The British have been particularly guilty of this in the handling of narcotic addiction. In 1924 the British wanted to know whether narcotic addiction should be dealt with in the medical model or some alternative (the criminal being the most viable alternative). To resolve this they turned to the Rolleston

---

[23]See *ibid.*, p. 251.

Committee, a committee of distinguished physicians. It never seems to have been realized that precisely at that point was the decision made—by the public—to place narcotic addiction into the medical model. The conclusion of the group of physicians—that narcotic addiction was an illness—was anti-climactic and theoretically unsound.

If the question is to determine whether a deviancy is in one model or another, the methodology must involve, as a minimum, not only the acceptance of the deviancy by the experts of one model, but also the rejection of the deviancy by the experts of all the other relevant models. Thus, one might use the Siegler-Osmond list of models and insist that the opinion of functionaries in each model be obtained. Since the moral model has the entire public as the expert class, in effect it is the public which must make the decision to classify a deviancy within or without a model. Turning to the experts within the medical model for this function is a theoretically confused move.

The behavior under consideration is non-organic, non-culpable, but negatively evaluated deviancies. The question is whether such types of behavior should be within the medical model. Recognizing that the medical model not only specifies the obligation to seek technically competent help, but also specifies that those experts are medical professionals, i.e. physicians, the implication is clear. Medically trained professionals are to be placed in control of such behavior and its correction if it is placed on the medical model. This seems to me both dangerous and unjustified in the light of the training and skills of such professionals. It is shocking to realize that, using the basic sub-systems as differentiation points, the psychiatrist is the only professional in Western society who receives his primary training in one of the sub-systems yet practices primarily in another.

The World Health Organization definition of health as encompassing total well-being means that, in effect, the medical professional is the one to turn to for technically competent help in such failures in well being as marriage problems, poverty, and unanswered prayers. This will require either radical retraining and redefinition of the medical professional or, more practically, the development of clearer categories of deviant roles.

In the medical model the early generation of a secondary deviant role places the deviant (ill) one under the control of the medical professional and removes control from the layman. We should, therefore, be careful not to extend this removal of individual freedom and dignity into non-organic forms of behavior too hastily. If the ratio of primary and secondary roles may be different in organic and non-organic deviancy, it may well be that the creation of technically competent experts in these non-organic realms may not follow the same patterns either. Perhaps we will be unable to produce such technically competent experts at all, or we may not be able to differentiate sub-specialties in the same way. The expansion of the medical model to cover such categories could only be dangerous.

D. Restoration of a Minimal Standard of Health

There is a fourth characteristic of the medical model, one which is probably the most difficult to grasp. I argued, in the first section of this paper, that even illness in the most traditional (i.e., non-culpable and organic) sense requires a social evaluation which is negative. The sick role is a socially disapproved, though legitimate, role. This is true by definition. One would not be sick but simply either unusual or super-healthy if he were abnormal in a manner which was not socially disapproved. We have purposely bracketed until now the question of the nature of the norm from which the deviant deviates in the medical model. Whatever it is, it is clear that the name for the norm is "health." Based on the previous discussion we would define health in a preliminary way as an organic condition of the body judged by the social system of meaning and value to be good.

Health, however, is an abstract norm, and abstractions in the human cultural symbol system function on at least two levels. On the one hand, in the abstract form, health exists as an ideal, a norm in the sense of being the highest or ideal type. Health in this meaning would be the organic condition of the body judged by the social system to be the best possible organic condition for a body. Abstract nouns also function in language to refer to some minimal standard, often, but not always, associated with a statistical mean or mode. In this sense, healthiness may be only a condition of the body judged by the social system of meaning and value to be better than a minimal standard. Thus, it is quite meaningful to say of two individuals that they are both healthy, but one is healthier. That statement would be impossible unless we could use the term in both senses simultaneously. "Healthy" refers simply to the minimal societal standard, but the "health" to which the word "healthier" refers is an ideal such that one individual approaches that ideal more closely. This dual function of abstract nouns in language is not unique to the concept health, but applies to all such abstract concepts.

In the medical model the most narrow reference seems to be to the minimal standard of healthiness. A deviancy fits most clearly in the medical model when it is perceived as falling below a minimal standard of healthiness. However, in the broader and more ambiguous sense, the problem of improving someone's health beyond the minimal standard to approach the ideal is only with difficulty assimilated to the medical model.

Our conceptualizations are frequently determined by the formulaiton of polarizations. Thus, the public health movement has posed the poles of restoring and preserving health. Both functions are clearly within the medical model in the more restricted sense. But this formulation often makes one lose sight completely of the possibility of an option to improve health beyond the normal. A number of somatic improvements are conceivable and perhaps technically feasible. They might include reduction of normal amounts of sleep needed, equipping the body to manufacture amino acids which now need to be obtained from animal protein, elimination of the menstrual cycle, and elimination of baldness. Would such activities be classed within the medical model? I think only with difficulty. They fit the medical model imperfectly and are analogous to other conditions which fit some, but not all, of the characteristics of the medical model.

While there is no necessary reason why medical practitioners should be limited to restoring and preserving minimal, socially defined standards of health, at least in Western medicine, the priority of these tasks seems well established. Even the normative principles of medical ethics reflect this orientation. At least according to one major strand of professional medical ethics, the primary moral principle is "first of all do no harm." This maxim differs in a significant way from classical utilitarianism even if it were applied solely with reference to the patient. The "don't harm rather than maximize the good" maxim is built on the same notion of a theoretical, socially defined minimal standard or base line. It gives rise to a philosophical problem which we might call the "baseline problem." The idea of normalcy from which one can measure health and illness, benefit and harm, commission and omission of an act, ordinary and extraordinary means, or positive and negative incentives, is not well explored in the philosophical literature—and should be. In any case, it seems to have been incorporated into the medical as well as the legal and normative ethical tradition. An action is less ambiguously included in the medical model when it is an effort to restore or preserve that baseline of minimally accepted health rather than to improve health beyond that baseline to an ideal.

III. THE MEDICAL MODEL AND MARGINAL DEVIANCIES

In the last section of this paper, I traced what I see as four essential defining characteristics of the medical model. For a type of deviant behavior to be interpreted as falling clearly within the medical model, it must first of all be negatively evaluated. Then it must be seen as (1) non-voluntary, (2) organic, (3) within the province of the medical professional, and (4) falling below some societally defined minimal standard of health. To the extent that the deviancy fits all of those characteristics, it will clearly be within the medical model. It is, however, when the behavior fails to meet one or more of these characteristics, or is called into question on one or more of them, that the medical model begins to seem less appropriate. The difficulty with such doubtful illnesses as narcotic addiction is thus apparent. For many, addiction remains a voluntary choice which sufficient will power could overcome. The testimonies of former addicts about how difficult the habit was to overcome only support this view. For many, addiction is non-organic at the stages of behavior, response (treatment), proximal or ultimate cause. In part because of these factors, these doubters may (but not necessarily will) reject the physician as the appropriate technical professional to respond to addiction. While addiction is clearly statistically aberrent, it may not always be considered below a minimal standard of health and may, especially in the case of marijuana, not be negatively evaluated as an alternative life style at all. With doubts at all of these levels, it is hardly surprising that narcotic addiction and similar deviancies are disputed in classification.

I believe that the bulk of the problem comes from reductionistic tendencies to polarize deviancy between the extremes of crime and illness and the use of the single category of illness to cover all non-voluntary deviancy. If all of the variables mentioned in this paper were cross tabulated, 48 models would result (voluntary/non-voluntary × organic/psychological/social/cultural × technical expert/no technical expertise × restoring health/preserving health/improving health). If differentiation within categories such as the social and cultural sub-systems were included, the figure would be that much higher. I feel that the expansion of the medical model to cover the other models is dangerous when unique characteristics exist for the other models and treating such deviancies as unique entites would be more realistic.

Particularly interesting and troublesome will be the models which combine the assumed need for technically competent biomedical experts with the characteristics of the other three dimensions which tend away from the medical model. We have seen that in relation to each of the characteristics of the medical model, there may be conditions requiring medical expertise for the resolution of perceived problems which are not considered to be unambiguously within the medical model. The clearest example may arise on the sub-system dimension. There are (or at least theoretically may be) deviancies which are considered non-organic in ultimate and proximal cause as well as in behavior, yet susceptible to chemical, surgical, or other medical "treatment" (response). We know, with a degree of certainty, that amygdalotomy will control violent behavior while we may not be certain that the "cause" of the behavior is somatic. We know chemical agents can condition avoidance of alcohol even if we are not sure the cause of alcoholism is biochemical. Likewise, we know that voluntarily induced somatic complaints are amenable to treatment by a physician. Recent discussion of hair implants has raised the question whether such procedures are sufficiently medical to justify tax deduction. This and other procedures may be medical in all senses except that they improve the bodily condition beyond societal standards of minimal acceptability. These cases will raise serious conflict for the medical professional as well as for the tax collector.

These ambiguous categories (voluntarily induced somatic complaint; non-voluntary, non-organic complaint; and somatic complaint requiring extension beyond societal standards of minimal acceptability) are frequently labelled "elective" in contrast to "therapeutic" procedures. The term applies equally well to abortions for serious social reasons or "cosmetic" surgery which is considered beyond the minimal standards of physicla health. These terms are terribly imprecise and probably misleading. In fact, in a country where free choice is valued, all medical procedures are elective for the patient (except in the case of incompetents where guardians elect medical treatments or, if necessary, courts will appoint a new guardian for the purposes of election). On the other hand, if "therapeutic" means simply "corrective" it might apply equally to non-somatic as well as somatic complaints provided the fourth criterion of intervention necessary to produce a minimal standard established by society is met. It might be better to abandon these terms, recognizing instead that, increasingly, medically trained experts will be called upon to provide responses to conditions which are not clearly in the medical model or are clearly not in the medical model.

This will be confusing and frustrating for professional and layman alike, but is a necessary concomitant to increasing biomedical technology which gives ever greater power to control, increasing sophistication about non-organic theories of causation, and expanding horizons about what is possible over and beyond that which is minimally acceptable. Nevertheless, the mere usefulness of intervention by technically competent medically trained individuals should not be a sufficient condition to place the deviancy into the medical model. Instead we would reserve that model for conditions which more nearly meet all four of the characteristics outlined here. Even deviancies clearly within the medical model rest upon a social judgment that the condition is unacceptable, so any such categorization cannot be used to isolate an "objective" value-free zone; but it can make clear our philosophical presuppositions about free will and determinism, our theories of causation linked to sub-systems, or judgments about distinctions between restoring, preserving, and improving healh, and differentiation in the role of the relevant technically competent professional as well as in the role of the actor whose behavior is in question.

5.4

On the Distinction between Disease and Illness

Christopher Boorse

In this century a strong tendency has developed to debate social issues in psychiatric terms. Whether the topic is criminal responsibility, sexual deviance, feminism, or a host of others, claims about mental health are increasingly likely to be the focus of discussion. This growing preference for medicine over morals, which might be called the *psychiatric turn*, has an obvious appeal. In the paradigm health discipline, physiological medicine, judgments of health and disease are normally uncontroversial. The idea of reaching comparable certainty about difficult ethical problems is an inviting prospect. Unfortunately our grasp of the issues that surround the psychiatric turn continues to be impeded, as does psychiatric theory itself, by a fundamental misunderstanding of the concept of health. With few exceptions, clinicians and philosophers are agreed that health is an essentially evaluative notion. According to this consensus view, a value-free science of health is impossible. This thesis I believe to be entirely mistaken. I shall argue in this essay that it rests on a confusion between the theoretical and the practical senses of "health," or in other words, between disease and illness.

Two presuppositions of my whole discussion should be noted at the outset. The first is substantive: with Szasz and Flew, I shall assume that the idea of health ought to be analyzed by reference to physiological medicine alone.[1] It is a mistake to view physical and mental health as equally well-entrenched species of a single conceptual genus. In most respects, our institutions of mental health are recent offshoots from physiological medicine, and their nature and future are under continual controversy. In advance of a clear analysis of health in physiological medicine, it seems an open question whether current applications of the health vocabulary to mental conditions have any justification at all. Such applications will therefore be put on

1. Thomas S. Szasz, *The Myth of Mental Illness* (New York, 1961); Antony Flew, *Crime or Disease?* (New York, 1973), pp. 40, 42.

probation in the first two sections below. The other presupposition of my discussion is terminological. For convenience in distinguishing theoretical from practical uses of "health," I shall adhere to the technical usage of "disease" found in textbooks of medical theory. In such textbooks "disease" is simply synonymous with "unhealthy condition." Readers who wish to preserve the much narrower ordinary usage of "disease" should therefore substitute "theoretically unhealthy condition" throughout.

I. NORMATIVISM ABOUT HEALTH

It is safe to begin any discussion of health by saying that health is normality, since the terms are interchangeable in clinical contexts. But this remark provides no analysis of health until one specifies the norms involved. The most obvious proposal, that they are pure statistical means, is widely recognized to be erroneous. On the one hand, many deviations from the average—e.g. unusual strength or vital capacity or eye color—are not unhealthy. On the other hand, practically everyone has some disease or other, and there are also particular diseases such as tooth decay and minor lung irritation that are nearly universal. Since statistical normality is therefore neither necessary nor sufficient for clinical normality, most writers take the following view about the norms of health: that they must be determined, in whole or in part, by acts of evaluation. More precisely, the orthodox view is that all judgments of health include value judgments as part of their meaning. To call a condition unhealthy is at least in part to condemn it; hence it is impossible to define health in nonevaluative terms. I shall refer to this orthodox view as *normativism*.

Normativism has many varieties, which are often not clearly distinguished from one another by the clinicians who espouse them. The common feature of healthy conditions may, for example, be held to be either their desirability for the individual or their desirability for society. The gap between these two values is a persistent source of controversy in the mental-health domain. One especially common variety of normativism combines the thesis that health judgments are value judgments with ethical relativism. The resulting view that society is the final authority on what counts as disease is typical of psychiatric texts, as illustrated by the following quotation:

> While professionals have a major voice in influencing the judgment of society, it is the collective judgment of the larger social group that determines whether its members are to be viewed as sick or criminal, eccentric or immoral.[2]

For the most part my arguments against normativism will apply to all versions indiscriminately. It will, however, be useful to make a minimal division of normativist positions into strong and weak. Strong normativism will be the

2. Ian Gregory, *Fundamentals of Psychiatry* (Philadelphia, 1968), p. 32.

view that health judgments are pure evaluations without descriptive meaning; weak normativism allows such jdugments a descriptive as well as a normative component.[3]

As an example of a virtually explicit statement of strong normativism by a clinician, consider Dr. Judd Marmor's remark in a recent psychiatric symposium on homosexuality:

> . . . to call homosexuality the result of disturbed sexual development really says nothing other than that you disapprove of the outcome of that development.[4]

If we may substitute "unhealthy" for "disturbed," Marmor is claiming that to call a condition unhealthy is *only* to express disapproval of it. In other words—to collapse a few ethical distinctions—for a condition to be unhealthy it is necessary and sufficient that it be bad. Now at least half of this view, the sufficiency claim, is demonstrably false of physiological medicine. It is undesirable to be moderately ugly or, for that matter, to lack the manual dexterity of Liszt, but neither of these conditions is a disease. In fact, there are undesirable conditions regularly corrected by physicians which are not diseases: Jewish nose, sagging breasts, adolescent fertility, and unwanted pregnancies are only a few of many examples. Thus strong normativism is an erroneous account of health judgments in their paradigm area of application, and its influence upon mental-health theorists is regrettable.

Unlike Marmor, however, many clinical writers take positions that can be construed as committing them merely to weak normativism. A good example is Dr. Marie Jahoda, who concludes her survey of current criteria of psychological health with these words:

> Actually, the discussion of the psychological meaning of various criteria could proceed without concern for value premises. Only as one calls these psychological phenomena "mental health" does the problem of values arise in full force. By this label, one asserts that these psychological attributes are "good." And, inevitably, the question is raised: Good for what? Good in terms of middle class ethics? Good for democracy? For the continuation of the social *status quo*? For the individual's happiness? For mankind? . . . For the encouragement of genius or of mediocrity and conformity? The list could be continued.[5]

3. R. M. Hare, in *Freedom and Reason* (New York, 1963), chap. 2, argues that no terms have prescriptive meaning alone. If this view is accepted, the difference between strong and weak normativism concerns the question of whether "healthy" is "primarily" or "secondarily" evaluative.

4. Judd Marmor, 'Homosexuality and Cultural Value System," *American Journal of Psychiatry* 130 (1973): 1208.

5. Marie Jahoda, *Current Concepts of Positive Mental Health* (New York, 1958), pp. 76–77. See also her remark in *Interrelations Between the Social Environment and Psychiatric Disorders* (New York, 1953), p. 142: ". . . inevitably at some place there is a value judgment involved. I think that mental health or mental sickness cannot be conceived of without reference to some basic value."

Jahoda may here mean to claim only that calling a condition healthy *involves* calling it good. Her remarks are at least consistent with the weak normativist thesis that healthy conditions are good conditions which satisfy some further descriptive property as well. On this view, "healthy" is a mixed normative-descriptive term of the same sort as "honest" and "courageous." The following passage by Dr. F. C. Redlich is likewise consistent with the weak view:

> Most propositions about normal behavior refer implicitly or explicitly to ideal behavior. Deviations from the ideal obviously are fraught with value judgments; actually, all propositions on normality contain value statements in various degrees.[6]

Redlich's term "contain" suggests that he too sees the goodness of something as merely one necessary condition of its healthiness, and similarly for badness and unhcalthiness.

Yet even weak normativism runs into counterexamples within physiological medicine. It is obvious that a disease may be on balance desirable, as with the flat feet of a draftee or the mild infection produced by inoculation. It might be suggested in response that diseases must at any rate be prima facie undesirable. The trouble with this suggestion is that it is obscure. Consider the case of a disease that has infertility as its sole important effect. In what sense is infertility primary facie undesirable? Considered in abstraction from the actual effects of reproduction on human beings, it is hard to see how infertility is either desirable or undesirable. Possibly those who see it as "prima facie" undesirable assume that most people want to be able to have more children. But the corollary of this position will be that writers of medical texts must do an empirical survey of human preferences to be sure that a condition is a disease. No such considerations seem to enter into human physiological research, any more than they do into standard biological studies of the diseases of plants and animals. Here indeed is another difficulty for any normativist, weak or strong. It seems clear that one may speak of diseases in plants and animals without judging the conditions in question undesirable. Biologists who study the diseases of fruit flies or sharks need not assume that their health is a good thing for us. On the other hand, there is not much sense in talking about the best interests of, say, a begonia. So it seems that normativists must interpret health judgments about plants and lower animals as analogical, in the same way as would be statements about the courage or considerateness of wolves and rats.

If normativism about health is at once so influential and so objectionable, one must ask what persuasive arguments there are in its support. I know of only three arguments, of which one will be treated in the next section. A germ of an argument appears in the passage by Redlich just quoted. Health judgments involve a comparison to an ideal; hence, Redlich concludes, they

---

6. F. C. Redlich, "The Concept of Normality," *American Journal of Psychotherapy* 6 (1952): 553.

are "fraught with value judgments." It seems evident, however, that Redlich is thinking of ideals such as beauty and holiness rather than the chemist's ideal gas or Weber's ideal bureaucrat. The fact that a gas or a bureaucrat deviates from the ideal type is nothing against the gas or the bureaucrat. There are normative and nonnormative ideals, as there are in fact normative and nonnormative norms. The question is which sort health is, and Redlich has here provided no grounds for an answer.

A second and equally incomplete argument for normativism is suggested by the first two chapters of Margolis' *Psychotherapy and Morality*.[7] Margolis argues in his first chapter that psychoanalysts have been mistaken in holding that their therapeutic activities can "escape moral scrutiny" (p. 13). From this he concludes that "it is reasonable to view therapeutic values as forming part of a larger system of moral values" (p. 37), and explicitly endorses normativism. But this inference is a non sequitur. From the fact that the promotion of health is open to moral review, it in no way follows that health judgments are value judgments. Wealth and power are also "values" in the sense that people pursue them in a morally criticizable fashion; neither is a normative concept. The pursuit of any descriptively definable condition, if it has effects on persons, will be open to moral review.

These two arguments, like the health literature generally, do next to nothing to rule out the alternative view that health is a descriptively definable property which is usually valuable. Why, after all, may not health be a concept of the same sort as intelligence, or deductive validity? Though the idea of intelligence is certainly vague, it does not seem to be normative. Intelligence is the ability to perform certain intellectual tasks, and one would expect that these intellectual tasks could be characterized without presupposing their value.[8] Similarly, a valid argument may, for theoretical purposes, be descriptively defined[9] roughly as one that has a form no instance of which could have true premises and a false conclusion. Intelligence in people and validity in arguments being generally valued, the statement that a person is intelligent or an argument valid does tend to have the force of a recommendation. But this fact is wholly irrelevant to the employment of the terms in theories of intelligence or validity. To insist that evaluation is still part of the very meaning of the terms would be to make an implausible claim to which there are obvious counterexamples. Exactly the same may be true of the concept of health. At any rate, we have already seen some of the counterexamples.

7. Joseph Margolis, *Psychotherapy and Morality* (New York, 1966).

8. Exactly what intellectual abilities are included in intelligence is, of course, unclear and may vary from culture to culture. (See N. J. Block and Gerald Dworkin, "IQ, Heritability and Inequality, Part I," *Philosophy and Public Affairs* 3, no. 4 [Summer 1974]: 333.) But this does not show that for any particular group of speakers "intelligent" is a normative term, i.e. has positive evaluation as part of its meaning.

9. The contrary view, which might be called normativism about validity, is defended by J. O. Urmson in "Some Questions Concerning Validity," *Revue Internationale de Philosophie* 25 (1953): 217–229.

Since the distinction between force and meaning in philosophy of languages is in a rather primitive state, it is doubtful that weak normativism about health can be either decisively refuted or decisively established. But I suggest that its current prevalence is largely the result of two quite tractable causes. One is the lack of a plausible descriptive analysis; the other is a confusion between theoretical and practical uses of the health vocabulary. The required descriptive analysis I shall try to sketch in the next section. As for the second cause, one should always remember that a dual commitment to theory and practice is one of the features that distinguish a clinical discipline. Unlike chemists or astronomers, physicians and psychotherapists are professionally engaged in practical judgments about how certain people ought to be treated. It would not be surprising if the terms in which such practical judgments are formulated have normative content. One might contend, for example, that calling a cancer "inoperable" involves the value judgment that the results of operating will be worse than leaving the disease alone. But behind this conceptual framework of medical practice stands an autonomous framework of medical theory, a body of doctrine that describes the functioning of a healthy body, classifies various deviations from such functioning as diseases, predicts their behavior under various forms of treatment, etc. This theoretical corpus looks in every way continuous with theory in biology and the other natural sciences, and I believe it to be value-free.

The difference between the two frameworks emerges most clearly in the distinction between disease and illness. It is disease, the theoretical concept, that applies indifferently to organisms of all species. That is because, as we shall see, it is to be analyzed in biological rather than ethical terms. The point is that illnesses are merely a subclass of diseases, namely, those diseases that have certain normative features reflected in the institutions of medical practice. An illness mut be, first, a reasonably *serious* disease with incapacitating effects that make it undesirable. A shaving cut or mild athlete's foot cannot be called an illness, nor could one call in sick on the basis of a single dental cavity, though all these conditions are diseases. Secondly, to call a disease an illness is to view its owner as deserving special treatment and diminished moral accountability. These requirements of "illness" will be discussed in some detail shortly, with particular attention to "mental illness." But they explain at once why the notion of illness does not apply to plants and animals. Where we do not make the appropriate normative judgments or activate the social institutions, no amount of disease will lead us to use the term "ill." Even if the laboratory fruit flies fly in listless circles and expire at our feet, we do not say they succumbed to an illness, and for roughly the same reasons as we decline to give them a proper funeral.

There are, then, two senses of "health." In one sense it is a theoretical notion, the opposite of "disease." In another sense it is a practical or mixed ethical notion, the opposite of "illness."[10] Let us now examine the relation between these two concepts more closely.

II. DISEASE AND ILLNESS

What is the theoretical notion of a disease? An admirable explanation of clinical normality was given thirty years ago by C. Daly King.

> The normal... is objectively, and properly, to be defined as that which functions in accordance with its design.[11]

The root idea of this account is that normal is the natural. The state of an organism is theoretically healthy, i.e. free of disease, insofar as its mode of functioning conforms to the natural design of that kind of organism. Philosophers have, of course, grown repugnant to the idea of natural design since its cooptation by natural-purpose ethics and the so-called argument from design. It is undeniable that the term "natural" is often given an evaluative force. Shakespeare as well as Roman Catholicism is full of such usages, and they survive as well in the strictures of state legislatures against "unnatural acts." But it is no part of biological theory to assume that what is natural is desirable, still less the product of divine artifice. Contemporary biology employs a version of the idea of natural design that seems ideal for the analysis of health.

The crucial element in the idea of a biological design is the notion of a natural function. I have argued elsewhere that a function in the biologist's sense is nothing but a standard causal contribution to a goal actually pursued by the organism.[12] Organisms are vast assemblages of systems and subsystems which, in most members of a species, work together harmoniously in such a way as to achieve a hierarchy of goals. Cells are goal-directed toward metabolism, elimination, and mitosis; the heart is goal-directed toward supplying the rest of the body with blood; and the whole organism is goal-directed both to particular activities like eating and moving around and to higher-level goals such as survival and reproduction. The specifically physiological functions of any component are, I think, its species-typical contributions to the apical goals of survival and reproduction. But whatever the

10. Thomas Nagel has suggested that the adjective "ill" may have its own special opposite "well." Our thinking about health might be greatly clarified if "wellness" had some currency.

11. C. Daly King, "The Meaning of Normal," *Yale Journal of Biology and Medicine* 17 (1945): 493–494. Most definitions of health in medical dictionaries include some reference to functions. Almost exactly King's formulation also appears in Fredrick C. Redlich and Daniel X. Freedman, *The Theory and Practice of Psychiatry* (New York, 1966), p. 113.

12. "Wright on Functions," to appear in *The Philosophical Review*.

correct analysis of function statements, there is no doubt that biological theory is deeply committed to attributing functions to processes in plants and animals. And the single unifying property of all recognized diseases of plants and animals appears to be this: that they interfere with one or more functions typically performed within members of the species.

The account of health thus suggested is in one sense thoroughly Platonic. The health of an organism consists in the performance by each part of its natural function. And as Plato also saw, one of the most interesting features of the analysis is that it applies without alteration to mental health as long as there are standard mental functions. In another way, however, the classical heritage is misleading, for it seems clear that biological function statements are descriptive rather than normative claims.[13] Physiologists obtain their functional doctrines without at any stage having to answer such questions as, What is the function of a man? or to explicate "a good man" on the analogy of "a good knife." Functions are not attributed in this context to the whole organism at all, but only to its parts, and the functions of a part are its causal contributions to empirically given goals. What goals a type of organism in fact pursues, and by what functions it pursues them, can be decided without considering the value of pursuing them. Consequently health in the theoretical sense is an equally value-free concept. The notion required for an analysis of health is not that of a good man or a good shark, but that of a good specimen of a human being or shark.

All of this amounts to saying that the epistemology King suggested for health judgments is, at bottom, a statistical one. The question therefore arises how the functional account avoids our earlier objections to statistical normality. King did explain how to dissolve one version of the paradox of saying that everyone is unhealthy. Clearly all the members of a species can have some disease or other as long as they do not have the same disease. King somewhat grimly compares the job of extracting an empirical ideal of health from a set of defective specimens to the job of reconstructing the Norden bombsight from assorted aerial debris (p. 495). But this answer does not touch universal diseases such as tooth decay. Although King nowhere considers this objection, the natural-design idea nevertheless suggests an answer that I suspect is correct. If what makes a condition a disease is its deviation from the natural functional organization of the species, then in calling tooth decay a disease we are saying that it is not simply in the nature of the species—and we say this because we think of it as mainly due to environmental causes. In general, deficiencies in the functional efficiency of the body are diseases when they are

13. The view that function statements are normative generates the third argument for normativism. It is presented most fully by Margolis in "Illness and Medical Values," *The Philosophy Forum* 8 (1959): 55–76, section II. It is also suggested by Ronald B. de Sousa, "The Politics of Mental Illness," *Inquiry* 15. (1972): 187–201, p. 194, and possibly by Flew as well in *Crime or Disease?* pp. 39–40. I think philosophers of science have made too much progress in giving biological function statements a descriptive analysis for this argument to be very convincing.

unnatural, and they may be unnatural either by being atypical or by being attributable mainly to the action of a hostile environment. If this explanation is accepted,[14] then the functional account simultaneously avoids the pitfalls of statistical normality and also frees the idea of theoretical health of all normative content.

Theoretical health now turns out to be strictly analogous to the mechanical condition of an artifact. Despite appearances, "perfect mechanical condition" in, say, a 1965 Volkswagen is a descriptive notion. Such an artifact is in perfect mechanical condition when it conforms in all respects to the designer's detailed specifications. Normative interests play a crucial role, of course, in the initial choice of the design. But what the Volkswagen design actually *is* is an empirical matter by the time production begins. Thenceforward a car may be in perfect condition regardless of whether the design is good or bad. If one replaces its stock carburetor with a high-performance part, one may well produce a better car, but one does not produce a Volkswagen in better mechanical condition. Similarly, an automatic camera may function perfectly and take wretched pictures; guided missiles and instruments of torture in perfect mechanical condition may serve execrable ends. Perfect working order is a matter not of the worth of the product but of the conformity of the process to a fixed design. In the case of organisms, of course, the ideal of health must be determined by empirical analysis of the species rather than by the intentions of a designer. But otherwise the parallel seems exact. A person who by mutation acquires a sixth sense, or the ability to regenerate severed limbs, is not thereby healthier than we are. Sixth senses and limb regeneration are not part of the human design, which at any given time, for better or worse, just is what it is.

We have been arguing that health is descriptively definable within medical theory, as intelligence is in psychological theory or validity in logical theory. Nevertheless medical theory is the basis of medical practice, and medical practice unquestioningly presupposes the value of health. We must therefore ask how the functional view explains this presumption that health is desirable.

In the case of physiological health, there are at least two general reasons why the functional normality that defines it is usually worth having. In the first place, most people do want to pursue the goals with respect to which physiological functions are isolated. Not only do we want to survive and reproduce, but we also want to engage in those particularl activities, such as eating and sex, by which these goals are typically achieved. In the second place—and this is surely the main reason the value of physical health seems indisputable—physiological functions tend to contribute to all manner of activities neutrally. Whether it is desirable for one's heart to pump, one's stomach to digest, or one's kidneys to eliminate hardly depends at all on what

14. For further discussion of environmental injuries and other details of the functional account of health sketched in this section, see my forthcoming essay "Health as a Theoretical Concept."

one wants to do. It follows that essentially all serious physiological diseases will satisfy the first requirement of an illness, namely, undesirability for its bearer.

This explanation of the fit between medical theory and medical practice has the virtue of reminding us that health, though an important value, is conceptually a very limited one. Health is not unconditionally worth promoting, nor is what is worth promoting necessarily health. Although mental-health writers are especially prone to ignore these points, even the constitution of the World Health Organization seems to embody a similar confusion:

> Health is a state of complete physical, mental, and social well-being, and not merely the absence of disease or infirmity.[15]

Unless one is to abandon the physiological paradigm altogether, this definition is far too wide. Health is functional normality, and as such is desirable exactly insofar as it promotes goals one can justify on independent grounds. But there is presumably no intrinsic value in having the functional organization typical of a species if the same goals can be better achieved by other means. A sixth sense, for example, would increase our goal-efficiency without increasing our health; so might the amputation of our legs at the knee and their replacement by a nuclear-powered air-cushion vehicle. Conversely, as we have seen, there is no a priori reason why ordinary diseases cannot contribute to well-being under appropriate circumstances.

In such cases, however, we will be reluctant to describe the person involved as ill, and that is because the term "ill" *does* have a negative evaluation built into it. Here again a comparison between health and other properties will be helpful. Disease and illness are related somewhat as are low intelligence and stupidity, or failure to tell the truth and speaking dishonestly. Sometimes the presumption that intelligence is desirable will fail, as in a discussion of qualifications for a menial job such as washing dishes or assembling auto parts. In such a context a person of low intelligence is unlikely to be described as stupid. Sometimes the presumption that truth should be told will fail, as when the Gestapo inquires about the Jews in your attic. Here the untruthful householder will not be described as speaking dishonestly. And sometimes the presumption that diseases are undesirable will fail, as with alcoholic intoxication or mild rubella intentionally contracted. Here the term "illness" is unlikely to appear despite the presence of disease. One concept of each pair is descriptive; the other adds to the first evaluative content, and so may be withheld where the first applies.

If we supplement this condition of undesirability with two further normative conditions, I believe we have the beginning of a plausible analysis of "illness."

---

15. Quoted by Flew, *Crime or Disease?* p. 46.

A disease is an *illness* only if it is serious enough to be incapacitating, and therefore is

(i) undesirable for its bearer;
(ii) a title to special treatment; and
(iii) a valid excuse for normally criticizable behavior.

The motivation for condition (ii) needs no explanation. As for (iii), the connection between illness and diminished responsibility has often been argued,[16] and I shall mention here only one suggestive point. Our notion of illness belongs to the ordinary conceptual scheme of persons and their actions, and it has developed to apply to physiological diseases. Consequently the relation between persons and their illnesses is conceived on the model of their relation to their bodies. It has often been observed that physiological processes, e.g. digestion or peristalsis, do not usually count as actions of ours at all. By the same token, we are not usually held responsible for the results of such processes when they go wrong, though we may be blamed for failing to take steps to prevent malfunction at some earlier time. Now if this special relation between persons and their bodies is the reason for connecting disease with nonresponsibility, the connection may break down when diseases of the mind are at stake instead. I shall now argue, in fact, that conditions (i), (ii), and (iii) all present difficulties in the domain of mental health.

III. MENTAL ILLNESS

For the sake of discussion, let us simply assume that the mental conditions usually called pathological are in fact unhealthy by the theoretical standard sketched in the last section. That is, we shall assume both that there are natural mental functions and also that recognized types of psychopathology are unnatural interferences with these functions.[17] Is it reasonable to make a parallel extension of the vocabulary of medical practice by calling these mental diseases mental illnesses? Let us consider each condition on "illness."

Condition (i) was the undesirability of an illness for its bearer. Now there are obstacles to transferring our general arguments that physiological health is desirable to the psychological domain. Mental states are not nearly so neutral to the choice of actions as physiological states are. In particular, to evaluate the desirability of mental health we can hardly avoid consulting our desires; but in

16. A good discussion of this point and of the undesirability condition (i) is provided by Flew in the extremely illuminating second chapter of *Crime or Disease?* Flew takes these conditions as part of the meaning of "disease" rather than "illness"; but since he seems to be working from the ordinary usage of "disease," there may be no real disagreement here.

17. The plausibility of these two claims is discussed at length in my essay, "What a Theory of Mental Health Should Be," to appear in *Journal for the Theory of Social Behaviour.*

the mental-health context it could be those very desires that are judged unhealthy. From a theoretical standpoint desires that are judged unhealthy. From a theoretical standpoint desires must be assigned a motivational function in producing action. Thus our wants may or may not conform to the species design. But if our wants do not conform to the species design, it is not immediately obvious why we should want them to. If there is no good reason to want them to, then we have a disease which is not an illness. It is conceivable that this divergence between the two notions is illustrated by homosexuality. It can hardly be denied that one normal function of sexual desire is to promote reproduction. If one does not have a desire for heterosexual sex, however, the only good reason for wanting to have such a desire seems to be that one would be happier if one did. But this judgment needs to be supported by evidence. The desirability of having species-typical desires is not nearly so obvious on inspection as the desirability of having species-typical physiological functions.

One of the corollaries of this point is that recent debates over homosexuality and other disputable diagnoses usually ignore at least onc important issue. Besides asking whether, say, homosexuality is a disease, one should also ask what difference it makes if it is. I have suggested that biological normality is an instrumental rather than an intrinsic good. We always have the right to ask, of normality, what is in it for us that we already desire. If it were possible, then, to maximize intrinsic goods such as happiness, for ourselves and others, with a psyche full of deviant desires and unnatural acts, it is hard to see what practical significance the theoretical judgment of unhealthiness would have. I do not actually have serious doubts that disorders such as neuroses and psychoses diminish human happiness. It is also true that what is desirable for a person need not coincide with what the person wants; though an anorectic may not wish to eat, it is desirable that he or she do so. But we must be clear that requests to justify the value of health in other terms are always in order, and there are reasons to expect that such justification will require more evidence in the psychological domain than in the physiological.

We have been discussing the value of psychological normality for the individual, as dictated by condition (i) on illness, rather than its desirability for society at large. Since clinicians often assume that mental health involves social adjustment, it may be well to point out that the functional account of health shows this too to be a debatable assumption requiring empirical support. Certainly nothing in the mere statement that a person has a mental disease entails that he or she is contributing less to the social order than an arbitrary normal individual. There is no contradiction in calling van Gogh or Blake or Dostoyevsky mentally disturbed while admiring their work, even if they would have been less creative had they been healthier. Conversely, there is no a priori reason to assume that the healthy human personality will be morally worthy or socially acceptable. If Freud and Lorenz are right about the existence of an aggressive drive, there is a large component of the normal psyche that is less than admirable. Whether or not they are right, the suggestion clearly makes sense. Perhaps most psychiatrists would agree anyway that antisocial behavior is to be expected during certain developmental stages, e.g. the so-called anal-sadistic period or adolescence.

It must be conceded that *Homo sapiens* is a social species. Other organisms of this class, such as ants and bees, display elaborate fixed systems of social adaptations, and it would be remarkable if the human design included no standard functions at all promoting socialization. On the basis of the physiological paradigm, however, it is not at all clear that contributions to society can be viewed as requirements of health except when they also contribute to individual survival and reproduction. No matter how this issue is decided, the crucial point remains: the nature and extent of social functions in the human species can be discovered only empirically. Despite the contrary convictions of many clinicians, the concept of mental health itself provides no guarantee that healthy individuals will meet the standards or serve the interests of society at large. If it did, that would be one more reason to question the desirability of health for the individual.

Let us now go on to condition (ii) on a disease which is an illness: that it justify "special treatment" of its owner. It is this condition together with (iii) that gives some plausibility to the many recent attempts to explain mental illness as a "social status" or "role."[18] The idea that the "sick role" is a special one is consistent with the statistical normality of having some disease or other. Some illnesses are serious diseases that incapacitate at the level of gross behavior, everyone can be minimally diseased without being ill. In the realm of mental health, however, many psychiatrists suggest the stronger thesis that it is statistically normal to be significantly incapacitated by neurosis.[19] A similar problem may arise on Benedict's famous view that the characteristic personality type of some whole societies is clinically paranoid.[20] A statistically normal condition, according to our analysis, can be a disease only if it can be blamed on the environment. But one might plausibly claim that most or all existing *cultural* environments do injure children, filling their minds with excessive anxiety about sexual pleasure, grotesque role models, absurd prejudices about reality, etc. It is at least possible that some degree of neurosis or psychosis is a nearly universal environmental injury in our species. Only an empirical inquiry into the incidence and etiology of neurosis can show whether this

18. An example of this approach is Robert B. Edgerton, "On The 'Recognition' of Mental Illness," in Stanley C. Plog and Robert B. Edgerton, *Changing Perspectives in Mental Illness* (New York, 1969), pp. 49–72.

19. Only one example of this suggestion is Dr. Reuben Fine's statement that neurosis afflicts 99 percent of the population. See Fine's "The Goals of Psychoanalysis," in *The Goals of Psychotherapy*, ed. Alvin R. Mahrer (New York, 1967), p. 95. I consider the issue of whether all neurosis can be called unhealthy in the essay cited in note 16.

20. See the descriptions of the Kwakiutl and the Dobu in Ruth Benedict, *Patterns of Culture* (Boston: Houghton Mifflin, 1934).

possibility is a reality. If it is, however, one can maintain the idea that serious diseases are illnesses only by abandoning one of the presuppositions of the illness concept: that not everyone can be ill.[21]

The last and clearest difficulty with "mental illness" concerns condition (iii), the role of illness in excusing conduct. We said that the idea that serious diseases excuse conduct derives from the model of the relation of agents to their own physiology. Unfortunately the relation of agents to their own psychology is of a much more intimate kind. The puzzle about mental illness is that it seems to be an activity of the very seat of responsibility—the mind and character—and therefore to be beyond all hope of excuse.

This inference is hardly inescapable; there is room for considerable controversy to which I cannot do justice here. Strictly speaking, mental disorders are disturbances of the personality. It is persons, not personalities, who are held responsible for actions, and one central element in the idea of a person is certainly consciousness. This means that there may be some sense in contrasting responsible persons with their mental diseases insofar as these diseases lie outside their conscious personalities. Perhaps from a psychoanalytic standpoint this condition is often met in psychosis and neurosis. The unconscious processes that surface in these disorders seem at first sight more like things that happen within us, e.g. peristalsis, than like things we do. But several points make this classification look oversimplified. Unconscious ideas and wishes are still *our* ideas and wishes in a more compelling sense than movements of the gut are our movements. They may have been conscious at an earlier time or be made conscious in therapy, whereupon it becomes increasingly difficult to disclaim responsibility for them. It seems quite unclear that we are more responsible for many conscious desires and beliefs than for these unconscious ones. Finally, the hope for contrasting responsible people with their mental diseases grows vanishingly dim in the case of a character disorder, where the unhealthy condition seems to be integrated into the conscious personality.

In view of these points and the rest of the discussion, I think we must accept the following conclusion. While conditions (i), (ii), and (iii) apply fairly automatically to serious physical diseases, not one of them should be assumed to apply automatically to serious mental diseases. If the term "mental illness" is to be applied at all, it should probably be restricted to psychoses and disabling neuroses. But even this decision needs more analysis than I have

21. A number of clinicians have seriously suggested that people who are ill can be distinguished from those who are well by their presence in your office. One such author goes as far as to calculate an upper limit on the incidence of mental illness from the number of members in the American Psychiatric Association. On a literal reading, this patient-in-the-office test implies that one could wipe out mental illness once and for all by dissolving the APA and outlawing psychotherapy. But the whole idea seems silly anyway in the face of various studies that indicate that the population at large is, by the ordinary descriptive criteria for mental disorder, no less disturbed than the population of clinical patients.

provided in this essay. It seems doubtful that on any construal mental illness will ever be, in the mental-health movement's famous phrase, "just like any other illness."

What are the implications of our discussion for the social issues to which psychiatry is so frequently applied? As far as the criminal law is concerned, our results suggest that psychiatric theory alone should not be expected to define legal responsibility, e.g. in the insanity defense.[22] Although the notion of responsibility is a component of the notion of illness, it belongs not to medical theory but to ethics, and one can fix its boundaries only by rational ethical debate. It seems certain such a simple responsibility test as that the act of the accused not be "the product of mental disease" is unsatisfactory. No doubt many of us have antisocial tendencies that derive from underlying psychopathology of an ordinary sort. When these tendencies erupt in a parking violation or negligent collision, it hardly seems inhumane or unjust to apply legal sanctions.[23] But this is not surprising, for no psychiatric concept is properly designed to answer moral questions. I am not saying that psychiatry is irrelevant to law and ethics. Anyone writing or applying a criminal code is certainly well advised to obtain the best available information about human nature, including the information about human nature that constitutes mental-health theory. The point is that one cannot expect to substitute psychiatry for moral debate, any more than moral evaluations can be substituted for psychiatric theory. Insofar as the psychiatric turn consists in such substitutions, it is fundamentally misconceived.

The other main implications of our discussion seem to me twofold. First, there is not the slightest warrant for the recurrent fantasy that what society or its professionals disapprove of is ipso facto unhealthy. This is not merely because society may disapprove of the wrong things. Even if ethical relativism were true, society still could not fix the functional organization of the members of a species. For this reason it could never be an infallible authority either on disease or on illness, which is a subclass of disease. Thus one main source of the tendency to call radical activists, bohemians, feminists, and other unpopular deviants "sick" is nothing but a conceptual confusion.

The second moral suggested by our discussion is that it is always worth asking, in any particular case, how strong the presumption is that health is desirable. When the value of health is left both unquestioned and obscure, it has a tendency to undergo inflation. The diagnosis especially of a "mental

22. The same conclusion is defended by Herbert Fingarette in "Insanity and Responsibility," *Inquiry* 15 (1972): 6–29.

23. Thus I disagree with H.L.A. Hart, among others, who writes: "... the contention that it is fair or just to punish those who have broken the law must be absurd if the crime is merely a manifestation of a disease." The quotation is from "Murder and the Principles of Punishment: England and the United States," reprinted in *Moral Problems*, ed. James Rachels (New York, 1975), p. 274.

illness" is then likely to become an amorphous and peculiarly repellent stigma to be removed at any cost. The use of muscle-paralyzing drugs to compel prisoners to participate in "group therapy" is a particularly gruesome example of this sort of thinking.[24] But there are many other situations in which everyone would profit by asking what exactly is wrong with being unhealthy. In a way liberal reformers tend to make the opposite mistake: in their zeal to remove the stigma of disease from conditions such as homosexuality, they wholly discount the possibility that these conditions, like most diseases, are somewhat unideal. If the value of health, as I have argued in this essay, is nothing but the value of conformity to a generally excellent species design, then by recognizing that fact we may improve both the clarity and the humanity of our social discourse.

Author's Note added for recent volume: Among many revisions I would make in this paper today, two are especially important. First, the view that illness is disease laden with values (i)-(iii) now seems a mistaken concession to normativism. Illness is better analyzed simply as systemically incapacitating disease, hence as no more normative than disease itself. Features (i)-(iii) are common social evaluations of illness, underlying the sick role, but they are probably no part of the meaning of 'illness'. On this view both a disease-illness distinction and a theory-practice distinction remain central to philosophy of medicine, without the former being a case of the latter. Second, as a terminological policy, I would avoid 'disease' as a generic term for all pathological conditions. Medical usage often contrasts diseases with injuries, static defects, poisonings, and other kinds of lesion. For these reasons the essay seems mistitled. A better title would be "On the distinction between the pathological and the sick role," although (remembering *Iolanthe*) I am also tempted to suggest "Not on the distinction between disease and illness." I hope to develop my revised position in a forthcoming book, *The Concept of Health.*

24. For this and other "therapeutic" abuses in our prison system, see Jessica Mitford, *Kind and Usual Punishment* (New York, 1973), chap. 8.

5.5

The Concept of Disease

Joseph Margolis

Austin Turk, surveying the literature of the criminal law, favored the view that "criminality is... the state of having been officially defined as punishable, whether or not one has been apprehended and punished" (Turk 1969, p. 18). He added that "efforts to determine causes of criminality have foundered on the fact that criminality is not a biological, psychologial, or even behavioral phenomenon, but a social status defined by the way in which an individual is perceived, evaluated, and treated by legal authorities" (p. 25).

It may seem surprising that such a view—rightly termed legal positivism—is fairly matched within medical theory and theories governing other domains concerned with deviance and maladaption. For instance, Ian Gregory maintains that, "While professionals have a major voice in influencing the judgment of society, it is the collective judgment of the larger social group that determines whether its members are to be viewed as sick or criminal, eccentric or immoral" (Gregory 1968, p. 32).[1] The conjunction of these specimen views serves to fix our minds on the essential issues concerning the concept of health. For, even on the most casual canvassing of the relevant literature, it is obvious that medicine and the law are the two principal professional disciplines of advanced societies systematically concerned with rendering judgments that are at once informed by selected norms of human functioning and characterizable as findings of fact (ignoring, here, a more restricted usage in the law); that the extension of 'illness' (or 'deviance' or 'maladaptation') and the extension of 'criminality' are quite often confused with one another and even sometimes subsumed under one another (see Glueck [1954]; Menninger [1968]; Menninger, Mayman, and Pruyser [1963]; also the review of the issue in Flew [1973]; Kittrie [1971]; Szasz [1970]); and that we are rather unwilling (though perhaps for different reasons) to regard illness and breaches of the law

---

[1]The reference, I should like to mention, is cited in an unpublished paper by Christopher Boorse (1975*a*) which came into my hands just at the moment of composing my own account and from which, allowing for disagreements, I have much benefited.

as matters merely of conventional classification—alterable without conceptual dislocation by whatever ingenious and imaginative historical turn given societies may have taken.

The question of the nature of illness and disease (as well as that of crime) depends very substantially, as may be shown, on how we understand the nature of factual and value judgments, norms and normality, and the functioning of organs, organisms, and human persons. Obviously, the latter are vexed matters and may even seem to be quite remote from the concern of practicing physicians and of therapists in allied disciplines. Hence, in developing a theory of health and illness, a certain initial tolerance is required regarding certain ground-level distinctions which, if not provided, will be found to render debate practically useless. Furthermore, in attempting a fair account, we should consider the lack of uniformity in speaking of disease and illness and the possible difference in focus intended in speaking of health and disease. Thus, in a recent pronouncement, the World Health Organization (1958) held that "health is a state of complete physical, mental, and social well-being and not merely the absence of disease or infirmity" (p. 459). Similarly, speaking of mental health, Marie Jahoda (1958) has stressed a comparable insufficiency when one thinks of health as the mere absence of mental disease. Also, a glance at the American Psychiatric Association's (1968; cf. *International Classification of Diseases* 1968) *Diagnostic and Statistical Manual of Mental Disorders* (*DSM II*), intended to adhere as closely as possible to the World Health Organization's *International Classification of Diseases*, confirms that the term 'disease' is hardly used in an explicitly systematic way.

1. VALUE JUDGMENTS

Begin, then, with value judgments.

For sentences of a predicative form, value judgments may be distinguished from nonvaluational judgments, by their predicates.[2] That a predicate is a valuational predicate depends solely on the explication of its sense in terms of norms of some sort. The concept of a norm is the concept of a condition or parameter in terms of which a range of relevant phenomena may be (valuationally) graded or ranked as satisfying the condition given: valuational predicates then, are used to grade or rank such phenomena relative to such norms. So seen, to admit a judgment to be a value judgment entails nothing at all about the defensibility or grounds for proposing particular norms; the distinction has to do only with the logical properties of different kinds of judgment. Construe illness as a lapse of some sort with respect to given norms of health: the judgment that Peter is ill (in whatever way may be specified) will

---

[2]The brief account given here is taken from Margolis (1971).

count as a value judgment. Furthermore, seemingly nonpredicative sentences used in making value judgments—for instance, 'ought'—judgments (whether moral or prudential or medical makes no difference)—may always be fairly construed in a predicative way by simply replacing 'ought' by some such locution as 'oughtful' and making the required grammatical adjustments (see Margolis 1971). The account is convenient because, at one and the same time, it frees the characterization of value judgments from disputes about the defensibility of particular norms and permits us to see the sense in which value judgments and factual judgments are not distinct species of a common genus. In fact, we may say that a factual judgment, of any sort whatsoever, is simply a judgment to which we may assign truth values, usually, truth and falsity. So seen, there is no difficulty at all in admitting that a given judgment may be both a factual judgment and a value judgment. For example, the judgment that "Peter is tubercular" (which is not to say merely that the bacillus may be found in Peter's system) and that "Peter murdered Paul" (which is not to say merely that something that Peter did was causally responsible for the death of Paul) are, at one and the same time, value judgments and factual judgments: both may, in an obvious sense, be true or false, and 'tubercular' and 'murdered' are predicates by means of which we manage to grade conditions and behavior relative to certain medical and legal norms. Such judgments may be called "findings." An alternative way of putting the point is this: human institutions normally embody norms; hence, institutional facts (e.g., as regarding murder) may entail reference to norms at the same time that they remain facts.

Even this general distinction is helpful with respect to certain well-known quarrels in the medical setting. For, it is very often maintained that one may have a disease without being ill, even if disease is still a normative concept, indicating "a state of affairs as undesirable and to be overcome" (cf. Engelhardt 1974; Feinstein 1967). It is also sometimes maintained that, while the concept of illness is a normative concept, that of disease is not. As Christopher Boorse puts it: "In our own culture and in others, the concept of *illness* is a compound of a theory of disease and a body of associated normative institutions"; "The physician as theoretician speaks of diseases, lesions, organs, functions, and the like: in his social capacity he speaks instead of illness, suffering, incapacitation, recovery, and the like. Statements made in this second vocabulary do typically have an evaluative component; but I believe statements made in the first do not" (Boorse 1975*a*).[3] Boorse cites the following view of Fredrick Redlich's as an instance of what he takes to be an error, the mistake of "normativism": "Most propositions about normal behavior refer implicitly or explicitly to ideal behavior. Deviations from the

[3]This manuscript (n. 1 above) has now appeared in somewhat revised form; see Boorse (1975*b*). Boorse pursues the same theme in two forthcoming papers; see (in press) and (forthcoming).

ideal obviously are fraught with value judgments; actually, all propositions on normality contain value statements in various degrees" (Redlich 1952). Boorse suggests that some idealizations—like that of ideal gases—are not normative, which is entirely fair; but the point of Redlich's remark remains entirely unaffected.[4]

A good deal hangs on this. The idealization involved in the gas laws concerns the provision of standard but nonexistence specimens to which actual gases may be compared in terms of resemblance only—and for the sake of simplifying causal explanation: the ideal gases are not thought to be excellent in any respect whatsoever. A similar methodological strategy is involved in Max Weber's ideal types (see Girth and Mills 1946). But the idealization involved in medical and related settings essentially concerns the provision of theoretical states of health with respect to which the actual states of organisms are to be suitably graded and ranked as relatively defective (as ill or not ill, or as more diseased or less disease than other specimens). From this viewpoint, it is quite possible to admit that an organism has a certain disease but is not ill, but it makes no sense to suppose that to ascribe a disease to an organism does not imply some reference to the very same normative states on which ascriptions of illness depend. The "presence of a disease" (usually bearing on infection or deficiency or abnormality) rather than the presence of a "diseased state" normally signifies that causal factors that might well make an organism ill (produce a diseased state that a patient might complain about or that might make him ail) are benignly present in the body under circumstances that invite concern about imminent or potentially imminent illness (that is, the occurrence of an actual diseased state that is likely to produce complaint or ailing imminently, or eventually does so). There are several reasons for insisting on the connection. First of all, it explains why it is that medical diagnosis and prognosis are conceptually linked to the norms of health and illness even where particular judgments, for instance judgments merely describing (nonevaluatively) the condition of the body, probable causal developments, and the probable causal consequences of initiating chemical and other physical changes, may involve no explicit reference to the norms of health and disease: the intent in pursuing the latter sort of inquiry is normally to determine the presence of a disease, that is, the presence of causal factors that are likely to produce illness (disease states palpable to the patient in virtue of his symptoms). Second, it explains the sense in which medicine is primarily an art and, dependently, a science: it is primarily an *institutionalized service concerned with the care and cure of the ill and the control of disease*, in facilitating which certain purely descriptive and causal inquiries are pursued. Third, it suggests the potentially controversial nature of the norms of health and disease and the prerogatives and obligations of medicine: the objectivity with which the norms

---

[4]The same charge is laid against my own book (1966).

of health and the constraints of medicine may be specified are not in the least assured by merely acknowledging that medicine is a doubly normative discipline. Controversy about the inclusion, say, of homosexuality as a medically designated disorder (see "Should Homosexuality Be in the APA Nomenclature?" 1973; "Ideas and Trends" 1973)[5] and about the revision of rights and obligations in the patient-doctor relationship (see Annas and Healey 174; Sade 1971) makes this quite clear.

But to collect the argument thus far advanced, we may say that value judgments are distinguished by their predicates, which entails that relevant ascriptions depend not merely on resemblances to standard but unexceptional specimens but, via grading and ranking, on approximations to, or deviations from, norms or standards of merit or worth (see Margolis 1971, chap. 5; cf. Hampshire 1959). Those norms, norms of health and illness, embody (in a way that needs to be specified) the relevant and legitimate concerns of human beings. The asymmetries between ascriptions of disease and illness reflect pragmatic distinctions relative to those concerns. And the proper constraints on the rights and obligations of patients and doctors, in the context of the practice of the medical arts, clearly must conform with those same concerns. There remains the problem, however, that, useful though they may be, these considerations are entirely formal.

2. NORMS

Two sets of contrasting distinctions conveniently fix the problem of medical norms: disease and illness, pathologist and clinician. It is obvious that there is a fair sense in which a certain disease may be present in one's system and in which one may be in a distinctly diseased state (through any of a range of stages from the benign to the lethal) without actually ailing or complaining of any symptoms because of the disease. And it is equally obvious that one may complain about or ail because of putative symptoms that either are not linked to disease at all or are, for reasons of technology or competence or the like, not detectably so linked; and even where symptoms are linked to disease, they may be associated with diseases other than the disease for which one's illness is classified. In this connection, Alvan Feinstein has usefully distinguished lanthanic diseases, that is, diseases that, though clinically evident, escape the patient's detection—as when there are no symptoms accessible to the patient or when, though there are, he is not a complainant. Feinstein here speaks of there being no iatrotropic stimulus. He adds the distinction of the comorbidity of diseases associated with the disease for which one may be a

[5]Dr. Robert L. Spitzer, who served as head of the APA task force on nomenclature and statistics, actually claims that 'normal' and 'abnormal' are "strictly speaking, not psychiatric terms" ("Ideas and Trends" 1973).

complainant, with respect to which some symptoms that serve as iatrotropic stimuli may really be the symptoms of an associated illness (Feinstein 1967, chap. 9).

Now, these distinctions presuppose a system of medical norms that Feinstein nowhere supplies. And yet, even with these formal distinctions in hand, it is clear why the concept of disease, though not entirely isomorphic with the concept of illness, makes no sense without reference to appropriate norms. A diseased state, on any plausible theory whatsoever, is a morbid or abnormal state of some sort, a state defective or deranged with respect to some condition of healthy functioning *or* suitably related to such a state, even if there is no complainant. A disease is either what is apt to cause a diseased state or that diseased state itself. Illness is simply a diseased state manifest to an agent through that agent's symptoms—sensations, introspective cognition, proprioceptive awareness, and the like; or, more informally and not narrowly the concern of medicine, a temporary condition of ailing (or complaint) not caused by a disease state at all. In that sense, plants may be diseased but never ill. But these distinctions still contribute very little to our understanding of the nature of disease itself.

In fact, what needs to be emphasized is that it is conceptually not at all implausible to hold that an incipient disease or diseased state may well obtain without any malfunctioning whatsoever—not merely in the lanthanic sense but in the sense that, on whatever professional criteria may be admitted, the palpable *onset* on some disease, as among the cancers, need not by synchronic with any determinate malfunctioning—provided that what is so designated is causally linked in an appropriate way with the onset of malfunctioning and is not trivially taken as a form of malfunctioning itself. Here, one must bear in mind a common equivocation on 'abnormal' and cognate terms—as designating determinate malfunctioning or what, under the circumstances, is likely to cause such malfunctioning.

To return to our initial distinctions: Feinstein (1967) also contrasts the clinician and pathologist. After listing characteristic diagnostic categories (e.g., myocardial infarction, phlebothrombosis), he observes:

> Not a single one of these diagnostic terms represents an entity that is ever actually seen, heard, or touched in the ordinary bedside observations of a clinician. Every one of these entities is an abnormality of internal anatomic structure. The clinician at the bedside never observes these abnormal structures directly; he observes the symptoms and signs that are their clinical effects. With roentgenography, a clinician may see the silhouettes and shadows of these abnormal structures; with endoscopy, he may see those portions of an abnormality visible in the accessible lumen; with laboratory tests, he may note the associated disorders in physiologic and biochemical function; with surgical exploration in suitable situations, he may see a larger view of the abnormal structure and of its anatomic relations. But the only doctor who regularly

> witnesses the actual, complete appearance of all these anatomic entities—the only doctor who can regularly see them, feel them, and even cut them— is a pathologist. [Pp. 73–74]

In effect, then, the clinician operates with the pathologist's categories. But Feinstein misleadingly concludes that the clinician is somehow confined to inferences from what he *observes* and that the pathologist actually *witnesses* the disease or diseased condition—which introduces an unexplained privilege. Thus he says: "To arrive at a diagnosis of morbid anatomy—such as *myocardial infarction, epidermoid carcinoma of the lung,* or *hepatic cirrhosis*—a pathologist makes no deductions or inferences. He classifies what he sees" (p. 80). The question remains, What makes what the pathologist observes classifiable as disease? Whatever the grounds may be, they will also provide a basis for claiming that the clinician observes the symptoms and signs of disease. Alternatively put, clinician and pathologist make their usual observations and inferences informed by a common theory of medical norms of health and illness.

There is another clue that the contrast between clinician and pathologist provides: the clinician normally attends to the complaints and therapy of his patient; the pathologist normally attends to the functioning of organs and other anatomical structures, systems of biochemical processes, and the behavior of cells. Psychiatry is at least a near exception. Clinician and pathologist, examining systematic behavior, tend to converge on the total condition of their human patients. But this is precisely what has raised the strenuous question of the medical status of psychiatric illness (see Szasz 1961; Margolis 1966). Nevertheless, two provisional conclusions may be drawn here. First of all, the conception of diseased cells, of microorganisms as disease entities (whether defensible or not) (see Virchow 1958), and of the diseases of organs must be dependent on the conception of the diseases and illnesses of human beings, animals, and plants as such. Second, the allegedly scientific and value-neutral status of medical pathology addressed to cells, organs, biochemical processes, and the like must be an abstraction (entirely defensible as such) from the value-freighted investigations of the world of disease and illness common to pathologist and clinician. The reason for both conclusions is the same, namely, reference to the medically relevant norms in terms of which alone diseases are construed as such.

A first approximation to the theory of medical norms—let it be stressed that it is only a first approximation—has it that the body is composed of certain structured systems each of which has an assignable range of normal functioning. Defect or disorder of such systems relative to such functioning constitutes a sufficient condition of disease; illness, then, is reflexively palpable disease. Psychiatry is once again problematic, since relative to mental illness, "functional" systems tend to be metaphorically identified and the norms that must be posited oblige us to assign functional characteristics to human nature as such (rather than to organs, limbs, or the like). In this regard, the norms of health and disease tend to correspond—often in a disputatious way—with putative norms of happiness and well-being (see Margolis 1966).[6] To the extent that this occurs, it becomes difficult to treat the norms of medicine as altogether independent of ideologies prevailing in different societies (see Hollingshead and Redlich 1958). A closer review of the matter reveals, however, both that the functional norms of psychiatry are capable of a fair measure of objective support relative to the norms of physical medicine and that the norms of physical medicine are themselves dependent on a deeper commitment to a more-than-medical conception of human functioning. Furthermore, pursuing the implications of the disease/illness distinction, we must realize that there cannot possibly be a thorough and detailed form/function correlation for all diseases. Feinstein (1967; see, also Ryle 1961), noting that "abnormal structure and abnormal function [cannot] always be correlated, so that one constantly implie[s] the other and vice versa," offers the following counterinstances:

> Anginal pain may arise from pulmonary hypertension, not coronary disease; coronary disease may produce no angina. Skin may look yellow because of hypercarotenemia; a serum bilirubin value may be elevated without evident clinical jaundice. Cyanosis may be due to methemoglobinemia; a hypoxemic patient may be too anemic to look cyanotic. Lid-lag may sometimes occur in healthy people or in euthyroid patients with pulmonary disease; the exophthalmos associated with lid-lag and hyperthyroidism may persist long after treatment has made the patient euthyroid or even hypothyroid; hyperthyroidism may produce no lid-lag; and an elevation of protein-bound iodine, associated with neither lid-lag nor hyperthyroidism, may be due to residual deposits of iodine dye used in a previous gall bladder X-ray examination. [Pp. 68–69]

Considerations of these sorts oblige us to admit that the functional conception in terms of which disease is to be specified cannot be read off directly by a scanning of observable form/function correlations, even if, for particular diseases, such correlations seem to present themselves (e.g., angina pectoris and coronary arteriosclerosis).

Here, also, several additional qualifications may be proposed. First of all, whatever it may be made out to be, the notion of normal or healthy functioning cannot be straightforwardly assigned to the localized processes and structures of the body. Even the concept of homeostasis must be construed in a molar and functional way (i.e., with respect to the functioning of the healthy organism as such), by reference to which *alone* the distribution of relatively localized functions is itself justified. Not only may the homeostatic mechanism itself be diseased—which obliges us to construe bodily functions

---

[6]Engelhardt (1974) cites the amusing "disease" drapetomania (the running away of slaves) (see Cartwright [1851, cited in Engelhardt]).

in terms of higher-order norms; the very "mechanism" of homeostasis presupposes "goal-directed activities" and "directively correlated processes"—which cannot be identified except in terms of some antecedently governing function (see Sommerhoff 1974; Wiener 1953).[7] Secondly, what is normal must be construed not as a fixed point but as a range of variations, tolerated in accord with some antecedent theory of the relationship between individual organisms and the populations of which they are members, a fortiori, between individual organisms and their environment. Species variation contributes to species survival in a changing world and individual variability may accommodate different careers and different kinds of tolerance (see Ryle 1961; Dobzhansky 1962). But to concede this much is to construe medicine as instrumental to ulterior values. What, then, is the nature of the disease?

3. FUNCTIONS

The notion that human beings have a natural function is essential to the eudaimonism of Plato and Aristotle and it is, in a way, presupposed by the claims of somatic and psychiatric medicine insofar as they suppose themselves to be value-neutral sciences.[8] The difficulty of defending functional norms is rather complex. For one thing, specimens of *Homo sapiens* are readily classified on the basis of resemblance to admitted specimens not otherwise distinguished in any way whatsoever regarding merit or excellence of any sort—hence, neutrally to the competing eudaimonistic visions of Plato, Aristotle, and their progeny. For another, even for such an organ as the eye—which one supposes to have a definite and assignable function, with respect to which, therefore, diseases may be objectively discerned—it is quite possible to imagine a set of circumstances in which eyes would lose their "function" and yet not be diseased. For example, imagine that, because of terrestrial pollution, the human race adopts, and adapts to, a life maintained at a submarine level unpenetrated by sunlight. The unlikelihood of the example is not important, because the lesson to be drawn is not that the eye has no function but only *what* is entailed in saying that it does have a function. Or, again, imagine that sickle-cell anemia conveys immunity from malaria and that,

---

[7]An essential consideration is that the application of (formal) homeostatic concepts to organisms must accommodate, within the margins or normality and health, the aging and death of individual organisms and favored forms of the viability of populations within their environments. Note the usual absence of discussion along these lines (see Engel 1953; van Bertalanffy 1950). But see the discussion of functions, below.

[8]A particularly explicit specimen view is offered by Heinz Hartmann (1960). The theme obviously underlies the comparatively recent debate on the medical status of homosexuality (see "Should Homosexuality Be in the APA Nomenclature?" 1973; Margolis 1975*b*).

among the black peoples of Africa, the first is significantly less lethal than the second and "functions" to insure the survival of given populations—admittedly at the expense of selected individuals (see Dubos 1959). What is the clear sense in which both are diseases on functional grounds? Finally, it is perfectly clear that absolutely no theory of disease construes death itself or aging as dysfunctional or the result, merely as such, of disease. Man is essentially mortal and the trajectory of life from birth to death sets the boundaries within which particular diseases are so designated. There are diseases that are lethal but *there are no diseases that are classified as such merely because they result in death.* On the contrary, the most interesting general feature about disease is that it is a disorder or the cause of disorder of a certain sort *within the functional range of ongoing life*: that death may result from disease is a mere contingency but that disease may cause death or aging *prematurely* is not another contingency of the same sort. Imagine, for instance, that an extraordinary discovery confirms that a certain drug could increase our life expectancy in general, at an "acceptable" level of activity, fourfold; that it would be inexpensive, accessible, and without unfavorable side effects; *and* that society would begin to adjust its expectations and social arrangements to the increased longevity of its members. Might not patterns of now-normal decline leading to eventual death "by natural causes" come to be viewed as disease syndromes, severely dysfunctional processes subject to medical correction? If not, why not? And if so, then what is the sense in which the functional norms of medicine may be objectively specified independently of social values and social expectations?

These questions set the essential puzzle,[9] but we are far from understanding the sense in which we speak of the functions of human beings or other animals and the functions of the various organs and processes within their bodily systems or the systems of their behavior and life.

One crucial distinction cannot be avoided. Whatever functions are assignable to organisms as such—human beings in particular—are behavioral, in the generous sense of the term, such that no norms regarding the "appropriate," "proper," "normal" life of given organisms (extending even to plants and not confined in any way to merely medical concerns) can fail to include reference to the molar behavior (informed, where relevant, by mental states) or to what is the molar analogue of behavior where sentience is minimal or nonexistent (as among lower animals, plants, and machines). But the functions that are assignable to organs and processes within the bodily or life systems of particular kinds of organisms are dependently assigned in virtue of putative

[9]It is interesting, in this connection, to consider the extremely convenient resumé of the development of the concept of disease offered by Sir Henry Cohen (1961). Cohen recommends that disease interpreted as "deviation from the normal... should dominate our teaching and our approach to medicine." But he obviously takes it for granted that the normal or normal functioning is a straightforward matter both professionally and philosophically.

molar functions and are themselves (on what may be called the molecular level) never directly construed in behavioral terms. That is, the functions of living organisms are to be understood in terms of the goal-directed activities of those organisms, but the functions of their organs and processes are teleologically defined by reference to such activities though they cannot themselves be construed as goal directed or goal seeking (an anthropomorphism that is intelligible only in the context of the fable of the contract between the stomach and the other organs and limbs to cooperate for the sake of their various and independent interests). This is not to say that all goal-directed activity is functional or has a function or that all behavior that has a function is goal directed (see the extremely interesting account by Wright [1973]). It is simply to say that, wherever they are assigned, functions are assigned in accord with some deliberate plan or design (as with human work and machines), or with "natural" goals (as with living organisms), *or* with some more informal approximation to either of these models (see Sorabji 1964).

The difficult cases, of course, are precisely those in which natural functions are assigned, and these are just the ones that concern medicinc and are usually specified in terms of the *sub*systems (e.g., the organs) of living organisms themselves. Where natural functions are assigned to those very organisms as integers of some sort—as, classically, by way of the eudaimonism of the Greeks—they are defined behaviorally and in terms of the "appropriate" goals or objectives of the creatures in question, favoring, of course, the full-blooded planning of human beings (though not exclusively). Still, the sense in which both artifacts and natural creatures *have* functions (and, by elaboration, the parts of artifactual systems and the organs and processes of organisms) is said to entail that the functions assigned be *essential* to their respective natures, not merely accidental or accidentally useful or the like.[10] The trouble is that animals, including *Homo sapiens*, may be classified without regard to norms of functional excellence of any sort, solely in terms of resemblance to standard specimens that are not themselves supposed to be functionally superior or to provide functional paradigms of any sort.[11] And this signifies that the ascription of "natural" functions to organisms—most controversially, natural functions to human beings or human persons (characteristically though not necessarily ethically freighted, as in the natural law tradition or the doctrine of eudaimonism)—cannot be straight-forwardly made on the basis of some *empirical inspection of the essential nature of such creatures.* This is not to lose the

---

[10]The point is effectively made in Wright (1973). He usefully analyzes the weakness of a number of accounts that are primarily concerned with the nature of the functions of the organs and processes of biological organisms; in particular, Beckner (1959); Canfield (1964); Beckner (1969).

[11]A standard argument that the mere classification of human beings (or of anything else) entails reference to grading and ranking notions appears in Hampshire (1959, p. 223). But it is untenable and unnecessary; see Margolis (1971, chap. 5).

notion of natural function but only to question in an important way the sense in which natural functions may be said to be discovered by an exercise of medical science or any other relevant science.

As it turns out, there is an extremely simple and straightforward sense in which natural functions may be assigned to human beings, which does not require that we think of them as fixed or determinate or essential or discovered. But to say this is, precisely, to provide for quarrels about the provision of medical norms—as, for instance, with regard to the longevity example already supplied or with regard to familiar controversies over sexual deviance and other psychiatrically sensitive categories. To see this, consider first the general analysis of functions advocated by Larry Wright: "The function of *X* is *Z means* (*a*) *X* is there because it does *Z*, (*b*) *Z* is a consequence (or result) of *X*'s being there" (1973, p. 161). Wright correctly notes that "functional ascriptions are... explanatory"; are, in particular, "etiological, concern the causal background of the phenomenon under consideration, [that is,] concern how the thing with the function got there" (pp. 154, 156). Nevertheless, in clarifying his formulation, Wright implicitly betrays its own limitations. For he says, "The first part, (*a*), displays the etiological form of functional ascription-explanations, and the second part (*b*), describes the convolution which distinguishes functional etiologies from the rest. It is the second part of course which distinguishes the combining with hemoglobin from the producing of energy in the oxygen-respiration example. Its combining with hemoglobin is emphatically not a consequence of oxygen's being in our blood; just the reverse is true. On the other hand, its producing energy *is* a result of its being there" (p. 161). The oxygen-respiration case concerns the fact that, although it is etiologically true that oxygen is found in human bloodstreams because it combines with hemoglobin, it is "colossally fatuous" to say that it is the function of oxygen to combine with hemoglobin—where it *is* the function of oxygen to produce energy. Nevertheless, Wright also maintains that, "if carbon monoxide, which we know to combine readily with hemoglobin, were suddenly to become able to produce energy by appropriate (non-lethal) reactions in our cells and, further, the atmosphere were suddenly (!) to become filled with CO, we could properly say that the reason CO was in our bloodstreams was that it combines readily with hemoglobin. We could not properly say, however, that CO was there because it produces *energy*. And that is precisely what we could say about oxygen, on purely evolutionary-etiological grounds" (pp. 159–60). This won't do, however, simply because one could well imagine sustained circumstances under which, on the hypothesis, the survival of the species depended on ingesting CO and on its combining with hemoglobin and thereupon producing energy—circumstances in which (on Wright's own hypothesis) the process noted obtained "suddenly." This shows the difficulty, in spite of what Wright says, of maintaining the asymmetry of the concept of "consequence" (that "'A is a consequence of B' is in virtually every context incompatible with 'B is a consequence of A'") (p. 161). But there is another fatal consideration, namely, that Wright's formulation fails to exclude cases of disease—in particular, cases in which the homeostatic mechanisms of an organism are themselves diseased. One has only to imagine the evolution of diseased populations to see that creatures and organs and processes may well be said to function in a certain characteristic way, although, on some relevant theory, we should not wish to say that the function of what is in question would then be given by the formulation cited (see pp. 141–43). Notice that such cases are quite different from cases (mentioned by Wright) in which "organismic mutations," though accidental, may yet confer in time functionhood on an organ or process. Obviously, something more is needed.

4. PRUDENCE AND DISEASE

When Wright attempts to explain the way in which functional explanations operate, he says explicitly: "When we explain the presence or existence of *X* by appeal to a consequence *Z*, the overriding consideration is that *Z* must be or create conditions conducive to the survival or maintenance of *X*" (1973, p. 164). But it may, for instance, be argued, as earlier remarked, that sickle-cell anemia, which is hereditary, functions, among African populations, in a way that is conducive to survival in malarial environments (see the suggestive summary in Brothwell [1971]). Is it the case, then, that, in such circumstances—relatively stable in fact for ages—the function of sickle-cell anemia is to confer immunity to malaria? This seems as "colossally fatuous" as what Wright had marked out in the oxygen-respiration case.

An essential part of the difficulty of all theories of these sorts applied to human beings depends on the important distinction between the human animal (the biological species *Homo sapiens*) and human persons (members of *Homo sapiens* who have been culturally trained in the mastery of language and who are, therefore, capable of self-reference and cultural contribution).[12] It is impossible, for instance, to speak of psychiatric disease and disorder exclusively in terms of the condition of the human animal: the disorders normally considered are formulable only in terms of the mental processes of culturally emergent persons. But this means that the ascription of "natural functions" to human persons cannot possibly be provided, in the context of psychiatry, in a way that ignores the culturally prepared goals of human societies. And if the functioning of the human animal (what may roughly but only very roughly be thought to provide the concern of soatic medicine) may be fairly said to be

[12]This very complicated matter I can only hint at here. It is the subject of my as yet unpublished book, *Persons and Minds*.

inseparable from the functioning and functional objectives of human persons and if, as has been suggested, natural norms are not simply straightforwardly discovered, then we need to provide a rather different rationale for the ascription of functions (a fortiori, for the norms of medicine) from what has so far been sketched.

A fair way of proceeding is to confine ourselves to what may be called rational minima, that is, constraints regarding normative matters, including the norms of health and disease, that are least controversial or objectionable to agents endowed with a minimal measure of rationality more or less presupposed by every significant human society.[13] Obviously, there will be quarrels here as well. But it may be said that human beings, viewed in a sense that is relatively neutral to their condition as animals or persons, subscribe to a characteristic set of (what may be called) prudential values—avoidance of death, prolongation of life, restriction of pain, gratification of desires, insuring security of person and body and property and associates, and the like. The evidence is empirical and statistically overwhelming and the argument does not in the least assume the discovery of what is essential or normatively natural to human existence. Now then, the set of prudential values that may be ascribed to human beings—and, by extension, adjusted for lower animals and, by analogy, adjusted for plants—is relatively open-ended, putative, and merely determinable. Any determinate recommendation regarding the management of prudential values for an entire society constitutes an ideology or part of an ideology—assuming that there are no discoverable natural norms of human existence, or at any rate in the absence of any compelling discovery of that sort.

Medicine and the law are the two principal professionalized disciplines of every complex society that have provided an institutionally determinate rule for managing a portion of our prudential interests: the law—in terms of restricting harm or the threat of harm to those interests, caused by another (criminal law), or of protecting the exercise of those interests, as in the use of rights and property, in the arena of social exchange (civil law); medicine—in terms of insuring the functional integrity of the body (or mind or person), as by care and cure, sufficient for the exercise of our prudential interests. Prudential interests, then, are merely enabling interests, that is, the general (determinable) condition on which any ethical, political, economic program viable for a complex society must depend; in that sense, the pursuit of prudential interests is prima facie rational—which of course is not to deny that, as in suicide and self-sacrifice, there may well be grounds on which prudential interests may be waived without being irrational (hence, without breaking the law or without being diseased or disordered) (see Margolis 1975*a*).

---

[13]The full account of the thesis presented here appears in Margolis (1975*a*).

Since the human body (unlike social institutions) has changed relatively little over millenia, the functional norms of somatic medicine are relatively conservative (unlike the norms of law). But since, understandably enough, medicine has expanded its purview to include the concerns of mental health and mental illness (see Margolis 1969, also 1966), and since medicine in general must subserve, however conservatively, the determinate ideology and ulterior goals of given societies, the actual conception of diseases cannot but reflect the state of the technology, the social expectations, the division of labor, and the environmental condition of those populations.

This is no more than a sketch of the nature of medical norms. Still, it is the conception rather than the details that is is so elusive. The apparent obviousness of the natural functions of the organs and bodily processes can only be understood in terms of the conservativism of our prudential interests, such that the shifting of ideologies leaves relatively intact—but only relatively—the detailed schedules of bodily disease and illness. What we see is that it is entirely fair to insist on the natural functions of the various parts of our system. What has been changed (or challenged) is "only" the theory of such functions: they are now seen to subtend the putative prudential interests of the race, which are themselves determinable values subserving in ideologically determinate ways the ulterior functional norms ascribed by different doctrines to the life of man (as in eudaimonism—even in the inverted form advanced by Freud—or the natural law doctrine or the like). In a sense, therefore, medicine is ideology restricted by our sense of the minimal requirements of the functional integrity of the body and mind (health) enabling (prudentially) the characteristic activities and interests of the race to be pursued. And disease is whatever is judged to disorder or to cause to disorder, in the relevant way, the minimal integrity of body and mind relative to prudential functions.

REFERENCES

American Psychiatric Association. *Diagnostic and Statistical Manual of Mental Disorders.* 3d ed. Washington, D.C.: American Psychiatric Association, 1968.

Annas, George J., and Healey, Joseph M., Jr. "The Patient Rights Advocate: Redefining the Doctor-Patient Relationship in the Hospital Context." *Vanderbilt Law Review* 27 (1974): 243–69.

Beckner, Morton. *The Biological Way of Thought.* New York: Columbia University Press, 1959.

Beckner, Morton. "Function and Teleology." *Journal of the History of Biology* 2 (1969): 151–64.

Boorse, Christopher. "The Descriptive Core of Mental Health Judgments." Unpublished manuscript. 1975. (*a*)

Boorse, Christopher. "On the Distinction between Disease and Illness." *Philosophy and Public Affairs* 5 (1975): 49–68. (*b*)

Boorse, Christopher. "What a Theory of Mental Health Should Be." *Journal for the Theory of Social Behaviour*, in press.
Boorse, Christopher. "Health as a Theoretical Concept," forthcoming.
Brothwell, Don. "Disease, Micro-Evolution and Earlier Populations: An Important Bridge between Medical History and Human Biology." In *Modern Methods in the History of Medicine*, edited by Edwin Clarke. London: Athlone Press, 1971.
Canfield, John. "Teleological Explanations in Biology." *British Journal for the Philosophy of Science*, vol. 14 (1964).
Cartwright, Samuel A. "Report on the Diseases and Physical Peculiarities of the Negro Race." *New Orleans Medical and Surgical Journal* 7 (1851): 707–9.
Cohen, Sir Henry. "The Evolution of the Concept of Disease." In *Concepts of Medicine*, edited by Brandon Lush. London: Pergamon Press, 1961.
Dobzhansky, Theodosius. *Mankind Evolving*. New Haven, Conn.: Yale University press, 1962.
Dubos, René. *Mirage of Health*. New York: Harper & Row, 1959.
Engel, George L. "Homeostasis, Behavioral Adjustment and the Concept of Health and Disease." In *Mid-Century Psychiatry*, edited by Roy R. Grinker. Springfield, Ill.: Charles C. Thomas, 1953.
Engelhardt, H. Tristram, Jr. "The Concepts of Health and Disease." In *Philosophy and Medicine*, edited by H. Tristram Engelhardt, Jr., and Stuart F. Spicker. Vol. 1. Dordrecht: D. Reidel, 1974.
Feinstein, Alvan. *Clinical Judgment*. Baltimore: Williams & Wilkins, 1967.
Flew, Anthony. *Crime or Disease?* London: Macmillan Co., 1973.
Girth, H. H., and Mills, C. Wright. Introduction to *From Max Weber: Essays in Sociology*. New York: Oxford University Press, 1946.
Glueck, Bernard. "Changing Concepts in Forensic Psychiatry." *Journal of Criminal Law, Criminology and Police Science* 45 (1954): 123–32.
Gregory, Ian. *Fundamentals of Psychiatry*. Philadelphia: W. B. Saunders Co., 1968.
Hampshire, Stuart. *Thought and Action*. London: Chatto & Windus, 1959.
Hartmann, Heinz. *Psychoanalysis and Moral Values*. New York: International Universities Press, 1960.
Hollingshead, A. B., and Redlich, F. C. *Social Class and Mental Illness*. New York: John Wiley & Sons, 1958.
"Ideas and Trends." *New York Times*, December 23, 1973.
International Classification of Diseases Adapted for Use in the United States. 8th revision. Public Health Service Publication no. 1693. Washington, D.C.: Government Printing Office, 1968.
Jahoda, Marie. *Current Concepts of Positive Mental Health*. New York: Basic Books, 1958.
Kittrie, Nicholas, N. *The Right to Be Different*. Baltimore: Johns Hopkins University Press, 1971.
Margolis, Joseph. *Psychotherapy and Morality*. New York: Random House, Inc., 1966.
Margolis, Joseph. *Values and Conduct*. New York: Oxford University Press, 1971.
Margolis, Joseph. "The Question of Homosexuality." In *Sex: From the Philosophical Point of View*, edited by Robert Baker and Fred Elliston. New York: Prometheus Books, 1975. (*b*)
Menninger, Karl. *The Crime of Punishment*. New York: Viking Press, 1968.

Menninger, Karl; Mayman, Martin; and Pruyser, Paul. *The Vital Balance.* New York: Viking Press, 1963.

Redlich, Fredrick. "The Concept of Normality." *American Journal of Psychotherapy* 6 (1952) 551–69.

Ryle, J. "The Meaning of Normal." In *Concepts of Medicine,* edited by Brandon Lush. London: Pergamon Press, 1961.

Sade, Robert M. "Medical Care as a Right: A Refutation." *New England Journal of Medicine* (1971), pp. 1288–92.

"Should Homosexuality Be in the APA Nomenclature?" *American Journal of Psychiatry* 130 (1973): 1207–16.

Sorabji, Richard. "Function." *Philosophical Quarterly* 14 (1964): 289–302.

Sommerhoff, Gerd. *Logic of the Living Brain.* London: John Wiley, 1974.

Szasz, Thomas S. *The Myth of Mental Illness.* New York: Harper-Hoeber, 1961.

Szasz, Thomas S. *The Manufacture of Madness.* New York: Harper & Row, 1970.

Turk, Austin. *Criminality and Legal Order.* Chicago: Rand McNally & Co., 1969.

van Bertalanffy, Ludwig. "The Theory of Open Systems in Physics and Biology," *Science* 111 (1950): 23–29.

Virchow, Rudolf. *Disease, Life, and Man: Selected Essays by Rudolf Virchow.* Translated by Lelland J. Rather. Stanford, Calif: Stanford University Press, 1958.

Weiner, Norbert. "The Concept of Homeostasis in Medicine." *Transactions and Studies of the College of Physicians of Philadelphia* 20 (1953): 87–93.

World Health Organization. *The First Ten Years of the World Health Organization.* Geneva: World Health Organization, 1958.

Wright, Larry. "Functions." *Philosophical Review* 82 (1973): 139–68.

5.6

The Medical Model of the Disease Concept

F. Kräupl Taylor

INTRODUCTION

Doctors talk freely about diseases and disease entities, but they rarely pause nowadays to examine the meaning of these concepts. When they do, they are liable to get ensnared in logical and philosophical traps. For example, when J. G. Scadding (1967) tried to elucidate the meaning of disease he allowed himself to be side-tracked into asserting that 'since the exact description of a disease depends on the defining characteristic we choose to adopt for it, it seems to me impossible to think of diseases as having any sort of independent existence;... and I think we must adopt an uncompromisingly nominalist viewpoint'. What Scadding obviously had in mind herc was a nominal definition of the term 'disease'. The term signifies a concept (a 'universal') which, accoding to the nominalist philosophers of the Middle Ages, has no independent existence, no ontological relevance. But defining characteristics are also used in so-called real definitions. They then refer to the attributes which members of a particular class have in common, for example the members of the class of patients. In that case, we would have to replace the term 'disease' in Scadding's argument by the term 'patient' and come to the absurd conclusion that patients do not have any sort of independent existence. This example suggests that in reasoning that patients and their diseases ancient scholastic doctrines are of less help than modern logical theories on classes and their attributes. The problem of ontological existence does not seem to be any more of much relevance in this context. Scadding was rightly undeterred by his argument in continuing his analysis of ontologically non-existent diseases.

DISEASE CONCEPT IN PSYCHIATRY

In psychiatry, a different attack on the concept of disease has been mounted. It is being spearheaded today by clinical psychologists. They have put forward the thesis that the concept of disease is justified in organic medicine, but that this medical model is not applicable in non-organic psychiatry. H. J. Eysenck (1960), for instance, has roundly declared: 'The first essential is probably the banishment of the notion of disease from the field of functional mental abnormalities.' He has pointed out that there is qualitative difference between the class of organically ill patients and the class of organically healthy person. The former are characterized by certain attributes which are absent in the latter. There is, he maintains, no such qualitative difference between psychologically normal and psychologically abnormal persons. For example, the factor (or dimension) of neuroticism indicates an attribute complex that is present in all persons, but to a greater or lesser extent. The number of people with different neuroticism scores is normally distributed. There is no bimodality or discontinuity which would indicate different classes of people whose neuroticism scores cluster around different values.

Findings of this kind have suggested to psychologists that the medical disease model has no place in abnormal psychology. It should be replaced there by a quantitative dimensional model. Psychologically abnormal persons cannot be assigned to mutually exclusive diagnostic classes, they can only be characterized by their various factor scores. Groups of persons with different profiles of factor scores may be distinguished, but they merge without boundary into other groups and therefore do not form separate classes.

These findings of clinical psychologists are certainly suggestive. Yet there is the possibility that psychologists have been unduly preoccupied with quantitative measurements and the manipulation of attribute scores. To make their argument conclusive they would have to prove that there are no attributes by which the class of psychologically healthy persons is adequately differentiated from the class of psychologically ill patients. To the medically trained, and therefore perhaps biased, mind, there are such attributes. Yet, before I examine their nature it will be profitable to look briefly at some relevant aspects of the theory of classes as developed by logicians. It will provide us, at the very least, with some useful concepts and terms.

Extension and intension

In formal logic, classes can be indicated in two ways: (a) by listing their members or by giving them their general name (e.g. 'patient' or 'psychologically abnormal person'); and (b) by mentioning the attribute complex which the members of the class share and which differentiates them from non-members of the class. The first way is known as 'extensional' because the class members can be regarded as an extension of the class concept (e.g. human beings are an extension of the class concept mankind). The second way is known as 'intensional' because the term 'intension' was specifically coined in the last century to designate the attribute complex shared by class members. A logical class is exactly demarcated because all its members are identically characterized by its intension so that there are no borderline members whose characterization is doubtful. An empirical class is inexactly demarcated because its members are only more or less fully characterized by its intension, so that there are borderline members that can be regarded with equal justification as members of non-members of the class.

It is our problem to find out whether the class of patients and the class of psychologically abnormal persons have a common intension which characterizes their members and only their members (disregarding borderline members). To my knowledge, only two solutions have been proposed. J. G. Scadding (1967) remarked that such an intension would consist of 'a specified common characteristic or set of characteristics by which [diseased living organisms] differ from the norm for a species in such a way as to place them at a biological disadvantage'. Since the concept of biological disadvantage seems to be itself in need of clarification, I (1971) have attempted another solution. It is less ambitious, as it does not consider living organisms in general but limits itself to the human species. It is based on the fact that patients with diseases or psychological abnormalities go, or are taken, to have treatment by doctors, psychologists or other therapists. I therefore suggested that the intension in question consists of the second-order attribute of abnormality (a statistically significant deviation of an attribute from a norm) and of the attribute of therapeutic concern for a person felt by the person himself and/or his social environment. Let us call the intension composed of these two attributes 'morbidity'. It is regarded as characterizing the empirical class of all human patients, i.e. of all the persons who are ill organically, psychologically, or otherwise.

My solution may claim to have the pragmatic merit of corresponding to the events that usually lead to the diagnosis of people as patients or possible patients. It lacks the virtue of an objective criterion, since it depends on subjective feelings and judgements. For, this reason, it is not an absolute criterion either, since it is bound to vary in different societies and cultures. It provides, for example, no guidance for the vexed question whether psychopaths or drug addicts should be treated as patients or punished as delinquent non-patients. But then, we live in a relativistic world in which the demand for absolute criteria is a counsel of unattainable perfection.

Morbidity

If we take the class of human beings as our domain, or universe of discourse, the intension of morbidity can be used as a classifying criterion to divide the domain into the two complementary classes of patients and nonpatients (disregarding borderline members). The former is characterized by morbidity, the latter is not; and the former includes the class of psychologically abnormal patients for whom there is therapeutic concern. Yet this still leaves us with the possibility that, though the class of organically ill patients can be adequately divided into different subclasses, there may be no way of adequately dividing the class of psychologically abnormal patients into such subclassses.

History of Disease Concepts

To get a clearer picture of the situation let us look at the concept of disease as it developed in medical history. Originally, a disease was not regarded as an attribute complex, an intension, that characterizes a class of patients. It was regarded as an entity that had ontological existence and was created by God just as everything else. These entities were, however, of the kind that the nominalist scholastics had denounced as non-existent, though 'realist' scholastics, supported by the Church, had strenuously asserted the opposite. The belief was that God had created species, or class concepts. Human beings, for instance, were only the concrete and ephemeral 'instantiations' of *the* human species which was 'real', unique, and permanent. Disease species were similarly 'real', unique, and permanent. Patients therefore suffered from *the* ague, *the* podagra, *the* dropsy, and so on.

To Sydenham, in the seventeenth century, diseases were parasitic entities in the bodies of patients. They were like 'the different species of excrescences, which tree and fruit exhibit in the shape of moss, and mistletoe, and fungi' (1848, orig. 1676). Two hundred years later, the scientific climate had become materialistic. Entities credited with ontological existence then were concrete and physical; they certainly were not abstract class concepts. Virchow could therefore state: 'In my view, a disease entity is an altered part of the body... disease is a living entity that leads a parasitic existence' (1895). The class of, say, gastric ulcers thus became a class of Virchowian disease entities. Consequently, a patient was said to suffer from *a* gastric ulcer, not *the* gastric ulcer.

Virchow knew that his disease entities were causally overdetermined. Yet he insisted that their names should reflect their pathological abnormalities and not their aetiological origin. For him, for instance, pulmonary tuberculosis and pulmonary phthisis were two different disease entities because they were pathologically different. Though he lost this particular battle against the then emerging science of bacteriology, his prestige and influence ensured that the term 'disease' acquired a new and narrower meaning. Instead of referring indiscriminately to clinical, pathological, and even aetiological events, its meaning began to be limited to structural pathological changes of a gross or microscopic kind. Clinical manifestations lost in status and esteem; they were mere symptoms and signs pointing diagnostically to the real thing, the pathological disease. New words were coined for the class of clinical manifestations, such as 'symptomatology' or 'semeiology', but they never had much general appeal. A. R. Feinstein (1967) has recently suggested that the term 'illness' best serves as an appellation for the class of clinical manifestations. If we accept this, we need an additional name for the umbrella concept consisting of a clinical illness and/or pathological disease component, usually both. The term 'morbus' seems to be suitable for this purpose.

The Morbus

The disease component of many morbi is of unknown causal origin. Sometimes, in a mood of frankness, such diseases are labelled 'cryptogenic'. The same epithet is used for clinical illnesses which are not due to a demonstrable pathological disease. However, the epithet with its confession of ignorance is not widely popular. It is generally replaced by others which absurdly imply an absence of all causation. Favourite terms are 'idiopathic', 'spontaneous', 'essential', 'primary', or 'autonomous'. In cryptogenic clinical illnesses, pathological functions are revealed which do not originate in structural diseases. For this reason, it became the custom to withhold the term 'disease' from the pathological component of such morbi. Instead, the pathological component was labelled a 'functional disorder'. This was the case with metabolic, endocrine, immunological and psychological morbi. The assumption was that the functional disorder originated in a faulty supply and distribution of energy. The energy in question was usually vaguely pictured as 'nervous' or 'mental' in character.

Psychological Morbi

There was a time in the nineteenth century when hopes ran high that a neuropathological basis would be found for psychological morbi. It was then customary to speak of nervous and mental 'diseases'. But the hopes were disappointed, and we speak today of nervous and mental 'disorders'. Indeed an expression like 'personality disease' strikes one as a solecism, a contradiction in terms. It has been otherwise with metabolic, endocrine, and immunological morbi. As the biochemical basis of their pathological components has been revealed in growing detail, the term 'disorder' for their pathological components has been giving way more and more to the term 'disease'. This terminological tendency is still absent from the field of psychological morbi, though evidence for some kind of biochemical pathology is accumulating even there. Indeed it has already yielded therapeutic dividends for patients with 'functional' psychoses. When Virchowian disease entities are occasionally found in the patients with a usually cyrptogenic morbus, its pathological component remains a disorder, though it is then called a 'symptomatic' one, e.g. a 'symptomatic psychosis', a 'symptomatic trigeminal neuralgia', and the like.

When we talk of disease entities today, we no longer have any ontological connotations of their parasitically separate existence in mind. Indeed, 'disease entity' in a non-Virchowian sense is now a misnomer, though I am not aware that this point has aroused the attention it deserves. It seems to me that the concept it signifies today can be equated with the concept of an elementary morbus. By this I mean a morbus whose disease component is a causal complex which originated in a particular kind of pathological event. By the time the illness component of the morbus has emerged that original pathological event belongs to the past. It is also the event that is remotest from clinical manifestations among their causal antecedents. The diagnosis of an elementary morbus is only possible, when this original pathological event can be inferred from pathological abnormalities which are more proximate to any clinical manifestations and also concomitant with them.

When the illness component of a morbus consists only of clinical symptoms, i.e. of manifestations which can be observed without special diagnostic procedures or expert knowledge, they are rarely of such a kind that it can eventually be shown that they indicate an elementary morbus. Almost invariably, illnesses composed of only symptoms belong to morbi which are still global in that they are a medley of as yet undetected elementary morbi. But there are exceptions.

First Example

I shall take as my first illustration a morbus whose clinical symptoms had been noticed and adequately described long before its elementary status could be demonstrated. The illustration will also support the argument that the medical disease model is applicable in the field of abnormal psychology despite the contrary assertions by clinical psychologists. The morbus is related to the first psychological factor that had been definitely and impressively established, namely the factor of intelligence. There are people with such low intelligence scores that their social competence is affected. If they arouse therapeutic concern they are regarded as belonging to the class of patients and liable to be sent to special hospitals, if such exist. Among patients of this kind, there is a special subclass whose characteristic clinical symptoms are readily observable. They were fully described for the first time in 1866 by Langdon Down, who had studied them among his patients at Earlswood Asylum. It took almost a hundred years before it could be demonstrated that the symptoms, when typically present, constitute the illness component of an elementary morbus. It was not till 1959 that the Virchowian disease entity of the morbus was discovered. It consists of cells that are pathologically altered through containing the substance of an extra chromosome 21. From this finding the original past pathological event can be confidently inferred. It must have been either the inherited occurrence of the extra chromosome substance in the zygote from which the patient developed or the acquired occurrence of this extra substance during the early segmentations of the zygote. All the adjuvant causal conditions must have been favourable at that time and subsequently to the eventual appearance of the Virchowian disease entity which is concomitant with the clinical illness of Down's syndrome.

Second Example

My second illustration of an elementary morbus is also taken from the same field of abnormal psychology. It was noticed by chance in 1934 that some intellectually subnormal patients excrete phenylketones in their urine. This clinial sign was christened 'phenylketonuria' three years later, or 'PKU' for short. As usual, however, the medical usage of the term has been careless, so that its meaning has become overloaded and must often be guessed from the context. It can designate the clinical sign by itself or the associated clinical illness or the morbus as a whole. For example, the parents of PKU patients, when given a diet rich in phenylalanine, may be said to have PKU, meaning the clinical sign, but not the illness nor the morbus. On the other hand, PKU patients on a low phenylalanine diet may be said to have PKU, meaning the morbus, but not the clinical sign nor the clinical illness.

The clinical sign of PKU indicates the occurrence of the proximate and concomitant pathological abnormality of hyperphenylalanineaemia. This is a functional metabolic disorder that is due to a structural disease, namely the pathologically altered stereo-molecular structure of the liver enzyme phenylalanine hydroxylase. The details of this stereo-molecular abnormality and of the changes in chemical composition responsible for it are not yet known, but there is no doubt that the morbus of PKU contains in its pathological component a molecular Virchowian disease entity which is beyond the horizon of visibility even through the most powerful electron microscope. This disease entity has its origin in the abnormal chemical composition of the homologous gene pair coding for it and activated in liver cells at birth or soon after. These gene pairs in the cells of PKU patients are descendants of the original pathological gene pair in the zygote from which the patient developed. For the morbus of PKU to have developed from this origin, all the adjuvant conditions must have been correct. Among these adjuvant conditions are some environmental ones which can be changed, and have been changed for therapeutic reasons, namely the phenylalanine content of a patient's diet.

The Medical Model

Opponents of the validity of the medical model in abnormal psychology may still argue that my two illustrations merely show that some psychological disorders are symptomatic of an organic disease. They are exceptions from which no generalizations should be drawn. Yet, despite such possible objections it seems to me that the illustrations significantly undermine the psychologists' case for the dimensional and against the medical model in the apparently non-organic psychiatric field. In the first place, morbi like PKU show clearly that one is not justified in assuming that failure to find structural pathological abnormalities in a morbus indicates their actual absence. They can still be present on a molecular level. In PKU, the stereo-molecular pathology occurs in the liver, and the brain is only secondarily affected. But there are good grounds today for the supposition that psychological abnormalities may be due to some biochemical dysfunctions in the brain itself. Psychologists are not averse to such conjectures. In Eysenck's view, for instance, 'the individual high on neuroticism is conceived to be a person with an over-reactive, labile type of nervous system' (1960). Whether it is justifiable to speak of 'types of nervous system' is a moot point, but we cannot doubt that brain functions have a biochemical basis. Moreover, it has become increasingly plausible that the stereo structures of protein molecules play an important part in cerebral and psychological functions and dysfunctions. Such assumptions agree well with the known fact that the production of proteins in the brain is as high as in the liver and higher than in any other organ of the adult body. Yet the brain neither grows in size nor has a protein output. This enormous protein turnover in the brain is unfortunately equalled by the still enormous extent of our ignorance of the biochemistry of neuronal processes.

Limitations of Statistical Methods

The case against the application of the medical model in abnormal psychology would have been strengthened, if it could have been shown that statistical procedures can sort out elementary or even near-elementary morbi. Yet is it almost certain that this would have been impossible in an unbiased sample of patients and with a number of variables that was not unwieldy in size. Indeed it may be argued that psychologists have largely set their face against the medical model because statistical procedures are not well suited for the classification of objects. A. E. Maxwell (1971) has specifically examined this classification problem with regard to three of the most commonly employed procedures. He has come to the conclusion that factor analysis 'does not enable the individuals in the sample to be classified in any clear-cut and acceptable manner'; that canonical variate analyses 'are seen not to be classificatory devices in their own right, as they require as their starting point an existing classification'; and that the only suitable procedure is cluster analysis, though 'unfortunately fully efficient methods have yet to be invented'.

CONCLUSION

To sum up, the argument has been presented that the class of patients can be distinguished from the class of non-patients (disregarding borderline patients) by the intension (attribute complex) of morbidity which is composed of abnormal attributes that arouse therapeutc concern. Through the influence of Virchow, 'disease' has come to signify some structural pathology. For clarity of discussion, the term 'illness' has been used for clinical manifestations, and the term 'morbus' for an umbrella concept, that is a form of morbidity having a clinical illness and/or pathological disease component. Most morbi are global in the sense that they are inextricably composed of as yet unknown elementary morbi. An elementary morbus originates in a particular kind of past pathological event. Its diagnosis depends on the discoverable presence of pathological abnormalities which are concomitant with clinical manifestations, if any, and from which the original past pathological event can be inferred. Elementary morbi are the disease entities of today. They differ from the Virchowian disease entities, which are pathological structures of a usually heterogeneous pathogenesis. The concept of Virchowian disease entities has been expanded to include pathologically structured molecules. This expansion has undermined the distinction between functional disorders and organic diseases, and strengthened the medical model based on the concept of elementary morbi. In abnormal psychology, the retention of the concept of functional disorders and the notion of a continuous variation in measurable psychological attributes has militated against the acceptance of the medical model. However, the dimensional model which has been put in its place may be no more than an interim solution of expedience, born of our ignorance of the biochemical structure and functioning of the brain and of the poor classificatory power of the statistical procedures used in abnormal psychology.

REFERENCES

Eysenck, H. J. (1960) *Handbook of Abnormal Psychology*. London: Pitman.
Feinstein, A. R. (1967) *Clinical Judgement*. Baltimore, Md.: Williams & Wilkins.
Maxwell, A. E. (1971) Multivariate statistical methods and classification problems. *British Journal of Psychiatry*, 119, 121–7.
Scadding, J. G. (1967) Diagnosis: the clinician and the computer, *Lancet*, *ii*, 877–82.
Sydenham, T. (1848, Orig. 1676) *Works*. London: Sydenham Society.
Taylor, F. Kräupl (1971) A logical analysis of the medico-psychological concept of disease. *Psychological Medicine*, 1, 356–64.
Virchow, R. (1895) *Hundert Jahre Allgemeine Pathologie*. Berlin.

5.7

The Need for a New Medical Model: A Challenge for Biomedicine

George L. Engel

At a recent conference on psychiatric education, many psychiatrists seemed to be saying to medicine, "Please take us back and we will never again deviate from the 'medical model.'" For, as one critical psychiatrist put it, "Psychiatry has become a hodgepodge of unscientific opinions, assorted philosophies and 'schools of thought,' mixed metaphors, role diffusion, propaganda, and politicking for 'mental health' and other esoteric goals" (1). In contrast, the rest of medicine appears neat and tidy. It has a firm base in the biological sciences, enormous technologic resources at its command, and a record of astonishing achievement in elucidating mechanisms of disease and devising new treatments. It would seem that psychiatry would do well to emulate its sister medical disciplines by finally embracing once and for all the medical model of disease.

But I do not accept such a premise. Rather, I contend that all medicine is in crisis and, further, that medicine's crisis derives from the same basic fault as psychiatry's, namely, adherence to a model of disease no longer adequate for the scientific tasks and social responsibilities of either medicine or psychiatry. The importance of how physicians conceptualize disease derives from how such concepts determine what are considered the proper boundaries of professional responsibility and how they influence attitudes toward and behavior with patients. Psychiatry's crisis revolves around the question of whether the categories of human distress with which it is concerned are properly considered "disease" as currently conceptualized and whether exercise of the traditional authority of the physician is appropriate for their help functions. Medicine's crisis stems from the logical inference that since "disease" is defined in terms of somatic parameters, physicians need not be concerned with psychosocial issues which lie outside medicine's responsibility and authority. At a recent Rockefeller Foundation seminar on the concept of health, one authority urged that medicine "concentrate on the 'real' diseases and not get lost in the psychosociological underbrush. The physician should not be saddled with problems that have arisen from the abdication of the theologian and the philosopher." Another participant called for "a disentanglement of the organic elements of disease from the psychosocial elements of human malfunction," arguing that medicine should deal with the former only (2).

THE TWO POSITIONS

Psychiatrists have responded to their crisis by embracing two ostensibly opposite positions. One would simply exclude psychiatry from the field of medicine, while the other would ahere strictly to the "medical model" and limit psychiatry's field to behavioral disorders consequent to brain dysfunction. The first is exemplified in the writings of Szasz and others who advance the position that "mental illness is a myth" since it does not conform with the accepted concept of disease (3). Supporters of this position advocate the removal of the functions now performed by psychiatry from the conceptual and professional jurisdiction of medicine and their reallocation to a new discipline based on behavioral science. Henceforth medicine would be responsible for the treatment and cure of disease, while the new discipline would be concerned with the reeducation of people with "problems of living." Implicit in this argument is the premise that while the medical model constitutes a sound framework within which to understand and treat disease, it is not relevant to the behavioral and psychological problems classically deemed the domain of psychiatry. Disorders directly ascribable to brain disorder would be taken care of by neurologists, while psychiatry as such would disappear as a medical discipline.

The contrasting posture of strict adherence to the medical model is caricatured in Ludwig's view of the psychiatrist as physician (1). According to Ludwig, the medical model premises "that sufficient deviation from normal represents *disease*, that disease is due to known or unknown natural causes, and that elimination of these causes will result in cure or improvement in individual patients" (Ludwig's italics). While acknowledging that most psychiatric diagnoses have a lower level of confirmation than most medical diagnoses, he adds that they are not "quantitatively different provided that mental disease is assumed to arise largely from 'natural' rather than metapsychological, interpersonal or societal causes." "Natural" is defined as "biological brain dysfunctions, either biochemical or neurophysiological in nature." On the other hand, "disorders such as problems of living, social adjustment reactions, character disorders, dependency syndromes, existential depressions, and various social deviancy conditions [would] be excluded from the concept of mental illness since these disorders arise in individuals with presumably intact neurophysiological functioning and are produced primarily by psychosocial variables." Such "non-psychiatric disorders" are not properly the concern of the physician-psychiatrist and are more appropriately handled by nonmedical professionals.

In sum, psychiatry struggles to clarify its status within the mainstream of medicine, if indeed it belongs in medicine at all. The criterion by which this question is supposed to be resolved rests on the degree to which the field of activity of psychiatry is deemed congruent with the existing medical model of disease. But crucial to this problem is another, that of whether the contemporary model is, in fact, any longer adequate for medicine, much less for psychiatry. For if it is not, then perhaps the crisis of psychiatry is part and parcel of a larger crisis that has its roots in the model itself. Should that be the case, then it would be imprudent for psychiatry prematurely to abandon its models in favor of one that may also be flawed.

THE BIOMEDICAL MODEL

The dominant model of disease today is biomedical, with molecular biology its basic scientific discipline. It assumes disease to be fully accounted for by deviations from the norm of measurable biological (somatic) variables. It leaves no room within its framework for the social, psychological, and behavioral dimensions of illness. The biomedical model not only requires that disease be dealt with as an entity independent of social behavior, it also demands that behavioral aberrations be explained on the basis of disordered somatic (biochemical or neurophysiological) processes. Thus the biomedical model embraces both reductionism, the philosophic view that complex phenomena are ultimately derived from a single primary principle, and mind-body dualism, the doctrine that separates the mental from the somatic. Here the reductionistic primary principle is physicalistic; that is, it assumes that the language of chemistry and physics will ultimately suffice to explain biological phenomena. From the reductionist viewpoint, the only conceptual tools availabe to characterize and experimental tools to study biological systems are physical in nature (4).

The biomedical model was devised by medical scientists for the study of disease. As such it was a scientific model; that is, it involved a shared set of assumptions and rules of conduct based on the scientific method and constituted a blueprint for research. Not all models are scientific. Indeed, broadly defined, a model is nothing more than a belief system utilized to explain natural phenomena, to make sense out of what is puzzling or disturbing. The more socially disruptive or individually upsetting the phenomenon, the more pressing the need of humans to devise explanatory systems. Such efforts at explanation constitute devices for social adaptation. Disease par excellence exemplifies a category of natural phenomena urgently demanding explanation (5). As Fabrega has pointed out, "disease" in its generic sense is a linguistic term used to refer to a certain class of phenomena that members of all social groups, at all times in the history of man, have been exposed to. "When people of various intellectual and cultural persuasions use terms analogous to 'disease,' they have in mind, among other things, that the phenomena in question involve a person-centered, harmful, and undesirable deviation or discontinuity... associated with impairment or discomfort" (*5*). Since the condition is not desired it gives rise to a need for corrective actions. The latter involve beliefs and explanations about disease as well as rules of conduct to rationalize treatment actions. These constitute socially adaptive devices to resolve, for the individual as well as for the society in which the sick person lives, the crises and uncertainties surrounding disease (*6*).

Such culturally derived belief systems about disease also constitute models, but they are not scientific models. These may be referred to as popular or folk models. As efforts at social adaptation, they contrast with scientific models, which are primarily designed to promote scientific investigation. The historical fact we have to face is that in modern Western society biomedicine not only has provided a basis for the scientific study of disease, it has also become our own culturally specific perspective about disease, that is, our folk model. Indeed the biomedical model is now the dominant folk model of disease in the Western world (*5, 6*).

In our culture the attitudes and belief systems of physicians are molded by this model long before they embark on their professional education, which in turn reinforces it without necessarily clarifying how its use for social adaptation contrasts with its use for scientific research. The biomedical model has thus become a cultural imperative, its limitations easily overlooked. In brief, it has now acquired the status of *dogma*. In science, a model is revised or abandoned when it fails to account adequately for all the data. A dogma, on the other hand, requires that discrepant data be forced to fit the model or be excluded. Biomedical dogma requires that all disease, including "mental" disease, be conceptualized in terms of derangement of underlying physical mechanisms. This permits only two alternatives whereby behavior and disease can be reconciled: the *reductionist*, which says that all behavioral phenomena of disease must be conceptualized in terms of physicochemical principles; and the *exclusionist*, which says that whatever is not capable of being so explained must be excluded from the category of disease. The reductionists concede that some disturbances in behavior belong in the spectrum of disease. They categorize these as mental diseases and designate psychiatry as the relevant medical discipline. The exclusionists regard mental illness as a myth and would eliminate psychiatry from medicine. Among physicians and psychiatrists today the reductionists are the true believers, the exclusionists are the apostates, while both condemn as heretics those who dare to question the ultimate truth of the biomedical model and advocate a more useful model.

HISTORICAL ORIGINS OF REDUCTIONISTIC BIOMEDICAL MODEL

In considering the requirements for a more inclusive scientific medical model for the study of disease, an ethnomedical perspective is helpful (*6*). In all societies, ancient and modern, preliterate and literate, the major criteria for identification of disease have always been behavioral, psychological, and social in nature. Classically, the onset of disease is marked by changes in physical appearance that frighten, puzzle, or awe, and by alterations in functioning, in feelings, in performance, in behavior, or in relationships that are experienced or perceived as threatening, harmful, unpleasant, deviant, undesirable, or unwanted. Reported verbally or demonstrated by the sufferer or by a witness, these constitute the primary data upon which are based first-order judgments as to whether or not a person is sick (*7*). To such disturbing behavior and reports all societies typically respond by designating individuals and evolving social institutions whose primary function is to evaluate, interpret, and provide corrective measures (*5, 6*). Medicine as an institution and as a discipline, and physicians as professionals, evolved as one form of response to such social needs. In the course of history, medicine became scientific as physicians and other scientists developed a taxonomy and applied scientific methods to the understanding, treatment, and prevention of disturbances which the public first had designated as "disease" or "sickness."

Why did the reductionistic, dualistic biomedical model evolve in the West? Rasmussen identifies one source in the concession of established Christian orthodoxy to permit dissection of the human body some five centuries ago (*8*). Such a concession was in keeping with the Christian view of the body as a weak and imperfect vessel for the transfer of the soul from this world to the next. Not surprisingly, the Church's permission to study the human body included a tacit interdiction against corresponding scientific investigation of man's mind and behavior. For in the eyes of the Church these had more to do with religion and the soul and hence properly remained its domain. This compact may be considered largely responsible for the anatomical and structural base upon which scientific Western medicine eventually was to be built. For at the same time, the basic principle of the science of the day, as enunciated by Galileo, Newton, and Descartes, was analytical, meaning that entities to be investigated be resolved into isolable causal chains or units, from which it was assumed that the whole could be understood, both materially and conceptually, by reconstituting the parts. With mind-body dualism firmly established under the imprimatur of the Church, classical science readily fostered the notion of the body as a machine, of disease as the consequence of breakdown of the machine, and of the doctor's task as repair of the machine. Thus, the scientific approach to disease began by focusing in a fractional-analytic way on biological (somatic) processes and ignoring the behavioral and psychosocial. This was so even though in practice many physicians, at least until the beginning fo the 20th century, regarded emotions as important for the development and course of disease. Actually, such arbitrary exclusion is an acceptable strategy in scientific research, especially when concepts and methods appropriate for the excluded areas are not yet available. But it becomes counterproductive when such strategy becomes policy and the area originally put aside for practical reasons is permanently excluded, if not forgotten altogether. The greater the success of the narrow approach the more likely is this to happen. The biomedical approach to disease has been successful beyond all expectations, but at a cost. For in serving as guideline and justification for medical care policy, biomedicine has also contributed to a host of problems, which I shall consider later.

LIMITATIONS OF THE BIOMEDICAL MODEL

We are now faced with the necessity and the challenge to broaden the approach to disease to include the psychosocial without sacrificing the enormous advantages of the biomedical approach. On the importance of the latter all agree, the reductionist, the exclusionist, and the heretic. In a recent critique of the exclusionist position, Kety put the contrast between the two in such a way as to help define the issues (*9*). "According to the medical model, a human illness does not become a specific disease all at once and is not equivalent to it. The medical model of an illness is a process that moves from the recognition and palliation of symptoms to the characterization of a specific disease in which the etiology and pathogenesis are known and treatment is rational and specific." Thus taxonomy progresses from symptoms, to clusters of symptoms, to syndromes, and finally to diseases with specific pathogenesis and pathology. This sequence accurately describes the successful application of the scientific method to the elucidation and the classification into discrete entities of disease in its generic sense (*5, 6*). The merit of such an approach needs no argument. What do require scrutiny are the distortions introduced by the reductionistic tendency to regard the specific disease as adequately, if not best, characterized in terms of the smallest isolable component having causal implications, for example, the biochemical; or even more critical, is the contention that the designation "disease" does not apply in the absence of perturbations at the biochemical level.

Kety approaches this problem by comparing diabetes mellitus and schizophrenia as paradigms of somatic and mental diseases, pointing out the appropriateness of the medical model for both. "Both are symptom clusters or syndromes, one described by somatic and biochemical abnormalities, the other by psychological. Each may have many etiologies and shows a range of intensity from severe and debilitating to latent or borderline. There is also evidence that genetic and environmental influences operate in the development of both." In this description, at least in reductionistic terms, the scientific characterization of diabetes is the more advanced in that it has progressed from the behavioral framework of symptoms to that of biochemical abnormalities. Ultimately, the reductionists assume schizophrenia will achieve a similar degree of resolution. In developing his position, Kety makes clear that he does not regard the genetic factors and biological processes in schizophrenia as are now known to exist (or may be discovered in the future) as the only important influences in its etiology. He insists that equally important is elucidation of "how experiential factors and their interactions with biological vulnerability make possible or prevent the development of schizophrenia." But whether such a caveat will suffice to counteract basic reductionism is far from certain.

THE REQUIREMENTS OF A NEW MEDICAL MODEL

To explore the requirements of a medical model that would account for the reality of diabetes and schizophrenia as human experiences as well as disease abstractions, let us expand Kety's analogy by making the assumption that a specific biochemical abnormality capable of being influenced pharmacologically exists in schizophrenia as well as in diabetes, certainly a plausible possibility. By obliging ourselves to think of patients with diabetes, a "somatic disease," and with schizophrenia, a "mental disease," in exactly the same terms, we will see more clearly how inclusion of somatic and psychosocial factors is indispensable for both; or more pointedly, how concentration on the biomedical and exclusion of the psychosocial distorts perspectives and even interferes with patient care.

1) In the biomedical model, demonstration of the specific biochemical deviation is generally regarded as a specific diagnostic criterion for the disease. Yet in terms of the human experience of illness, laboratory documentation may only indicate disease potential, not the actuality of the disease at the time. The abnormality may be present, yet the patient not be ill. Thus the presence of the biochemical defect of diabetes or schizophrenia at best defines a necessary but not a sufficient condition for the occurrence of the human experience of the disease, the illness. More accurately, the biochemical defect constitutes but one factor among many, the complex interaction of which ultimately may culminate in active disease or manifest illness (*10*). Nor can the

biochemical defect be made to account for all of the illness, for full understanding requires additional concepts and frames of reference. Thus, while the diagnosis of diabetes is first suggested by certain core clinical manifestations, for example, polyuria, polydipsia, polyphagia, and weight loss, and is then confirmed by laboratory documentation of relative insulin deficiency, how these are experienced and how they are reported by any one individual, and how they affect him, all require consideration of psychological, social, and cultural factors, not to mention other concurrent or complicating biological factors. Variability in the clinical expression of diabetes as well as of schizophrenia, and in the individual experience and expression of these illnesses, reflects as much these other elements as it does quantitative variations in the specific biochemical defect.

2) Establishing a relationship between particular biochemical processes and the clinical data of illness requires a scientifically rational approach to behavioral and psychosocial data, for these are the terms in which most clinical phenomena are reported by patients. Without such, the reliability of observations and the validity of correlations will be flawed. It serves little to be able to specify a biochemical defect in schizophrenia if one does not know how to relate this to particular psychological and behavioral expressions of the disorder. The biomedical model gives insufficient heed to this requirement. Instead it encourages bypassing the patient's verbal account by placing greater reliance on technical procedures and laboratory measurements. In actuality the task is appreciably more complex than the biomedical model encourages one to believe. An examination of the correlations between clinical and laboratory data requires not only reliable methods of clinical data collection, specifically high-level interviewing skills, but also basic understanding of the psychological, social, and cultural determinants of how patients communicate symptoms of disease. For example, many verbal expressions derive from bodily experiences early in life, resulting in a significant degree of ambiguity in the language patients use to report symptoms. Hence the same words may serve to express primary psychological as well as bodily disturbances, both of which may coexist and overlap in complex ways. Thus, virtually each of the symptoms classically associated with diabetes may also be expressions of or reactions to psychological distress, just as ketoacidosis and hypoglycemia may induce psychiatric manifestations, including some considered characteristic of schizophrenia. The most essential skills of the physician involve the ability to elicit accurately and then analyze correctly the patient's verbal account of his illness experience. The biomedical model ignores both the rigor required to achieve reliability in the interview process and the necessity to analyze the meaning of the patient's report in psychological, social, and cultural as well as in anatomical, physiological, or biochemical terms (*7*).

3) Diabetes and schizophrenia have in common the fact that conditions of

life and living constitute significant variables influencing the time of reported onset of the manifest disease as well as of variations in its course. In both conditions this results from the fact that psychophysiologic responses to life change may interact with existing somatic factors to alter susceptibility and thereby influence the time of onset, the severity, and the course of a disease. Experimental studies in animals amply document the role of early, previous, and current life experience in altering susceptibility to a wide variety of diseases even in the presence of a genetic predisposition (*11*). Cassel's demonstration of higher rates of ill health among populations exposed to incongruity between the demands of the social system in which they are living and working and the culture they bring with them provides another illustration among humans of the role of psychosocial variables in disease causation (*12*).

4) Psychological and social factors are also crucial in determining whether and when patients with the biochemical abnormality of diabetes or of schizophrenia come to view themselves or be viewed by others as sick. Still other factors of a similar nature influence whether or not and when any individual enters a health care system and becomes a patient. Thus, the biochemical defect may determine certain characteristics of the disease, but not necessarily the point in time when the person falls ill or accepts the sick role or the status of a patient.

5) "Rational treatment" (Kety's term) directed only at the biochemical abnormality does not necessarily restore the patient to health even in the face of documented correction or major alleviation of the abnormality. This is no less true for diabetes than it will be for schizophrenia when a biochemical defect is established. Other factors may combine to sustain patienthood even in the face of biochemical recovery. Conspicuously responsible for such discrepancies between correction of biological abnormalities and treatment outcome are psychologial and social variables.

6) Even with the application of rational therapies, the behavior of the physician and the relationship between patient and physician powerfully influence therapeutic outcome for better or for worse. These constitute psychological effects which may directly modify the illness experience or indirecty affect underlying biochemical processes, the latter by virtue of interactions betwen psychophysiological reactions and biochemical processes implicated in the disease (*11*). Thus, insulin requirements of a diabetic patient may fluctuate significantly depending on how the patient perceives his relationship with his doctor. Furthermore, the successful application of rational therapies is limited by the physician's ability to influence and modify the patient's behavior in directions concordant with health needs. Contrary to what the exclusionists would have us believe, the physician's role is, and always has been, very much that of educator and psychotherapist. To know

how to induce peace of mind in the patient and enhance his faith in the healing powers of his phsyician requires psychological knowledge and skills, not merely charisma. These too are outside the biomedical framework.

THE ADVANTAGES OF A BIOPSYCHOSOCIAL MODEL

This list surely is not complete but it should suffice to document that diabetes mellitus and schizophrenia as paradigms of "somatic" and "mental" disorders are entirely analogous and, as Kety argues, are appropriately conceptualized within the framework of a medical model of disease. But the existing biomedical model does not suffice. To provide a basis for understanding the determinants of disease and arriving at rational treatments and patterns of health care, a medical model must also take into account the patient, the social context in which he lives, and the complementary system devised by society to deal with the disruptive effects of illness, that is, the physician role and the health care system. This requires a biopsychosocial model. Its scope is determined by the historic function of the physician to establish whether the person solicitng help is "sick" or "well"; and if sick, why sick and in which ways sick; and then to develop a rational program to treat the illness and restore and maintain health.

The boundaries between health and disease, between well and sick are far from clear and never will be clear, for they are diffused by cultural, social, and psychological considerations. The traditional biomedical view, that biological indices are the ultimate criteria defining disease, leads to the present paradox that some people with positive laboratory findings are told that they are in need of treatment when in fact they are feeling quite well, while others feeling sick are assured that they are well, that is, they have no "disease" (*5, 6*). A biopsychosocial model which includes the patient as well as the illness would encompass both circumstances. The doctor's task is the account for the dysphoria and the dysfunction which lead individuals to seek medical help, adopt the sick role, and accept the status of patienthood. He must weight the relative contributions of social and psychological as well as of biological factors implicated in the patient's dysphoria and dysfunciton as well as in his decision to accept or not accept patienthood and with it the responsibility to cooperate in his own health care.

By evaluating all the factors contributing to both illness and patienthood, rather than giving primacy to biological factors alone, a biopsychosocial model would make it possible to explain why some individuals experience as "illness" conditions which others regard merely as "problems of living," be they emotional reactions to life circumstances or somatic symptoms. For from the individual's point of view his decision between whether he has a "problem of living" or is "sick" has basically to do with whether or not he accepts the sick role and seeks entry into the health care system, not with what, in fact, is responsible for his distress. Indeed, some people deny the unwelcome reality of illness by dismissing as "a problem of living" symptoms which may in actuality be indicative of a serious organic process. It is the doctor's, not the patient's, responsibility to estalish the nature of the problem and to decide whether or not it is best handled in a medical framework. Clearly the dichotomy between "disease" and "problems of living" is by no means a sharp one, either for patient or for doctor.

WHEN IS GRIEF A DISEASE?

To enhance our understanding of how it is that "problems of living" are experienced as illness by some and not by others, it might be helpful to consider grief as a paradigm of such a borderline condition. For while grief has never been considered in a medical framework, a significant number of grieving people do consult doctors because of disturbing symptoms, which they do not necessarily relate to grief. Fifteen years ago I addressed this question in a paper entitled "Is grief a disease? A challenge for medical research" (*13*). Its aim too was to raise questions about the adequacy of the biomedical model. A better title might have been, "When is grief a disease?," just as one might ask when schizophrenia or when diabetes is a disease. For while there are some obvious analogies betweeen grief and disease, there are also some important differences. But these very contradictions help to clarify the psychosocial dimensions of the biopsychosocial model.

Grief clearly exemplifies a situation in which psychological factors are primary; no preexisting chemical or physiological defects or agents need be invoked. Yet as with classic diseases, ordinary grief constitutes a discrete syndrome with a relatively predictable symptomatology which includes, incidentally, both bodily and psychological disturbances. It displays the autonomy typical of disease; that is, it runs its course despite the sufferer's efforts or wish to bring it to a close. A consistent etiologic factor can be identified, namely, a significant loss. On the other hand, neither the sufferer nor society has ever dealt with ordinary grief as an illness even though such expressions as "sick with grief" would indicate some connection in people's minds. And while every culture makes provisions for the mourner, these have generally been regarded more as the responsibility of religion than of medicine.

On the face of it, the arguments against including grief in a medical model would seem to be the more persuasive. In the 1961 paper I countered these by comparing grief to a wound. Both are natural responses to environmental trauma, one psychological, the other physical. But even at the time I felt a vague uneasiness that this analogy did not quite make the case. Now 15 years later a better grasp of the cultural origins of disease concepts and medical care systems clarifies the apparent inconsistency. The critical factor underlying man's need to develop folk models of disease, and to develop social adaptations to deal with the individual and group disruptions brought about by disease, he always been the victim's ignorance of what is responsible for his dysphoric or disturbing experience (*5, 6*). Neither grief nor a wound fits fully into that category. In both, the reasons for the pain, suffering, and disability are only too clear. Wounds or fractures incurred in battle or by accident by and large were self-treated or ministered to with folk remedies or by individuals who had acquired certain technical skills in such matters. Surgery developed out of the need for treatment of wounds and injuries and has different historical roots than medicine, which was always closer in origin to magic and religion. Only later in Western history did surgery and medicine merge as healing arts. But even from earliest times there were people who behaved as though grief-stricken, yet seemed not to have suffered any loss; and others who developed what for all the world looked like wounds or fractures, yet had not been subjected to any known trauma. And there were people who suffered losses whose grief deviated in one way or another from what the culture had come to accept as the normal course; and others whose wounds failed to heal or festered or who became ill even though the wound had apparently healed. Then, as now, two elements were crucial in defining the role of patient and physician and hence in determining what should be regarded as disease. For the patient it has been his not knowing why he felt or functioned badly or what to do about it, coupled with the belief or knowledge that the healer or physician did know and could provide relief. For the physician in turn it has been his commitment to his professional role as healer. From these have evolved sets of expectations which are reinforced by the culture, though these are not necessarily the same for patients as for physician.

A biopsychosocial model would take all of these factors into account. It would acknowledge the fundamental fact that the patient comes to the physician because either he does not know what is wrong or, if he does, he feels incapable of helping himself. The psychobiological unity of man requires that the physician accept the responsibility to evaluate whatever problems the patient presents and recommend a course of action, including referral to other helping professions. Hence the physician's basic professional knowledge and skills must span the social, psychological, and biological, for his decisions and actions on the patient's behalf involve all three. Is the patient suffering normal grief or melancholia? Are the fatigue and weakness of the woman who recently lost her husband conversion symptoms, psychophysiological reactions, manifestations of a somatic disorder, or a combination of these? The patient soliciting the aid of a physician must have confidence that the M.D. degree has indeed rendered that physician competent to make such differentiations.

A CHALLENGE FOR BOTH MEDICINE AND PSYCHIATRY

The development of a biopsychosocial medical model is posed as a challenge for both medicine and psychiatry. For despite the enormous gains which have accrued from biomedical research, there is a growing uneasiness among the public as well as among physicians, and especially among the younger generation, that health needs are not being met and that biomedical research is not having a sufficient impact in human terms. This is usually ascribed to the all too obvious inadequacies of existing health care delivery systems. But this certainly is not a complete explanation, for many who do have adequate access to health care also complain that physicians are lacking in interest and understanding, are preoccupied with procedures, and are insensitive to the personal problems of patients and their families. Medical institutions are seen as cold and impersonal; the more prestigious they are as centers for biomedical research, the more common such complaints (*14*). Medicine's unrest derives from a growing awareness among many physicians of the contradiction between the excellence of their biomedical background on the one hand and the weakness of their qualifications in certain attributes essential for good patient care on the other (*7*). Many recognize that these cannot be improved by working within the biomedical model alone.

The present upsurge of interest in primary care and family medicine clearly reflect disenchantment among some physicians with an approach to disease that neglects the patient. They are now more ready for a medical model which would take psychosocial issues into account. Even from within academic circles are coming some sharp challenges to biomedical dogmatism (*8, 15*). Thus Holman ascribes directly to biomedical reductionism and to the professional dominance of its adherents over the health care system such undesirable practices as unnecessary hospitalization, overuse of drugs, excessive surgery, and inappropriate utilization of diagnostic tests. He writes, "While reductionism is a powerful tool for understanding, it also creates profound misunderstanding when unwisely applied. Reductionism is particularly harmful when it neglects the impact of nonbiological circumstances upon biologic processes." And, "Some medical outcomes are inadequate not because appropriate technical interventions are lacking but because our conceptual thinking is inadequate" (*15*). How ironic it would be were psychiatry to insist on subscribing to a medical model which some leaders in medicine already are beginning to question.

Psychiatrists, unconsciously committed to the biomedical model and split into the warring camps of reductionists and exclusionists, are today so preoccupied with their own professional identity and status in relation to medicine that many are failing to appreciate that psychiatry now is the only clinical discipline within medicine concerned primarily with the study of man and the human condition. While the behavioral sciences have made some limited incursions into medical school teaching programs, it is mainly upon psychiatrists, and to a lesser extent clinical psychologists, that the responsibility falls to develop approaches to the understanding of health and disease and patient care not readily accomplished within the more narrow framework and with the specialized techniques of traditional biomedicine. Indeed, the fact is that the major formulations of more integrated and holistic concepts of health and disease proposed in the past 30 years have come not from within the biomedical establishment but from physicians who have drawn upon concepts and methods which originated with psychiatry, notably the psychodynamic approach of Sigmund Freud and psychoanalysis and the reaction-to-life-stress approach of Adolf Meyer and psychobiology (*16*). Actually, one of the more lasting contributions of both Freud and Meyer has been to provide frames of reference whereby psychological processes could be included in a concept of disease. Psychosomatic medicine—the term itself a vestige of dualism—became the medium whereby the gap between the two parallel but independent ideologies of medicine, the biological and the psychosocial, was to be bridged. Its progress has been slow and halting, not only because of the extreme complexities intrinsic to the field itself, but also because of unremitting pressures, from within as well as from without, to conform to scientific methodologies basically mechanistic and reductionistic in conception and inappropriate for many of the problems under study. Nonetheless, by now a sizable body of knowledge, based on clinical and experimental studies of man and animals has accumulated. Most, however, remains unknown to the general medical public and to the biomedical community and is largely ignored in the education of physicians. The recent solemn pronouncement by an eminent biomedical leader (2) that "the emotional content of organic medicine [has been] exaggerated" and "psychosomatic medicine is on the way out" can only be ascribed to the blinding effects of dogmatism.

The fact is that medical schools have constituted unreceptive if not hostile environments for those interested in psychosomatic research and teaching, and medical journals have all too often followed a double standard in accepting papers dealing with psychosomatic relationships (*17*). Further, much of the work documenting experimentally in animals the signficance of life circumstances or change in altering susceptibility to disease has been done by experimental psychologists and appears in psychology journals rarely read by physicians or basic biomedical scientists (*11*).

GENERAL SYSTEMS THEORY PERSPECTIVE

The struggle to reconcile the psychosocial and the biological in medicine has had its parallel in biology, also dominated by the reductionistic approach of molecular biology. Among biologists too have emerged advocates of the need to develop holistic as well as reductionistic explanations of life processes, to answer the "why?" and the "what for?" as well as the "how?" (*18, 19*). Von Bertalanffy, arguing the need for a more fundamental reorientation in scientific perspectives in order to open the way to holistic approaches more amenable to scientific inquiry and conceptualization, developed general systems theory (*20*). This approach, by treating sets of related events collectively as systems manifesting functions and properties on the specific level of the whole, has made possible recognition of isomorphies across different levels of organization, as molecules, cells, organs, the organism, the person, the family, the society, or the biosphere. From such isomorphies can be developed fundamental laws and principles that operate commonly at all levels of organization, as compared to those which are unique for each. Since systems theory holds that all levels of organization are linked to each other in a hierarchical relationship so that change in one afffects change in the others, its adoption as a scientific approach should do much to mitigate the holist-reductionist dichotomy and improve communication across scientific disciplines. For medicine, systems theory provides a conceptual approach suitable not only for the proposed biopsychosocial concept of disease but also for studying disease and medical care as interrelated processes (*10, 21*). If and when a general-systems approach becomes part of the basic scientific and philosophic education of future physicians and medical scientists, a greater readiness to encompass a biopsychosocial perspective of disease may be anticipated.

BIOMEDICINE AS SCIENCE AND AS DOGMA

In the meantime, what is being and can be done to neutralize the dogmatism of biomedicine and all the undesirable social and scientific consequences that flow therefrom? How can a proper balance be established between the fractional-analytic and the natural history approaches, both so integral for the work of the physician and the medical scientist (*22*)? How can the clinician be helped to understand the extent to which his scientific approach to patients represents a distinctly "human science," one in which "reliance is on the integrative powers of the observer of a complex nonreplicable event and on the experiments that are provided by history and by animals living in particular ecological settings," as Margaret Mead puts it (*23*)? The history of the rise and fall of scientific dogmas throughout history may give some clues. Certainly mere emergence of new findings and theories rarely suffices to overthrow well-entrenched dogmas. The power of vested interests, social, political, and economic, are formidable deterrents to any effective assault on biomedical dogmatism. The delivery of health care is a major industry, considering that more than 8 percent of our national economic product is devoted to health (*2*). The enormous existing and planned investment in diagnostic and therapeutic technology alone strongly favors approaches to clinical study and care of patients that emphasize the impersonal and the mechanical (*24*). For example, from 1967 to 1972 there was an increase of 33 percent in the number of laboratory tests conducted per hospital admission (*25*). Planning for systems of medical care and their financing is excessively influenced by the availability and promise of technology, the application and effectiveness of which are often used as the criteria by which decisions are made as to what constitutes illness and who qualifies for medical care. The frustration of those who find what they believe to be their legitimate health needs inadequately met by too technologically oriented physicians is generally misinterpreted by the biomedical establishment as indicating "unrealistic expectations" on the part of the public rather than being recognized as reflecting a genuine discrepancy between illness as actually experienced by the patient and as it is conceptualized in the biomedical mode (*26*). The professionalization of biomedicine constitutes still another formidable barrier (*8, 15*). Professionalization has engendered a caste system among health care personnel and a peck order concerning what constitute appropriate areas for medical concern and care, with the most esoteric disorders at the top of the list. Professional dominance "has perpetuated prevailing practices, deflected criticisms, and insulated the profession from alternate views and social relations that would illuminate and improve health care" (*15*, p. 21). Holman argues, not convincingly, that "the Medical estalishment is not primarily engaged in the disinterested pursuit of knowledge and the translation of that knowledge into medical practice; rather in significant part it is engaged in special interest advocacy, pursuing and preserving social power" (*15*, p. 11).

Under such conditions it is difficult to see how reforms can be brought about. Certainly contributing another critical essay is hardly likely to bring about any major changes in attitude. The problem is hardly new, for the first efforts to introduce a more holistic approach into the undergraduate medical curriculum actually date back to Adolf Meyer's program at Johns Hopkins, which was initiated before 1920 (*27*). At Rochester, a program directed to medical students and to physicians during and after their residency training, and designed to inculcate psychosocial knowledge and skills appropriate for their future work as clinicians or teachers, has been in existence for 30 years (*28*). While difficult to measure outcome objectively, its impact, as indicated by a questionnaire on how students and graduates view the issues involved in illness and patient care, appears to have been appreciable (*29*). In other schools, especially in the immediate post—World War II period, similar efforts were launched, and while some flourished briefly, most soon faded away under the competition of more glamorous and acceptable biomedical careers. Today, within many medical schools there is again a revival of interest among some faculty, but they are few in number and lack the influence, prestige, power, and access to funding from peer review groups that goes with conformity to the prevailing biomedical structure.

Yet today, interest among students and young physicians is high, and where learning opportunities exist they quickly overwhelm the available meager resources. It would appear that given the opportunity, the younger generation is very ready to accept the importance of learning more about the psychosical dimensions of illness and health care and the need for such education to be soundly based on scientific principles. Once exposed to such an approach, most recognize how ephemeral and insubstantial are appeals to humanism and compassion when not based on rational principles. They reject as simplistic the notion that in past generations doctors understood their patients better, a myth that has persisted for centuries (*30*). Clearly, the gap to be closed is between teachers ready to teach and students eager to learn. But nothing will change unless or until those who control resources have the wisdom to venture off the beaten path of exclusive reliance on biomedicine as the only approach to health care. The proposed biopsychosocial model provides a blueprint for research, a framework for teaching, and a design for action in the real world of health care. Whether it is useful or not remains to be seen. But the answer will not be forthcoming if conditions are not provided to do so. In a free society, outcome will depend upon those who have the courage to try new paths and the wisdom to provide the necessary support.

SUMMARY

The dominant model of disease today is biomedical, and it leaves no room within its framework for the social, psychological, and behavioral dimensions of illness. A biopsychosocial model is proposed that provides a blueprint for research, a framework for teaching, and a design for action in the real world of health care.

REFERENCES AND NOTES

1. A. M. Ludwig, *J. Am. Med. Assoc.* **234**, 603 (1975).
2. *RF Illustrated*, **3**, 5 (1976).
3. T. S. Szasz, *The Myth of Mental Illness* (Harper & Row, New York, 1961); E. F. Torrey, *The Death of Psychiatry* (Chilton, Radnor, Pa., 1974).
4. R. Rosen, in *The Relevance of General Systems Theory*, E. Laszlo, Ed. (Braziller, New York, 1972), p. 45.
5. H. Fabrega, *Arch. Gen Psychiatry* **32**, 1501 (1972).
6. ———, *Science*, **189**, 969 (1975).
7. G. L. Engel, *Ann. Intern. Med.* **78**, 587 (1973).
8. H. Rasmussen, *Pharos* **38**, 53 (1975).

9. S. Kety, *Am. J. Psychiatry* **131**, 957 (1974).
10. G. L. Engel, *Perspect. Biol. Med.* **3**, 459 (1960).
11. R. Ader, in *Ethology and Development*, S. A. Barnett, Ed. (Heinemann, London, 1973), p. 37; G. l. Engle, *Gastroenterology* **67**, 1085 (1974).
12. J. Cassel, *Am. J. Public Health* **54**, 1482 (1964).
13. G. L. Engel, *Psychosom. Med.* **23**, 18 (1961).
14. R. S. Duff and A. B. Hollingshead, *Sickness and Society* (Harper & Row, New York, 1968).
15. H. R. Holman, *Hosp. Pract.* **11**, 11 (1976).
16. K. Menninger, *Ann. Intern. Med.* **29**, 318 (1948); J. Romano, *J. Am. Med. Assoc.* **143**, 409 (1950); G. L. Engel, *Midcentury Psychiatry*, R. Grinker, Ed. (Thomas, Springfield, Ill., 1953), p. 33; H. G. Wolff, Ed., *An Outline of Man's Knowledge* (Doubleday, New York, 1960), p. 41; G. L. Engel, *Psychological Development in Health and Disease* (Saunders, Philadelphia, 1962).
17. G. L. Engel and L. Salzman, *N. Engl. J. Med.* **288**, 44 (1973).
18. R. Dubos, *Mirage of Health* (Harper & Row, New York, 1959); *Reason Awake* (Columbia Univ. Press, New York, 1970); E. Mayr, in *Behavior and Evolution*, A. Roe and G. G. Simpson, Eds. (Yale Univ. Press, New Haven Conn., 1958), p. 341; *Science* **134**, 1501 (1961); *Am. Sci.* **62**, 650 (1974); J. T. Bonner, *On Development. The Biology of Form* (Harvard Univ. Press, Cambridge, Mass., 1974); G. G. Simpson, *Science* **139**, 81 (1963).
19. R. Dubos, *Man Adapting* (Yale Univ. Press, New Haven, Conn., 1965).
20. L. von Bertalanffy, *Problems of Life* (Wiley, New York, 1952); *General Systems Theory* (Braziller, New York, 1968). See also E. Laszlo, *The Relevance of General Systems Theory* (Braziller, New York, 1972); *The Systems-View of the World* (Braziller, New York, 1972); Dubos (*19*).
21. K. Menninger, *The Vital Balance* (Viking, New York, 1963); A. Sheldon, in *Systems and Medical Care*, A. Sheldon, F. Baker, C. P. McLaughlin, Eds. (MIT Press, Cambridge, Mass., 1970), p. 84; H. Brody, *Perspect. Biol. Med.* **16**, 71 (1973).
22. G. L. Engel, in *Physiology, Emotion, and Psychosomatic Illness*, R. Porter and J. Knight, Eds. (Elsevier-Excerpta Medica, Amsterdam, 1972), p. 384.
23. M. Mead, *Science* **191**, 903 (1976).
24. G. L. Engel, *J. Am. Med. Assoc.* **236**, 861 (1976).
25. J. M. McGinnis, *J. Med. Educ.* **51**, 602 (1976).
26. H. Fabrega and P. R. Manning, *Psychosom. Med.* **35**, 223 (1973).
27. A. Meyer, *J. Am. Med. Assoc.* **69**, 861 (1917).
28. A. H. Schmale, W. A. Greene, F. Reichsman, M. Kehoe, G. L. Engel, *Adv. Psychosom. Med.* **4**, 4 (1964); G. L. Engel, *J. Psychosom. Res.* **11**, 77 (1967); L. Young, *Ann. Intern. Med.* **83**, 728 (1975).
29. G. L. Engel, *J. Nerv. Ment. Dis.* **154**, 159 (1972); *Univ. Rochester Med. Rev.* (winter 1971–1972), p. 10.
30. ______, *Pharos* **39**, 127 (1976).
31. This article was adapted from material presented as the Loren Stephens Memorial Lecture, University of Southern California Medical Center, 1976; the Griffith McKerracher Memorial Lecture at the University of Saskatchewan, 1976; the Annual Hutchings Society Lecture, State University of New York-Upstate Medical Center, Syracuse, 1976. Also presented during 1975 to 1976 at the University of

Maryland School of Medicine, University of California—San Diego School of Medicine, University of California—Los Angeles School of Medicine, Massachusetts Mental Health Center, and the 21st annual meeting of Midwest Professors of Psychiatry, Philadelphia. The author is a career research awardee in the U.S. Public Health Service.

Part 6

New Directions

The selections in this section have not been previously published. They represent ongoing efforts to extend and refine available analyses of the concepts of health and disease.

Whitbeck argues that the concept of health ought not to be understood as an antonym of the concept of disease. She argues that health is a state in which persons can effectively engage in a wide range of activities of their own choosing. As such, the individual must have the final say as to the need or desirability of a particular medical intervention in the pursuit of health.

Siegler is sympathetic to the notion that medicine must view the pursuit of health and the alleviation of disease as a process involving shared expertise between physician and patient. Functional assessments, while objective for Whitbeck and Siegler, are viewed as only part of the data base for guiding decision making in health care.

Moreno traces the historical development of psychotherapy in the nineteenth and early twentieth centuries in America and shows how the moral treatment movement evolved under the influence of American pragmatism. His historical analysis leads him to posit a number of ways in which biomedical and social approaches to mental illness might be accommodated. Bayles, in contrast to Siegler and Moreno, investigates the role that contemporary physicians play and finds much evidence favoring a strict, reductionistic approach to understanding health and disease. The Bandmans discuss the ways in which the practice of nursing has been altered by shifts in the definitions of health and disease. They argue that broad definitions may be most useful for attaining certain morally desirable social and political ends in the nursing profession.

Ruse and Caplan attempt to use current analyses of the concept of disease in assessing two areas in which medical intervention has created great controversy—homosexuality and aging. Both authors conclude that close attention to models of disease leads to direct implications for change in current health care practice. Ruse finds that arguments over homosexuality often result from the application of incommensurate models of disease and that, in light of some of these models, homosexuality ought not to be viewed as a disease. Caplan argues that, while the processes involved in aging are not classified as indicative of disease, grounds exist for reclassifying aging as a disease. Both selections illustrate the central role that the concept of disease plays in organizing and directing efforts in the health professions.

Contributors

Contributor	Chapter
Bertram Bandman Department of Philosophy Brooklyn Center, Long Island University, Brooklyn	Health and Disease: A Nursing Perspective
Elsie L. Bandman Hunter College—Bellevue School of Nursing Hunter College of the City University of New York	Health and Disease: A Nursing Perspective
Michael D. Bayles Westminster Institute for Ethics and Human Values Westminster College London, Ontario, Canada	Physicians as Body Mechanics
Authur L. Caplan The Hastings Center Hastings-on-Hudson, New York, and Columbia University New York, New York	The "Unnaturalness" of Aging—A Sickness Unto Death?
Jonathan D. Moreno Department of Philosophy George Washington University Washington, D.C.	The Continuity of Madness: Pragmatic Naturalism and Mental Health Care in America
Michael Ruse Department of Philosophy University of Guelph Guelph, Ontario, Canada	Are Homosexuals Sick?
Mark Siegler Department of Medicine University of Chicago Chicago, Illinois	The Doctor–Patient Encounter and Its Relationship to Theories of Health and Disease
Caroline Whitbeck Institute of Medical Humanities University of Texas Medical Center University of Texas Galveston, Texas	A Theory of Health

6.1

A Theory of Health

Caroline Whitbeck

I. THE INITIAL DEFINITION OF HEALTH

People generally recognize the value of having the psychophysiological capacity to act or respond appropriately in a wide variety of situations. By "appropriately," I mean in a way that is supportive of, or at least minimally destructive to, the agent's goals, projects, aspirations, and so forth.[1] This good, I claim, is the good of health. The absence of any restrictions on a person's goals, projects, and aspirations in this definition is intentional. Even if we consider such unusual goals as the wish to die, we would find that it, too, is more easily and surely attained by a person with a wide range of capabilities.

To understand *fully* the concept of health, we need more than a definition of the term, we need to understand how the concept of health relates to a host of others, including those of disease, injury, fitness, prevention, "health hazard," motivational disturbance, health promotion, and medical care.[2] In what follows, I develop such a philosophical theory of health, and argue that health is a concept of a different order from the concept of disease (and, *mutatis mutandis*, those of injury and impairment). Although medicine, in the broad sense, is the body of knowledge and practice concerned with the prevention of disease and the treatment of disease and injury (and, to some extent impairment), and diseases and injuries frequently *do* compromise the health of those who bear them, nonetheless, health promotion goes *beyond* the scope of medical care.

I am most grateful to the Committee on the Status of Women of the American Philosophical Association for the invitation to present an earlier version of this paper at the Eastern Division Meetings in December 1977, to the late Jane English and other attenders and participants at that session for their comments and criticisms, and to the many people who have given me suggestions since that time, especially James Speer, Marilyn Thompson, Maradee Davis, Arthur Caplan, Edmund Erde, Joseph Margolis, and Christopher Boorse.

II. THE CONCEPT OF HEALTH AND PROPOSALS TO REFORM MEDICINE

If we bear in mind the human interest in health as here defined, we will have a perspective on the institution of medicine, in terms of which its scope and limits may be properly assessed. One implication of the theory outlined here is that *expertise* in medicine, even in the broad sense of medicine as we have defined, will not be relevant to many health decisions. The term "medicine" is used in a number of narrower senses, for example, to mean a discipline distinct from nursing, clinical nutrition, or public health. I refer to this as the "narrow sense." This is the sense in which we speak of "a license to practice medicine." Of course, the term is used still more narrowly to mean the nonsurgical specialties, or just one among these, internal medicine. When I speak of "medicine" without giving further qualification, I mean medicine in the broad sense, that is, all of those disciplines concerned with the treatment and prevention of disease and injury.

A number of recent proposals to change the emphasis or practice of medicine in both the broad and narrow sense of "medicine," have been couched in terms of "health." Although many of these proposed changes have merit, overuse of the term "health" has created new confusions about what health is. Among these proposed changes has been one to integrate a concern for prevention back into medicine in the narrow sense. Thus physicians are encouraged to help people recognize behavior that increases their risk of future disease and injury, by using some instrument like the Health Hazard Appraisal List. Unfortunately the new emphasis on recognizing the way in which certain ways of living predispose a person to injury or disease is often phrased as though it concerned health per se, whereas, in fact, it often involves *only* the prevention of disease and injury. (There are additional problems posed by the way in which this valuable re-emphasis on prevention is discussed. For example, the relevant variables are often termed "lifestyle variables" which makes it seem that *most* people have a wide range of choices in these matters, whereas, in fact, only the privileged have such a range of choices.)

Another proposal is one designed to combat the fragmentation of patient care, which has been one of the untoward side effects of the growth of specialty medicine. First nursing and, more recently, other provider groups have explicitly addressed the issue of developing a more comprehensive approach to patient care, because they have recognized that at present medical care often harms in one way while helping in another. Unfortunately, this proposal to make patient care more comprehensive has been phrased in terms of providing "health care." At the same time, greater appreciation of the fact that in developed nations most major illnesses are chronic illnesses, and thus not susceptible to cure, has led to greater attention to finding ways to care for people whose conditions can only be managed (as opposed to cured). Although such continuing care generally does enhance people's health, it does so only by coping with particular problems.

Until recently, the term "health" was hardly mentioned in medical circles—the term does not even appear in the index of many standard medical texts, such as Beeson and McDermott, *Textbook of Medicine*. Then, the only danger of conceptual confusion regarding health arose from the attempt to define health entirely in terms of medical concepts, such as those of disease and injury. This attempt generated the so-called "negative notion" of health, health as the absence of disease, injury, and impairment. The term "health," however, was only rarely used in this way. Even in such expressions as "restoring the patient to health," "health" often does not mean "the absence of disease." Instead, "restoring the patient to health" merely means restoring the patient to a *premorbid* level of functioning where "premorbid" refers only to *a particular episode* of illness, so that the "health" of the "restored" patient still includes all his or her chronic diseases as well as poor physical condition, neurotic malaise, and so forth.

If there are any clear assets for human beings, health (considered as the psychophysiological capacity to respond appropriately to a wide variety of situations) is one. This evaluation of health accords with the historical one. Those philosophers from Aristotle to Rawls who have believed that there are some "natural goods" for human beings have placed health among those goods. In contrast, it is easy to find conditions that are generally agreed to be cases of disease, injury, or impairment, which could hardly be counted as the loss of a natural good by those who use this category, but, indeed, which under plausible circumstances would *benefit* their bearers. Sterility and cowpox are examples that come quickly to mind. Indeed, as will be argued presently, the concepts of disease and health are value-laden in different respects.

My general thesis is that not only is health something over and above the absence of disease, injury, and impairment, but also that a high degree of health is compatible with some degree of disease, injury, and impairment. Moreover, the relationship between concepts of health and disease is an intimate one: people's interest in health, together with their aversion to pain, is the *origin* of their interest in having the means to prevent and effectively treat disease, injury, and impairment.

In taking the position that the concepts of health and disease are *not* complementary concepts, I differ with Engelhardt, Margolis, Boorse, and most recent writers on this subject, but concur with the ancient writers, for whom medicine and hygiene (the science of health promotion) were different disciplines.[3] To understand the intimate and complex relation between the concepts of health and disease, it is necessary to clarify what is meant by the terms "disease," and "impairment" and to elaborate the respects in which they are value-laden.

III. WAYS IN WHICH CONCEPTS MAY BE VALUE-LADEN

It is sometimes argued that the distinctions drawn in the language of a human community are, largely, the distinctions needed to carry out the projects recognized by that community, and as such, reflect the value commitments of that community. I think that there is something to the view that the distinctions made in a language reflect what the community using that language take to be important, and to the extent that it is correct, there is a sense in which all general terms are value-laden.[4] The assertion that the concept of health and the concept of disease are value-laden only in this particular sense, could not be an interesting claim about *these* two concepts.

Some terms, such as "discovery," (an act of) kindness," "hideous," "vicious," "sacred," "blunder," and "worthwhile," are value-laden in a very strong sense: to use these terms is to say that that to which they are applied is good or bad, valuable or worthless, in some way—aesthetically, ethically, religiously, prudentially, epistemically, or hedonistically. Health considered as the psychophysiological ability to act or respond appropriately, is a concept that is value-laden in this very strong sense.

I claim that the concept of disease[5] is value-laden in a third sense, which is distinct both from the very strong sense and from the weak sense in which all general terms may be said to be value-laden. I shall call this intermediary sense "the capability sense" and define it as follows: a concept or term will be said to be value-laden in the capability sense if, and only if, the concept or the definition of the term warrants the conclusion that people have an interest in *being able* to influence things of that type. The failure to recognize this third sense has obscured the understanding of the ways in which terms may be value-laden; the implicit assumption of most examinations of the extent to which concepts are value-laden has been that *either* a term is no more value-laden than the other general terms of a language, *or* it is value-laden in the very strong sense that application of the term implies the judgment that the particular to which it was applied is valuable (or worthless) in some respect.

In particular, people's interest in *being able* to prevent and treat diseases may be inferred from the concept of disease. Indeed, the interest in prevention and treatment is the basis of the distinction between disease processes and other atypical psychophysiological processes.

All human societies have devoted some of their resources to the development of medicinal or healing arts. This allocation represented the society's attempt to acquire these desired capabilities. Yet notice that, according to what I have argued, to say that a *particular* psychophysiological process is a case of disease is to say only that it is an instance of a kind of psychophysiological process that one wishes *to be able* to prevent or to treat effectively, not that the particular *case* of a disease itself is necessarily a misfortune for the bearer and hence necessarily something that is in the bearer's interest to have treated. The impairment, sterility, is one which people frequently go to some trouble and expense to acquire through medical intervention. The same was true of cases of cowpox before the development of smallpox vaccine. These examples of disease and impairment, which are commonly of net benefit to their bearer, together with the desirability of *being able* to prevent or treat diseases, shows that the concept is value-laden in what I have called, "the capability sense," rather than being value-laden in the very strong sense. The concepts of food, shelter, flood, and infestation are all capability-valued. One generally wishes *to* be able to produce or maintain a supply of food or shelter and to *be able to* prevent or eliminate infestations and floods, but on a given occasion it may not be in anyone's interest to produce or possess more food or shelter or to prevent or eliminate every infestation or flood.

Consider two identical physiological processes, one of which is counted as the early stages of a disease, and the other of which is regarded as a normal reaction to a vaccination. This disparity casts doubt on any attempt to define "disease" purely in terms of physiological functioning, and hence, on the claim that disease is value-laden only to the same extent as biological concepts.

The definition of disease that I have offered is that *diseases* are, first of all, psychophysiological processes; second, they compromise the ability to do what people commonly want and expect to be able to do; third, they are not necessary in order to do what people commonly want to be able to do; fourth, they are either statistically abnormal in those at risk or there is some other basis for a reasonable hope of finding means to effectively treat or prevent them.[6]

According to these criteria, what qualifies as a disease is relative to a societal context insofar as what people are understood as wanting to do is relative to societal context. Statistical abnormality in those at risk (worldwide), however, is *independent* of societal context. Therefore, a psychophysiological process may qualify as a disease even if a society fails to *recognize* its presence because of its near ubiquity in those at risk in that society. The last three characteristics provide the basis for the interest in *being able to do something about* processes of this sort. It is the desirability of *being able to do something about things* of this sort which is the valuational component of terms like "disease," "food," or "flood."

The value of having a capability with respect to things of some type does not presume *anything* about the worth of particular things of that type. It is therefore as misleading to say that calling something a case of disease is to assert a prima facie case for preventing or eliminating it, as it is to say that calling an item "food" is to make a prima facie case that we want to produce or provide it.

IV. THE AGENT AND THE PATIENT

Health is frequently pursued through a variety of intermediary goals. One is the prevention and termination of particular processes and states that compromise health. Sometimes the way diseases compromise health is taken to be so important that the person whose health is at stake is thought of as an actual or potential "patient," that is, one who bears, or is *afflicted* with, or *suffers* from the process or condition in question. The passivity that is central to the concept of a "patient" is the person's passivity vis-à-vis the disease. (Passivity of the patient in the treatment process or as the client of the health professionals may or may not also exist as part of the social role of being a patient.) Notice that in talking about people's health, and not just the actual or potential diseases that may compromise that health, it is misleading to start by viewing these persons as actual or potential patients or bearers of disease.

The notion of health as the capacity to act or respond appropriately explicates the positive conception of health, which has been particularly evident in the practice of the self-help and mutual aid movements of this century and the last. It is closely connected with the idea of wholeness, rather than with a high level of functioning in some isolated areas or in some limited respects. Deriving from "hale," which means whole, health, in the positive sense, connotes wholeness of a person. Wholeness of a person is more than the wholeness of an organism, although the wholeness of the organism contributes to the health or wholeness of the person. This sense of wholeness of a person implies the ability to engage in distinctively human activities. I will use the term "capabilities" hereafter to mean the ability to engage in activities that are characteristically intentional actions. In contrast, the term "capacity" is used for biological functioning, whether of organisms (as respiratory capacity) or of parts of organisms such as organs or cells (as the heart's capacity to pump blood).

To assess people's health, one must take into account their capabilities and not merely their biological capacities. Therefore, the notion of health or wholeness is closely associated with the notions of autonomy, with the ability to act to achieve one's purposes, and with the ability to live as a member of a human community. Accordingly, health, rather than being something that happens or fails to happen to a person in the way that diseases and injuries do, is the ability to act or participate autonomously and effectively in a wide range of activities. The term "wholeness" should not, however, suggest that there exists an upper limit, a state of optimum health. Such a suggestion would be foreign to the account given here since, presumably, people can always increase their ability to act appropriately in *some* situations. The absence of an upper limit on health does not make that concept any more obscure than concepts such as wealth, which also have no upper limit.

I will not address here the question of just what are the components of human life, because the theory of health that I am advancing does not require specification of these components. The best method is to begin by accepting an account of human life that is as broad as possible, since if some human activity is a mistaken, or stupid, or sloppy, or naive way of undertaking some other, quite different, human activity, this will eventually become clear as the two enterprises are examined further. However, if one starts from an assumption that some activity is just a mistaken way of doing something else and it turns out not to be, there will never be an opportunity to discover the error.[7]

It may be objected that some goals are themselves irrational and thus that it is odd to include such goals among those that the actions of a healthy person would contribute to attaining. To the extent that we believe that some goal is itself peculiar, however, or even irrational, we are inclined to say that it is something else that the person "really wants." The peculiar goal is only a means to some other end, and that if the further end were attained, the person would be satisfied and abandon the peculiar one. Thus if someone asserted that he or she wished to become miserable, one would assume either that this was only a means to some end, such as being so tranquil or resigned as to be beyond repulsion or attraction, or that this was an attempt to expiate some guilt, and if the guilt were lifted in some other way, the person would be satisfied. Nothing in this argument turns on a specification of the goals that are thought to be irrational or peculiar. The point is only that if we are willing to apply the term "irrational" to a goal, we are also inclined to say that the goal is only a means to some further end which we may regard as rational. Therefore, it should not seem paradoxical to define health in terms of a person's ability to act or respond in a way that is supportive of the person's goals, projects, and aspirations.

The notion of health expounded here, while much broader than the notion of a mere absence of disease, is not as broad as the much criticized definition of the World Health Organization: "the state of complete physical, mental and social well-being and not merely the absence of disease or infirmity." By this definition, all elements of social well-being, including wealth, legal capacity, political power, and social prestige, are a *part* of health. Although there are important *causal* connections between the components of social well-being and health (for example, people with social advantages do tend to have less disease), people do not become healthier just by becoming wealthier or by gaining the right to vote. Thus, wealth, legal capacity, political power, and social prestige should *not* be considered a part of health, even if possession of them increases the likelihood that people will be healthier or less subject to disease.

Health as the ability to act or respond appropriately in a variety of situations requires more than many individual human capabilities and functional capacities. This conception requires the integration of such capabilities and capacities so that each is exercised in ways that serve the interests of the person in question. In particular, the psychophysiological changes that constitute a stress response will serve a person's interests in some situations but, in others, will simply be painful and taxing. (Contrast the situation in which a stress response permits someone to lift a heavy object that has fallen on someone else, with another situation in which the person undergoes these changes but no physical action is required and the person experiences the changes as anxiety and disturbed sleep.) Much more could be said about the compatibility or incompatibility of a person's projects and goals, and thus about the ease or difficulty with which appropriateness can be assessed in a particular case. But we have at least some idea of what it is to function or act in an appropriate way. We may then understand the claim that health is the capacity for a high level of integrated psychophysiological functioning, which enables the agent to act or respond to situations in a way that promotes the agent's projects and goals (and that promotes the availability of a wide range of responses in the future).

The failure of some writers on the concept of health to recognize the integration of functioning that characterizes health has led them to assume that an increase in health, in any positive sense of health, would be identical with an increase in isolated abilities, specifically *athletic* abilities. Such an approach to positive health predictably runs afoul of the fact that the development of a physique to perform some particular athletic feat with unusual excellence generally interferes with developing the physique to perform some *other* feat. The lesson to be learned from this fact is not that health cannot be conceived positively, but rather that an increase in health should not be confused with an increase in isolated capabilities and capacities. Although an increase in health cannot be identified with an increase in *isolated* capabilities, it is nonetheless possible to specify some significant components of health.

V. SIGNIFICANT COMPONENTS OF HEALTH

Consider the notion of physical fitness. In addition to being a significant component of health (so that, other things equal, a more physically fit person is healthier, that is, is more able to respond appropriately in a wide range of situations), physical fitness is a concept that resembles the concept of health. That is, it is best characterized in general terms, which make no mention of the excellence with which a person performs specific feats. This may come as a surprise to those who measure fitness in terms of, say, the ability to run laps, and who confuse the concept of fitness with the procedure for measuring it. A high level of physical fitness is usually characterized as a state in which there is good muscle tone and improved circulation, bones are less brittle, and the person has greater cardiac reserve. It may be evident that one result of these changes, in addition to an increase in a variety of athletic abilities, is that an increase in the capacity to withstand a wide range of insults with a minimum of injury or to retard or forestall the development of a wide range of diseases. The consequence that being healthy (or having a high level of fitness) makes a person less liable to disease and injury is not an accidental feature of the concept of health that I have proposed. Since acting or responding in a way that minimizes disease and injury (that prevents its occurrence *or* lessens its severity) is a way of responding that generally promotes people's goals and projects, *any psychophysiological state* that makes one better able to ward off a wide variety of diseases and injury would for that reason be considered a significant component of health.

It is important to highlight two points implicit in what has just been said. First, it is *not* suggested that a significant component of health, such as fitness, is itself health. Quite to the contrary, the conception of health as a wholeness of the agent entails the *integration* of capabilities and capacities. Knowing that one person is more fit than another person does not by itself tell us which is healthier. Second, a decreased susceptibility to a specific disease, or injury, or to a narrow subclass of either, is not a significant component of health. Specific immunity is just that. Although immunity to a disease (say, measles) is useful in diminishing one's chance of becoming a patient, the capacity to respond in a desirable way only when exposed to measles virus is too specific to be a significant component of health in my theory. People who have lower risk of some specific type of injury may well have a greater life expectancy, but it is misleading to call them healthier. Such persons are only more likely to be healthy in the future than persons with greater risks. One may have increased risks for many reasons other than that of not being very healthy. For example, one may have a dangerous job. It is, therefore, misleading to use the Health Hazard Appraisal List in a way that puts not wearing seat belts on a par with smoking as an indication of being "less healthy," since smoking compromises health by compromising lung capacity *in addition* to increasing the risk of other diseases. Primary prevention, which increases safety, should be distinguished from primary prevention through promotion of health, since only the latter entails a change in psychophysiological state.

The distinction between a significant component of health, like fitness, and health itself, is important in other respects. If other things are equal, an increase in one significant component of health may make one healthier. But other things are rarely equal, and one can readily imagine a case in which a physically fit person would be less healthy than one who was out of condition. Suppose that the first was so ridden by phobias and neuroses that, in many situations, the most appropriate responses would be blocked by an anxiety reaction. Compared to such a person, a less neurotic but out-of-condition individual would be better able to respond in most situations, regardless of whether we view neuroses as disease. Suppose, on the other hand, that a person with a high level of one or more significant components of health (that is, being physically fit, or being aware of her or his emotions, or having a realistic view of both and of him/herself and others, or being able to handle stressful situations well), has a sprained finger or acne. It seems clear that such a persons would be healthier than another person who was out of condition, out of touch with feelings, had an unrealistic view of people, or stayed in a state of high anxiety long after a stressful situation, but had no detectable disease or injury.

These possibilities illustrate again the crucial point that not only is health something over and above the absence of disease, but a high level of health may be compatible with some degree of disease, injury, and impairment. One reason for choosing *not* to seek treatment or not following recommended treatment for some disease, injury, or impairment would be that undergoing the treatment excessively undermined the person's exercise of his or her capacities and capabilities, that is, the treatment would be detrimental to the person's health. This might occur not only in cases in which the treatment carried risk of further disease and injury, but in cases in which the treatment caused disruption of health maintenance routines, or resulted in loss of social supports (for example, because of travel required) or in other ways undermined the person's ability to deal with stress. Notice that refusal of treatment for health reasons contrasts with the refusal of treatment for economic or social reasons, although refusal of recommended treatment (often unfortunately called "noncompliance") for reasons such as these may also be a sensible decision.

VI. THE RELATION BETWEEN THE CONCEPTS OF HEALTH AND HAPPINESS

To recapitulate, health is a person's psychophysiological capacity to act or resond appropriately (in a way that is supportive of the person's goals, projects, and aspirations) in a wide variety of situations. Health encompasses certain significant components: among them, maintaining physical fitness, having a generally realistic view of situations, and having the ability to discharge negative feelings. The *net* effect of having a disease is frequently, although not invariably, to undermine a person's health. The institution of medicine is society's collective attempt to develop the means of preventing and treating conditions that are likely to undermine health.

The foregoing survey of the scope of the concept of health invites further statement about its limits. (The demarcation of health from such aspects of social well-being as wealth, social status, and legal capacity has already been discussed.) The distinction between health and happiness is particularly apropos. I argue that, to be happy, a person needs to be able to act in ways that serve *many goals, aspirations, and projects simultaneously*. The opportunity to do this is a function of at least four things: the range and relative importance of a person's goals, aspirations, and projects; the person's health (as previously characterized); the person's creativity; and the person's access to resources of all types (social, economic, and so forth). To consider creativity (as opposed to originality) as a significant component of health is consistent, at least, with the account of health we have given, although it is not entailed by it. The range and relative importance of a person's goals, aspirations, and projects, as well as a person's access to resources, however, are excluded from health in the presented theory. This demarcation accords with the intuition that having a diversity of interests, say, promoting social justice, pursuing truth, building close friendships, and living close to nature, can make it difficult to pursue all one's goals simultaneously, and can create unhappiness, yet does not compromise health. This demarcation is also consistent with the distinction between health and other social goods.

VII. CONDITIONS OF SELF-ALIENATION OR ALIENATED-SELF CONDITIONS

Other sorts of conditions, in *addition* to those of disease, injury, and impairment, *compromise a person's* ability to act or respond appropriately, but yet are not diseases, injuries, or impairments. These I call conditions of self-alienation, which may be classified into three or four general types. The first of them is what Thalberg has called "motivational disturbance," namely, a condition in which a person has thoughts, feelings, or attitudes, or expresses types of behavior that are experienced as being at odds with his or her beliefs, basic attitudes, and habits. The second is akrasia or "weakness of will," a situation in which the person fails to act as he or she has resolved to act. (Akrasia may or may not have motivational disturbance admixed in a given case.) The third is a self-deception, which has been most aptly characterized by Fingerette as the condition in which people systematically avoid avowing some aspect of their engagements in the world. (The cardinal sign of avowing is the act of spontaneously spelling out that aspect of the engagement to oneself or others.) Fourth is what I will call remorse/self-hatred, which encompasses everything from rejection and deidentification with an aspect of the self (remorse) to rejection of the self in its entirety or at least in its central aspects (self-hatred).

Although it is undoubtedly evident that many of the conditions that I have characterized here as conditions of self-alienation would be classified as neuroses from the point of view of psychoanalytically oriented psychotherapy, I wish to leave open the question of whether, and to what extent, psychoanalytic nosology is correct and, in particular, whether some of what are now termed neuroses may turn out to be diseases (like toxic psychoses[8]) or impairments (like mental retardation), whereas others will be self-alienation problems as defined here. Psychiatric nosology is fluid and is likely to remain so for the foreseeable future.

These conditions are not discussed in detail here, but several points about them should be noted. First, they are value-laden in the capability sense, that is, in the way that medical conditions (diseases, injuries, and impairments) are. Furthermore, alienated-self problems frequently, but not invariably, compromise health. In particular, self-deception might enable a person to behave appropriately under circumstances that were too painful to acknowledge immediately, and hence *contribute* to health in this instance. Remorse might be necessary for rapid change and growth, and hence could contribute to integrated development.

Second, in the many societies the institutions that address these problems most directly have been religious, even where medicine and religion have been separated. This latter point may be important to make since we may be so struck by the popularity in our own culture of psychoanalysis or other secular approaches, such as EST, which have dealt with these problems, that we may lose sight of other conceptions that historically have dealt with the same phenomena. Commonly, the adherents of one practice claim that alternative practices actually increase self-alienation problems in general, and self-deception in particular, but I will not examine those controversies here.

The third point about these conditions is that, although they may predispose a person to medical problems or may frequently be aggravated by medical problems, this is no reason to regard them as medical problems. In the absence of evidence that they ought to be considered diseases, injuries, or impairments, we have no reason to think that expertise in medicine will be relevant to preventing or treating these conditions. This is not to say that *the presence* of such conditions may be ignored by medical personnel in the course of treating medical problems. In view of their causal connections to medical problems, they need to be *taken into account* in devising any plan for *comprehensive* medical care, even if they cannot be eliminated by medical intervention. In this respect, having an alienated-self condition is like having low income, or undergoing a grief reaction.

The subject of alienated-self conditions raises the question of agent competence in deciding what actions will promote health. Although diseases, injuries, and impairment *can* make people incompetent (such as when a person is delirious due to fever, or acutely psychotic due to a brain tumor or due to the ingestion of toxic substances, or unconscious due to a concussion of the brain), these situations are relatively easy to recognize. Furthermore, the effects of disease are more often less severe, and make the person more vulnerable and more in need of support, rather than incompetent. Self-alienation, however, creates a different sort of problem in that, when severe, it does not make the person incapable of acting in any coherent way at all, but may distort a person's decisions so that they fail to reflect the person's (integrated) self-interest. The burden of proof must be on the side of those who say that a particular person is so self-alienated as to be unable to make decisions that promote her or his own health.

Suppose, however, that a person is so self-alienated as to choose against his or her own interests. Suppose, for example, that a person's self-hatred is so great that he or she elects to have a succession of mutilating surgical procedures that are not warranted by evidence of grave health risks. In such a case, both medical practitioners as well as those who care about the person, might have a moral duty to try to dissuade the person from the operations. Such cases, though, are relatively rare. Since numerous studies show that the various (lay and professional) forms of psychotherapy have about the same recovery rate, there is no reason to think that self-alienation is not at least as amenable to self-care and mutual aid approaches as it is to medically and nonmedically oriented professional psychotherapies (although this will depend on the exact nature of the self-alienation). Certainly, the practice of self-care and mutual aid is especially conducive to enhanced self-esteem and reduced self-hatred.

VIII. THE ROLE OF MEDICINE IN HEALTH PROMOTION

Expertise in medicine—skill in the prevention of disease and the treatment of disease and injury—is not sufficient to make many decisions concerning health. What then is the role of medicine in health promotion? Because diseases and injuries frequently do compromise health, the ability to prevent disease and injury is an important component in an individual's or a society's attempts to promote people's health. However, I submit that the paradigm instance in which one person appropriately makes decisions about the promotion of another's health is not the situation in which a medical practitioner (nurse, physician, physical therapist) makes decisions about care of patients, but rather is the situation in which a parent reaches a decision on the care of a young child. Typically the parent considers such possible consequences of a course of action, as how it will affect the child's self-esteem, body awareness, trust of adults, relation to peers, and general comfort, as well as whether it will prevent disease or facilitate recovery from it. Now I am not suggesting that it would be appropriate for a practitioner, or any one else, to make decisions for another in the way in which the parent does for a child. Indeed, as I have argued, the person whose health is in question is in the best position to be aware of all of the factors involved. When that person is unconscious or otherwise incompetent to do so, those closest to the person and who care about him or her are in the best position to be aware of all of the factors that bear on their overall health. Of course, the person may not have anyone who cares about him or her deeply, in which case, there will be no good proxy to make the decision.

In some respects, consulting a medical practitioner is like consulting an architect: both have information about what can be done to achieve the ends of the client, what future options will be foreclosed by taking a given course of action, and the likely time and expense required for each option. The analogy breaks down, however, when the patient is significantly affected by fear, pain, or confusion due to the threat of disease or death or due to disease itself or to diagnostic and treatment procedures. Furthermore, those who care about the sick person may also be distraught. People generally are not fully articulate about all of the important factors in their lives, and those who are sick and stressed are still less so. Thus patients who are distraught cannot be expected to transfer all of the necessary information to a practitioner. Practitioners, therefore, need the skills to provide clients with support and an opportunity to discharge their pain and distress, so that they can make the momentous and often painful decisions with which they are faced. It is only when practitioners are themselves able to do this, or see that it is adequately done by others, that medical knowledge will be correctly applied, that is, applied in a way that promotes and enhances people's health.

IX. SUMMARY OF THE ARGUMENT

I might have called this chapter "a theory of health as the context for an adequate understanding of medicine," were that title not so long and awkward, since it gives a more precise specification of the subject. I began by observing that people generally recognize the value of having the psychophysiological capacity to act or respond appropriately in a wide variety of situations and claimed that this good is the good of health. I examined the ways in which the term "health," has been used in recent years, in order to unravel some of the confusions concerning it. I argued that whereas the term "health" is properly understood to be value-laden in the very strong sense, that is, to say something is healthy or that it promotes health, is to give a reason for saying that it is good. In contrast, the term "disease" is value-laden in a distinct and hitherto unrecognized sense, that is, when we apply it to a psychophysiological process, we judge that the process is one that would be good (for people) to *be able* to prevent or treat effectively. The concepts of health and disease are not complementary concepts, therefore, but turn out to be concepts of different orders. This point is brought out further by the contrast between disease as something that befalls its bearer and health as the integrated ability to engage effectively in a wide range of activities.

Although it is important to understand the integrated character of a high state of health, significant components of health can be identified. Among these are physical fitness, having a realistic view of oneself and others, and having the ability to handle stressful situations. Although the concept of health is much more than the absence of disease, and indeed a high level of health is compatible with having some disease, health contrasts both with other aspects of social well-being and with happiness. In addition to medical conditions, there is another class of conditions that often compromise health, which I call "self-alienation conditions." Because of the importance of the consideration of these and other factors that bear on a person's health and lie outside of the scope of medical expertise, decisions about the appropriateness of some medical intervention, that is, decisions about whether that intervention is likely to produce a net increase or enhancement in a person's health, cannot be decided on the basis of medical expertise alone. I argue that usually these are best made by the person whose health is at stake.

NOTES

1. If one is able to respond appropriately, of course, one is also *able* to respond inappropriately.
2. In my discussion of medicine and medical concepts, such as the concept of disease, I assume to some extent the perspective of Western allopathic medical science. Specifically, I assume that medical science is generally correct in believing that certain sorts of things exist in nature: disease entities, microbes, cells, malignant cells, DNA, and so on. I do not assume, however, that every customary application of those concepts is correct. Thus, if it were true that pregnancy is frequently construed as a disease in medical theory and practice, I would not take that empirical fact about the explicit and implicit ascription of disease status as sufficient warrant to decide that pregnancy is a disease. Furthermore, although I do not assume anything about the existence or nonexistence of natural entities answering to the description of the theoretical terms in nonallopathic medicine, theoretical notions such as "chi," I accept on its own merits any evidence for the efficacy of practices, like acupuncture, which are explained in terms of notions like "chi" in those nonallopathic traditions.
3. Today one scarcely hears "hygiene" used to mean the promotion of health except in such contexts as the "Natural Hygiene Movement." The term "hygienic" (and its cognate, "sanitary") have lost their connection with health and have come to mean merely clean (although modern usage dictionaries do not seem to have caught on to this fact). Sometimes, the cleanliness involved has at least a prophylactic function, as is the case with dental hygiene, but often "hygiene," and "sanitary" mean only clean, that is, free from matter that is regarded as ugly or taboo, but in no way is the meaning related to health or the prevention or treatment of disease. This is aptly illustrated by the application of the term "sanitary napkin" to a product which, like a table napkin, merely serves to keep clothes clean.
4. It is surprising how often people will speak as though value commitments are "subjective" in the pejorative sense of being preferences which may be based as easily on individual or collective whim as on considered judgment. Since one hears this from nonphilosophers as often as from philosophers, it is more than the legacy of the philosophical thesis of emotivism. However, since many, if not most, of the projects recognized in a human community are requisite for the survival of the

community in its present form, the community's interest in these projects can hardly be viewed as capricious.

5. From here on when I speak of disease my remarks apply, *mutatis mutandis*, to injury and impairment as well. I take the latter concepts to be value-laden in the same way as those of disease. What is required to fulfill the *mutatis mutandis* clause is spelled out in my "Four Basic Concepts of Medical Science," *PSA 1978*, vol. 1, pp. 210-222. There I also delineate the confusions that may arise if the differences between disease, injuries, impairments, and symptoms are not recognized. The distinctions between these concepts, however, are not important for the present discussion.
6. I have explained and argued for this definition in "Four Basic Concepts of Medical Science" in *PSA, 1978*, vol. 1, pp. 210–222.
7. This way of putting the matter assumes that any activity to which people have devoted a good deal of time and effort is, at worst, a mistaken way of doing something else, and not *just* a mistake.
8. I have argued elsewhere that it is unlikely that the separation of organic or somatic factors from psychosocial factors in the determination of the etiology of diseases, or the etiology of self-alienation, can be done so clearly and unequivocally that there will be any generally useful distinction to be marked by calling some diseases "mental" and others "physical," or "somatic."

REFERENCE

Whitbeck, Caroline, "Four Basic Concepts of Medical Science." *PSA, 1978,* 1(1978): 210–222.

6.2

The Doctor-Patient Encounter and Its Relationship to Theories of Health and Disease

Mark Siegler

I. INTRODUCTION

A relationship may exist between clinical medicine and theories of health and disease; if so, this relationship will likely prove to be complex and multidimensional. It must be discovered and analyzed. The practice of clinical medicine probable influences what counts as health and disease, and simultaneously theories of health and disease probably modify the nature and limits of clinical medicine. Theoretical constructs of various models of health and disease are tested ultimately in the realities of medical practice. It might be useful to explore the nature of clinical medicine in an effort to derive further insight into various models of health and disease.

The nature of clinical medicine is not an entity to be discovered like a truth of nature; rather it is defined and created in the context of a negotiated accommodation between a doctor and a patient. There is no single "nature of clinical medicine," but many such natures. What counts as a problem of clinical medicine is mutually decided in a doctor-patient accommodation which may lead to a deeper, longer lasting, doctor-patient relationship. Without such a doctor-patient accommodation problems do not exist in clinical medicine, even though there may exist health problems, or diseases, or even problems in preventive, social, community, or research medicine. Clinical medicine requires accommodations between individual patients and physicians which are designed to achieve mutually agreed on goals.

The determination that a problem falls within the boundaries of clinical medicine (rather than saying that a problem is a disease or a health problem) is an elaborate process and is usually the result of a mutually agreed on transaction between patient and physician in which the physician's eventual agreement with the patient that a problem is a medical problem (again, rather than saying that a problem is a disease or a health problem) decides the case, but in which many preliminary developments have been necessary. In general, a necessary, although not a sufficient, condition for a problem to become one for clinical medicine is that the doctor and patient agree that it is one. However, when conflicts arise between patients and physicians in which either claims that a medical problem does not exist, then, with rare exceptions, for their purposes the issue is not a problem of clinical medicine. Of course, negotiations between doctors and patients are governed and partially constrained by such external forces as the availability of resources and the political demarcation of boundaries for medicine.

My contention is that these negotiations, carried on by thousands of physicians who interact with millions of patients, determine at the individual doctor-patient level the nature and limits of clinical medicine, and further, they provide valuable data from which can be inferred societally accepted norms on the nature and limits of clinical medicine and on societal attitudes towards health and disease.

Note that although an understanding of clinical medicine may illuminate our concepts of health and disease, the distinction between clinical medicine and health and disease models must be maintained. If it could be agreed that the legitimate goal of clinical medicine is the pursuit of physical and mental health, it would be crucial to indicate that clinical mdicine is merely one means by which health can be pursued or regained. Without laboring this point, it is clear that health can be maintained or regained in the absence of clinical medical intervention by improving living conditions, nutrition, sanitation, education, and by strengthening an individual's personal responsibility for the maintenance of his own health. Not all health problems are appropriately problems of or for clinical medicine. Some health problems would be entirely legitimate as problems of clinical medicine if they ever came to the attention of the traditional medical system. However, whether because of the unavailability or inaccessibility of health services, or because of an individual's failure to recognize problems as medical, or because of an individual's own decision to seek treatment of these problems in nonmedical systems, these problems never become problems for clinical medicine. For example, a patient being treated for asthma by a physician has both a health problem and a clinical medical problem. However, another person with asthma who goes to church to pray for the relief of symptoms may have a health problem, but does not have a clinical medical problem.

II. MODELS OF HEALTH AND DISEASE

Physicians and philosophers have developed many theories of health and disease. Such constructions attempt to describe the nature of health and disease and usually attempt secondarily to use such descriptions to prescribe the proper range and scope of clinical medicine. The analyses often turn on the issue of whether disease is an objective biological state, describable and verifiable by objective criteria, or alternatively whether disease is relative to social and cultural values.

As its limit, the model of disease as an objective biological state represents an analytic, scientific view in which disease and specific etiology serve as the paradigm, and in which it is argued that dysfunctional assessments involve no value judgments. In this view, sometimes referred to as the functionalist model of medicine, disease is a fact. In contrast, the extreme relativistic model of disease holds that biological derangements may not be very relevant to dysfunctional states and that all functional assessments—both somatic and psychological—involve only value judgments. An intermediate claim might hold that functional assessments frequently involve value judgments, but nevertheless it is possible to arrive at an objective assessment of dysfunction even while acknowledging the presence of a series of value judgments. Each of these three models is represented in the writings of clinicians, although the narrow, scientific model of medicine has been in the ascendancy in recent decades (or perhaps recent centuries) and has only recently been challenged again by proponents of a broader psychosocial concept of disease.

Recently a distinguished physician (Seldin, 1977) defended the traditional scientific medical model and argued that modern medicine ought to narrow and restrict its scope to those medical, surgical, and psychiatric conditions for which effective drug or surgical therapy was available. In this view, medicine is regarded as narrowly disease-oriented and is enjoined from accepting a variety of social or political missions which it is not capable of accomplishing. This functionalist model of medicine considers the maintenance or restoration of health to be the goal of medicine. Any departure from "normal" functioning is regarded as a disease, and the goal of medicine is to alleviate such dysfunctional states. Some supporters of the functional hypothesis maintain a narrow, often merely physical view of health, and do not indicate clearly how psychological well-being falls within the purview of medicine (Kass, 1975).

In contrast to these positions describing limited goals for medicine, some have defended the functionalist model, but have suggested that medicine has been far too narrow in its scope and that what medicine needs is precisely a broader model sometimes referred to as a biopsychosocial model of medicine. This view of medicine includes as disease, that is, dysfunctional states, physical-biological derangements, psychological difficulties, and even social problems. In this model, a physician would be held responsible for evaluating and managing almost any problem with which a patient presented to a medical setting. An extreme statement of this model could be referred to as "the complaint model" of medicine, in which physicians are responsible for responding to almost all patient complaints. In this view, the range of medicine is defined by complaints people make in a medical setting, and the art of medicine is regarded as responding in the most effective way to treat patient complaints (Engelhardt, 1979).

I do not deny the importance of developing these kinds of conceptual models to account for actual behavior. Nor do I deny the potential usefulness of such models in modifying the behavior of physicians and patients in the future. On the one hand, such theoretical models may, if agreed upon, influence the medical profession's own sense of the range and extent of its medical obligations. For example, if an intraprofessional consensus emerged on the limits of medicine, for example, on a narrow scientific model or on a broad "complaint model," it might be reflected eventually in medical education—perhaps in the selection process of the medical students and in the curriculum for undergraduate and postgraduate medical students—and it might also be reflected eventually in the medical marketplace. Alternatively, if health planners and legislators could agree on a particular theoretical model for medicine, whether or not the profession concurred entirely with such a model, in time, practical limits could be established (perhaps through financing mechanisms) on the scope of clinical medical activities.

My concern with these theories is that none of them quite wrestles with the actualities of medical practice in an effort to describe what clinical medicine is, what its limitations are, and what the relationship is between theories of health and disease and the practice of medicine. Specifically, neither the functional model nor the complaint model provides usable guidelines that could be followed by conscientious physicians who encounter a patient in a clinical setting. Attempts to limit the scope of medicine to physical derangements fails to take into account psychological and psychosomatic illness and also founders in a more fundamental way in an inability to define adequately the concept of boundaries to healthy existence. In contrast, a broad vision of medicine, in which all patient complaints are to be counted and addressed, fails to indicate except in the most general ways how patient demands are to be restrained in such a system. It has been suggested that certain complaints transgress medical boundaries and should be seen as educational or political problems, but frequently criteria are not offered for making such a determination. One commentator notes that certain "medical" matters ought not be addressed by physicians because a physician would be involved in unethical, immoral, frivolous, or costly endeavors, but again, the question of how this conclusion is to be arrived at and who is responsible for reaching this judgment is left unanswered (Engelhardt, 1979). My essential criticism of these theoretical constructions about the nature of health and disease centers on the unclarity of how and in what circumstances such models are to be used by health planners, and more importantly, by physicians and patients.

These various theoretical models suppose that a univocal sense of health and disease appropriately describes modern medicine and captures its nuances. Proponents of such theories believe that such encompassing constructs are context-free and are beneficial to society. It should be asked, however, whether any single theory of health and disease can satisfactorily describe a system of modern medicine that includes neurosurgery, cosmetic surgery, psychoanalysis, acupuncture, and the management of aging.

I wish to suggest that a context-dependent, rather that a context-free definition of medicine would be considerably more useful for physicians and patients, and also for health planners, in determining the goals and ends of medicine. For example, in the case of emergency surgery, a narrow functional model provides a reasonably accurate description of events, whereas in other areas of medicine, such as the psychiatric management of unhappiness, alternative constructs such as a broader biopsychosocial model are needed.

An alternative approach, one that will be pursued in this chapter, is to begin not with theories of health and disease, but rather with the actuality of health and disease. If we can understand how clinical medicine works in the realities of daily practice, we may achieve a better understanding of the nature of clinical medicine and its relationship to disease and health. It seems important, even necessary as a crucial preliminary step, to understand how patients and physicians currently behave and how they describe and justify their actions before formulating any theoretical basis for such actions. It is even possible that such an approach would indicate how theories of health and disease could be applied more appropriately to resolve practical medical dilemmas. Thus, in contrast to those who propose a theoretical model of medicine and then attempt to deduce conclusions that may be useful in clinical medicine, I propose a more inductive model that moves from the actual experience of medicine, from the negotiation processes carried on by patients and doctors, to a definition of what clinical medicine is and what its goals are.

III. THE PATIENT-DOCTOR ENCOUNTER

In an effort to explore further the thesis that a problem becomes one for clinical medicine only when the patient and doctor agree that it is one, the medical encounter can be divided into four logical moments (or stages or phases): 1) the person in a pre-patient phase, 2) the physician in the context of the initial encounter with the person who now presents as a patient, 3) the negotiated accommodation between the doctor and the patient, and 4) the doctor-patient relationship. Strictly speaking, these are moments in the logical rather than in the chronological sense, because they attempt to distinguish, for purposes of analysis, elements of an interconnected process that begins when patient and physician first meet, or in fact, when they first communicate. It is important to describe accurately what occurs in such circumstances and to avoid false compartmentalization or linearization of these moments. Nevertheless, most of the pre-patient phase of this encounter is logically prior to physician involvement, and considerable action occurs in the second clinical moment, the physician phase, which is required before concluding a patient-physician accommodation. At each stage of this process, both the patient and the doctor formulate hypotheses in their minds about what kind of problem exists and what should be done about it. It is unlikely that either the doctor or the patient relies on a theoretical construction during most of the stages of their encounter.

The Pre-Patient Phase of Clinical Medicine

The pre-patient phase of clinical medicine represents the first clinical moment. An individual's decision that he has a health problem must precede the actual medical encounter. This pre-patient phase surely represents a necessary, although not a sufficient, factor to decide that the problem is appropriate to clinical medicine. The perception of a state of ill health and a decision to seek medical help is influenced by many social, cultural, political, and economic factors, in addition to the biological manifestations of the perceived state of ill health (Parsons, 1951; Merton, 1957).

Except in instances of acute medical problems where medical care is sought in an emergency, persons usually have considered their bodily sensations, that is, their symptoms, the persistence of symptoms, and the effect such symptoms have on disrupting their ordinary personal and social activities. Further, individuals will have considered their own values and beliefs, those of their immediate family and community, and the availability, cost, and quality of medical care, before determining that a particular sensation or feeling is one that should be attended to by physicians rather than, for example, by priests or teachers or social workers or by themselves.

Some commentators have suggested that medical symptoms or physiological abnormalities may be detected in as many as 90 percent of the population, but what converts such symptoms into medical problems is the failure of individuals to adapt to the stress that accompanies these symptoms. These analysts do not indicate why this failure of adaptation to stress should cause individuals to seek care from medical sources rather than from other helping professionals.

In an effort to understand the relationship of the first clinical moment—the self-definition of illness by the prospective patient—to concepts of health and disease, a case example may be useful.

A Case Example of the Pre-Patient Phase of Clinical Medicine. An eighty-one-year-old man had long-standing, moderately severe atherosclerotic coronary and cerebrovascular problems, which manifested with chronic congestive heart failure and recurrent transient ischemic attacks. Nevertheless, assisted by a devoted wife, and on medication, he had adjusted to his functional limitations and considered his lifestyle satisfactory. Three weeks before calling me, he noted the development of ankle swelling which he treated himself by increasing his dosage of diuretic medication. One week later, he noted the onset (for the first time) of fecal incontinence and began soiling his clothes and bed. He and his wife attributed this problem to advancing age. They did not seek medical assistance. His wife consulted a social worker and inquired about the possibility of obtaining the services of a nurse to assist her in caring for her husband. The social worker replied that such continuous nursing service was unavailable, but that she would submit an application for both husband and wife at a nursing home. About four days before contacting me, the patient stopped urinating. Although he and his wife were disturbed by this development, they decided that he was probably dehydrated from taking too many diuretic pills and from his repeated episodes of loose, watery bowel movements. They therefore discontinued the diuretic pills and began to push fluids. Over the course of the next four days, he experienced gradually increasing lower abdominal pains and noted the development of a large abdominal mass below the umbilicus. He also noted breathlessness on exertion. When he finally presented to my office, three weeks after the onset of his new problems, his chief complaint was severe, unremitting lower abdominal pain and an abdominal mass, and he stated: "Doc, I'm afraid I've recently developed a cancer." He and his wife mentioned the fecal incontinence and his failure to urinate only after these problems were suspected during the physical examination.

By examining the early phases of this patient's illness and his decision to seek a medical opinion, it is possible to reach some tentative conclusions concerning the relationship between clinical medicine and theories of health and disease:

1. The distinction between a problem of health and a nonhealth matter, for example, the fecal incontinence, is frequently obscure.
2. Many social, cultural, and psychological factors may influence a particular person's judgment that he has a health problem rather than a problem whose relief should be sought from other agencies, or that he has any problem at all.
3. Even if a problem is actually perceived as a "health" problem, for example, the anuria, one may choose not to make it a problem for clinical medicine by not presenting with it to physicians.
4. Some people may be entirely asymptomatic or may suppress or deny the existence of symptoms even while harboring a serious condition, such as an occult malignancy. Some individuals may define a symptomatic problem as a nonmedical problem even when severe "disease," such as cancer, exists.
5. The existence of a pre-patient phase of clinical medicine severely limits the

direct application of either a functionalist or a complaint model of medicine. Unquestionably, for three weeks this patient's usual functional capacity was severely compromised, and yet his problem was not one of clinical medicine because he chose not to make it one. Further, the complaint model of medicine is hard-pressed to explain whether this man was appropriate in seeking relief from a social service agency rather than from medicine, and whether such an individual decision would mean that he did not have a medical problem. Cases such as these indicate clearly that one can have serious dysfunctional states and diseases and still deny or misinterpret symptoms and thus delay in presenting with complaints to physicians. This man could have died from one of several possible complications of his problems before he chose to enter the medical setting.

The Initial Encounter of Patient and Physician

David Mechanic has written that "people visit the physician because they have a problem; most frequently they come because they are ill. In one sense, at least, all persons seeking advice from a physician and presenting a symptom are 'diseased.' There is something in their life condition that impels them to seek help" (Mechanic, 1978, p. 418).

From a patient's perspective the issue appears settled at the time he requests help. His problem should be counted and responded to as a medical problem. But, the question remains: do patients present to physicians based on a theory of health and disease? At some level, I suppose they do. Some patients may respond to one level of pain or discomfort or unhappiness which they consider to be disturbing, and thus may conform to the medical model theory of disease. Other patients may present with various individual dysfunctional conditions (say, a sprained ankle in a world class runner) which more closely resembles the functionalist model of health and disease. But, in general, these theoretical constructs probably exert considerably less influence on when patients come to physicians than do the social, cultural, educational, economic, and political factors noted in our consideration of the first clinical moment.

Nevertheless, I believe that in these circumstances the physician's response is guarded and reserved. Indeed, in many instances the physician is frankly suspicious of the patient and may question at least in his own mind why the patient has chosen to appear at this time and whether the patient is in ill health and has a clinical medical problem. Some might regard this suspicion as contrary to the spirit of medicine, to the physician's duty to respond to a patient's request for help. Others might regard it as an inappropriate extension of the physician's expertise. These views, which often emanate from nonphysician critics of the medical endeavor (Veatch, 1973), are naive and misguided. In fact, this stage of the physician's thinking is a crucial technical step. The physician must analyze with precision why the patient chose to present at this particular time and the physician also must elucidate the nature of the patient's symptom formation. Psychiatrists are quite adept at these analyses, particularly for psychological symptoms, but other excellent clinicians will pursue the same conceptual analysis for physical as well as for psychological complaints.

Physicians have a theoretical notion of health and disease and it is applied in these circumstances. By and large, physicians in general (excluding perhaps psychiatrists and family practitioners) are disease-oriented. This disease orientation represents the scientific model of medicine that is emphasized during medical education and postgraduate training and it also tends to be the model perpetuated by the reimbursement schemes of insurance companies and government. Physicians get paid for treating disease.

In my discussion of the first clinical moment, the individual's perspective on his illness, I indicated how a person's decision that a problem is a medical one is based on a complex interaction of biological, psychological, and social factors. These factors may culminate in a decision to seek medical care and then the person becomes a patient. Similarly, the physician now embarks on the difficult task of disentangling these multiple factors to determine whether the patient has found his way to the proper institutional setting, i.e., a medical setting, and whether the patient's problem is properly "medical" rather than being a social, religious, political, or economic problem. An essential part of this process is to determine, to borrow Alvan Feinstein's term (Feinstein, 1967, pp. 141–155), what was the iatrotropic stimulus, that is what immediate event or events convinced the patient to seek medical attention at this time.

What usually follows after the patient's initial presentation is a process which we have come to call the clinical method. Its efficacy has been established since Hippocratic times. The clinical method may appear to some to be a mechanical, stereotyped procedure, but this view is simplistic and incorrect. The clinical method as I will describe it has two central components: 1) data-gathering, and 2) data-reduction and diagnosis. Both of these features of the clinical method, but especially the data-gathering phase, require a considerable amount of personal interaction and an exchange of information about both technical and value-laden concerns between the patient and the physician.

Data-Gathering. I want to emphasize that the heart of data-gathering occurs in the verbal and paraverbal exchanges between the patient and physician. All expert clinicians agree that no laboratory tests or technological innovations in medicine can compare to the efficiency and effectiveness of the clinician's history and physical examination, which remain unrivaled tools for gathering information about patients' problems. Medical students know very well that most diagnoses, perhaps 70 to 90 percent, are made on the basis of the medical history. This stage of the clinical encounter is absolutely and critically dependent on the interaction of two persons. By contrast, a patient-computer encounter or the collection of a written medical history questionnaire are inadequate substitutes for the interaction of the patient with a sensitive and skilled physician.

The success of the data-gathering phase of the second clinical moment depends on the interaction of the patient and doctor and on their ability to communicate effectively. As Tumulty (1970) suggests, the measure of a clinician's skill is his ability to communicate successfully with a broad and diverse group of patients. It is essential to acknowledge and to appreciate that individual responses—some conscious and some subconscious—of patients to physicians and physicians to patients can modify the effectiveness of the patient-doctor interaction.

Data-Reduction and Diagnosis. The second stage of the clinical method is designed to reduce the enormous amount of information from the history, physical examination, and laboratory studies to a useful and workable amount. The data is structured and used in some taxonomic standard of classification, as the clinician engages in the process of differential diagnosis in an effort to give a disease name to the complaint with which the patient presented. Physicians will be engaged simultaneously in attempting to generate a diagnosis or a differential diagnosis and in testing the complaints of the patient to determine for themselves whether the patient legitimately falls within the clinical medical model. The second moment is not an end in itself, but is a necessary preliminary step in deciding whether to proceed to the succeeding clinical moments: the doctor-patient accommodation and the doctor-patient relationship.

The second clinical moment, the patient's encounter with the physician, has traditionally been regarded as the doctor's domain and is too often considered to be cold, analytic, objective, rational, and ultimately, that final pejorative epithet, "scientific." But even in the second clinical moment, while the physician wears his persona of objective scientist, an enormous amount of human, personal, subjective interaction is occurring between patient and doctor. The eliciting of a medical history is no job for machines and requires the profound subtlety that only trained, sensitive humans can bring to it. As Lain Entralgo (1969) has indicated in his analysis of the doctor-patient relationship, the relationship commences when patient and physician look at each other and interact for the first time, and it deepens during the physical examination phase.

Nor do I believe that the data-reduction phase which generates a diagnosis and a differential diagnosis is a mechanical process. The apparently scientific, mechanical second clinical moment—just like the first clinical moment—is full of personal drama, and it leads inexorably to the individualization of the patient which is the central event in the third clinical moment, the doctor-patient accommodation.

The case presented earlier indicates that a complete understanding of the patient's medical problem would require that the physician recollect and recount the events that unfolded over a three-week period. Only then would the physician be able to understand fully the nature of the illness and its pathophysiology and diagnosis. The historical details presented in the case example were elicited by the physician only after repeated questioning of the patient and his wife. The patient ignored certain relevant details, had forgotten them, or was sufficiently embarrassed by them (for example, the fecal incontinence) that the original history given by the patient was substantially different from the one finally described in the case report. Some physicians might not have pursued repeatedly the historical features of the case and thus might have reached an erroneous or incomplete diagnosis. This case illustrates the essential importance of subjective interaction even in the second clinical moment, which sometimes masquerades as an entirely objective, "scientific" encounter.

The second clinical moment allows the physician to answer the patient's concerns of whether he is sick and whether he has a serious disease. It permits the physician to reach a determination of whether the patient has a disease that can be named and treated. Theories of health and disease are applied at this stage, particularly by the physician. The physician's response to the patient will be modified by his beliefs concerning the kinds of problems that ought to "count" as diseases. The physician's interpretation and management of a patient's presenting complaint will depend to a large degree on whether the physician has a commitment to a narrow medical model of disease or whether he believes in a broader biopsychosocial model.

The Doctor-Patient Accommodation

The third clinical moment, the doctor-patient accommodation (DPA), is one in which a joint decision is reached relative to the specific clinical problem for which the patient presented on whether this particular doctor will agree to care for this particular patient and in which the patient also decides whether or not to place his care in the hands of this physician (Siegler, 1981). The DPA is both a process and an outcome. The participants in the DPA process have been prepared for their encounter by a complex series of preliminary experiences which have led the patient to seek counsel from the physician and which have prepared the physician to serve the patient as knowledgeable counsellor. The process is one of communication and negotiation—sometimes short and to the point, sometimes extended—on what rights and responsibilities each of the participants wishes to retain and which will be relinquished in the context of their medical relationship. From the moment the patient originally presented to the physician's attention, testing has been undertaken by both parties to decide whether this patient and this doctor wish to work together.

During the negotiations that may culminate in a DPA, the patient and the physician are each silently thinking about a series of questions, which, if answered in the affirmative, will encourage them to conclude the DPA. It may be helpful to try to make explicit what some of these questions are. The patient wishes to know: 1) Are my symptoms serious (my fear) or trivial (my hope)? 2) Is this doctor a good doctor (for me)? 3) Can he help me? Simultaneously, the physician is thinking: 1) Are the patient's symptoms "real?" 2) Does the patient have a "disease" or just a "problem of living" which may not be a matter proper for medicine? 3) Is the patient's problem serious (his fear) or trivial (his hope)? 4) Is this patient a good patient (for me)? 5) Can I help him? 6) Can I help him and still remain loyal to my obligations as a physician and as a participant in the medical enterprise?

The accommodation process depends on all of the particularities of the medical encounter. The nature of the patient involved—personality, character, attitude, and values—and the factors which led him to seek a medical encounter with this particular physician, are a central component of the process. Similarly, the personality, character, attitude, values, and technical skills of the physician affect the DPA process. Further, the quality of the interaction between patient and physician—the chemistry of the interaction—modify the process. Other considerations that may affect the achievement of a DPA include the clinical setting, for example, a hospital, doctor's office, a prepaid medical group, or the patient's home, and also, occasionally, the claims of relevant third-party interests, such as those of family, insurers, or the state. Of course, the nature of the medical problem, including its type, acuity, gravity, and its potential for remediation, will be a major determinant of whether a DPA is achieved. For example, the entire DPA process will be modified profoundly if the patient is acutely or critically ill and alternative medical resources are unavailable.

If the process of negotiation referred to as the DPA is concluded successfully, the result will be an outcome also called a DPA. This outcome is an agreement between the patient and doctor to work together on a particular problem subject to mutually acceptable specifications. There are as many results and styles of outcome for the DPA as there are configurations of the variables which enter into the process of negotiating the DPA.

The DPA is not a permanent, stable, and unchanging relationship between a doctor and a patient; it is a dynamic model and is always in flux. In one sense, the DPA as an outcome exists only as a concept; it is always in the process either of developing or of dissolving. Patients and physicians must achieve accommodations repeatedly, even regarding the same basic conditions for which the original DPA was concluded. For example, a patient's agreement to be cared for by a cardiologist for anginal chest pain would not commit the patient to agree with the cardiologist's recommendation to undergo coronary angiography or subsequently to accept a recommendation for cardiac surgery. Or, in the case example, the person's decision to be treated for congestive heart failure and transient ischemic attacks, presumably do not commit the patient to see the same physician (or any physician, for that matter) regarding his new problems of fecal incontinence and "cancer."

Some DPAs are stronger than other. The resilience of a DPA is determined largely by the extent of trust and confidence exchanged between patient and physician. However, the stability of a DPA is constantly threatened by new circumstances. For example, changes in the patient (the development of new problems, new attitudes, or new demands), changes in the physician (a change in specialization, restriction of practice, or the development of new attitudes), or changes in the disease (for example, when chronic renal disease progresses to its end stages and a new technology such as renal dialysis is needed), all may result in a reassessment of the DPA and perhaps a failure to reach an accommodation on the same or a new issue. The DPA outcome could be regarded as a dynamic equilibrium model in which medical trust tends to drive the equation toward maintaining the stability of the accommodation, but in which new circumstances constantly force patients and physicians to reassess the stability of the accommodation. If an accommodation is not achieved on an important matter (a situation roughly analogous to a prime minister who loses a vote of confidence), the patient and/or the physician legitimately could decide to dissolve their professional relationship (again with the proviso, that the patient's emergency health care needs are attended to).

In contrast to previous descriptions of the doctor-patient relationship (DPR) which tend to regard it as an established, static arrangement between doctor and patient, the DPA provides a more dynamic and more realistic model of the medical encounter. Perhaps DPRs as such rarely exist; rather, what we regard as a DPR may really be repeatedly negotiated DPAs. More likely, a DPR represents a specific, and increasingly uncommon variant of the DPA. It may be distinguished from the DPA by its duration, depth, and maturity. The DPR is characterized by mature and enduring exchanges of trust between the patient and the physician which establish an almost inseparable bond. If such an exchange of trust occurs, it serves as a stabilizer of the medical relationship even during periods of new and difficult stresses. A decline in personal medicine and a rise in high technology and in institutional, specialized medical care probably have accelerated the decline of the traditional DPR model and have contributed to the emergence of the DPA model.

The model of medicine that is implied by my emphasis on the need for physicians and patients to achieve a DPA repeatedly is one of mutuality and voluntariness. I regard such mutual consent of patient and physician to arrive at a doctor-patient accommodation to be a necessary condition for morally acceptable medical practice. Thus, the concept of accommodation is essential in defining the nature and limits of clinical medicine. From the patient's viewpoint what is sought is help in the care of a problem that he regards as a health problem. From the physician's perspective what is important is being able to help the patient while remaining loyal to the professional responsibilities to the enterprise of medicine.

Let me emphasize again my notion that the nature of clinical medicine is defined and created in the context of a DPA which must be mutually agreed on by both participants. The concept that the nature of clinical medicine can be defined with reference to the DPA required justification. I am suggesting that medicine is defined not only by its scientific knowledge base or by its technological capabilities or by theories of health and disease. Rather, in essence, my definition of clinical medicine closely parallels the definition offered by Otto Guttentag when he states that medicine "deals with the care of health of human beings by human beings" (Guttentag, 1981). This immediate and requisite involvement of two human personalities in clinical medicine distinguishes clinical medicine from other activities in which technological skills developed from basic science discoveries are applied (ultimately) for human benefit. For example, I am distinguishing medicine from such technological enterprises as bridge building, architecture, veterinary medicine, and others that are not centered in a human-to-human encounter.

Theories of health and disease partially influence whether a DPA will be concluded. How individual patients and physicians regard the medical encounter and how they conclude their negotiations leading to a particular DPA is partially affected by their individual understandings of health and disease theories. Nevertheless, I do not believe such theories provide either a general or even a societal standard to which patients and physicians can appeal to determine whether a particular problem should be addressed by clinical medicine. Thus, despite theoretical constructs, a degree of uncertainty will always prevail, and neither patient nor physician can rely on a universal, fixed standard to decide on the appropriateness of concluding a particular DPA. The enormous latitude for negotiation between the individual patient and physician, rather than theories of health and disease, is a more important determinant of whether a DPA is concluded.

Reasons Patients Choose Not to Enter a Doctor-Patient Accommodation. We could surely imagine grounds for the patient not wishing to continue with a particular doctor. For example, if the doctor had a bad bedside manner, seemed incompetent, had the wrong diplomas on the wall or none at all, maintained a shabby office, charged excessive fees, had too long a queue, or did not have the proper hospital privileges, the patient might choose to go elsewhere. The patient has a choice, at least this is so in our current medical system. The patient selected this doctor initially, but if he is now dissatisfied, he can vote with his feet. Few of us would have any difficulty accepting this position theoretically; we might differ on such empirical questions as whether our system truly provides all patients with free choices of physicians or how frequently patients as a class exercise such options to find another doctor, but we would agree that the possibility for switching from one physician to another certainly exists.

Reasons Physicians Choose Not to Enter a Doctor-Patient Accommodation. From the point of view of the physician, the decision to enter a doctor-patient accommodation is also a critical determination, although in many regards the physician is less free to choose than the patient. Legally, a doctor-patient accommodation probably exists from the first encounter with the patient, and morally, a therapeutic relationship has begun at least from the moment doctor and patient first see each other, or more likely, from the moment the patient first makes an appointment. Despite these restraints on the physician's freedom of choice, I think it is appropriate, even obligatory, for the physician to make a conscious decision to assume the care of the person who presents asking for medical assistance.

A decision to care for a patient is based on the physician's ability to help the patient (which is a central concern in clinical medicine) and his own concept of professional standards and norms of behavior for physicians. Clinical medicine is defined in this accommodation between doctor and patient. The discipline balances the need of patients (the physician's responsibility to individuals) and the science of medicine (the physician's responsibility to professional standards). In this context, the "good" physician might be viewed as one who most successfully balances responsibility to individual patients with responsibility to the medical enterprise.

One major reason why a physician might choose not to enter a doctor-patient accommodation is because he perceives that he is not able to benefit the patient. Some reasons why a physician may be unable to help a particular patient are: lack of technical skills, profound personality conflicts with the patient, or the pursuit by patient and physician of mutually incompatible medical goals.

A second general reason why a physician might choose not to enter a DPA is because he concludes that his involvement would violate his own professional standards of what it is to be a "good" physician. The physician must consider at this point his responsibilities to the art of medicine and to its standards. A physician is not required to depart from his own standards of conscientious behavior to engage in illegal or immoral practices, to act in ways contrary to his own perception of what it is to be a good physician, or to participate in practices he believes to be outside of the legitimate medical sphere. If the physician cannot help the patient, or if he can do so only by sacrificing his own conscientious standards of loyalty to the profession, I believe it is the physician's moral and medical obligation not to enter into a DPA.

The Limited Applicability of Theories of Health and Disease. A third reason why the good physician might decide not to enter a DPA would be his personal conviction, possibly based on some broad societal notion, that the patient's problems were not medical problems and ought not to be addressed by clinical medicine. I am not suggesting that we are dealing here with a radical relativism. There exist some widely shared notions of what constitute medical problems. We could probably muster a consensus that a broken leg, hemorrhagic shock, the need for open-heart surgery, acute appendicitis, and congestive heart failure were problems that were appropriately addressed by clinical medicine. However, we would likely discover that individual physicians had widely divergent views on whether the following were properly medical matters: amniocentesis for gender identification, the management of exogenous obesity, drug addiction, control of hyperactive school children, malnutrition resulting from poverty, nonspecific anxiety, elective abortions, aging, accident-proneness, unhappiness, and unattractiveness.

This situation differs from one in which the patient and the physician were each desiring different and incompatible ends from the medical encounter, but in which both participants agreed that their encounter was one that had found its way to the appropriate institutional setting, that is, the medical setting. The decision by a physician that a particular complaint is medical or not is based on the diagnosis he has reached, on his sense of the patient's motivations for coming to the doctor, and on his own attitudes and values. Some of these values may be broadly shared by society (for example, certain norms about health and disease) and some may be quite peculiar to physicians as a group or to a particular physician as an individual. Some of these values peculiar to physicians as a group may have developed in the course of training in medicine, and some of these values may have antedated professional education and, indeed, may have contributed to an individual's choosing medicine as a career.

Models of health and disease, either those articulated by philosophers or those taught to physicians in medical school, probably find their widest application at this stage of the doctor-patient encounter. I have indicated previously that some physicians have a restricted vision of medicine which views the purpose of the medical interaction as "the treatment of illness conceived as deranged biomedical function" (Seldin, 1977, p. 39). Other commentators have described a quite different medical model, a biophyshosocial model, in which almost all complaints count (Engel, 1977). I wish to emphasize that a particular physician may place a particular patient's complaints out of the sphere of clinical medicine based on the physician's own perception of what clinical medicine is about and what the standards of the profession require.

IV. CONCLUSION

In a sense, I am rejecting the proposition that any complaint that patients present to physicians counts as a medical matter. Rather, I believe that every patient presentation generates a claim to be heard by physicians. But physicians have the professional and personal responsibility, based on their training, expertise, and values, and modified by the existence of political, economic, and scientific boundaries to medicine, to weigh patient requests and to determine if they are to be managed, at least by *this* physician, as medical problems. I also reject the functionalist position which would determine what problems ought to count as medical ones based either on theoretical dysfunctional states or on narrow notions of biomedical effectiveness. I have not denied that theories of medicine, health, and disease may influence individual decision making for both patients and physicians. I have argued, however, that such theories serve only as the intellectual background of the human encounter between patient and physician. The nature of clinical medicine, at any time, is not determined by such theories, but rather is defined and discovered principally by the resolution of individual doctor-patient accommodations.

REFERENCES

Engel, G. L. 1977. The need for a new medical model: A challenge for bio-medicine. *Science* 196:129–36.

Engelhardt, H. T., Jr. 1979. Doctoring the disease, treating the complaint, helping the patient: Some of the works of Hygeia and Panacea. In *Knowing and valuing: The search for common roots,* ed. H. T. Engelhardt, Jr. and D. Callahan. Hastings on Hudson, N. Y.: The Hastings Center.

Feinstein, A. R. 1967. *Clinical Judgment*. Baltimore: Williams and Wilkins Co.

Guttentag, O. E. 1981. *The attending physician as a central figure.* In *Changing values in medicine*, ed. E. J. Cassell and M. Siegler. Chicago: Univ. of Chicago Press.

Kass, L. R. 1975. Regarding the end of medicine and the pursuit of health. *The Public Interest* 40:11–42.

Lain Entralgo, P. 1969. *Doctor and patient.* Translated by F. Partridge. New York: McGraw-Hill Book Co.

Mechanic, D. 1978. *Medical sociology*. 2d ed. New York: Free Press.

Merton, R. K. 1957. *Social theory and social structure.* Revised ed. New York: Free Press.

Parsons, T. 1951. *The social system.* New York: Free Press.

Seldin, D. W. 1977. The medical model: Bio-medical science as the basis of medicine. In *Beyond tomorrow: Trends and prospects in medical science*, ed. Helene Jordon. New York: Rockefeller University Press.

Siegler, M. 1981. On the nature and limits of clinical medicine. In *Changing values in medicine*, ed. E. J. Cassell and M. Siegler. Chicago: Univ. of Chicago Press.
Tumulty, P. A. 1970. What is a clinician and what does he do? *New England Journal of Medicine* 283:20–24.
Veatch, R. M. 1973. Generalization of expertise. *The Hastings Center Studies* 1:29–40.

6.3

The Continuity of Madness: Pragmatic Naturalism and Mental Health Care in America*

Jonathan D. Moreno

> The treatment of the insane has ever varied with the philosophy and intelligence of the age. That they are treated better in modern times, more kindly and judiciously, is not owing to any increase in benevolence, but to an increase of knowledge.
>
> *The American Journal of Insanity*, 1847–48

We have witnessed in recent years a renewed interest in the history and philosophy of care for the mentally ill. Researchers have had a large and detailed literature to draw upon, and have considered issues implied by this experience that range from the metaphysical to the institutional. In America the public record is particularly expansive and exciting since the response to all sorts of deviance was relatively undirected by an existing body of technique or structure. The resulting experience in this area has attracted many curious observers from abroad, Tocqueville probably being the most renowned.

In this context I shall not be concerned directly with reiterating all the well-documented details of policy or theory in American mental health care since the colonial period, but rather with one tradition in what might be called America's "mental health culture": the complex of philosophical assumptions and wider social *Zeitgeist* which has characterized the care of America's insane, especially during the nineteenth century. The development of a distinctive American philosophy, here called pragmatic naturalism, will be seen to highlight and in effect to ameliorate some of the philosophical views tacitly

*Roderick S. French, Lawrence B. McCullough, and Arthur L. Caplan offered several important criticisms of an earlier version of this paper; of course, its errors are solely the author's responsibility.

held by earlier mental health workers. One might also say, as I hope to show, that American psychiatry in the early nineteenth century anticipated, in deed if not usually in word, an important doctrine American philosophy would later develop. The relevance of this development will be highlighted through the psychiatry of Adolf Meyer, and applied to a current dispute in psychiatric policy.

I. COLONIAL MENTAL HEALTH CULTURE: THE REVISED VIEW

Traditional accounts of the treatment of deranged persons in colonial America have tended to emphasize a conceptual picture corrupted by superstition and issuing in cruelties. Authors of this standpoint cite the extraordinary isolation of American physicians from British and European developments, the prevalence of demonic etiologies, and "the scourge, the rack, the stake and the gallows" as "common methods of treatment."[1] It was Phillipe Pinel's liberation of French asylum inmates, on the traditional view, that marked the watershed in humane treatment of the mentally ill.[2]

A more recent account challenges both the dark image of most standard treatment and the force of the break from it in the nineteenth century. While not denying the superstitions and primitive chemistries associated with mental disease, either in Europe or America, Rothman[3] is careful to point out that the insane in the colonies were not particularly distinguished from any other indigent population. The mentally ill, the vagrant, the physically handicapped, the unfortunate of any sort, were classified together by virtue of a singularly important condition from the viewpoint of social management: they were all poor. Thus, "[t]he lunatic came to public attention not as someone afflicted with delusions or fears, but as someone suffering from poverty."[4]

The link between insanity and poverty also held in Europe, but with an important difference in social conditions that permitted Europeans an approach to lunacy not available to the colonists. Foucault has argued[5] convincingly that the dependence of the insane on public assistance, in combination with Enlightenment attitudes toward idleness, a new work ethic, and social obligation, lent reason and significance to the massive confinement of the mentally ill. The confinement tradition was given impetus by the existence of institutions that had once housed large numbers of lepers. Here, by forced labor, the insane could at least be made to pay for the inconvenience they had caused. But no such ready-made structures could be called upon in the English colonies, nor was there a crisis-ridden industrializing economy to call attention to sloth. Rather, in the New World the problem of social dependence, like all other social problems, had to be treated through a balancing and adjustment of the Puritan conscience in light of the constraints of a primitive natural context.

Part of this balancing had to do with the actions of church members in the pursuit of grace—though admittedly grace was not something to be achieved but was already granted or not, unbeknownst to all but God. And the presence of the poor, including the insane, had a great role in this, for they provided a God-given opportunity for the performance of good works. Their role in the orderly hierarchy of creatures was considered to be divinely established, so the indigent were not only not a danger to colonial society, but were actually converted into a functional necessity for the Puritan community. Owing to these factors, and combined with the relatively small size of colonial towns, care of the local poor became an obligatory community project. Provision of modest support for the indigent often included removal of "distracted persons" to a place designated as a house of correction, should that become necessary for public safety. Little legislation and public record was designed and kept on these matters because poor relief was an unchallenged public responsibility. Hence, statutory attention was paid, not to internal dependents, but to external stragglers. Settlement conditions were strict, often apparently beyond reason, mostly in order to prevent the community from incurring new obligations.[6]

For our purposes, what was especially important about colonial mental health policy was what distinguished it from that of Europe. Granted that sadism and superstition were not wanting, that when deemed necessary bloodletting and exorcism prevailed, and that "care" in this sense is largely a euphemism, the cultural variations in treatment of the insane can be linked directly to differences in brute historic conditions. Europeans, struggling with the hazards of emergent industrialization, found themselves with distraught casualties, existing structures, and the memory of the miserable, huddling lepers; American colonists, seeking to actualize a covenant on which survival of all depended, found it necessary, and theologically convenient, to extend this community to the poor insane.

II. PSYCHOTHERAPY NATURALIZED: THE RISE AND FALL OF MORAL TREATMENT

In 1779, four years before Pinel unchained the inmates at Salpetriere, Benjamin Rush petitioned for reform at the Pennsylvania Hospital. Certainly the lot of the institutionalized insane improved dramatically both in Europe and America for at least fifty years, but a certain ambiguity characterized the American embrace of the new "moral treatment," one which eventuated in an extraordinarily muddy and ambivalent conceptual situation.

It is possible broadly to distinguish two dominant "models" of mental illness in the nineteenth century, though these may seem rather uninformative, for such was the level of generality at which specialists worked. Probably the most efficient way to categorize the various positions turns on the issue of curability. Since the late seventeenth century the notion that insanity is an incurable condition was in decline among specialists, whether this incurability was attributed to irreversible occupation by demons or disintegration of brain tissues or some other factor. Still, by the early nineteenth century, "once insane always insane" remained a popular slogan. But the example set by Pinel and others, and the admission of mentally disturbed persons to institutions called hospitals rather than prisons or almshouses, indicated opinion was shifting to the side of curability. On this more or less "medical" model, mental disturbance is a kind of disease, characterized at least in part by somatic pathology, which is not only preventable by proper social design but curable as well. These two positions competed for acceptance throughout the nineteenth century in America, with curability winning the stage from around the 1830s to the 1870s, then being pushed aside somewhat, and then regaining currency by the turn of the century.

But the curability theorists were by no means unified in their views. To see this we can take the case of the pioneering Rush himself, who was not only typical of the modest schizophrenia on this matter, but due to his influence on later Americans arguably set the pace for it. Rush, generally regarded as the father of American psychiatry, served at Pennsylvania Hospital for thirty years until his death in 1813. During that time he turned his considerable inductive powers to designing the first course by an American for the study of mental disease, the first American treatise on psychiatry, and a most influential theoretic systematization of mental illness. Besides this, Rush rivaled his fellow Philadelphian Benjamin Franklin in his energetic reformism in several fields, especially education of the poor and of women, and in periods as treasurer of the United States Mint and as president of the Society for the Abolition of Slavery.[7]

Rush located pathology in the inflammation of blood vessels in the brain; etiology in unrestrained passions or "appetite" causing the swelling; and treatment strategy in methods to reduce inflamed arteries, including bloodletting, purging, dosing with emetics and other chemicals, and stimulating terror as a kind of shock therapy. However, Rush was incensed by the miserable conditions of hospital cells for the insane, and lobbied successfully for occupational therapy and systematically kind treatment of patients by qualified and gentle attendants. Rush did not try to integrate these latter concepts into his etiological views; although "moral," that is, social and psychological, conditions were admitted to play a role, they were secondary to those that followed from a mechanistic pathology.

Hence Rush had a direct if somewhat ambivalent influence on the American version of the moral treatment movement which was also emerging in Europe before the early eighteen hundreds. Proponents of moral treatment of course were committed to curability, but they further emphasized a well-ordered therapeutic environment, since it followed from their Lockean psychology that the surface of the brain is susceptible to impressions from without. The well-ordered asylum was to influence and correct the disordered minds of inmates, hence also their inflamed, infected, or deteriorated brains. Concrete results were anticipated from programs of manual labor and recreational therapy. Isolation of the patient from family and friends especially reflected the view that the theoretic purpose of moral treatment was to give physical lesions time to heal.[8]

If the theory and practice of moral treatment were not quite inconsistent, they were only rather ambiguously related. From the theoretical standpoint "the proximate cause producing the deranged manifestation of mind, is always located in the brain," although the "initial disturbance" may have been "moral or physical."[9] Supposing that we are able to skirt the Cartesian mind-body problem, it is astonishing how the slightest social and psychological factors seemed to work their way into the form of actual, neural lesions. These ranged from conditions associated with modernity, such as rigid social changes and political crises, to the proper location of ducts and pipes in asylums; the latter was specified in an important treatise by Thomas Kirkbride of the Pennsylvania Hospital.[10] Whatever the mechanism at work translating moral agents into physical effects, it could not be accused of insensitivity.

But it is worth pointing out that moral treatment was not an isolated phenomenon, limited to a few liberal institutions. Whatever limitations existed in the application of moral treatment they were largely due to administrative and financial constraints. But the American commitment to moral treatment, under the important auspices of the curability model, was immense: by 1850 asylums following some versions of these methods dominated the institutional landscape in America, literally as well as figuratively. Many were built deliberately for moral treatment, and many of the rest came to help champion the cause. In contrast to Europeans, because the terrain was virtually empty in 1800, Americans felt they had to make a choice, and they opted for a formula of confinement and moral treatment in a big way.[11]

From the perspective of cultural history a powerful case can be made that moral treatment was especially congenial to American attitudes because of its emphasis on the curative powers of an environment. "Nature" sometimes named America's physical setting, sometimes seemed to have broader, cosmic connotations, but there was wide agreement since the Puritan days that these spaces ought to be held in high regard. In the words of James Brooks in 1835, "God has promised us a renowned existence, if we will but deserve it. He speaks this promise through the sublimity of Nature."[12] Little wonder that an orderly institution, reflecting God's orderly universe, in combination with a little Christian care, would amount to a quasi-sacred environment for the restoration of the deranged. Naturally there were more direct reasons for the popularity of moral treatment,[13] but a uniquely American stage was set. For example, when Kirkbride, waxing Jeffersonian, remarked that "no life is so generally conducive to good health as one that, like agriculture, gives exercise in the open air,"[14] he showed that American psychiatry was not immune to the legendary virtues of nature.

Although our concern is more with the philosophical undertones of moral treatment, it is curious that the question of its actual efficacy is still very much a live issue. Proponents note with excitement the early claims for a 90 percent recovery rate and defend their validity; not so long ago an American psychiatrist called on modern mental hospitals to regard nineteenth century institutions "as pilot hospitals which demonstrated the value of social and psychological factors in treatment."[15] But others question the criteria on which data on recovery rates were based.[16] There is little doubt, however, that moral treatment died a slow and painful death with the overcrowding by chronic cases of hospitals designed to give individualized care to a few, especially after the Civil War period. The formula of moral treatment and confinement, when the former dropped out, yielded custodial care.

While the incurability model did not quite regain its foothold with the decline of moral treatment, the somatic "cum" medical model became its functional replacement. Mental hospital inmates came more and more to be characterized as patients who were ill, thus helping complete a medical attitude, but the prospects of most for cure were regarded as severely limited by the lack of knowledge and techniques for investigating and repairing the microscopic material damage associated with pathology.

The advocates of curability found it difficult to defend their view as wards overflowed and strictly somatic pathologies were advanced. In large measure this was because no systematic philosophical commitment had been made to the curative powers of a certain sort of environment. For most American moral treatment supporters, "moral" considerations in diagnosis were never quite on an ontological par with somatic ones, hence it was difficult to make a case for their retention as institutional problems worsened. The reasons for this early lack of commitment included the concrete problem of attracting philanthropy to a cause that was not as "concrete" as a physical disease. Philosophically, psychiatrists could not reconcile themselves to the notion that the mind, as finally identical with the soul, could itself ever be diseased, for then the very spiritual integrity of the individual is at hazard. Rush himself led this concern, though the respected Dr. Pliny Earle of Northampton State Hospital in Massachusetts made the concise and representative statement:

> Were the arguments for the hypothesis that in insanity the mind is diseased tenfold more numerous than they are, and more weighty, I could not accept them. My ideas of the human mind are such that I cannot hold for a moment

> that it can be diseased, as we understand disease. That implies death as a final consequence, but Mind is eternal. In its very essence and structure (to use the terms we apply to Matter), in its elemental composition and organization, it was created for immortality. Consequently, beyond the scope of the wear and tear and disorganization and final destruction of the mortal part of our being.[17]

Thus as important as the environment was to social and psychological factors in mental illness, at least from the standpoint of etiology and treatment, extrapsychiatric commitments required that it take a second place to somatic considerations. Of course, this is only one of the seemingly numberless such instances that can be analyzed by the sociology of science. Also damaging to the continuity of moral treatment in America during the latter half of the nineteenth century, and in similarly broad cultural terms, was perhaps the fact that the very idea of the environment as "nature" came to lose some of its grandeur. For while America's idealized natural spaces seemed to provide a model environment for the insane, these spaces were not immune to onrushing urbanization, nor to a Civil War that turned open fields of sacred possibility into bloody battlegrounds. It is true that Americans turned their naturalistic expectations towards a fantasy called "the Northwest," but even this evidenced the decline in faith in the curative powers of a certain sort of *actual* environment.

Still some practitioners attempted to associate the apparently impressive results of early moral treatment with a more adequate philosophical framework, though most were Europeans. Pierre Cabanis suggested that, since a combination of psychological and somatic factors seemed to explain the success of moral treatment, the mental and physical may be at most parts of an integrated whole person.[18] Despite the extensive American involvement with moral treatment one is surprisingly hard-pressed to find a similar statement from an American psychiatrist. In 1838 the distinguished superintendent of the Rhode Island asylum, Dr. Isaac Ray, allied himself with the received view: "No pathological fact is better established... than that deviations from the healthy structures are generally present in the brains of insane subjects."[19] But in Ray's *Mental Hygiene* of 1863 he wrote, in light of the apparent efficacy of moral treatment, "[I]t may be doubted if it is quite correct to consider the individual as composed of two things essentially distinct (mind and brain) both in origin and nature, instead of regarding him as being endowed with various powers which, though serving each a special purpose, form an harmonious whole—a single, individual man."[20]

Ray's selection of the expression "powers" in this context anticipated the language of another physician, William James, by several decades, but his remark was in passing, limited in scope, and virtually unique among American psychiatrists of his time. Moral treatment, whether deservedly or not, could not survive a lack of vision, let alone a lack of funds. Hence the insane overcrowding the hospitals were more and more usually restrained on the grounds that they required protection from themselves. The superintendent of the Cincinnati Sanitarium, Orpheus Everts, expressed what became the received view that no amount of sentimental social engineering could alter the facts of persons "who are depraved and vicious because of an arrest of human development short of the higher and more complex intellectual capabilities that are essential to high, complex intellectual perceptions." Like the "children or savages" they truly are, the insane must be disciplined "for their own good and the welfare of society."[21]

III. NATURALISM IN AMERICAN PSYCHIATRY: ADOLF MEYER

I have been somewhat abstractly describing the impression that "nature" or the "environment" or even "the land" made on early American psychiatrists as a factor in the origin and treatment of madness, though the dominant pathologies were somatic. This vagueness was characteristic of the way Americans spoke of their surroundings. Nor were they any more certain about the nature of the relation between the person and his or her environment, at least not since the earliest Puritan views of a divine covenant lost their explicit hold. Waiting in the wings, equally unsure of its role, was the problem of community in America, also a Puritan concern. Asylum superintendents in the nineteenth century could consistently stress the import of popular understanding of the naturalness of mental disease and its social origins, while specifying a minimum distance from the city and fortress walls for the institution itself. The philosophers and social scientists of a later generation attempted to formulate answers to these questions, and American psychiatry was ably represented in these deliberations by Adolf Meyer, whose work can be seen, in part, as an articulation of the implicit principles of moral treatment from the standpoint of a pragmatic naturalism.

We need to address Meyer's historic connection to the moral treatment movement, his personal and philosophic connection to pragmatic naturalism, and the meaning of that latter expression. Taking these matters "seriatim," moral treatment has been linked to twentieth-century community psychiatry,[22] though the extent of this connection is unclear;[23] and Adolf Meyer was a pioneer of community psychiatry. The outlines of Meyer's position as conceptualizer of the successor to moral treatment will take us directly into the philosophies of William James and John Dewey.

It is astonishing that Meyer, the dean of American psychiatry for much of this century, is today so little discussed. His relatively unsystematic manner of presentation and failure to provide many detailed clinical histories at a time when the psychoanalysts were doing this have been cited as reasons for this neglect; but so has the incorporation of his ideas into mainstream psychiatry.[24] Meyer was an immigrant, born in Zurich, who came to this country in 1892, when he joined the staff of the Illinois Eastern Hospital for the insane at Kankakee. In 1895 he became pathologist at the Worcester Hospital, which had been a leader in the moral treatment movement.[25] But when Meyer arrived on the scene that period was long past, for after 1850 the apparent incurability of insanity had combined with a newly aggressive school of strictly physiological theory to discourage the notion that the environment in any sense could be important for treatment purposes. Mental illness came to be regarded as mainly a result of innate and often microscopic weaknesses in the brain.[26] In the interim, Worcester had succumbed to national tendencies and problems, becoming largely a custodial institution.

By the 1890s, however, there were important new, or perhaps renewed, stirrings in American psychiatry. A younger generation of specialists candidly surveyed the post-Civil War scene and admitted widespread institutional deterioration. They were also impressed by the neurophysiological studies of Fritzsch, Hitzig, Ferrier, and others which suggested that external influences were recorded in a vastly complex neural network in the brain. As William James put it in his epic, *The Principles of Psychology*, "[o]ur nervous system grows to the modes in which it has been exercised."[27] Here was a novel reply to psychiatric dualism[28] and a new motivation for an environmentally informed psychotherapy: the system of engrained neural pathways in the brain is personal experience writ small. An Ohio psychiatrist named A. B. Richardson took seriously Briton Henry Maudsley's maxim that "[i]nsanity marks a failure in organic adaptation to external nature"[29] and concluded: "the surroundings of an insane person seriously affect the diseased conditions of the brain," besides having an important effect on the establishment of habits dangerous to maintenance of sanity. Hence the old moral treatment had some force, at least, for twentieth-century psychiatry.[30]

American philosophers, too, were influenced at this time by developments in European experimental psychology. Charles Peirce's pragmatic maxim, although not itself a direct result of this activity, was warmly embraced by James as most harmonious with the new view of mind the psychologists were bringing about. The maxim, in its early expression, asserted that the *meaning* of a concept for a thinker is exhausted by the sensible consequences suggested by thinking about the concept. Hence concepts, or ideas, are not only verified by their sensible consequences but actually help instrumentally to bring about those consequences. In turn, these concepts are modified by the often surprising results of their application. In this way the pragmatists generally sought to move mentality into the actual world, where activity is inherently experimental. James and John Dewey, noting that traditionally person and mind have been identified, saw the further opportunity to eliminate problematic Cartesian dualism and make the person continuous with the environing natural world. Therefore the term used to denote this position is pragmatic naturalism.[31]

While in Illinois, Meyer knew John Dewey, then teaching at the University of Chicago, and became familiar with Charles Peirce's pragmatism in *The Monist.*[32] Then, during his seven years at Worcester, Meyer was in close touch with William James,[33] so it is not surprising that they should exercise an important influence on Meyer's thought. However, the depth of the relationship between Meyer's "psychobiology" and pragmatic naturalism is seldom appreciated, in spite of Meyer's reflections:

> The factors involved in the development of a psychobiological conception had much support in American thought. Pluralism and pragmatism were liberating factors in throwing off dogmatic dualism and making unnecessary an ideal and forced monism which disregarded the specificity of many biological data. William James' clear vision of the significance of the "pragmatism" of Charles S. Peirce and the "instrumentalism" of John Dewey and the healthy encouragement given to natural spontaneity of thought and work in the American environment, were all sympathetic to a realignment of concepts in harmony with what was essentially an urge to place one's confidence in the actual potency of experience.[34]

Although a thorough examination of Meyer's psychiatric thought in relation to that of American philosophers is not possible here, we can highlight those premises common to Meyer and the pragmatists which, in retrospect, also seem congenial to much of the practice of moral treatment.

As indicated earlier, Meyer was a pluralist, but not an eclectic. The latter is willing to bring many techniques to bear on a problem, because he or she does not believe one will do from a practical standpoint. But Meyer believed that the original human situation is itself a locus of various aspects, each requiring a particular approach. Zilboorg noted that for Meyer "the total picture is first the summation, then a possible synthesis of all the forms and aspects of the life of the individual—organic, sociological, general, cultural, and pure psychological."[35] James called his own philosophy a "radical empiricism," since its basic proposition was that experience originally comes as a whole "pure experience," the relations as real as the features related, and that we divide and categorize the fields of consciousness as we entertain and adjust to the passing show. For both Meyer and James there could be no a priori single system of description, whether it be mind-body dualism in philosophy or physiology in psychiatry, for example, because in its immediacy experience is a seamless web of as yet undifferentiated factors.

Thus Meyer and James shared a broad conception of human experience. One upshot in terms of a study of the person is that he or she is taken "as a whole," in terms of the entire range of kinds of experience that constitutes an organism: "We respect the facts as they are and as they work in and for the life of the person, before they are ripped from their settings or are actually torn asunder under a division of labor no longer compatible with our best critical and trained sense."[36] In effect, Meyer applies James' warning against "vicious intellectualism" to the psychiatric context. This occurs when we forget that our definitions and analyses are not gleaned passively from experience, but are interpretations.[37] Fundamentally, therefore, people find themselves in *situations*, the facets of which are many and in organic relation prior to analysis.

Meyer called the study of the whole, situated person the study of "integrates" or "personal units." The principle of integration, he claimed, permits the researcher to distinguish between what "the structural *parts* or organs could do by themselves, working as detached preparations, and what the unit would do with these parts, which serve in actual life in ever-adjusting organismal adaptations when asleep or awake, at rest and in action."[38] The description of the person as a dynamic, functioning whole is reminiscent of Dewey's more dramatic account of the person as in the first instance a "live creature," an expression which encompasses at least two important propositions. First, the life of any organism "goes on in an environment," "through interaction with it," because "its subcutaneous organs are means of connection with what lies beyond its bodily frame, and to which, in order to live, it must adjust itself by accommodation and defense but also by conquest."[39] Secondly, and as a corollary to this observation, the creature that is fully alive is "fully present, all there, in all of its actions; in its wary glance, its sharp sniffings, its abrupt cocking of ears. All senses are equally on the *qui vive*."[40] The live creature is thus sensitively continuous with its context.

I advert to Dewey so that we may more adequately appreciate what a profound disorientation Meyer believed mental illness to be, one that seemingly involves all relations, from the most basic biological to the most seemingly ethereal psychological, going on in a particular and often inhospitable setting. The whole creature is at hazard in the psychiatric crisis:

> Our patients are sick not merely in the abstract mind but actually living in ways which put their mind and the entire organism and its activity in jeopardy, and we are now free to see how this happens—since we study the biography and life-history, the resources of adaptation and of shaping the life to success or to failure.
>
> The study of life problems always concerns itself with the interaction of an individual organism with life situations.[41]

Hence Meyer, partly under the influence of James and Dewey, came to support a pluralistic conception of the person.

On this account no single human science has priority over others; the psychological and the biological describe different aspects of the human situation, as do the sociological, anthropological, political, and economic, rather than different substantial kinds associated in an individual under divine auspices. They are each admitted as authentic aspects only insofar as they contribute to the grasp and reform of the conditions of living. Thus there followed a psychiatric epistemology informed by all disciplines in the science of man, and a naturalistic view of mental life as, in its healthy state, contextually adaptive. In this way Meyer articulated the underlying rationale of moral treatment, unencumbered by a dualism that both denies the deep engagement of mentality in the affairs of the environment, and regards explanations in all but the most rigidly materialistic terms as incompatible with scientific psychiatry. On the contrary, the psychiatry that Meyer described, in his opinion, "has furnished a concrete setting for the interplay of emotions and their effects."[42] Descartes "left the mental world outside nature, with a consequent naturalization by the new sciences of only a part of man";[43] Meyer believed that his new psychobiology would help to bring mentality into nature.

As has been noted Meyer, like Dewey, posited a dynamic human organism adjusting to its environment based on "the products of experience, as well as those of heredity and growth."[44] From the therapeutic standpoint the next step is to refine the general notion of environment in a manner that is consistent with Meyer's position concerning the nature of the person. This refinement took the form of a conception of community in psychiatric treatment: the mental health specialist must build bridges between the institution and society, to "attain a collaboration beyond the hospital walls."[45] This sort of cooperation yields preventive results insofar as the community can be educated concerning the sources of mental disorder, and assists the specialists in gathering information about the patient that is relevant for treatment.[46] Both envisioned consequences of community psychiatry return us to older principles of moral treatment, including the sense of continuity between person and environment.

But it is not yet clear what the link is between community and environment in a view such as Meyer's, besides the obvious fact that the latter term more generally describes the organismic context. Meyer's conception of mental hygiene has as its background the view that the emotionally healthy organism in general adjusts competently to novel situations. Much of this competence is thought to spring from the funded experience of the organism as a species being shared among humans through significant speech communication. Hence, to give society a role in the patient's treatment is to begin to make that patient a part of the community once more, and so to avail him or her of the collective experience relevant to successful living. The caricature of the patient's removal from the community was the exhibition of lunatics for a fee at regular intervals in Europe and America until the end of the eighteenth century. On the preventive side, the mental health worker can enter the community and encourage the development of those shared characteristics which tend to inhibit the development of emotional problems. The asylum superintendents had also written on the social causes of insanity in the eighteen hundreds and commonly visited families to advise them on the progress of relatives; Meyer's approach entailed promoting the growth of persons as individual members of a community, whole creatures who are social integrates and natural parts of a wider world. By way of indicating how this general therapeutic strategy connects with Meyer's pluralistic and naturalistic view of the person, it is helpful to recall again Dewey's "live creature," whose career and destiny...are bound up with its interchanges with its environment, not externally but in the most intimate way."[47] Thus, "[i]nner harmony is attained only when, by some means, terms are made with the environment."[48] Meyer evidently regarded continued membership in the human community as a crucial means of coming to terms.

As was the case in our discussion of moral treatment, no defense of the claims Meyer made for his research results is offered here. Rather, we have been interested in historically situating these movements from a philosophical perspective. However, one sort of attack on Meyer's approach seems worth remarking on because it so seriously misconstrues the nature of his project.

This position, exemplified in an otherwise helpful study of psychiatric models,[49] attributes the recent eclipse of Meyer's reputation to what is called his "holistic" doctrine. Meyer, it is claimed, urged the examination of the person "as a whole," while the thrust of inquiry is properly to set out different parts of the individual for specialized study. Hence, on this view, Meyer's position "happens to be in direct contradiction to the whole methodology of modern science,"[50] it was really trying "to introduce a new kind of science" for "it was not proper science as we now understand it."[51]

Certainly it would have been an extraordinary but not impossible oversight for a scientist of Meyer's acknowledged skill and influence to be operating in "contradiction" to the method of science for so long. But this is too strong a claim, since any method "contradictory" to that of science would have to deny precisely what scientific method affirms, and Meyer hardly denied the authority of rational inquiry in science. The critics in question seem to have confused the *method* of science with the *techniques* of science. From the technical standpoint, Meyer never advocated abandoning laboratory work, for example, with its attendant analytical techniques ranging from dissection to the control of relevant variables. Indeed, Meyer explicitly called for continued study of "data anatomically and for their physiological part-relations." This is entirely consistent with a method, that is, an heuristic device that is informed by certain philosophical premises concerning the fundamental nature of the object of study, which urges us "to recognize... the unit or whole utilizing these parts for its own ergasic [the overt and implicit products of psychological integration] or expressive purposes."[52] It is analogous to the contemporary physicist's quest for a unified field theory, a methodological presupposition that provides a broad framework lending significance to technical research in various physical subdisciplines. Further, insofar as "non-holistic" views encourage interdisciplinary competition based on notions of ontological priority, for example, the superiority of somatic explanation and the priority of a materialist metaphysic, the opportunity for various approaches to inform one another and share fruitful results is inhibited. In this respect nonholism as an heuristic principle runs counter to "progress" in science, however that term is sliced. Finally, no reader of Meyer can fail to be impressed with his determination that his method is not unreasonable given the wealth of information yielded by scientific technique during the last several centuries, for this information continues to describe a world of continuities and relationships that renders ancient substantial dualism more and more doubtful. Again, if Meyer's method is today little discussed, it is probably because it is widely assumed. Whether or not the assumptions have been translated into effective action is another matter.

IV. PROSPECTS FOR A NATURALIZED PSYCHIATRIC MODEL

We have found a significant conceptual continuity running through the history of American mental health care, from the development of moral treatment to the community psychiatry of Adolf Meyer. Moral treatment was seen as at least anticipatory of a naturalistic approach to care of the insane, while Meyer's psychiatry understood itself as a naturalistic account of the person with implications for treatment. It is tempting to suggest that we have yet to align theoretical and practical considerations in American mental health policy. There is little doubt that this country has at least as rich a reservoir of medical talent as any other, while the coherence of its program lags behind. Wing, in a comparative study of mental health services in the United States, the United Kingdom, and the Soviet Union, finds the greatest difference between the American system and the two others to be the absence in the American system of a national standard of care, one that cuts across regional and socioeconomic lines. As a partial result opportunities for experimentation and innovation are greater in the United States, though delivery of services thus designed is hampered by lack of a "state administrative structure."[53] Furthermore, the re-emergence of social psychiatry in the late 1950s, perhaps yet another chapter in the tale of American successors to moral treatment, failed to mobilize public and professional support for what suggested "welfarism" to many. As a society, we have yet to make a commitment to a mental health policy that recognizes social factors in etiology and epidemiology and thus enlivens a sense of public responsibility. In this respect we have hardly advanced from conditions in the 1870s, when the curability model was admitted but social considerations, and social responsibility, were not.

Still, Meyer's psychiatry, bolstered by the literature of pragmatism and neo-pragmatism, provides a rubric that remains to be explored in contemporary terms. That these authors proffer an appropriate philosophical framework for a novel program in psychiatry is attested to by medicine's "extraordinary correlation between knowledge and implementation,"[54] as a current follower of the pragmatic tradition expresses it, for in documenting the relations between knowing and doing the pragmatist is one with the physician.

One way in which division in approaches to provision of mental health care continues to infect both the philosophy and the policy decisions relating to these services is the current dispute among "models" of mental illness. Proponents of the competing models often seem to suppose that from both a philosophical and a practical standpoint their positions are mutually exclusive, that theory and practice require commitment to a single approach. Yet I would argue that eclecticism and systematic pluralism are confused here. Admittedly, survey of the terms describing popular models, including the medical model, the social science model, the psychoanalytic model, and the family interaction model, does not make for optimistic expectations of compatability.[55] And confusion is aggravated by the absence of a full-blown, red-blooded *theory*, properly so-called, to provide a systematic explanation for any of the rather vague perspectives called models. However, there are at least two reasons to think that cross-model cooperation is possible: first, such cooperation is actual, that is, practitioners adhering to different approaches in institutional settings do, as a matter of fact, manage somehow to communicate and agree on diagnoses, commitment recommendations, and even treatment strategies, albeit often with difficulty; second, alleged incompatibility between and among competing models is, in at least some cases, more apparent than real.

By way of illustrating briefly the second claim, we might consider the lively debate between advocates of the medical model and of the social science model. Formulations of each position differ significantly, but a serviceable summary of the medical model for psychotherapy runs as follows: the focus is on "the causes of abnormal or maladaptive behaviors, rather than on the behaviors themselves, construing 'real' disorder in terms of an underlying disease state of the organism," where the disease state is further construed on an analogy with physical medicine in terms of clusters of symptoms with underlying causes corresponding to germs, viruses, and lesions. Notice that no "ontological" commitment is made concerning the types of causes underlying the syndromes; causes need not be organic according to the model so formulated.[56] The social science model, as proposed by a contemporary sociologist of mental illness, Thomas Scheff, emphasizes the "societal reaction" to mental illness, that is, the reaction of fellow community members to the disease insofar as this affects the patient's prospects for recovery and reintegration. Notice that this version of the social science model does not necessarily propose a contribution to etiology or pathology, but it does seek to call attention to social factors in epidemiology and therapy which rigid adherents to the medical model have tended to ignore.[57]

At the very least, the issues that arise between these characterizations of the models are considerably more subtle than a mere reduction to a metaphysic of the physical or psychical. While a social science modelist may still wish to make a case for a social etiology or even pathology, this more modest proposal opens the door to an intelligent reconciliation within the boundaries of current information concerning the importance of social influences on those who have acquired the role of mental patient. Even without making the more radical claims concerning onset and causes of mental illness, there is a place here for a naturalistic psychiatry on the order Meyer sought to work out.[58] This would amount to what Macklin has called for: "a rapproachment between proponents of the medical model and adherents of the 'social scientific' approach."[59]

That, however, is work that remains to be done; here we have only indicated the historic background and philosophical parameters of the project. It is easy enough for the nonspecialist to proselytize, but the layperson's urgings must be informed by history, restrained by facts, and governed by confidence in the physician's art. With these regulations we can fairly participate in the tradition, compelled and heartened by the conviction that, in Dubos' words, "[b]ecause they are concerned with all the various aspects of man's humanness, the biomedical sciences in their highest form are potentially the richest expression of science."[60]

NOTES

1. Albert Deutsch, *The Mentally Ill in America* (New York: Doubleday, Doran and Company, 1937) pp. 24–27.
2. Norman Dain, *Concepts of Insanity in the United States, 1789–1865* (New Brunswick: Rutgers University Press, 1964), pp. 3–5.
3. David J. Rothman, *The Discovery of the Asylum* (Boston: Little, Brown, 1971). Gerald Grob has directly attacked Deutsch's account. See his *Mental Institutions in America* (New York: Free Press, 1973), fn. p. 12.
4. Ibid, p. 4.
5. Michel Foucault, *Madness and Civilization* (New York: Random House, 1965).
6. Rothman, *The Discovery of the Asylum*, pp. 7–19. Significantly, the rigorousness of these codes was probably proportional to the level of community already achieved: "In New England towns the new settler may never have come to feel comfortable. In some Middle Atlantic communities he was probably accepted in full after presenting his credentials. In frontier areas, no one may have questioned his presence at all." Rothman, p. 19.
7. For a concise discussion of Rush's career and thought see Deutsch, *The Mentally Ill in America*, ch. V.

8. An overview of moral treatment can be found in Ruth B. Caplan, *Psychiatry and the Community in Nineteenth Century America* (New York: Basic Books, 1969), ch. 1; and in Rothman, *The Discovery of the Asylum*, ch. 6.
9. Friend's Asylum, *Annual Report* (1837):9.
10. Thomas Kirkbride, *On the Construction, Organization, and General Arrangements of Hospitals for the Insane, with some Remarks on Insanity and its Treatment*, (Philadelphia, 1847).
11. This is not to suggest that all asylums reached the high standards set by moral treatment, nor to deny that some did not strive to reach them at all. Most Southern asylums, for example, could not afford to institute superior treatment. A major exception was Virginia, which established the first hospital exclusively for the insane. See Henry Hurd, *The Institutional Care of the Insane in the United States and Canada* (Baltimore: Johns Hopkins Press, 1916), p. 81; and Grob, *Mental Institutions in America*, p. 25.
12. Cited in Perry Miller, "Nature and the National Ego," *Errand Into the Wilderness* (New York: Harper Torchbooks, 1956), p. 210.
13. Among these were probably the vision of liberation from tyranny Pinel's actions projected; the fear that insanity by the 1830s had become a serious threat to America's social order; the emergent American philanthropy; and the liberalized theology of the Second Great Awakening, supporting the prospect of individual regeneration.
14. Cited in Grob, *Mental Institutions in America* p. 156.
15. J. Sanbourne Bockhoven, "Moral Treatment in American Psychiatry," *Journal of Nervous and Mental Disease*, 124 (1956):130–131
16. Rothman, *The Discovery of the Asylum*, p. 13; and Dain, *Concepts of Insanity in the United States*, p. 133. A still different position is taken by Grob, who regards the recovery claims as reasonable given the contemporary minimal claims for release from the institutions. See Grob, *Mental Institutions in America*, p. 68.
17. F. B. Sanborn, *Memoirs of Pliny Earle, M.D.* (Boston: Donnell and Upham, 1898), p. 281.
18. Cited in Dain, *Concepts of Insanity in the United States*, p. 12.
19. Isaac Ray, *A Treatise on the Medical Jurisprudence of Insanity*, 3rd ed. (Boston, 1853), p. 69.
20. Isaac Ray, *Mental Hygiene* (Boston: Ticknor and Fields, 1863), p. 6.
21. Orpheus Everts, "Treatment of the Insane," *The American Journal of Insanity*, XL (1884–1885):164–165.
22. Caplan, *Psychiatry and the Community*, p. 3.
23. Grob is especially critical of attempts anachronistically "to interpret this therapeutic system (moral treatment) in modern psychological terms and relate it to 'milieu therapy.' " Fortunately, we need not assert any direct connection, and we can agree with Grob that moral treatment's "vague theoretical foundations" let it be "interpreted and applied in a variety of ways." Our thesis relates not to similarity of theory, for as we have shown there was hardly any, but to similarity of practice. See Grob, *Mental Institutions in America*, p. 47.
24. George Mora, "Adolf Meyer," *Comprehensive Textbook of Psychiatry*, ed. A. M. Freedman, H. I. Kaplan, and B. J. Sadock (Baltimore: Williams and Wilkins Company, 1975), vol. I, p. 632.

25. Gregory Zilboorg, *A History of Medical Psychology* (New York: Norton, 1941), p. 503.
26. Caplan, *Psychiatry and the Community*, pp. 131–133.
27. William James, *The Principles of Psychology* (New York: Henry Holt, 1890).
28. There was of course a relation between older psychiatric traditions, such as phrenology, and the new notions of neural engraining, but beyond the shared conception of experience manifest in organic matter the similiarities begin to fall away.
29. Cited in Mark D. Altshule, *Roots of Modern Psychiatry* (New York: Grune and Stratton, Inc., 1957), p. 124.
30. Cited in Caplan, *Psychiatry and the Community*, p. 252. I have not recited the various innovations that grew out of this rebirth of environmental interest. They are surveyed in Caplan, *Psychiatry and the Community*, ch. 25.
31. For characteristic impressions of pragmatic naturalism in each author see Charles S. Peirce, "How to Make Our Ideas Clear," *Philosophical Writings of Peirce*; Justus Buchler, ed. (New York: Dover, 1955); William James, *Pragmatism* (New York: Longmans, Green and Co, 1907); John Dewey, *Logic: The Theory of Inquiry* (New York: Holt, Rinehart and Winston, 1938).
32. Alfred Lief, *The Commonsense Psychiatry of Adolf Meyer* (New York: McGraw-Hill, 1948), p. 44.
33. Adolf Meyer, *Psychobiology* (Toronto, Ryerson Press, 1957), p. 232.
34. Ibid, p. 47. Meyer called his philosophy "critical commonsensism" à la Peirce. See p. 108.
35. Zilboorg, *A History of Medical Psychology*, p. 503.
36. Meyer, *Psychobiology*, p. 11.
37. William James, *A Pluralistic Universe* (New York: Dutton and Company, 1971), p. 225.
38. Meyer, *Psychobiology*, p. 52.
39. John Dewey, *Art as Experience* (New York: Capricorn Books, 1958), p. 13.
40. Ibid., p. 19.
41. Adolf Meyer, "The Contributions of Psychiatry to the Understanding of Life Problems," in Lief, *The Commonsense Psychiatry of Adolf Meyer*, p. 5.
42. Ibid., p. 8.
43. Meyer, p. 26.
44. Ibid., p. 60.
45. Adolf Meyer, cited in Caplan, *Psychiatry and the Community*, p. 308.
46. Ibid., p. 307.
47. Dewey, p. 13.
48. Ibid., p. 15.
49. Miriam Seigler and Humphry Osmond, *Models of Madness, Models of Medicine* (New York: Macmillan, 1974).
50. Ibid., p. 148.
51. Ibid., p. 149.
52. Meyer, p. 52.
53. J. K. Wing, *Reasoning About Madness* (Oxford: Oxford University Press, 1978) pp. 198–217.
54. McDermott, p. 151.

55. See Seigler and Osmond, *Models of Madness*, pp. 1–20. Unfortunately, this study conflates the very different positions of Scheff and Szasz under the heading of the "conspiratorial" model. See pp. 65–73.
56. Ruth Macklin, "The Medical Model in Psychoanalysis and Psychotherapy," *Comprehensive Psychiatry*, vol. 14, no. 1 (January/February, 1973):50–51.
57. Ibid., pp. 52–53.
58. This need not be a "half-hearted" naturalism. As a recent commentator on Dewey's metaphysics has pointed out, "we must not think of the prefix 'psycho' in 'psycho-physical' as the addition of something 'physical' or as the negation of the physio-chemical level but rather as *the manifestation of additional properties,* namely, *the capacity to elicit support from the environment,*" [emphasis added] John E. Smith, *Purpose and Thought* (New Haven: Yale University Press, 1978), p. 153.
59. Macklin, *Medical Model in Psychoanalysis and Psychotherapy*, p. 67.
60. René Dubos, *Man, Medicine and Environment* (New York: Mentor Books, 1968), p. 168.

6.4

Physicians as Body Mechanics

Michael D. Bayles

Much has been written about the physician-patient relationship.[1] The traditional relationship, many people claim, has broken down under the conditions of modern medical practice, and it is not yet clear what will replace it. Many writers on medical ethics consider the relation to be a special one, not paralleled elsewhere in society. Aiming to downgrade that special claim without denigrating the profession of medicine, this article compares the automobile mechanic-owner relationship to the physician-patient relationship. The occupation of auto mechanic has arisen in society almost simultaneously with the progress of medicine and the breakdown of the traditional physician-patient relationship. Despite one's initial aversion to this analogy, it soon seems a very strong and informative one for the concepts of health and illness as well as the ethical relations involved.

A preliminary caution is needed. There is no single appropriate model of the physician-patient relation; there are at least several important variations, depending on the context. The focus is on one common medical context, that of a patient with a nonfatal physical illness seeing a primary care physician. Particularly excluded are the relations of patients to health care teams and patients with mental illnesses.

I. WHY SEE A MECHANIC?

Reasonable persons may have others make judgments on their behalves for three basic reasons. First, although capable of doing so, one may not wish to be bothered making them. One allows another to do so if that person will make them as oneself would, or if the differences are insignificant. For example, one authorizes a secretary to order any needed office supplies. Second, the judgments may require knowledge or expertise one does not have. For example, a tax accountant knows the tax laws. One is not necessarily incapable of acquiring the needed knowledge, but it is not worth the effort.

Nobody can acquire all the knowledge needed for all the activities and decisions of modern life One primarily goes to an expert for information and service. Third, one may allow others to make judgments if one will be or is already mentally incompetent. Thus, some people voluntarily enter mental hospitals.

The ordinary person visits an auto mechanic or physician for the second reason; lack of personal knowledge about how to diagnose or repair a misfiring engine, or how to treat fever and nausea. At least four basic models exist of the relation between nonexpert and expert. (1) In the *agency* model, an expert is a technician who acts in behalf and at the direction of a nonexpert. (2) In the model of a *contract between equals* dealing at arms length, an expert sells services just as a grocery store sells food. (3) In the *paternalistic* model, an expert with superior knowledge and skills stands to the nonexpert as a parent to a child. (4) In the *fiduciary* model, although there is a contract, it is not between equals at arms length. Because of superior knowledge and the nonexpert's vulnerability, an expert has a special obligation to consider the nonexpert's interests.

Which model is appropriate depends on the characteristics of the people involved and the situation in which the relationship develops. The relationship between automobile mechanic and owner is obviously not that of paternalism. It would be gratuitous for mechanics to treat as children adult owners with the mental ability and experience to fend for themselves in society. Nonetheless, the paternalistic model has been, and still is, applied to the physician-patient relationship. However, in recent years it has been widely criticized and rejected as inappropriate for most situations. Rather than refight that battle, the remainder of this discussion focuses on the other three models.

Several authors have provided reasons for rejecting the agency and contract models for the physician-patient relationship.[2] Agency assumes the principal knows what needs to be done and directs the technician or agent in doing it. The principal is in a superior position relative to the agent. Contract generally assumes bargaining between equals. At least four factors are frequently cited for rejecting these assumptions in the physician-patient relation. (1) The physicians' knowledge far exceeds that of the patients. (2) The patients are concerned and worried about their health and have more at stake than physicians who can find other patients more easily than the patients can locate alternate physicians. (3) The patient cannot shop around for another physician; the market mechanism does not work.[3] (4) Third-party payers (insurance companies) limit the services or amounts for which they will pay.

These same four factors also generally apply to the automobile mechanic-owner relationship thereby rendering the agency and contract models equally inappropriate. Consequently, to the extent that they support applying the fiduciary model to the patient-physician relationship they also support applying it to the mechanic-owner relationship. (1) The mechanic and owner are not equally knowledgeable. The mechanic possesses technical information and expertise that many owners lack. Many owners do not know what a distributor cap is, let alone the functioning of an alternator or the automatic transmission. Evidence for the general ignorance of owners about automobiles may be found in the number of unneeded shock absorbers and tires sold to tourists along the highways. (2) An owner may be psychologically disturbed by anxiety about a malfunction and have more at stake than the mechanic. When an expensive automobile will not start or run properly, an owner is psychologically disadvantaged vis-à-vis a mechanic. The owner needs the car to get to work and complete essential errands. The mechanic does not have a comparable or urgent need. (3) An owner is often limited in seeking repairs elsewhere. There may be no opportunity to shop around for the best buy as the contract model assumes, and indeed the owner may need the car repaired as soon as possible. If the car will not run at all, then to go to another mechanic involves having the car towed. Moreover, often only one or two available mechanics are competent to work on a particular type of car. Many mechanics may lack the necessary training, tools, or parts to do the work. (4) Third-party payers are often involved, and these of course restrict the bargaining freedom of both parties. Although automobile insurance companies frequently allow the insured to obtain estimates for accident repairs, they may pay only the lowest amount.

Charles Fried argues against the analogy between the physician-patient and the mechanic-owner relationships. His chief contention is that patients' relationships to their bodies are different from owners' relationships to their automobiles. The latter relationship is one of property, but not the former. People's bodies are not productive goods they own, but part of the persons themselves.

Although Fried's claim about the difference between one's relationships to one's body and automobile is correct, it does not necessarily follow that there is or should be a difference in one's relationships to physicians and mechanics. The range of interests that the physician's treatment may affect is often much broader than the range affected by a mechanic. Moreover, what a physician does may more directly and immediately affect one's mental state, for example, painful treatments or drugs affecting mental state. These factors go to the degree of concern a physician should show and the manner of treatment rather than the kind of relationship between the expert and nonexpert. Moreover, Fried contends that the physician-patient relationship should be viewed as a fiduciary one,[5] and the argument here is that the mechanic-owner relationship should also be viewed as a fiduciary one.

This objection is based on alleged differences in the relationships of the experts or nonexperts to the subject matters of their transactions. This form of objection is mistaken in principle. Differences in the relationships of experts (*E*s) or nonexperts (*N*s) to the subject matters of their transactions or relationships does not imply that the relationships between them vary. If *E* and *N* have a relationship with respect to *S*, it is the differences between *E* and *N*, rather than differences in their separate relationships to *S*, that are primary for the nature of the relationship between *E* and *N*.

This argument, it may be said, holds for extensional relations, such as "being further away from," but not for intensional relations of the sort involved between physicians and patients or automobile mechanics and owners. Once one considers the purposes patients and automobile owners have in consulting physicians and mechanics, the analogy fails. In particular, patients go to physicians and are treated for illnesses, while owners see mechanics for malfunctions. Illness and health cannot be defined without reference to the values of the patient or society, but the malfunction of an automobile can be.[6] Thus, the physician-illness relationship necessarily involves reference to the patient and may affect the physician-patient relationship.

This point is mistaken—not about illness, but about the malfunction of an automobile. Perhaps one can determine whether a particular automobile part or subsystem, such as a carburetor, functions without reference to values, just as one can determine whether a plant grows without reference to values. However, that does not settle whether an automobile needs repair. The owner may not want the part to function, for example, a fasten-seatbelt buzzer.

Whether an automobile functions satisfactorily depends on the particular values and goals of the owner. Likewise, whether one is physically healthy or ill depends on the goals and values of the individual patient. For example, whether the shock absorbers are functioning satisfactorily depends on how smooth a ride the owner wants. Similarly, whether one's body is functioning satisfactorily and is healthy depends on one's particular goals and activities. My big toe occasionally aches and is weak if strain is put on it. This condition does not bother me or prompt me to see a physician, but if I were a football kicker, I would see a physician and consider myself ill. Thus, as Robert Brown has argued in greater detail, a standard of health must be relative to the activities in which particular people wish to engage.[7]

Two qualifications must be made to this last point. First, many bodily conditions, for example, paralysis of the legs, will prevent almost any person from engaging in the activities he or she wants, so one need not pay much attention to the particular activities in which a person wishes to engage. Of course, the same applies to automobiles. If they will not run at all, most people will find them unsatisfactory. Second, a condition may not presently prevent any desired functioning, but it may be an indication of a possible future inability to function. When I had a prostate infection, none of my desired functioning was impaired, but a blood discharge made me apprehensive that incapacitation might develop. Similarly, a pinging sound in my automobile's engine, even while it continues to function satisfactorily, may prompt me to take my automobile to a mechanic. To sum up, persons are physically ill if they have bodily conditions that prevent them from engaging in desired activities they could have engaged in before the condition developed or which, if uncorrected, may prevent their doing so. Similarly, automobiles do not function satisfactorily if they have conditions that prevent their owners using them as they desire and could have before or which, if uncorrected, may prevent their doing so in the future.[8]

Finally, it may be said that one crucial point distinguishes illness from a malfunctioning automobile. Illness, many writers contend, excuses one from obligations, and physicians thus certify one's excuse (a doctor's excuse for being absent from school). A malfunctioning automobile does not necessarily excuse one from anything, so the mechanic has no such certifying function. This argument, which rests on Fried's point that the relationship between patient and body differs from that between owner and automobile, misunderstands excuses. A condition excuses a person if it shows he or she could not have fulfilled an obligation, or could not have done so without unreasonable effort. Bodily illness often incapacitates one from engaging in activities required to fulfill obligations. However, often one is still capable of fulfilling many obligations and is not excused, for example, from paying one's rent. In any case, excuses need not refer to bodily or mental conditions.[9] Automobile trouble is a frequent and commonly accepted excuse for being late for or missing activities.

A final objection to the analogy is that although one often goes to a mechanic for maintenance, one rarely goes to a physician for maintenance. Automobiles are not always in need of repairs, but they need oil changes, lubrication, and tune-ups. However, people are not always ill when they go to a physician. They may merely want an eye examination or Pap test. They may simply wish to be certified as healthy, for example, for life insurance. Preventive medicine is concerned to provide just such "scheduled maintenance." If people go to physicians for preventive medicine less than they do to mechanics for preventive maintenance, it may be because they are more concerned and worried about their cars than themselves. Also, tune-ups and other such services are not mere preventive maintenance, often the engine is not working at full efficiency when they are performed. A change of oil or antifreeze might be comparable to taking vitamins.

II. WHY TRUST A MECHANIC?

If an analogy between the mechanic-owner and physician-patient relationships is thus plausible, one might get a handle on the analysis of physician-patient relationships by considering what an automobile owner desires or expects of a mechanic. Probably the question asked most often is: Can this mechanic be trusted? One wants a mechanic who is trustworthy to look after one's interests in the automobile, and one wants a mechanic who can be trusted to protect and further those interests. Thus, the virtues of a mechanic are those that indicate trustworthiness. Since trust is crucial to the relationship, it is best described by the fiduciary model.

Physicians emphasize the concept of patient trust. However, when some physicians speak of patients having trust, they mean trust in physicians to make decisions about them and to provide appropriate treatment. In short, they mean patients should trust physicians as children should trust their parents. The element of trust involved in the fiduciary model is different from that of the paternalistic one. One must always ask, "Trust to do what?" A virtue of the analogy between the mechanic-owner and the physician-patient relationships is that it provides a new perspective on what patients might trust physicians to do.

Although many of the ethical or moral features of the physician-patient relationship derive from a physician being worthy of a patient's trust, the whole of medical ethics cannot be derived from this source. The physician-patient relationship can at best ground the ethical obligations between these two parties. Physicians, like automobile mechanics, have obligations to others that do not arise from the relationship. These obligations depend on the role of the profession or occupation in society. Also, there will at least be variations in the fiduciary relationship, depending on the situation; and in some situations (for example, that of an unconscious emergency patient) another model, such as the paternalistic one, may be more appropriate. Only a few ethical elements of the physician-patient relationship can be briefly considered here by use of the automobile mechanic-owner analogy.

In New York state, automobile repair shops, like physicians, are licensed. The explicit purpose of such licensing is to indicate that the shop and its mechanics are worthy of trust. (Of course, implicitly, licensing is frequently advocated by professions and occupations in order to restrict admission and increase fees or prices.) One major point of licensing is to certify competence. Mechanics must know what they are doing or they may make matters worse. Incompetence may be grounds for suspending their licenses.

Two interesting points arise from the licensing of both mechanics and physicians. First, no one seriously argues that mechanics should be a self-regulating group. Public control by the state is readily assumed to be appropriate. However, although some control of physicians by the state exists, the medical profession puts much emphasis on self-regulation. The analogy suggests that self-regulation has at least been overemphasized. Second, repair garages may be fined or have their licenses suspended or revoked for overcharging automobile owners. There is no parallel practice with physicians. Overcharging patients is not a widely recognized reason for suspending or revoking physicians' licenses. By analogy, however, physician "theft" in the form of overcharging or performing unnecessary services should be grounds for so doing.

The mechanic-owner analogy also provides a basis for analyzing two much discussed issues in medical ethics, namely, a physician's obligation of full, truthful disclosure and patient consent. When an automobile owner or patient goes to a mechanic or physician, that person is seeking the latter's expert knowledge. An owner wants a mechanic to describe what is wrong with the automobile and then, usually, to repair it. A person goes to a physician to obtain a diagnosis of an illness and a recommendation of what drug to take, surgery to have, or other treatment regimen to pursue. To be worthy of trust, the mechanic must make a full, truthful disclosure of what has been found. Similarly, to be worth of trust, a physician must make full, prompt, and truthful disclosures.

A physician's obligation of full, truthful disclosure is not absolute. There may be, or at least many physicians believe there may be, occasions on which it is outweighed by other obligations. The most frequently discussed situation concerns informing a patient of terminal illness, of cancer in particular. The argument for nondisclosure is that the information would be harmful to the patient's well-being, particularly the individual's mental well-being.[10] On what is this obligation to the patient's well-being based? Physicians usually rest it on the traditional principle that a physician's first obligation is to do no harm. This principle merely moves the issue back one step. The problem then becomes whether the information and psychological distress are, in the total situation, harm. Although the patient may suffer psychological depression, he or she may also want to know the truth.[11] One might compare the situation to that confronting an automobile mechanic who discovers that an automobile needs such major repairs that it would be cheaper to buy a new one. Suppose the mechanic does not tell the owner, because it would produce psychological distress and nothing can be done to fix the automobile anyway. The mechanic might even contend that the owner either "really knows" the automobile is shot or else does not want to know. In that case, the mechanic has clearly stepped beyond the bounds of the relationship and failed in his responsibility to the owner.

The trust one may repose in a mechanic is to provide accurate, relevant information and to perform authorized work competently, but not to make important decisions for the owner. Automobile mechanics cannot make repairs without authorization to do so. Most repair shops use order forms on which the work to be done is specified and then signed by the owner. If the mechanic discovers other problems requiring further significant repairs, further authorization must be obtained. However, if an owner trusts a mechanic, the latter may be authorized to check out the engine (or automobile) and do whatever is needed, provided it does not cost more than some specified dollar amount. Permitting a mechanic to make such decisions falls under the first reason for allowing others to make judgments on one's behalf, namely, that the matter is not significant enough to attend to oneself.

Analogously, physicians must have informed consent from patients.[12] A physician cannot legally or morally perform diagnostic tests or make therapeutic interventions without a patient's consent. Such consent must be informed, which means that the obligation of truthful disclosure of all materially relevant facts must be met before the consent is acceptable. An automobile mechanic should explain how bad the brakes, shocks, or whatever are before seeking permission to repair them. When major repairs are indicated, owners may go to another mechanic for a second opinion, just as patients may want a second doctor's judgment about an elective operation. Finally, a mechanic may describe alternative procedures, such as tightening and relining the present brakes or putting in a new set. So also, a physician should explain to a patient alternative procedures, for example, surgery or radiation therapy for a malignancy.

An automobile owner may be dissatisfied with the work done by the mechanic. The engine may stall at stop lights after a tune-up, the hand brake may not hold, and so on. The owner has recourse for slipshod, careless, or incompetent work. Likewise, a patient may be dissatisfied with the ministrations of a physician. The pain may continue; the medicine may produce considerable nausea; the illness may persist. In either case, an owner or patient may sue for negligent work. With respect to negligence, some people may claim that the analogy between the mechanic-owner and physician-patient relationships breaks down. A physician will probably respond that a cure cannot be guaranteed, though a mechanic can of course guarantee repairs. A complete and strongly confirmed scientific theory or theories explain the functioning of automobiles and their subsystems or parts. However, no complete theories exist of the functioning of human beings, or many of their subsystems. Although there is, of course, considerable and growing scientific knowledge about the functioning of human beings and their organs, much remains unknown. It has even been argued that medical knowledge is necessarily fallible.[13] Because of this difference in knowledge, a physician cannot guarantee the outcome of treatments, though a mechanic can. Hence, untoward results are conclusive evidence of negligence or incompetence on the part of a mechanic but not of a physician.

Although these claims have some force, the differences and their significance are easily exaggerated. First, even if a complete (or nearly complete) theory of the operation of automobiles and their parts exists, it does not follow that significant differences exist at the practical level. The methodology of clinical physicians and mechanics is similar. Both usually start from verbal reports of symptoms. On this basis, a physical examination is made of particular parts and subsystems to determine the cause (disease). The same symptoms may result from different causes. Once I had difficulty with headlights failing. The cause could have been the alternator, a short in the wiring, or something else. As it turned out, the difficulty was a new fan belt that had stretched and slipped. A few years later, I had a fever, sore throat, cough, and general weakness. It could have been bronchitis (as I thought) or influenza (as the physician first thought). It turned out to be strep throat. As multiple possible causes exist for symptoms of automobiles as well as human bodies, even a complete theory does not ensure that a correct diagnosis will be made.

Second, some philosophers define diseases as the causes of illness.[14] This definition does not quite conform to ordinary usage, for a person may be critically ill as a result of injuries incurred in an automobile accident yet not be diseased. Working with a similar concept of disease as a structural change in an organ for which there is a unique cause, Eric J. Cassell is led to claim that most people have a disease, arteriosclerosis, most of their adult lives.[15] If one accepts some such notion of disease and considers the function of physicians to be to cure disease, then of course cures cannot be guaranteed. However, an analogous argument for automobile mechanics can be constructed. The parts of automobiles begin to rust (a chemical, structural change) and sooner or later malfunction may result. If one expects mechanics to be able to guarantee to fix all such potential causes of malfunction, then they cannot do so either. In short, physicians are to cure or alleviate illness (not disease) and mechanics, malfunctioning. Neither can repair all such problems, let alone guarantee that if one part is repaired the whole will function satisfactorily.

Third, the limits of medical knowledge and ability to cure do not, of course, imply that physicians cannot be negligent. They cannot guarantee to cure all illnesses any more than mechanics can guarantee to repair all automobiles no matter how badly damaged. Nor can they guarantee to cure any specific illness, as mechanics can guarantee that, except for defective parts from the supplier, they can repair specific parts. Nonetheless, physicians can guarantee that they will conform to a standard of care—that of other physicians in similar communities and specialties.[16] Failure to fulfill that guarantee is negligence, for which they are properly liable.

Finally, neither the mechanic-owner nor the physician-patient relationship is isolated from the wider community. Consequently, there are limits on the devotion of mechanics and physicians to owners and patients. There are some laws and obligations on a mechanic for the benefit of the wider community. Legally, an odometer cannot be turned back unless it is necessary and a record made. A mechanic also has a responsibility to the wider public that automobiles be safe for operation when lives other than the owner's may be at risk. Physicians also have responsibilities to the wider public that may limit their relations to patients. An obvious area of such responsibility pertains to communicable diseases. The confidentiality of physician-patient communications may need to give way for notification of others of their exposure to venereal disease. Similarly, heart defects or other problems of airline pilots and other employees may justify notifying employers of their illnesses.

A comparison of the auto mechanic-owner and physician-patient relationships indicates that the latter is not as unique and difficult to ethically analyze as is sometimes thought and sheds some light on the concepts of illness and health. Further similarities could be developed. Although the physician-patient relation is not the sole basis for medical ethics, in many contexts it is illuminating to view physicians as body mechanics.

NOTES

1. This paper has been revised for this volume to indicate the implications of the analogy for the concepts of health and illness. It was originally published in *Contemporary Issues in Biomedical Ethics*, ed. John W. Davis, Barry Hoffmaster, and Sarah Shorten (Clifton, New Jersey: The Humana Press, 1978), pp. 167–77.
2. See, for examples, Roger D. Masters, "Is Contract an Adequate Basis for Medical Ethics," *Hastings Center Report* 5 (December 1975): 25; William F. May, "Code, Covenant, Contract, or Philanthropy," *Hastings Center Report* 5 (December 1975): 35; and H. Tristram Engelhardt, Jr., "Rights and Responsibilities of Patients and Physicians," in *Medical Treatment of the Dying: Moral Issues*, ed. Michael D. Bayles and Dallas M. High (Boston: G. K. Hall & Co. and Schenkman Publishing Co., 1978), pp. 9–28. See also *Cobbs* v. *Grant*, 8 Cal. 3d 229, 502 P.2d 1, 9, 104 Cal. Rptr. 505 (1972).
3. See also, Kenneth Arrow, "Uncertainty and the Welfare Economics of Medical Care," *American Economic Review* 53 (1963): 948–54.
4. *Medical Experimentation*, Clinical Studies, vol. 5 (New York: American Elsevier Publishing Co., 1974), p. 96.
5. Ibid., p. 34.
6. Much has been written as to whether the concept of disease is value laden. See both Joseph Margolis, "The Concept of Disease," and H. Tristram Engelhardt, Jr., "Ideology and Etiology," in *Journal of Medicine and Philosophy* 1 (1976): 238–68. Cf. Christopher Boorse, "On the Distinction between Disease and Illness," *Philosophy and Public Affairs* 5 (1975): 49–68. However, all participants to this debate agree that illness is a value laden concept.
7. "Physical Illness and Mental Health," *Philosophy and Public Affairs* 7 (1977): 22.
8. Genetic defects may be compared to defects in particular cars of a certain model. By the definition given here, genetic defects are not illnesses, but they may provide good reasons for seeing physicians for treatment, just as one may have a mechanic replace a defective choke with another one. Boorse claims that if one replaces a Volkswagen's stock carburetor with a high-performance one, the result is not a Volkswagen in better mechanical condition. "On the Distinction between Disease and Illness," p. 59. This claim is ambiguous and puzzling. Does he mean the automobile is no longer a Volkswagen, that it is not better, or that it is not a better

Volkswagen? The first claim is mistaken (it is not a Chevrolet); the second depends on one's values; and the third is irrelevant. Suppose a Jewish person has his or her nose shortened. The person is still a Jew, may or may not be better (looking), and the fact that the person is not a better Jew (or his or her nose is not a better Jewish nose) is irrelevant to medicine.

9. Hyman Gross, *A Theory of Criminal Justice* (New York: Oxford University Press, 1979), pp. 23–24.
10. See Donald Oken, "What to Tell Cancer Patients: A Study of Medical Atitudes," *Journal of the American Medical Association* 175 (1961): 1125. Physicians' practices in this respect have greatly changed in the last decade and a half so that they now usually inform cancer patients of their disease. See Dennis H. Novack et al., "Changes in Physicians' Attitudes Toward Telling the Cancer Patient," *Journal of the American Medical Association* 241 (1979): 897–900.
11. William D. Kelly and Stanley R. Friesen, "Do Cancer Patients Want to be Told?" *Surgery* 27 (1950): 822–26.
12. *Cobbs* v. *Grant,* 8 Cal. 3d 229, 502 P.2d 1, 11, 104 Cal. Rptr. 505 (1972).
13. Samuel Gorovitz and Alasdair MacIntyre, "Toward a Theory of Medical Fallibility," *Hastings Center Report* 5 (December 1975): 13–23. Elsewhere I criticize their view; Michael D. Bayles and Arthur Caplan, "Medical Fallibility and Malpractice," *Journal of Medicine and Philosophy* 3 (1978): 169–86.
14. Engelhardt, "Ideology and Etiology," p. 257.
15. "Illness and Disease," *Hastings Center Report* 6 (April, 1976): 32.
16. Restatement (Second) of Torts, § 299A.

6.5

Health and Disease: A Nursing Perspective

Elsie L. Bandman
and Bertram Bandman

I. INTRODUCTION

Broadened definitions of health and disease have significantly altered the conceptions and practices of nursing away from a narrow preoccupation with the sick. Attention has turned toward environmental, social, economic, psychological, and political factors affecting health. These altered beliefs which broaden the concept of health are reflected in a position paper by the American Nurses Association.[1] This paper maintains that health care is the right of all and that society has the duty to provide the physical, social, economic, psychological, educational, and political conditions necessary to the promotion, maintenance, and restoration of the health of individuals in families and communities.

The change from a narrow to a broad definition of health has been a twentieth-century phenomenon. The traditional nursing view of health was oriented by the concept of disease as an intensive, pathological body process, one to be vanquished by vigorous, directed nursing activity. This narrow view prevailed until Florence Nightingale demonstrated the significance of the environment as either a source of disease or as a factor in maintaining health. Her work contributed toward broadening the concept of health.

Some current nursing definitions of health associate "levels of wellness" with such terms as "peak wellness" or maximum wellness" and "death" or "minimum" at either end of the spectrum. On this conception, little attention is paid to traditional disease entities, regarded as evaluative labels, which convey negative or static attitudes towards diseased body states. Instead, terms such as "problems," "dysfunctions," "disorders," and "impairments" are used to connote lowered levels of wellness and to emphasize the dynamic, functional self-healing processes of the body.

The notion of "holistic nursing" is associated by some nursing scholars with the notion of "wellness." It has been maintained by some adherents of this position, for example, that

> Optimum healing depends upon the interaction of both patient and professional as whole human beings. This view is then translated into concern for the patient as a unique psychological whole (who) is self-responsible and self-healing.[3]

One view that associates "wellness" with "holism" emphasizes the underlying assumption that the person is able to heal himself or herself if the therapeutic encounter occurs between whole persons. Moreover, the nurse's concern is for the physical, psychological, social, cultural, and "spiritual" concerns of the patient as aspects of the whole person.

An independent nurse practitioner, M. Lucille Kinlein, states the focus of her practice to be the client's exercise of "self-care practices in regard to a person's health state."[4] She says that visits to her office and physical examinations are conducted for the purpose of identifying "what is right, how well and how healthy the person is... [and for] improving on the total health of a person... who is the primary giver of care to himself."[5] Anatomical and physiological norms are her base lines for definitions of normality or its absence. Kinlein admits to the unattainability of a criterion of absolute health. She measures health on a scale of such factors as nutrition, sleep, responsibilities, emotions, and metabolism. She cites the need for a body of scientific data regarding health states and practices.[6]

The trend in nursing education toward the development of educational programs preparing primary care, family, pediatric, and geriatric practitioners is similarly supported by the disposition to care for the whole person and to support "health" as a dynamic, achievable high level of function, within the limits of age, infirmity or impairment, and socioeconomic status.

These definitions and practices are illustrative of the theoretical developments in nursing that have moved from a definition of health and disease consistent with the biophysiological medical model to one that is broad and comprehensive in scope and eclectic in origin, and that draws on the social sciences and moral philosophy more than on the physical and natural sciences.

II. HISTORICAL ROOTS OF NURSING CONCEPTIONS OF HEALTH AND DISEASE

Florence Nightingale concluded her *Notes on Nursing* with these observations of health and disease:

> We know nothing of the principle of health, the positive of which pathology is the negative, except from observation and experience... [which] will teach us the

> ways to maintain or to bring back the state of health. It is often thought that medicine is the curative process. It is no such thing... Nature alone cures. Surgery removes the bullet..., but nature heals the wound... the function of an organ becomes obstructed; medicine... assists nature to remove the obstruction.... And what nursing has to do in either case, is to put the patient in the best condition for nature to act upon him.[7]

Nightingale thus defined nursing as the art of actively assisting the body to heal itself as its natural function. This rested on the further assumption that bodily health was an achievable state through control of the water supply, sewerage disposal, food shortage, hygiene, wound asepsis, and proper nutrition, for example. During the Crimean War she demonstrated, by dramatic reductions in the morbidity and mortality statistics of soldiers, the beneficial consequences of environmental control and nursing care on the body's recuperative powers.

Nightingale's influence on public health and nursing education was extensive and prolonged. Her concept of health and disease as two ends of a continuum with one present in the absence of the other was qualified by her metaphor of health as an economy with reserves upon which the individual may draw capital.[8] Presumably she meant that health, like capital, may be earned and conserved (by healthful living in a safe environment) and through the expenditure of accrued interest (through the utilization of reserve strength in overcoming disease or repairing injury) will restore the economy to a state of solvency and the body to a state of health. Here she assumed that health is the natural state of the person supported by the body's self-curative healing process with nursing as the ally of nature. The economy metaphor further suggests that she conceived health to be an achievable state through healthful living. She apparently evaluated health primarily in narrow physical terms with disease as its opposite. Her prime objective seemed to have been the recovery and maintenance of health through defeat of illness by physiochemical manipulation of the environment.

The turn of the century ushered in an innovative era of nursing education characterized by the objective of "training... [nurses] for useful service to the people in all matters which affect their health and well-being."[9] This is an early recorded nursing definition of health as well-being, one which suggests that health pervades all aspects of life in homes, schools, and communities.

The curriculum of the Department of Nursing and Health established at Teachers College, Columbia University, in 1910 was designed to support this concept of health as well-being. The two-year curriculum for graduate nurses supported these ambitious goals. The leading public health physicians of the time, such as C. E. A. Winslow of Yale, were guest lecturers who taught the promotion of health and the prevention of disease as achievable goals attainable through public education and control of the environment.

III. CURRENT NURSING CONCEPTIONS OF HEALTH AND ILLNESS

The identification of nursing with "useful service to the people in all matters which affect their health and well being"[10] by these nursing scholars becomes the basis for their more extensive definitions of health and illness. In 1951 the National League of Nursing Education broadened the concept of health. On this view, levels of health ranged from states of dependency to independence and responsibility for self-direction of health.[11] The words "disease" and "illness" were conspicuously absent from the new emphasis on health as the ability to care for and direct the self.

Virginia Henderson places the terms "health" and "illness" on a continuum with independence and health at one end and sickness, dependence, and death on the other. The special function of nursing is to help the patient's return to self-care and self-direction. These reforming definitions of health and illness imply that peak or optimal health or well-being is the ability to function independently. As yet health-producing conditions were regarded as not extending far beyond the narrow confines of the immediate care environment.[12]

A decade later, Ernestine Wiedenbach summarized her experiences in nursing education and practice in a statement which foreshadows the broad definition of health now endorsed by the profession.

> To facilitate the efforts of the individual to overcome the obstacles which currently interfere with his ability to respond capably to demands made of him by his condition, environment, situation and time.[13]

All that was needed to completely modernize this definition and make it consistent with the American Nurses Association position on health care was to add the qualifying statement that it is the individual's right and society's duty to provide the conditions that promote this level of health and adaptation.

To emphasize the "wholeness" of persons in their interaction with nature, Martha Rogers asserts that "nursing seeks to promote symphonic interaction between" persons and their "environment" as well as "to strengthen the coherence and dignity of" persons, and to make use of the environment to achieve the "realization of maximum health potential."[14] To Rogers, disease categories are "subsumed within the larger perspective of ecological relationships."[15] This means that categories such as cancer, high blood pressure, and hyperactivity in children, are "paranormal events." The notion of "field theory" in physics and applied to social psychology by Kurt Lewin[16] seems to provide a basic assumption to Roger's view of a unitary human science. This unified human science rules out "health" and "disease" as evaluative, dichotomous terms. Rogers characterizes living systems as negentrophic, that is, manifesting increasing complexity and heterogeneity in contrast to entropy as a "trend toward... homogeneity."[17] Rogers's view is associated with holistic nursing.

Ruth Wu provides several models of illness. The first model identifies illness as an autonomous being or force that occupies the body against which the person is rendered helpless.[18] The second, the medical-physiological model, correlates objective observations of pathological change with laboratory findings in the process of identifying and classifying disease entities.[19] The equilibrium model views illness as a disturbance in the interaction between the human and the changing environment.[20] Finally, the social model, which Wu prefers for nursing, regards illness as the impaired ability to perform social roles and tasks[21] appropriate to that person's status and disruptive to the ordinary course of life. Wu's concern is to find a definition that "includes the range of possible conditions from illness to wellness."[22]

Wu endorses Marie Jahoda's view of concepts of health and illness as qualitatively different.[23] Individuals possess both aspects simultaneously with one predominant. This concept of the health capacity in ill or disabled persons is a prevailing motif in nursing literature. The implication is that an amputee with a well-fitting prosthesis who is mobile and fulfills activities of daily living, including sexual activity, is functioning at a high level of wellness despite the loss of limbs. This conception places emphasis on both "care of the disability and... on developing the person's well potentials."[24]

Wu is critical of placing illness and wellness on one continuum, as it tends to focus attention on the illness aspects of the patient. Wu's approach is to consider illness and wellness as separate entities and behaviors, which give the nurse opportunities to assess and support both components of health and disease in the case given. Thus the nurse can promote health through teaching and counseling, and encouraging responsibility for self-direction and care while intervening therapeutically to resist the disease. An example is the nurse's teaching of proper diet, insulin administration, exercise, hygiene, and skin care to a diabetic.

Ann Burgess states that ideally all aspects of human experience should be included in a comprehensive definition of health.[25] Burgess defines the equilibrium model[26] as a continuum with health and disease as polar opposites and the individual at different points at different times. Health thus becomes a changing and dynamic process. In Burgess's view, health is the successful adaptation to environmental changes, while disease is the failure to adapt.[27]

Burgess defines the community model as a still broader concept in which health is measured from the viewpoint of families, communities, and society as interacting, interdependent components of the environment. In addition to attention to environmental levels of sanitation and hazard, broad social parameters, such as crime rates, unemployment, and pollutants, are considered indicators of the health of a community. This conception reorders social values, such as employment and a safe environment, into an all-inclusive health care system in which each variable may be evaluated from the viewpoint of its health- or disease-producing characteristics. In short, Burgess's definition of health is all-inclusive, with the unstated assumption that health is identified as complete adaptation. This definition involves all aspects of society and its institutions.

In a recent medical surgical nursing text written for baccalaureate students in nursing, Gretchen Dery presents an account of disease as "objective, observable and quantifiable... with a knowledge of anatomy and physiology essential."[28] Dery views Maslow's hierarchy of needs as relevant to a concept of health. Satisfaction of physiological needs and needs for safety, love, belonging, and esteem are stepping stones to self-actualization as characteristic of persons achieving their potential. Dery views total need gratification and ideal health as synonymous.[29] Dery cites Dunn's concept of high-level wellness as goal-directed behavior of the individual toward optimal self-fulfillment achieved by balance with one's environment. Key concepts in defining individual high-level wellness include movement toward higher levels of function, based on an open-ended future with challenges to function at a still higher level by a person who has achieved integration, somewhat like a jogger who becomes better and faster than before.

High-level wellness in families provides security, love, shared values, and an integrated approach to problem solving. Community well-being, in this view, includes proper sanitation, safe water, sufficient space, no crime, decentralization of industry, intergenerational relationships, and an appreciation for beauty and wildlife.[31]

A concept of high-level social wellness calls for nurses to "focus on the wellness of people" instead of on their illness.[32] Thus, this author supports the holistic approach as care and concern for the total person and for those factors related to achievement of health at the highest level.

IV. A CRITIQUE OF A NURSING CONCEPTION OF HEALTH

The first thing to note is that some of the foregoing nursing scholars have developed a broader, more dynamic, flexible, and more patient-oriented concept of health than the traditional view of health as the absence of disease. While a nursing definition of health, one that associates environmental conditions with levels and degrees of health, is not without some serious conceptual and practical drawbacks, it reveals insights and has some important advantages in understanding the concept of health.

Critique of the Narrow Conception of Health

In contrast to the broad nursing definition of health, the traditional medical concept of health as "the absence of disease" violates the logical rule that a definition is not to be formulated in the negative.

A further, substantive difficulty with the traditional medical definition of health is that it is too narrow to account for complex explanatory and causal factors existing in the physical, social, and economic web of circumstances, such as the quality of food and water, that contribute to one's health or ill health.

A third difficulty with the concept of health as the absence of disease is that, in some of its traditional interpretations, the concept of health, and its cognate terms such as "disease" and "illness," has been claimed to be value-free. To argue that the concept of "health" is value-free fails to account for normative, value-laden, arguable, dynamic boundaries between "health" and "disease," and ignores the evaluative conclusion made in ordinary usage that health is good, that disease is bad, and that boundaries between health and disease are consequently not so easily drawn, and certainly not drawn on purely factual grounds.[33] The concept of health as the absence of disease emphasizes quantifiable criteria of disease, such as measurements of elevated blood pressure. This narrow concept of health gives little or no attention to the environmental causes of disease. Instead the emphasis is on the patient as the symptom bearer of disease and in need of medical and nursing care. The physician's and nurse's responsibility then becomes the treatment of the disease within the person. A result of the narrow definition of health is the denial of responsibility by the traditional medical model of such health deterrents as air, water, and soil pollution, and the lack of the American Medical Association's direct and concerted involvement with eliminating the tobacco industry in the interest of public health.

A Critique of the Broad Conception of Health

A difficulty with the American Nurses Association's broad position, which substantially endorses the World Health Organization (WHO) definition of health as a "state of complete physical, mental and social well-being," is that it is too broad to account for the special role of health professional services that explain the relation of health and disease.[34] A result of excessive broadening of the concept of health is that responsibilities are imputed to health professionals which they could not possibly perform.

Health professionals, for example, cannot be held entirely responsible for policies concerning the production and distribution of food, clothing, shelter, education, and other services that contribute to health care; nor can health professionals be responsible for population policies. Proponents of the narrower medical model are understandably reluctant to redescribe and reduce social and economic problems into medical issues to which the efforts of Thomas Szasz, who criticizes "mental illness as a myth," provide but one example. In contrast, some nurses use organized political activities to convert economic and social issues into health-related ones. The American Nurses Association reported that in 1978, more than 1,200 congressional bills were monitored for their implications to nursing and to health care. Testimony was presented for 29 hearings in addition to consultation to congressional staffs on considered legislation.[35]

A further argument against the broad view of health is that it assimilates social, moral, economic, political, religious, aesthetic, and other prefixed social goals. Thus, it begs questions as to well-made distinctions between the goals and process of health and social and economic well-being.

The logical possibility of qualifying the definition of health shows that the WHO definition is not an accurate reportive or lexical definition of health as one would find in a dictionary; it is rather a reforming, revelatory, or persuasive definition—a proposal to use "health" in a new way.[34]

However, this objection need not concern writers like Wu, Jahoda, Burgess, Rogers, and Dunn, for example, who defend a broad concept of health by appealing to ecology, adaptation, or dynamic "levels of wellness," since this seems to mean that one is healthy if, given the optimal conditions, one can function as well as one can. A reason these writers need not be concerned with the objection that their definitions are not reportive is that their aim may well be to reform the concept of health. However writers like Burgess, who define health as encompassing all aspects of human experience, are burdened with contending, for example, that the physically sound Nazis herding Jews into the gas chamber is not healthy.

This example shows a difficulty for both the narrow and broad views. In the narrow view, identifying health with physical health would result in regarding the Nazi as healthy without contradiction. This view, however, rules out serious aspects of psychopathic and sociopathic properties of a Nazi, which may qualify as instances of disease under the rubric of "psychiatric illness."

If, however, in the broad view one identifies the Nazi as unhealthy and extends this "unhealthy" designation to other forms of social and psychological "deviations in behavior," there is a danger in not being able to stop the "slippery slope" slide. The consequence may be to rule against designated social deviations on the pretext that unpopular views are illnesses. In the narrow view, one can say, in accordance with common usage, that "the Nazi is healthy, but morally evil," which would seem a preferable way to handle moral deviations of that type.

Counting all those factors, such as crime and unemployment or being a

Nazi as ill health precludes such normal distinctions as "X is healthy, but is a criminal" or "Y is healthy, but unemployed." In Burgess's view, one could not say without contradition, "Y is healthy and able bodied, but he is not employed." In Burgess's analysis, Y would not be healthy, which is absurd. This view identifies health so broadly as to make it synonymous with every social ideal.

These broad concepts of health lead to a position widely defended by writers in nursing representing the position known as "holism," to which we previously referred. Sally Gadow, for example, writes that "the nurse attends the individual as a unity rather than as a single problem or system."[37]

Gadow points out that "optimal healing depends upon the interaction of both patient and professional as whole human beings." She suggests that "the concern for holistic, or whole persons, healing of the patient... requires whole person involvement of the nurse" as well.[38] Leah Curtin contends that "the concerns of the physician are primarily directed toward physical entities, whereas the concerns of the nurse are primarily directed toward the entire person of the patient—the wholeness of the person."[39] On the basis of these and other accounts—including one's perception of nursing reality—it seems to us that "holism" in nursing is girded by an explicit belief in either the whole patient or the whole nurse as "emergent entities" as is evident in Martha Rogers's work, for example. Additionally, "holism" in nursing serves to secure moral and political standing, status, and significance for the role of the bedside nurse.

The notion that the nurse takes care of the whole patient whereas the physician treats the disease, however, is not a clearly defensible distinction. A view of a person as a unity may be so broad as to fail to account for the undeniable existence of disease and its adverse effects on a person's well-being. Even though nursing is responsible for coordinating the care and safety of each patient for twenty-four hours a day, the nurse no more takes care of the "whole patient" than the physician; only some of the psychological, physiological, and social needs of the patient are met. Moreover, each nurse takes care of an aspect, part, or condition of the patient. The nurse applies a dressing, gives a medication or counsels the patient or the family; but in doing so, the nurse treats part of the patient or an aspect of the patient. Nor does the nurse solely treat for health while the physician solely treats disease. In caring for the patient with the goal of raising "levels of wellness," the nurse also treats disease or illness and a physician, in treating illness or disease, is treating to restore health.[40]

An Attempted Reconciliation Between the Narrow and the Broad Concepts of Health

It seems that both concepts of health suffer—the traditional medical definition of health from being too narrow and the conventional nursing definition of health from being too broad to be serviceable or very useful.

Nevertheless, from both concepts of health, we may, with the help of a distinction suggested in recent social and political philosophy, find a solution to the dilemma other than discarding both concepts. That move consists in distinguishing between the core and the scope of "health."[41] Analogously, the scope of a person, for example, includes all of his or her limbs, but if a person has to lose a limb or if a person is even a quadraplegic, we still identify him or her as a person whose core (or essential) features are nevertheless intact. Returning to the concept of health, let us imagine two concentric circles, with the inner circle identified as the core of health and the outer circle identified as the scope of health. We perceive both concepts as complementary rather than as mutually exclusive, and perceive the complementary roles of two main levels of health professionals, namely physicians and nurses. An adequate concept of health calls for both the narrow and broad views of health and disease. Thus the core of both terms "health" and "disease" is the narrow physiological circle with the larger one being social and cultural. In this view, nurses and allied health professionals primarily promote health in the broad sense, whereas physicians primarily identify and treat diseases and illnesses in the narrow sense. Neither approach need be exclusive.

We contend, contrary to Christopher Boorse and more in accord with R. M. Hare, that disease and illness have both descriptive and normative features. We believe that the core of health and disease is heavily descriptive, but that the scope of these health-related terms is partly evaluative; and an understanding of both descriptive and evaluative aspects is helpful. The core of these concepts depends on verifiable descriptions of physiological processes; whereas the scope of these concepts may be said to depend on cultural and individual value judgments of what is good or bad. A concept of disease without physical signs and symptoms of impairment lacks the core of meaning of that term and is therefore purely evaluative, a danger to the broader concepts of health and disease. Do away with the descriptive and quantifiable aspect of health and the difference between health and disease becomes purely political and identical to the interests of the powerful.

However, the descriptive core of the concepts of health and disease without their "evaluative" scope lacks a goal or purposive orientation of health aimed at the good life. Medical research and practice is pointless unless oriented by human values on behalf of the good life.[42] In this view, distinguishing the core from the scope of health and illness, some forms of psychiatric illness or of personality deviations, such as masturbation, alcoholism, homosexuality, and Nazism, may be regarded under the scope rather than the core of illness.

The broader, more dynamic concept of health proposed by WHO, by nurse reformers, and in nursing manifestoes may be interpreted as a linguistically penetrating reminder that health-promoting conditions, like clean air and water and affluence, education, and full employment, causally contribute to health. Since "health" is partly evaluative, it may well be that incorporating more of the conditions that are health-promoting, invites us to put more emphasis on the broad conditions of health, which in turn, causally contributes to the narrow concept of health.

In this view, the social, economic, political, moral, and religious conditions of health and illness, singled out by defenders of the broad scope of these terms, are health-promoting conditions of health and illness, and are given greater emphasis than that given by defenders of the traditional core of "health" and "illness." Some social and economic conditions which bring about well-being or its opposite, such as wealth and poverty, knowledge and ignorance, crime, Nazism, mental illness, freedom, security and justice, are health-promoting or illness-promoting conditions and give some support to the attempted conceptual identification of health with complete well-being.

If a definition of health as well-being is interpreted as persuasive or reformative, one can judge whether such a definition, although in part exaggerated and misleading, if clarified, may nevertheless be illuminating and useful. The broad concept of health, for example, directs more attention to health-promoting and disease-promoting conditions than the narrow, traditional concept of health, and thereby reveals aspects of health previously ignored.

V. HEALTH-PROMOTING VALUES AND THE RIGHT TO HEALTH CARE

Some nursing defenders of the broader view of health express their support by advocating comprehensive health care as a right. Hildegard Peplau, for example, writes that the Bill of Rights on behalf of the right to life, to liberty, and to the pursuit of happiness, "is a kind of promissory note" and that "the right to health care is an implementation of the Bill of Rights; for without health... the rights to life, liberty and the pursuit of happiness become relatively meaningless, because hunger, ignorance, pain and illness and disease" interfere with these pursuits."[44]

The position paper of the American Nurses Association concerning a national health policy clearly states the predominant values of the nursing profession regarding the conditions of life conducive to the achievement of health. These may be summarized as the "belief that health care is a basic right of all people,"[45] as is an environment that provides safety. Adequate nutrition, housing, educational employment, and public services, and equal rights and opportunities "that will sustain an acceptable quality of life"[46] are to be provided. Income maintenance is supported as a necessary condition for individual dignity and family integrity. Thus, provision of the conditions that contribute to the quality of life is seen as a necessary condition of health at the levels of promotion, maintenance, and restoration.

VI. IMPLICATIONS OF IMPLEMENTING THE BROAD VIEW OF HEALTH

This concern for the right to health care is advanced through proposals for major changes in the delivery of health care services. Martha Rogers views the purpose of nursing to be service and accountability to society for "building a health people . . . by the maintenance and promotion of health . . . through the concept of community health services . . . [now] critically inadequate and notably obsolete."[47]

One proponent who recommends comprehensive change in the purpose, organization, and delivery of health care services, incorporating the aspirations of some nurses and some trends already underway, is Patti Hamilton. She discusses the need for expanded roles for nurses that are "definitive in nature, that anticipate and prevent health problems and that manage primary and secondary prevention of illness and accidents and maintain health."[48] The nurse would receive direct payment for services. Independent nursing practice at this level is viewed as indispensable to the implementation of the "National Health Priorities, identified in Section 1502 of PL 93-641."[49] These priorities call for providing primary care to the underserved and to persons in rural areas, the prevention of illness, health education, and the utilization of health resources.[50] Hamilton regards independent nursing practice, nursing diagnosis, and intervention as different from "managing only what the physician neglects."[51] The cost of paying for two practitioners for every health problem is cost ineffective. Tragically, nurses in most states are effectively constrained by medical and nurse practice acts from independent practice in primary care. Hamilton views a hierarchical system of health care delivery with physicians in control to be "not only labor intensive, inefficient and extremely costly, but also resistant to change from within." The author concludes that a coalition of nurses and consumers offers the best hope of developing sufficient clout to bring about significant change in health care delivery systems. The combination of consumer and nursing forces within such political and regulatory organizations as regional health systems agencies, could support the nurse's provision of a full range of nursing services independently and participation in health care services collaboratively on a colleague basis.

Jo Ann Ashley, a nursing historian, criticizes the prevailing authority relation of physician and nurse as one of dominance and submission, which defines nursing as a "supportive" profession.[52] Ashley points to the historical fact that nurses have lowered hospital mortality rates and brought about reforms through emphasis on preventive health care. However, disease, hospitals, and physicians have been supported—health and nursing have not. The training and practice of physicians in disease supports the medical professions' virtual control over the operations of hospitals in this country. Nurses become subordinate to medical authority through state laws, which effectively defined nursing as handmaiden to the physician. Ashley alludes to the the 1970 statement by the American Medical Association's Committee on Nursing, which assumes "that nurses will remain in their 'logical place at the physician's side' functioning 'under the supervision of physicians' for the purpose of 'extend[ing] the hands of the physician.'"[53] Ashley concludes that the intellectual and operational devaluation of the nurse has verifiable consequences. Nurses are limited in what they can do for patients because of medical paternalism. Health care, of which medicine is a part, is unnecessarily expensive and scarce. The quality of health care possible by the combination of complementary professions has suffered. Significantly, nurses are reluctant to advocate in support of patient's rights on important issues because of their perceived lack of power, thus contributing to further decline of health care services. Ashley recommends the remedy to be the formulation of national health policies that will fully utilize nursing abilities and educational preparation. She contends that as a consequence of underutilization of nurses, neither the best quality nor the sufficient quantity of nursing, medical, or health care has been made available to the general public.

Ashley, Hamilton, and Rogers are but three key nursing critics of the current health scene who identify the political, economic, and philosophical assumptions of the current state of health care services. Their conceptual move on behalf of the broad definition of health emphasizes factors that promote or hinder health in its widest application.

VII. THE HEALTH PLATITUDE

A persistent problem about health-promoting values, such as those supported by the American Nurses Association and the nurses cited, is to decide which social value or goal best promotes health. Every social value promotes or hinders health, it seems. A second question asks: Whose health is being promoted or contributed to? And to what extent? Everyone's? Is support of this broad scope of health feasible in an economy of scarce resources? Thus, one is forced to point to the broad definition as the health platitude, one admittedly impossible to fulfill in all its particulars. Yet the program of the health platitude of the kind referred to by visionary nurses has affected more health changes than conventional curative medicine. This has been accomplished through such measures as the public water supply, sewerage, immunization, and the development of antibiotics. The next large reduction in morbidity and mortality statistics may come about as a consequence of changing lifestyles in habits of smoking, as well as exercise and overconsumption of food and alcohol. The concept of peak wellness may contribute to public understanding and may be relevant as the product of health-promoting factors.

VIII. CONCLUSION

Despite the rhetorical excesses of the broader, reformative concept of health emphasized by some nursing scholars and supported by the American Nurses Association, this definition includes reference to a right to health care in a manifesto sense. This broad concept of health sets down a norm in the sense that, if there were social justice in health care, the concept of "health" would be expanded to include both the right to health care and the social, economic, and political conditions necessary for its achievement.[54]

NOTES

1. American Nurses Association, *A National Policy for Health Care* (Kansas City, Missouri: American Nurses Association, 1977).
2. Wilma J. Phipps, Barbara C. Long, and Nancy F. Woods, eds., *Medical-Surgical Nursing: Concepts and Clinical Practice* (St. Louis: C. V. Mosby, 1979), pp. xi–xiv.
3. Sally Gadow, "Nursing and the Humanities: An Approach to Humanistic Issues in Health Care," in *Bioethics and Human Rights: A Reader for Health Professionals*, eds. Elsie L. Bandman and Bertram Bandman (Boston: Little, Brown, 1978), p. 310.
4. M. Lucille Kinlein, *Independent Nursing Practice with Clients*, Philadelphia: J.B. Lippincott, 1977), p. 24.
5. Ibid., p. 77.
6. Ibid., pp. 19–20.
7. Florence Nightingale, *Notes on Nursing: What It Is And What It Is Not* (New York: Appleton and Company, 1860; unabridged republication, Dover Publications, 1969), p. 133.
8. Ibid., p. 123.
9. M. Adelaide Nutting, Fourteenth Annual Report, 1908," in *Cornerstones for Nursing Education*, ed. Teresa M. Christy (New York: Teachers College Press, Columbia University, 1969), p. 38.
10. Ibid.
11. Joint Nursing Curriculum Conference, *Curriculum Bulletin*, 2 (New York: National League of Nursing Education, 1951), p. 21.
12. Bertha Harmer, *Textbook of the Principles and Practices of Nursing*, 5th ed., revised by Virginia Henderson (New York: Macmillan Co., 1955), p. 4.
13. Ernestine Wiedenbach, *Clinical Nursing: A Helping Art* (New York: Springer Publishing, 1964), p. vii.
14. Martha Rogers, *An Introduction to the Theoretical Basis of Nursing* (Philadelphia: F.A. Davis, 1970), p. 122.
15. Ibid., p. 130.
16. Ibid., p. 133.
17. Ibid., p. 51.

18. Ruth Wu, *Behavior and Illness* (Englewood Cliffs, N.J.: Prentice-Hall, 1973), p. 8.
19. Ibid., p. 10.
20. Ibid., p. 12.
21. Ibid., p. 13.
22. Ibid., p. 78.
23. Ibid., p. 82.
24. Ibid., p. 83.
25. Ann Burgess, *Nursing: Levels of Health Intervention* (Englewood Cliffs, N.J.: Prentice-Hall, 1978), p. 13.
26. Ibid., p. 17.
27. We endorse a helpful comparison, suggested by Arthur Caplan, between Ann Burgess's application of health as dynamic adaptation and an earlier analysis by René Dubos. According to Dubos, "health can be regarded as an expression of fitness to the environment, as a state of adaptedness." R. Dubos, "Health as Ability to Function," in *Contemporary Issues in Bioethics,* eds. T. Beauchamp and L. Walters (Encino and Belmont, California: Wadsworth, 1978), p. 98.
28. Gretchen Dery, "Concepts of Health and Illness," in *Medical-Surgical Nursing*, p. 3.
29. Ibid., p. 4.
30. Ibid., p. 5.
31. Ibid., p. 6.
32. Ibid., p. 7.
33. There are some parallel points with R. M. Hare's paper, "What Can Philosophy Do For Medicine?" read at the New York University Medical School, December 17, 1979.
34. Although some recent philosophical writers, such as Daniel Callahan, Tristram Engelhardt, Christopher Boorse, and Caroline Whitbeck, criticize the excessively broad WHO definition of health, they seem also to be making moves away from the excessively narrow, traditional concept of health. For an account and critique of the World Health Organization definition of health, see H. T. Engelhardt, "Health and Disease: Philosophical Perspectives" in *Encyclopedia of Bioethics*, Vol. 2, ed. W. Reich (New York: Macmillan Co., 1978), p. 605.
35. Myrtle K. Aydelotte, "A Report from the ANA's Executive Director," *The American Nurse* 11 (November 30, 1979): 10.
36. For an instructive discussion of reformative definitions of health and disease, see T. L. Beauchamp, "Health and Disease," in *Contemporary Issues in Bioethics*, eds. T. Beauchamp and L. Walters, p. 87.
37. Sally Gadow, "Advocacy Nursing and the New Meanings of Aging," in *The Nursing Clinics of North America* 70 (March, 1979):81–91.
38. Sally Gadow, "Nursing and the Humanities: An Approach to Humanistic Issues in Health Care," in *Bioethics and Human Rights*, p. 310.
39. Leah Curtin, "Nursing's Fundamental Right" (Paper given at Conference on Nursing and Human Rights, Long Island University, Brooklyn Center, May 3, 1978).
40. There is an analogy between holism in nursing and the progressive education slogan that "we teach the whole child, not the subject." As some philosophical critics point out, however, one cannot teach the whole child but teach it nothing by way of some subject matter, skill, or value. Analogously, one cannot treat a

patient but not treat something in particular. For a criticism of the progressive education slogan, see I. Scheffler, *The Language of Education* (Springfield, Ill.: Charles Thomas, 1960), pp. 37–39.

41. See Joel Feinberg, *Social Philosophy* (Englewood Cliffs, N. J.: Prentice-Hall, 1973), pp. 80–82, for an analysis of this distinction between the core and the scope of a concept and its application to First Amendment freedoms. See also Laurent Frantz, "The First Amendment in the Balance," *Yale Law Journal* LXXI (1962):1438.
42. See Peter Sedgwick, "What is 'Illness'?" in *Contemporary Issues in Bioethics*, ed. T. Beauchamp and L. Walters, pp. 114–119, for an account of the importance of attaching human values to health and illness.
43. For a view of masturbation as a disease, see H. T. Engelhardt, "Health and Disease: Philosophical Perspectives," in *Encyclopedia of Bioethics*, ed. W. Reich, p. 605.
44. Hildegard Peplau, "Is Health Care a Right?" *Image* 7 (1974): 5.
45. American Nurses Association, *A National Policy for Health Care.*
46. Ibid.
47. Martha E. Rogers, "Nursing: To Be or Not to Be?" *Nursing Outlook* 20 (January 1972): 42–46.
48. Patti Hamilton, "ANS Open Forum," *Advances in Nursing Science* 2(2) (January 1980): 111–113.
49. Ibid.
50. Ibid.
51. Ibid.
52. Jo Ann Ashley, *Hospitals, Paternalism, and the Role of the Nurse* (New York: Teachers College Press, 1976), p. 128.
53. Ibid., p. 129.
54. We wish to thank Arthur Caplan for important criticisms and suggestions of an earlier draft. We also appreciate two anonymous nursing scholars for their critical comments of an earlier draft.

6.6

Are Homosexuals Sick?[1]

Michael Ruse

There is much controversy today about whether a homosexual orientation is in itself a disease or sickness.[2] If one is attracted sexually to members of one's own sex rather than to members of the opposite sex, then is this a sign that one is ill—standing in need of a cure? Or is it the case that having a homosexual orientation is simply a matter of having an attribute different from heterosexuals—something on a par with having blue eyes rather than brown?

Not surprisingly, militant homosexuals tend to see homosexuality as nothing more than a variant form of sexual orientation. "I have come to an unshakable conclusion: the illness theory of homosexuality is a pack of lies, concocted out of the myths of a patriarchal society for a political purpose. Psychiatry dedicated to making sick people well has been the corner-stone of a system of oppression that makes gay people sick." (Gold, 1973, p. 1211) But there are medical people who argue in much the same way. The influential psychiatrist Judd Marmor states: "Surely the time has come for psychiatry to give up the archaic practice of classifying the millions of men and women who accept or prefer homosexual object choices as being, by virtue of that fact alone, mentally ill. The fact that their alternative lifestyle happens to be out of favor with current cultural conventions must not be a basis in itself for a diagnosis of psychopathology. It is our task as psychiatrists to be healers of the distressed, not watchdogs of our social mores." (Marmor, 1973, p. 1209.)

Conversely however, Irving Bieber states that "homosexuality is not an adaptation of choice: it is brought about by fears that inhibit satisfactory heterosexual functioning." (Bieber, 1973, p. 1210) Similarly, Charles Socarides states that "homosexuality represents a disorder of sexual development and does not fall within the range of normal sexual behaviour." (Socarides, 1973, p. 1212)[3] And in line with the views of these two psychiatrists, the endocrinologist Gunther Dörner speaks of homosexuality as involving "inborn disturbances of gonadal functions and sexual behaviour in man," and he thinks it is a "sexual deviation" in need of cure (Dörner, 1976).

Obviously whether or not homosexuality is to be judged a sickness or a disease or an illness depends in part on the facts, both at what one might call the "empirical" or "phenomenal" level and at the causal level. One wants to know something about homosexuality, how it affects people, and what putative causes have been proposed for it. But there is more than this. One must also learn how terms like "disease" and "illness" are used. Only when one has done a philosophical analysis at this level can one then examine the empirical and causal claims and properly judge how to assess the status of people's sexual orientations, and in particular to judge the healthiness or sickness of homosexuality.

This then is my task in this paper. I shall begin with brief exposition of two recently proposed philosophical models of health, disease, and illness. I shall not be critical of these models, although I do think that in the course of the discussion certain strains will appear in at least one of the models. Then I shall run quickly both through some recent findings about homosexuals at the empirical level and through the three main categories of putative explanatory causes for homosexuality: psychoanalytic, endocrinal, and sociobiological. Again, my main intent will be expository rather than critical. At each point I shall see what light is thrown on the "homosexuality as sickness" question by comparison of the scientific claims with the philosophical models. What I shall argue is that, given different scientific claims and different philosophical models, we get different answers to our main question. This, I shall suggest is the reason why we get such a controversy over the medical status of homosexuality.

I. TWO MODELS OF HEALTH AND SICKNESS[4]

There are I believe currently two main models of health and sickness. The first is due primarily to Christopher Boorse (1975, 1976, 1977) and for obvious reasons I shall label it the *naturalist* model. Boorse sees health and disease as being opposite sides of the same coin. Health is the absence of disease. Disease is what one has when one is not healthy. The key to Boorse's position is that one makes no judgments about good or bad, desirable or undesirable, when one judges something a disease. "On our view disease judgements are value-neutral... their recognition is a matter of natural science, not evaluative decision." (Boorse, 1977, p. 543) What then is disease (and health)? Boorse centers in on the notion of normality. The normal is the natural, that is to say, the healthy. Approvingly, Boorse refers both to ancient and to modern writers who have seized on this idea.

> There is a definite standard of normality inherent in the structure and effective functioning of each species of organism.... Human beings are to be considered normal if they possess the full number of... capacities natural to the human

> race, and if these... are so balanced and inter-related that they function together effectively and harmoniously. (Boorse, 1977, p. 554, quoting Marston et al., 1931, p.434, 437)

In other words, to be healthy is to fit the average or full standards of a functioning member of one's species, in our case of *Homo sapiens*. To be diseased is to fall below these standards, and diseases are what brings this about.

More formally and fully Boorse's position is as follows:

1. The *reference class* is a natural class of organisms of uniform functional design; specifically, an age group of a sex of a species.

2. A *normal function* of a part or process within members of the reference class is a statistically typical contribution by it to their individual survival and reproducion.

3. *Health* in a member of the reference class is *normal functional ability*: the readiness of each internal part to perform all its normal functions on typical occasions with at least typical efficiency.

4. A *disease* is a type of internal state which impairs health, i.e., reduces one or more functional abilities below typical efficiency. (p. 555)

As far as we are concerned, the key notion in this definition is that of a function, more particularly, a *normal function*. Boorse sees a function as something which contributes to a goal or an end. In human beings, the functions of the parts of the body are, specifically, "contributions to individual survival and reproduction." (p. 556) In other words, for Boorse an organ is healthy if it is doing what is typical of it for the (human) species, with respect to the ends of survival and reproduction—if it is part of the "species design." Otherwise it is diseased.

To complete his analysis, Boorse makes a distinction between "disease" and "illness." (Boorse, 1975) Disease for Boorse is neither good nor bad. It is just a thing or a state. But sometimes, often, we want to express our unhappiness about having a disease. Lung cancer, for instance, is surrounded by negative connotations. Boorse suggests that we categorize the subclass of diseases that we do not want by introducing the term "ill." When one is "ill," one has an unwelcome disease. Lung cancer is a disease, and as such is a state. However, people with lung cancer are ill, meaning that they have something they would rather not have.

Formally, Boorse offers the following definition.

> A disease is an *illness* only if it is serious enough to be incapacitating, and therefore is
> (i) undesirable for its bearer;
> (ii) a title to special treatment; and
> (iii) a valid excuse for normally criticizable behavior. (Boorse, 1975, p. 61)

Against Boorse, we have the *normativist* position, endorsed in recent years particularly by Joseph Margolis and H. Tristram Engelhardt Jr. Take Margolis first. Although there is obvious overlap between his position and that of Boorse, he is quite explicit in seeing values both in the concepts of disease and of illness. For Margolis, the difference between the two lies, not in the fact that only the latter has value connotations, but in that only the latter has a directly, apparent, troublesome nature. "A first approximation to the theory of medical norms—let it be stressed that it is only a first approximation—has it that the body is composed of certain structured systems each of which has an assignable range of normal functioning. Defect or disorder of such systems relative to such functioning constitutes a sufficient condition of disease; illness, then, is reflexively palpable disease... the norms of health and disease tend to correspond—often in a disputatious way—with putative norms of happiness and well-being.... To the extent that this occurs, it becomes difficult to treat the norms of medicine as altogether independent of ideologies, prevailing in different societies." (Margolis, 1976, p. 245)

In a like fashion, H. Tristram Engelhardt Jr., (1975, 1976) writes that "we identify illnesses by virtue of our experience of them as physically or psychologically disagreeable, distasteful, unpleasant, deforming—by virtue of some form of suffering or pathos due to the malfunctioning of our bodies or our minds. We identify disease states as constellations of observables related through a disease explanation of a state of being ill." Engelhardt, 1976, p. 259) In other words, although both Margolis and Engelhardt agree with Boorse that disease involves functioning, or rather malfunctioning, of the body or person, they disagree in how they feel it should be regarded. For them, a disease is a bad thing. Consequently, obviously they do not tie functioning directly to the biological ends of survival and reproduction (although of course it could involve these). They see functioning as more "cultural": "working in a satisfactory manner," or the like.

We have now before us our two positions, the naturalist and the normativist models. We must now turn to what is known, or at least claimed, about homosexuality. But as we do so, let me note one area of controversy that I am avoiding entirely. In recent years the notions of mental health and mental illness have come under strong attack, both as incoherent and as socially dangerous (especially Szasz, 1961). Clearly this attack has to be defused to open the way for a positive judgment about the disease/illness status of homosexuality, because (whether or not there be physical causes) homosexual orientation as such is a "mental" phenomenon. However, at this point I shall not get side-tracked into a discussion of the logical/ethical status of mental illness. I sympathize very much with the intentions of the critics—I hate the way that so many today refuse to judge behavior because of popular half-baked psychological theses. But as a general charge, I think the attack against the concept of mental illness fails, and that others have already adequately shown this. Hence, presupposing the defenses, I shall assume that one can legitimately ask questions about mental health and mental disease/illness. (See Margolis, 1966; Macklin, 1972, 1973; Moore, 1975a, 1975b; Klerman, 1977; Flew, 1973; Brown, 1977.)

II. THE EMPIRICAL FACTS ABOUT HOMOSEXUALITY

For my empirical information I rely heavily on the recent Kinsey Institute–endorsed study of homosexuals (and heterosexuals) drawn from the San Francisco area. (Bell and Weinberg, 1978) This study will hardly be the last word on homosexuals, their perceptions of themselves, their lifestyles, and so forth. But it does seem to be the most comprehensive and best evidence that we have so far. The authors of the study, Alan Bell and Martin Weinberg, gave extensive questionnaires to 972 homosexuals and 477 heterosexuals.[5] Since we are already in a situation where people are making judgments about health and illness with respect to homosexuality, it is not as if I am being that premature in thus turning to the Bell-Weinberg report.

With an eye to our models, we want to answer two kinds of questions. The first question is: How does a homosexual orientation affect people's functioning, particularly their biological functioning? Unfortunately, dead people tend not to complete questionnaires, so there is no information on the survival chances of homosexuals as compared to heterosexuals. However, there is pertinent information on reproduction. As might be expected, it really does seem that having a homosexual rather than heterosexual orientation reduces one's chances of having offspring (in biological language, one has "reduced fitness").[6] As tables 1 and 2 clearly show, the chances of getting married if one is a homosexual is very much less than if one is a heterosexual, and even if one does get married, one tends to have fewer children.

Of course, there are obvious questions about gaps in this information. For instance, one certainly does not have to get married to have children. But, in the absence of evidence to the contrary, one can assume that the missing information would not seriously distort the conclusion that homosexuals have fewer children than heterosexuals. Indeed, what additional evidence we do have points the other way. For instance, while they were married, homosexuals had significantly less intercourse (with their spouses) than heterosexuals, as tables 3 and 4 show.

Table 1

"Have you ever been married?"

	WHM *N=575* %	*BHM* *N=111* %	*WHTM* *N=284* %	*BHTM* *N=53* %	*WHF* *N=229* %	*BHF* *N=64* %	*WHTF* *N=101* %	*BHTF* *N=39* %	*Pilot Study* *N=458* %
0: No	80	87	26	49	65	53	27	31	83
1: Yes	20	13	74	51	35	47	73	69	17

This was originally Table 17.1 from Bell and Weinberg (1978), p. 374. I have omitted the statistical analysis here and in the succeeding tables, as I think the raw data speak for themselves.

WHM = white homosexual male
BHM = black homosexual male
WHTM = white heterosexual male
BHTM = black heterosexual male
WHF = white homosexual female
BHF = black homosexual female
WHTF = white heterosexual female
BHTF = black heterosexual female
(Pilot study refers to the preliminary study in Chicago.).

The second kind of question we want answered is: How do people feel about themselves? Generally speaking, is one happy as a homosexual? Would one be happier were one a heterosexual? The findings do not point unambiguously in one direction.

Take first the question about how homosexuals feel about being homosexual. Are they happy with their orientation? Or would they wish (have they

Table 2

"How may children (have you had/did you have) in this [first] marriage?"

	WHM *N=116* %	*BHM* *N= 14* %	*WHTM* *N=210* %	*BHTM* *N=26* %	*WHF* *N=80* %	*BHF* *N=30* %	*WHTF* *N=74* %	*BHTF* *N=27* %	*Pilot Study* *N=80* %
0: None	50	29	34	27	50	27	31	26	30
1: None	25	50	22	31	29	40	19	33	25
2: Two	15	21	26	27	6	13	15	22	26
3: Three	5	0	10	15	6	3	26	4	15
4–6: Four or more	5	0	8	0	9	17	9	15	4

This was originally Table 17.3, Bell and Weinberg (1978) p. 391.

Table 3

"How often (have/did) you (had/have) intercourse or sexual relations with your (husband/wife) during the first year of your [first] marriage?"

	WHM *N=116* %	*BHM* *N=14* %	*WHTM* *N=208* %	*BHTM* *N=27* %	*WHF* *N=80* %	*BHF* *N=30* %	*WHTF* *N=74* %	*BHTF* *N=27* %	*Pilot Study* %
0: Never	9	0	0	0	10	3	0	0	
1: Less than once a month	4	0	1	4	6	13	3	0	
2: once a week, once a month	8	0	3	4	10	13	5	4	
3: 1–1.9 times a week	10	7	10	0	19	10	9	4	
4: 2–3.9 times a week	31	50	30	26	30	17	36	22	
5: 4–5.9 times a week	19	21	32	33	14	13	27	26	
6: 6 or more times a week	18	21	24	33	11	30	19	44	

This was originally Table 17.5, Bell and Weinberg (1978) p. 382.

Table 4

"How often (have/did) you (had/have) intercourse or sexual relations with your (husband/wife) during the last year of your [first] marriage?"

	WHM *N=97* %	*BHM* *N=11* %	*WHTM* *N=182* %	*BHTM* *N=25* %	*WHF* *N=52* %	*BHF* *N=27* %	*WHTF* *N=71* %	*BHTF* *N=22* %	*Pilot Study* %
0: Never	29	0	7	4	31	26	8	5	
1: Less than once a month	21	18	5	8	13	19	10	5	
2: $<$ once a week, $\geq$ once a month	18	18	18	16	31	11	18	5	
3: 1–1.9 times a week	13	27	32	20	15	22	25	23	
4: 2–3.9 times a week	10	27	26	16	6	11	27	36	
5: 4–5.9 times a week	5	9	7	32	2	7	10	14	
6: 6 or more times a week	4	0	3	4	2	4	1	14	

This was originally Table 17.6, Bell and Weinberg (1978) p. 384.

wished) to change? (No comparable questions were asked of heterosexuals. I assume the authors believed that although some heterosexuals have sexual problems, they do not wish to become homosexual.) The answers are mixed, although on balance they strongly support the claim that most homosexuals are reasonably satisfied with their sexual orientation. The pertinent figures on sexual-orientation regret are shown in table 5.

Among those who did feel a sense of regret, societal rejection was the main cause (about 50 percent), followed by the inability to have children (about 25 percent). In their conclusions on these findings, the authors (Bell and Weinberg) suggest that the reason why more men than women regret their homosexuality is that probably more women than men have had a chance to sample both hetero- and homosex, and that consequently women have more feeling that they themselves have freely chosen their homosexuality. They point out also that they find far more satisfied homosexuals than do surveys restricted to people in treatment and they suggest that such latter surveys suffer from the fallacy of biased statistics. Many homosexuals in treatment are there precisely because they cannot handle their sexual orientation. I suppose a critic might object that a sample drawn from the San Francisco population is not that representative either. If one can live openly as a homosexual one might adjust a lot more readily to one's orientation than if one is in a society like Guelph, Ontario, where it is politic to conceal it.

Next, let us look at happiness perceptions ("psychological adjustment"). The most obvious, and not necessarily the worst way of finding out how people feel is to ask them. When the question was put to people the Kinsey researchers found that most people were pretty satisfied with their lot, and that there was not indeed a great deal of difference between homosexuals and heterosexuals. The pertinent findings are shown in table 6.

Bell and Weinberg drew up a five-point typology of homosexuals. "Close-coupled," those living reasonably monogamously with a partner; "Open-

Table 5

Acceptance of Homosexuality

	WHM	*BHM*	*WHF*	*BHF*	*Pilot Study*
Amount of Regret	(N=575)	(N=111)	(N=229)	(N=64)	(N=458)
0: None	49%	59%	64%	73%	45%
1. Very little	24	21	20	17	24
2. Some	21	18	14	9	20
3: A great deal	6	3	2	0	10

This was originally from Table 12, Bell and Weinberg (1978) p. 337.

Table 6

"Taking things altogether, how would you say you are feeling these days? Very happy, pretty happy, not too happy, or very unhappy?"

	WHM *N=575* %	*BHM* *N=111* %	*WHTM* *N=284* %	*BHTM* *N=53* %	*WHF* *N=229* %	*BHF* *N=63* %	*WHTF* *N=101* %	*BHTF* *N=39* %	*Pilot Study* %
0: Very unhappy	3	2	1	0	2	3	1	3	
1: Not too happy	14	18	11	4	16	22	10	10	
2: Pretty happy	55	61	67	53	57	59	57	61	
3: Very happy	28	19	20	43	25	16	32	26	

This was originally Table 21.3 Bell and Weinberg (1978) p. 432.

coupled," with a partner but quite promiscuous; "Functional," unattached, promiscuous, but satisfied; "Dysfunctional," unattached, promiscuous, and not satisfied; and "Asexual," not really that turned on by sex. As might be expected, in terms of this typology, Close-coupleds and Functionals tended to score highest on the happiness scale, and Asexuals and Dysfunctionals lowest. One interesting finding was that "although the Asexuals and the Dysfunctionals were less happy than the heterosexual men, the Close-coupleds tended to report even more happiness than those in the heterosexual group" (p. 199).

A critic is going to object that a major problem with questions like "Are you happy?" is that people simply do not always tell the truth, either about how they feel now or how they have felt in the past. This is simply a function of the fact that we all a remarkable capacity for self-deception. I suspect that there is some force in the first objection. Although one must certainly take people's self-perceptions seriously (I do not belong to the school which assumes that one should never take people's explicit claims seriously), it is undoubtedly true that people do deceive themselves. And luckily, many of us have a great capacity to blank out unhappy memories. ("Oh yes, it was a wonderful holiday. So relaxing!")

There is however one question which the researchers asked which perhaps helps us to edge a little closer to finding out how people really feel about themselves. This was to do with suicide—about whether people had actually attempted it or thought seriously about it. It is certainly not a perfect gauge of mental happiness. Thankfully people who have been suicidal at one point do not always remain so. But the topic of suicide would seem to tell us something about how people feel about themselves, how stable they are, how they adjust to life, how happy they are, and how content they are with their lot. The differences between homosexuals and heterosexuals, particularly homosexual and heterosexual men, are really quite staggering. As table 7 shows, homo-

Table 7

Suicidal Feelings and Impulses

	WHM N=575 %	BHM N=111 %	WHTM N=284 %	BHTM N=53 %	WHF N=229 %	BHF N=64 %	WHTF N=101 %	BHTF N=39 %	Pilot Study %
0: Never imagined	26	37	43	77	25	39	36	45	
1: Imagined, but never seriously considered	37	39	44	21	34	36	39	37	
2: Seriously considered, but never attempted	19	4	10	0	16	8	16	3	
3: Attempted at least once	18	20	3	2	25	17	10	16	

This was originally Table 21.12, Bell and Weinberg (1978) p. 450.

sexuals are far more likely than are heterosexuals to have attempted or seriously considered suicide.

One might wonder how representative these figures are, especially given that San Francisco has one of the highest suicide rates in the United States, but in fact the pilot study in Chicago found much the same suicide-attempt rate for homosexuals. Also plausibly one might suggest that the high homosexual ratio in San Francisco is not independent of a high suicide/suicide-attempt rate.

One wants to know to what extent the high figures for homosexuals are a function of their homosexuality, and whether this be internal (e.g., personal dissatisfaction with their homosexuality) or external (e.g., societal disapproval of homosexuals). The findings shown in tables 8 through 11 seem relevant.

It is not an entirely straightforward matter interpreting all of this data, but (summarizing) apparently about 20 percent of homosexuals attempt suicide and another 20 percent think seriously about it. Although the ratios are closer for women, this is at least a 3 to 1 imbalance for homosexuals over heterosexuals. Not all of the suicide attempts or thoughts are related to homosexuality, but something of the order of a half are. (This rather involves averaging things that probably should not be averaged!) This means about 1 homosexual in 5 is troubled by homosexuality to the extent of trying or seriously thinking about suicide. And about half of these are really having severe personal problems over their homosexuality—these problems not simply a function of societal disapproval.

One interesting fact is that suicide attempts tend to be the province of the young, for both homosexuals and heterosexuals, as table 12 clearly shows.

Table 8

"What were the reasons you considered it [suicide]?"

	WHM N=212 %	*BHM N=27* %	*WHTM N=36* %	*BHTM N=1* %	*WHF N=92* %	*BHF N=16* %	*WHTF N=26* %	*BHTF N=8* %	*Pilot Study* %
Distress not related to homosexuality	57	52	100	100	66	88	100	100	
Difficulty with sociosexual homosexual adjustment (external)	26	41	0	0	36	12	0	0	
Acceptance of one's homosexuality (internal)	18	7	0	0	7	6	0	0	
Other reasons	16	19	0	0	8	0	0	0	

This was originally Table 21.13, Bell and Weinberg (1978) p. 452.

Table 9

"What were the reasons you tried it [suicide] the first time?"

	WHM N=105 %	*BHM N=22* %	*WHTM N=8* %	*BHTM N=1* %	*WHF N=57* %	*BHF N=11* %	*WHTF N=10* %	*BHTF N=7* %	*Pilot Study N=75* %
Distress not related to homosexuality	48	59	100	100	58	82	100	100	29
Difficulty with sociosexual homosexual adjustment (external)	38	46	0	0	51	0	0	0	25
Acceptance of one's homosexuality (internal)	16	9	0	0	4	9	0	0	3
Other reasons	16	9	0	0	5	9	0	0	43

This was originally Table 21.16, Bell and Weinberg (1978) p. 455.

Table 10

"Did this [first suicide attempt] have anything to do with the fact that you are homosexual?"

	WHM *N=105* %	*BHM* *N=22* %	*WHF* *N=68* %	*BHF* *N=11* %	*Pilot Study* *N=78* %
0: No	38	59	59	73	24
1: Yes	62	41	41	27	76

This was originally Table 21.17, Bell and Weinberg (1978) p. 456.

Table 11

"In what way [was homosexuality involved in first suicide attempt]?"

	WHM *N=65* %	*BHM* *N=9* %	*WHF* *N=23* %	*BHF* *N=3* %	*Pilot Study*
Problems generated in a homosexual relationship (breaking up with partner, etc.)	43	33	67	33	
General homosexual adjustment (acceptance of one's homosexuality, etc.)	37	56	21	67	
Other (social, legal, parental problems, etc.)	20	11	8	0	

This was originally Table 21.18, Bell and Weinberg p. 457.

This rather implies that whatever conclusions one might draw about disease and illness may well be more applicable to younger people than to older people.

But what conclusions might we want to draw from all of these facts and figures? Fairly obviously I think we would want to say that most homosexuals are pretty content with their lot. Some indeed, particularly Close-coupleds and Functionals, are very positive about their homosexuality, apparently being at least as satisfied if not happier than comparable heterosexuals. There really seems no reason to pretend otherwise. On the other hand, there are homosexuals who have trouble accepting their sexual orientation, and there are

Table 12

"How old were you when you tried it [suicide] the first time?"

	WHM *N=105* %	*BHM* *N=22* %	*WHTM* *N=9* %	*BHTM* *N=1* %	*WHF* *N=58* %	*BHF* *N=11* %	*WHTF* *N=10* %	*BHTF* *N=7* %	*Pilot Study* %
1–17: 17 or younger	27	32	11	0	21	36	50	43	
18–20: 18–20	25	27	11	100	21	18	10	0	
21–25: 21–25	27	23	56	0	29	27	20	43	
26–87: 26 or older	22	18	22	0	29	1	20	14	

This was originally Table 21.15, Bell and Weinberg (1978) p. 454.

homosexuals (I would imagine much the same group) who are not very happy. Moreover, many homosexuals have gone through crises of one kind or another which have driven them to serious thoughts of, or even attempts at, suicide. One simply cannot deny this fact, or that we are looking at a minority of the order of 10 to 20 percent (admittedly, this might in part be a transitory phase of development, say pre-25, which is then followed by a happier maturity).

So, how do these empirical findings fit in with out models of health, disease, and illness? Taking first the naturalist position promulgated by Boorse, and concentrating on the negative notions (i.e., disease and illness), we have seen nothing directly about how homosexuality affects survival prospects. Only if we link attempted suicide with successful suicide (which seems a major assumption) can we suggest that homosexuality may in some respects reduce survival chances. However, we have got reasonably strong evidence that being a homosexual reduces reproduction, and this clearly seems to be a function of homosexuality itself, rather than something else. Hence, on one prong of Boorse's criterion, homosexuality must be judged a disease.[7]

However, illness is another matter. Some homosexuals, indeed most homosexuals, cannot be judged ill by Boorse's criterion. They are at least as satisfied with their lot, specifically with their sexual orientation, as are heterosexuals. Nevertheless, I do think we have to allow that by the naturalist criterion, a small minority of homosexuals are ill, and that this illness must be laid at the feet of their homosexuality. There are, for instance, some who would really like to be heterosexual, to marry, and to have children, and because of their orientation they cannot and this makes them unhappy. These people are ill, as perhaps are others who at various times in their lives are driven to the brink because of their sexual orientation.

The normativist conclusion overlaps in part with the naturalist conclusion, but not entirely. Those homosexuals that the naturalist would judge to be *both* diseased and ill (because of their homosexuality) would seem to be judged both diseased and ill (because of their homosexuality) by the normativist. Certainly, these are people who are not much enjoying life because of their sexual orientation, and this all seems to fit the normativists' criteria for disease and illness. However, the normativist parts company with the naturalist's claim that, judgments of illness apart, homosexuality generally is a disease. For Boorse, homosexuality is a disease because it reduces biological fitness. For the normativist, whether loss of biological fitness is a disease is a contingent matter, dependent on whether such loss makes the loser in any way regretful or unhappy. And apparently, since many homosexuals are happy in their homosexuality, the normativist would have no reason to judge them diseased (or ill). One can put matters this way. Boorse would say of the integrated happy homosexual that he/she had a disease but was not thereby ill. (See Boorse, 1975) The normativist would deny both disease and illness.[8]

In concluding this section, a number of points of clarification and qualification seem appropriate. First, even if one does judge (some) homosexuals diseased/ill on the basis of the empirical data, this does not imply that they are diseased/ill all of their lives. If anything, the data seem to imply that homosexuality-as-disease/illness is more of a young person's problem—perhaps giving the lie to the popular notion about the tragedy of the aging homosexual, a sentiment that Bell and Weinberg (1978) endorse. Whether spontaneously or through human intervention, the possibility that homosexuality-as-disease/illness will vanish is certainly not barred.

Second, if one talks in terms of "cure" at this point (and the argument does seem to imply that such talk is appropriate for some), note that such cure does not necessarily entail changing a person's sexual orientation (even if this be at all possible). The way to dissolve homosexuality-as-disease/illness may be to come to accept one's sexual orientation, and to appreciate and cherish it for its own values and virtues. Third, related to this point, total cure might well (undoubtedly will?) involve the heterosexual majority as well. If the majority stop thinking of homosexuality as a handicap and as something unpleasant, and if they stop hating homosexuals, then if nothing else we shall get a rise in the self-image of presently troubled homosexuals. (However, the evidence does seem to be that there is more to the problem than societal attitudes. For instance, some homosexuals dislike their homosexuality because they want to be heterosexual, get married, and have children. Admittedly society endorses the having of children, but the happiness of child-rearing transcends societal approval.)

The final point is directed against those who might be inclined to say that homosexual happiness cannot in any way be compared to heterosexual happiness—it is obviously lower and therefore even your integrated homosexual is sick as compared to your average heterosexual. All one can say in reply to an objection like this is that there is not the slightest bit of evidence for such an ad hoc assumption. The closest parallel would perhaps be the case of a child with Down's Syndrome. We would want to say that such children have both disease and illness (judged by either naturalist or normativist criteria) even though people with Down's Syndrome tend to have exceptionally cheerful and loving natures. I take it that at this point we have to introduce some element of paternalism, saying that if only Down's Syndrome sufferers knew better, they would be unhappy with their lot. But the reason why paternalism is justified here is that people with Down's Syndrome cannot know better—they are retarded. However, no similar case can be made against homosexuals—if anything, the evidence is that they are more intelligent than heterosexuals. (Weinrich, 1976) Nor do homosexuals seem lacking in other human virtues which might make us feel permitted to judge for others (as, for instance, in the case of the intelligent paranoid schizophrenic). Hence, in the absence of contrary evidence, the objection fails.

It might be felt at this point that there is really no need to take the discussion any further. One might feel that judgments of disease and illness (although, of course, not necessarily of cure) can and should be made directly and exclusively on the basis of empirical studies. If a homosexual has more or fewer children, is more or less happy, that is all we need to know. For our present purposes, there is no necessity to inquire after causes.

However, I would suggest to the contrary that it does in fact seem worthwhile looking into causes. Obviously the Bell-Weinberg study, although the best of its kind, is somewhat limited in value. Furthermore, a look at causal claims might throw a different light on some of the answers to the empirical questions (although I hasten to add, not necessarily a *truer* light). One might for instance plausibly suggest that people tend to claim to be more happy than they really are (although this is not to deny my defense just above of the claim that a happy homosexual is apparently just as happy as a happy heterosexual. For these and like reasons, let us turn to causes.

III. PSYCHOANALYTIC CAUSAL EXPLANATIONS

I find two main explanations of homosexuality in the psychoanalytic literature.[9] One I shall term the "classical Freudian" explanation; the other explanation stems from Freud's ideas but was developed in part in reaction to Freud, and is for fairly obvious reasons called the "adaptationist" or "phobic" theory.

Freud (1905) argues that we are all essentially, physiologically and psychologically, bisexual—with elements of male and female mingled in our nature. In the case of biological males (which was Freud's paradigm), psychologically speaking we start out with the male side predominant, as we are attracted to mother. Then the female side comes to the fore, as we turn narcisstically towards our own bodies. And then comes the swing back to the male side, first to mother again, and then hopefully with a successful resolution of the Oedipus complex, to other females at adolescence. Females take a comparable path, although as every critic has been happy and eager to point out, Freud gives female psychosexual development little study in its own right, and that shows a desperately sexist bias. Fortunately, Freud's problems are not our problems here.[10]

For Freud, therefore, a person is not really turned into a homosexual—rather, it is more a question of the homosexual side of our nature coming to the front and pushing back or out our heterosexual side. This can happen for a number of reasons. One can be born innately having a strong homosexual disposition. One might for various environmental reasons just stay in the homosexual phase of childhood. In boys, this could be because one had a very overpowering and affectionate father. Freud (1905) speculated that the reason why homosexuality was so common in Ancient Greece was because male slaves attended and reared the young boys. Or one might later have trouble breaking from a dominant and overaffectionate mother, and then coming up against the universal incest taboo (Freud, 1913) one rejects females in favor of males.

Consequently, for Freud homosexuality was not so much "abnormal," but more a question of arrested development or regression to an earlier stage. This means that, in his language, it is a "perversion" rather than a "neurosis," which latter involves repression (of memories, ideas, and so forth, from full consciousness). Hence, the method of analysis is inappropriate, since this is designed to bring unconscious elements to the front. Freud was therefore not very sanguine about curing homosexuality (in the sense of changing one predominantly homosexual into one predominantly heterosexual). Indeed, as he explained in his famous "Letter to an American Mother," he did not even think that homosexuality is an illness.[11]

The question we want to ask is whether, if one accepts Freud's position as true (please not the hypothetical[12]), we would want to modify or in any way alter the conclusions arrived at in the last section.[13] Freud himself seems to imply that if one regards homosexuality as a case of arrested development (which he does), then this means it cannot be an illness. However, this seems not to follow. In girls, if a piece of one of their sex chromosomes is missing, there is a failure to develop sexually at puberty. We would (and do) certainly want to classify this phenomenon, Turner's Syndrome, as a disease/illness. (Levitan and Montagu, 1977) Therefore, analogously, such judgments seem not to be ruled out in the case of homosexuality. But of course this is not to say conversely that even if homosexuality is arrested development, that it is thereby either a disease or an illness.

And in fact it would seem that accepting this classical Freudian position would not really much affect judgments made on the empirical evidence alone. The Freudian position implies nothing new about survival or reproduction, nor about the happiness or unhappiness of homosexuals. Perhaps indeed it does imply (as certainly Freud's letter assumes) that there is no reason why a homosexual cannot be perfectly happy and content with his/her lot—that such happiness is genuine. Some people are content to stay in or go back to a phase of childhood development. This being so, both naturalist and normativist can agree with Freud that many homosexuals are not ill at all. (This is not to deny the other conclusions we arrived at, for instance that Boorse would judge homosexuality a disease, or that both normativists and naturalists think some homosexuals ill. In fact, as we shall now see, inasmuch as Freud subscribed to a version of the phobic theory—which certainly grew out of his ideas—he too would probably have judged some homosexuals sick, in the sense of neurosis. Certainly, the letter shows that Freud thought analysis could bring comfort to some homosexuals. Thankfully, it is not my task here to bring full consistency to Freud's thinking.)

For Freud, one thing which can drive someone back to a homosexual phase, that is which can lead to an incomplete resolution of the Oedipal Strife, is an overly close mother. Another thing, one which often accompanies such a mother, is a hostile threatening father. The developing boy sees father as a rival threat to his love of mother. Since father is stronger than the son, the son does the safest thing, which is to take himself out of the heterosexual running! Often this is all bound up with the fact that at an earlier stage in life when the boy had discovered his own penis (the "phallic phase"), there was also the discovery that females do not have penises—in the boy's view, they are castrated. Hence, the threatened son fears that the father will geld him, if he continues to look towards the female side of the human race.

These sorts of ideas have been taken up by a number of analysts and developed into the adaptationist or phobic theory. (Bieber et al, 1962; Bieber, 1965; Kardiner et al, 1959a, 1959b, 1959c, 1959d; Ovesey, 1954, 1956; Rado, 1940, 1949; Salzman, 1965) Breaking from Freud, they see our natural state as heterosexual—we are not constitutionally bisexual. Normally a boy (they are good Freudians in that they continue to take males as the paradigm!) will grow up to be attracted to females, but certain things—fears—may deflect him into homosexuality. Homosexuality is therefore an adaptive move in the face of perceived threats. The fears may start at an early stage in life. Seeing the gash caused by the girl's castration, the boy will fear that a like fate awaits him, and on learning of the mechanism of sexual intercourse the boy might hypothesize that this is the main source of danger—that the vagina contains teeth that lie in wait, ready to bit off the penises of would-be copulators. (This line of argument is taking place subconsciously. A little lesson in gynecology or dentistry is not going to remove the fear.) Again, the fears might start in the family, as Freud suggested, as a function of an inadequate resolution of the Oedipus complex, bought about by dominant mother and hostile father.

But whatever the cause, the homosexual male is deflected from his "true" heterosexual nature through fear. And unlike Freud, the phobic theorists think that cure (that is, change to heterosexuality) is theoretically and in many cases practically possible. Through analysis, one must remove the fear and curb the false adaptation. (Significantly, both Bieber and Socarides, quoted at the beginning, subscribe to versions of this theory.)

Clearly, if one adopts this position, then some revisions in our conclusions based on the Bell-Weinberg report are called for. There is no change in the belief that homosexuals have lower biological fitness, so the naturalists' claim that homosexuality is a disease is unaltered. But serious doubt is thrown on the claim that one can really be homosexual and happy. All homosexuals are walking on something of an emotional tightrope—one is thinking and acting to cover up dreadful, threatening, irrational fears of castration and death. The happiness one can achieve is at best phony, at worst fictitious. Hence, the phobic theorist will be inclined to disregard the claims of homosexuals that they get any measure of real and lasting happiness—his theory tells him otherwise. Hence, as a naturalist he will judge all homosexuals ill (as well as diseased), and as a normativist he will judge homosexuals both diseased and ill. (Again, significantly, it is the phobic theorists who are loudest about the claim that homosexuals are sick, deluded people.)

We see therefore that we get different answers to our main questions according to which psychoanalytic theories we support. In concluding this section, let me make brief reference to one interesting side claim of the phobic theory. Human beings are essentially heterosexual. This gives the phobic theorists something which needs explaining, namely the fact that sometimes heterosexuals (men especially) have fleeting homosexual dreams, fantasies, or even when they are under stress, encounters. The phobic theorists argue that these are not genuine homosexual phenomena—they are "pseudo." In fact, in an important sense they are not really sexual phenomena at all. Rather, they are defense, adaptive reactions to personal problems, like losing out on a professorship to a younger rival. (Ovesey, 1955a, 1955b, 1965)

The reaction can go one of two ways. Either one fantasizes about getting on top of things. In a case like that of the rival, one might dream about buggering him, thus acting out one's need to dominate, perhaps even kill, him. Or one retreats to safe ground. A typical pattern would be to identify the penis with that organ which is the symbol of security, the maternal breast. In this case, one wants to suck on the penis as on the breast, and subconsciously one draws up the simple equations: "penis = breast," and "semen = milk."

I take it that by definition a key aspect of this "pseudo-homosexuality" is that it is a fleeting aspect of a heterosexual's life, although one may need therapy to get over it entirely. I take it also that it is a rather unpleasant frightening phenomenon. Life is tense enough as it is, without losing grip on one's sense of sexual identity. I rather suspect however that at this point (if we accept the theorizing) we get an interesting reversal in our analyses. To now, it has been the naturalist who has been more ready than the normativist with his ascription of a disease. Clearly here the normativist could and would talk of disease and illness—certainly there is the drop in the quality of life that the normativist would seek in applying such labels. But could the naturalist even talk of disease here? I doubt it, because by definition we are dealing with people fundamentally and continuously heterosexual. I see no real loss of biological fitness. Hence, unless one commits suicide there is no loss of life or survival prospects: there is no disease. And hence there can be no illness either. At most, the naturalist seems locked in to regarding pseudo-homosexuality as one of those unpleasant things which happens to us in the course of life, like grief or fear. One is not sick when one grieves a loss or fears a bull, even though one is not happy. Perhaps this is how the naturalist must categorize pseudo-homosexuality.

IV. ENDOCRINOLOGICAL CAUSAL EXPLANATIONS OF HOMOSEXUALITY

There have been two main sets of attempts at pinning the causes of homosexual orientation on hormonal levels (specifically sex hormonal levels). One set argues that the crucial causal period is during development; the other that it is during adulthood. Initial work centered on the second set of hypotheses, suggesting that sexual orientation is primarily a function of male/female sex hormone ratios (androgen/estrogen ratios) in the adult. However, empirical studies have not really borne much fruit in this direction, and so although such hypotheses are certainly not discredited entirely, more and more attention is being directed towards the effects of hormones on development. (See Meyer-Bahlburg, 1977; Dörner, 1976) For brevity in this section I shall concentrate exclusively on these developmental hypotheses, although I suspect that much (if not all) of what I have to say would apply to all endocrinological explanations.

Fundamentally, what is argued is about as simple as the psychoanalytic theories are complex. According to the chief spokesman of this position, Gunther Dörner in East Germany, the key organ in sexual orientation is the hypothalamus, and the key time is during its formation which is (approximately) from the third to sixth months of fetal development. Dörner argues straightforwardly that, for males, if at this time the androgen/estrogen level ratio surrounding (or in) the fetus is lower than normal, the adult will grow up sexually directed towards other males. Conversely, for females, if the androgen/estrogen level ratio is higher than normal, the adult will grow up sexually directed towards other females. And that is that. No change or cure is possible after the hypothalamus is fixed, beyond a vague as-yet-unrealized hope of psycho-surgery to alter sexual orientation.

As we have seen, Dörner himself has no doubts that homosexuality is a dreadful disease and that homosexuals are ill. He has all sorts of plans for testing amniotic fluid and checking sex hormone ratios, tampering with them if need be in order to prevent future adults with homosexual orientations. But these are Dörner's views. The question we want answered is to what extent (if at all), in the light of Dörner's scientific hypotheses, we must modify conclusions about homosexuality qua disease/illness drawn just on the empirical evidence.

First, there is the question of biological functioning. It will be remembered that Boorse explicated this both in terms of reproduction and of survival. In fact, biologists are concerned only with reproduction, but really Boorse cannot avoid mention of survival, because otherwise he would have to say that cancer in an old person is no disease. Now as far as reproduction is concerned, Dörner has nothing new to say. However, most interestingly, he does think his theory has implications about survival. In particular, Dörner suggests that life-expectancy is a direct function of sex-hormone levels as they have affected the developing hypothalamus. The owners of "male type" hypothalami live shorter lives than the owners of "female type" hypothalami. This is why, on average, females live ten years longer than males. The implication is therefore that male homosexuals will (on average) live longer lives than male heterosexuals, and female homosexuals will live shorter lives than female heterosexuals.

If this claim is true, what happens to an analysis of disease, considered from a Boorsian viewpoint? As far as lesbians are concerned, both reproduction and survival prospects are lowered, and so we have a disease either way. But as far as males are concerned, the model comes apart somewhat. From a reproductive viewpoint male homosexuals are diseased, but from a survival viewpoint male homosexuals are anything but! They are perfectly healthy.

Going on to illness, I think a major reason why Dörner thinks homosexuality must be an illness (and a disease too for that matter) is that he believes anything that comes about by accident, for instance atypical sex hormonal level ratios, must be bad for the organism. However, irrespective of whether homosexuality is really a disease, this argument seems not to hold. In the first place, if there is any truth in some of the sociobiological speculations (to be discussed shortly), it is a moot point whether the ratios are all that accidental. But this apart, even though accidents normally cause trouble, judgments of illness must be made solely on the effects. If by accident a child got more growth hormone, taking him from the expected 5′ 6″ to 6′, we would certainly not speak of illness. So similarly we must judge homosexuality.

Staying with Boorse's model, with illness as in the case of disease we get a certain amount of confusion. Döner's ideas do not really seem to have any direct implications about how people feel about their homosexuality. Hence, if (concentrating on reproduction) one thinks of it as a disease, probably some will have it as an illness also. But not all. However, if by concentrating on survival, one thinks there is no disease, then there can be no illness (although no doubt some homosexuals are unhappy with their condition). Lesbians are easier to handle. By either criterion they have a disease. Some will be ill also (although this latter is not a judgment based directly on Dörner's work).

I suppose one might speculate about how homosexuals would feel about finding out about life expectancies! Presumably if anything this would tend to make lesbians more miserable (and hence more would be ill), whereas male homosexuals would be cheered (and hence fewer would be ill). But I wonder if at this point we are not entering the world of fantasy. My experience is that males (including myself) do not go around in a state of permanent gloom because our life expectancy is less than that of women. So I am not sure how relevant all of this is to the emotional states of homosexuals.

The normativist model does not run into the problems that plague Boorse's model when it faces Dörner's hypotheses. For the normativist, reproductive and survival expectancies are secondary to how one feels about oneself and life in general. Discounting the rather tenuous speculations in the last paragraph, it really does not seem that, were one to endorse Dörner's putative causes for homosexual orientation, as a normativist one would much alter conclusions about disease/illness drawn on the empirical evidence of the Bell-Weinberg study. Those homosexuals who are unhappy with their homosexuality we might be prepared to speak of as diseased and ill, but there is no reason to alter the conclusion that for most homosexuals their orientation is not a disease, and consequently such homosexuals are no more ill than comparable heterosexuals. That Dörner himself draws other conclusions stems not from his causal theorizing, but from his different perception of the mental state of the average homosexual: a perception which the Bell-Weinberg study suggests is distorted. (One suspects that another major reason Dörner draws such a gloomy picture of the mental state of homosexuals, is that like many psychiatrists he is working from a biased sample. He draws his conclusions from homosexuals who are sufficiently troubled to seek help. Happy homosexuals, like successful murderers, tend not to get into the statistics.)

V. SOCIOBIOLOGICAL CAUSAL EXPLANATIONS

We come now to the most recent set of explanations of human homosexual orientation. These are the explanations proposed primarily by biologists who want to explain human social behavior as a function of the genes, which have in turn been molded by the forces of evolution, primarily natural selection. (See Wilson, 1978; Caplan, 1978; Ruse, 1979) Since selection puts a premium on reproductive efficiency, indeed success in evolution is seen as a success in reproduction, and since prima facie homosexual orientation leads to a drop in reproductive efficiency, human homosexuality has attracted much attention from these thinkers, the "sociobiologists." At least four putative causal explanations have been proposed from this quarter, and I shall run quickly through them, as before asking whether their truth would require modification of conclusions based on empirical data. (I discuss in detail the sociobiology of homosexuality in Ruse, 1981.)

The first explanation invokes the so-called phenomenon of "balanced heterozygote fitness." The genes, the units of heredity and also the units causally responsible for the developed organism (the units of "function"), come in pairs in an organism, one of each pair contributed by each parent. If paired genes (genes at the same "locus") are identical then the organism is "homozygous"; otherwise "heterozygous." Now, if in a population of organisms there are only two kinds of a gene ("alleles") which can occupy corresponding loci in population members, then one has two homozygotes and one heterozygote (if A_1 and A_2 are the alleles, one can represent these as A_1A_1, A_1A_2, A_2A_2). Suppose now that the heterozygote A_1A_2 is "fitter" than either homozygote, that is, on average it reproduces more than either A_1A_1, or A_2A_2. What this means is that in each generation the A_1A_2's will be pouring their genes into the next generation, which in turn will then contain members with A_1 genes and members with A_2 genes—and this is whether or not either homozygote reproduces at all!

In fact, one can show quite simply that with the heterozygote fitter than either homozygote, one can get a "balanced" situation. (Ruse, 1973) This means that in each generation one will get a certain proportion of all three types (A_1A_1, A_1A_2, A_2A_2). And this situation can continue indefinitely, by virtue of the superior reproductive power of the heterozygote, even though one or other homozygote (say A_2A_2) does not reproduce at all. (One will continue to get A_2A_2's regardless, because if an A_1A_2 breeds with an A_1A_2, by Mendel's first law ¼ of their offspring will be A_2A_2.)

The applicability of this model to the homosexuality situation is obvious. (Hutchinson, 1959; Wilson, 1975) One simply assumes that there is a gene with two forms, say *h* and *H*. If one is an *hh* homozygote, one is just a normal heterosexual. If one is an *HH* homozygote, one is a low-reproducing homosexual. And if one is a *hH* heterozygote, one is not just heterosexual but a superreproducer. Indefinitely, one can expect to get homosexuals in each generation of the human species.

Our concern here is not to check whether this model is true or adequate. For the purposes of this discussion we are assuming that it is. Our concern is whether the model's truth leads to qualifications of our empirically based decisions about the disease/illness status of homosexuality. It seems clear that the model does cause a change of mind for the naturalist, although whether this is a change someone like Boorse would welcome is perhaps another matter. The naturalist sees disease as a failure in proper or adequate functioning. But what is proper or adequate functioning? Not the absolute best in a species; but that which fits into the "species design." In other words, that which has been brought about and maintained by natural selection. (Hence, it is no disease that we cannot synthesize our own vitamin C, because that ability is not something selection has left us with.) But the whole point of the balanced heterozygote fitness explanation, is that the homosexual homozygote is just as much a product of and just as much maintained by selection as its heterosexual siblings! In other words, the homosexual is part of the species design, and homosexuality cannot therefore be considered a disease. By definition consequently no homosexual can be made ill by his or her homosexuality, however unhappy it may make him or her feel.[14]

The normativist seems unaffected by this line of reasoning. That the homosexuality might have been caused by homozygous possession of two alleles seems to make no difference at all to how one feels (except in the indirect and somewhat unpredictable way that knowledge that one's homosexuality is genetic may have on one). Hence, in this case there seems no reason to modify conclusions based on the empirical data.

The second sociobiological model takes us right to the heart of the new biological work on social behavior, for it rests on the most exciting mechanism yet proposed by the sociobiologists: kin selection. When one reproduces, one passes on one's genes—only not really, because what one is doing is passing on *copies* of one's genes. However, one shares genes with close relatives, and so there is really no reason why one should not reproduce by proxy, as it were. Inasmuch as relatives reproduce, one reproduces oneself (or rather, one reproduces a portion of oneself—relatives are not genetically identical, just genetically overlapping). Hence, a viable biological strategy (kin selection) is to aid relatives to reproduce, even though it may mean reduction of one's own direct reproductive effort. Normally one will not adopt this strategy—the optimum course is to maximize one's genes transmitted, and since one is more closely related to oneself than one is to relatives (identical twins excepted), direct reproduction is usually the preferable course. However, if for some reason one's own reproduction is liable to be low, or one's skill at aiding relatives high, then kin selection and vicarious reproduction can come into play.

Some sociobiologists have seen in kin selection a mechanism for the production of homosexuals. (Weinrich, 1976; Wilson, 1978) If, for some reason people would be likely themselves to be low reproducers, or good at aiding relatives (or both), then there might be good biological sense in a condition which would turn one entirely or primarily from attempts at direct personal reproduction: such a condition being a homosexual orientation.

This kin selection explanation has rather interesting implications for the naturalist model of disease/illness. If nothing else, one suspects that Boorse had not thought too hard about kin selection when he set up his criteria. On the surface, the explanation seems to imply that homosexuals will themselves be rather poor reproducers. Furthermore, it rather seems to imply that homosexuals would be the kind of people who (homosexuality apart) would not be very good at reproducing anyway! One proponent of this model has suggested that the reasons for this might be a childhood illness (with possible long-term effects) like tuberculosis, or just general physical slightness or weakness. (Weinrich, 1976) Hence, even though one might not know much about the survival and reproductive chances of homosexuals, in Boorse's sense they seem diseased, and many if not all seem either to be or have been quite ill.[15]

But there are two major points of qualification. First, the proponents suggest that kin selection might have been at work at fullest force amongst our ancestors, when we were all primitive people living close to nature. In such a state, it might have paid to switch sexual orientation, given a childhood disease. But in our modern society, biology might not have caught up to today's medicine. A childhood illness may still trigger homosexuality, even though today the child might recover completely (or alternatively, in today's society the fragility which would count against one in a hunter-gatherer society may be no handicap). Hence, we cannot immediately presume that all homosexuals today are either ill or show the effects of such illness.

Second, the explanation does not make homosexuality an illness, or even a disease for that matter. First there is the fact that the sexual orientation of the homosexual is supposed to have come about in part through selection and this in itself means that the naturalist has trouble talking in terms of "disease" at this point. But secondly, and more importantly, the whole point of the kin selection explanation is that one has reduced reproductive potential and one is perhaps also ill, in the first place. Homosexuality is a biologically adaptive move to *increase* one's reproduction in the face of this. In other words, from Boorse's viewpoint, homosexuality is no disease—it is a cure! What one is doing is exchanging the reasonably certain prospects of vicarious reproduction for the uncertain prospects of direct reproduction. On this model therefore, we may be facing people with diseases and illnesses in Boorse's sense (although this is questionable)—but homosexuality itself seems no disease in Boorse's sense.

Turning to the normativists' analysis of disease and illness, little more needs to be added to what has just been said in the context of our discussion about Boorse's analysis. There is certainly no especial implication that homosexuality itself is a (normativist) disease or illness, although this is not to deny that it might be an adaptive move in the face of other disease and illness. The one thing about the normativist position different from the naturalist position that we can say is that, even supposing homosexuality is increasing someone's biological fitness, if the homosexuality makes the bearer unhappy, then we can start to think in terms of disease and illness. I rather think that Boorse has cut off this option. However unhappy homosexuality makes someone, if it does not reduce reproductive (or survival) potential, then it is neither disease nor illness.

The third sociobiological model is parental manipulation. Normally, it is in an organism's biological interests to raise as many fully fertile, reproductive-eager offspring as possible. But suppose that if one of one's offspring were a nonreproductive, "altruistically" aiding its siblings, one would then have more grandchildren than one would otherwise (i.e., if all of one's offspring were attempting direct reproduction). From a biological viewpoint it would pay one to "manipulate" one offspring into a non-reproductive altruist. (Weinrich, 1976; Trivers, 1974) and obviously, one good way of making such a non-reproducer is by making him/her a homosexual. (Precisely how this "manipulation" would take place is left unspecified by the model. It is certainly not necessarily done consciously. I have suggested elsewhere that it could take a Freudian path, showing incidentally that these different sets of explanatory models are not necessarily incompatible rivals—they could be complementary parts of the whole picture. Ruse, 1979)

It is clear that this model causes trouble for Boorse's analysis similar to problems encountered before. On the one hand the manipulated child's personal reproduction is depressed and this is not compensated for by kin selection. For this reason, according to Boorse, one ought to be thinking in terms of disease. On the other hand, the mechanism of parental manipulation is preserved in the species by natural selection. So for this reason the homosexuality of the manipulated child is no disease. Who is to say what is "statistically typical" in a species where parental manipulation is operating? The manipulated child is just as typical as anyone else.

If we assume for Boorse that (viewed in the light of this model) homosexuality is a disease, is it then also an illness? Obviously there is no direct implication that the parentally manipulated homosexual will be unhappy or dissatisfied with his/her lot. I am not sure either that there is any implication that being manipulated would be all that unpleasant. It might perhaps involve a hostile unloving father, but then again relations with parents might be very close as one is directed away from a heterosexual role. However, one point should be noted. In the parental manipulation case, it is not in the child's reproductive interests to be a homosexual. One has parental and child reproductive strategies in conflict. (This of course excludes cases where the child's interests also dictate homosexuality, because of kin selection.) This could mean that at the behavioural level there is conflict between parent(s) and child, and possibly the child's sexual orientation ends up somewhere between the extremes of heterosexuality and homosexuality. Perhaps some of these middle people belong to that subclass of people who are torn by their homosexuality, even to the extent that we would classify them as ill. Clearly this is but a speculation—there is an awfully big gap between premises and conclusion—however, one feels that there must be some reason why, whereas most homosexuals are happy with their lot, a minority are bitterly unhappy. Once again, the normativist position does not have the same conceptual confusion as the naturalist position over whether or not we are faced with a disease. What counts as a "normal" amount of reproduction for a member of the human species is not relevant. However, inasmuch as parental manipulation might be expected to lead to conflict in the child, so presumably the normativist would be prepared to agree that there was something wrong, even to the extent of disease and illness. The man or woman torn and tormented by conflicting sexual emotions, because of the conflict between his/her reproductive strategy and that of his/her parent(s), would undoubtedly be judged sick by the normativist, as much as by Boorse.

The final sociobiological speculation is one applicable only to males.[16] It has been hypothesized that masturbation has a biological value, particularly in young adolescent males. If nothing else, they thereby learn a little about the mechanics of sex—erection, stimulation, ejaculation, and so forth. But if for some reason males cannot switch to heterosexual conduct at a sufficiently early age, it has been speculated that then perhaps this autosexuality could lead to a life-long preference for the kind of organ involved in (male) masturbation, namely the penis. In other words, one would get a sort of transference from one's own body to other bodies of the same sex.

A number of reasons have been suggested why this transference might happen. Perhaps social factors (e.g., English private schools) could prevent boys getting to know girls before they get imprinted with penis-obsession. Perhaps future homosexuals start masturbating before other boys (so that they are already imprinted by the time heterosexual contact becomes possible). Perhaps it is simply that homosexuals are physiologically different from heterosexuals—there is some evidence that homosexuals have bigger penises than heterosexuals, which could have an imprinting effect, given that one's first sexual experience involves looking at and fondling one's own sex organ.

But, however the fixation on penises comes about, one point is clear. Biologically speaking, (male) homosexuality caused in this way is seen as a straight loss of fitness: it is maladaptive, without any compensations. To be a good heterosexual requires adolescent masturbation. Homosexuality is a function of this requirement backfiring in some sort of way. One has gambled and lost. (This mechanism is not proposed for females, first because they neither do nor need to masturbate so early and frequently as males—their sexual role is more passive—and second because a masturbating female is hardly as visually conscious of her clitoris, as is a masturbating male of his penis.)

Obviously for Boorse, the homosexual viewed in the light of this explanation suffers from a disease. The homosexual is indeed below species par when it comes to reproduction. On the other hand, there seems no immediate implication of illness. Having an overly large penis would not normally be considered a matter of regret. I suppose in some circles masturbation still sets up feelings of guilt, and that consequently the early and persistent masturbator might be expected to suffer from feelings of remorse and inadequacy. But whether this would lead to a lack of self-esteem so severe that one would want to label it "illness" is surely open to debate.

The normativists would of course disagree flatly with Boorse over the question of whether a disease is involved here. The fact that homosexuality is maladaptive is neither necessary nor sufficient to label something a disease. Furthermore, since for them disease and illness go together, they would see no more reason than would a Boorsian to conclude that the model under discussion implies always that male homosexuals are ill. Even if this putative explanation has any validity, they would surely argue that judgments of disease and illness must be made on other grounds. In particular, there seems no call to modify conclusions reached on empirical grounds.

VI. CONCLUSION

With this brief survey of the sociobiological explanations of homosexual orientation, we reach the end of our attempt to compare the two major models of disease and illness against the known and speculated facts about homosexuality, empirical and causal. Have we answered our initial question: "Are homosexuals sick?" In fact, we have done so rather too well, because we have come up with a whole set of answers—answers which are far from uniform. However, while in a sense having too many answers is almost as bad as having too few answers, all is far from lost. We now know at least three things we did not know when we set out. First, one of our models of illness and disease, the naturalist model, needs a certain amount of revision if it is to remain a plausible approach to analyzing ill-health. The model has led to counterintuitive results and shown internal strains. If one likes the general approach, it can probably be revised—but revision is necessary.[17] Second, the reason why people differ on the homosexuality and health question is most probably because they bring different assumptions about disease, illness, and homosexuality to their arguments. Now, at least we are in a much better position than previously to sort out what information (or misinformation) is leading to what result. We are closer to finding out why particular people differ. And third, towards an adequate ultimate answer of our own, we do now know what the options are—philosophical and scientific. We have discovered what assumptions to check and evaluate. But this checking and evaluation is, I am afraid, going to need another paper.

NOTES

1. This paper is based on a chapter in my forthcoming book, *Homosexuality: A Philosophical Perspective.*
2. I distinguish between homosexual orientation and homosexual behaviour, taking the former as the primary concept. Weinrich (1976).
3. See also Stoller (1973), Green (1973), Spitzer (1973).
4. I use the terms "sick" and "sickness" loosely to cover disease, diseased state, ill-health, illness, and so forth. I shall be separating out some of these latter terms.
5. There was also a pilot study run in Chicago.
6. The implication is *not* that there is anything wrong with the sperm or ova of homosexuals: rather, that having a homosexual orientation tends to lead to homosexual behaviour, and that homosexual behaviour does not lead to conception.
7. I realize that the figures show that some homosexuals apparently reproduce very efficiently. My point is that, *on average*, it seems that homosexuality reduces reproductive efficiency. In this sense I claim (in the present context) that it is a disease for all, just as lung cancer is a disease for all, even though some with lung cancer live as long as some without. But this is mainly a semantic quibble. If you do not like the universal quantification, substitute "most" for "all" here and, wherever appropriate, later.
8. In Appendix 1, I have drawn up a matrix trying to incorporate all the results I get in this paper. It should help the reader to keep things reasonably clear!
9. I use the term "psychoanalytic" to refer, not simply to strict Freudianism, but also to all hypotheses which see attitudes and behaviour primarily or exclusively a function of mental causes, molded strongly in childhood.
10. I am afraid nevertheless that in this section, in particular, my emphasis will be on males rather than females. This sexist bias, if such it be, is a function of the materials with which I am working. See also, for example, Fisher and Greenberg (1977) for more details of Freud's position.
11. As will become clear however, I am not sure that Freud would want to argue—as he seems to do in the letter—that homosexuality is *never* an illness.
12. I must emphasize again that mine is somewhat of a preliminary inquiry. I am checking models of disease against claims about homosexuality. The claims here are going unquestioned. In my forthcoming book I raise all the questions about truth.
13. Note that in dealing with causal speculations my prime question is not whether they *alone* tell us if homosexuality is disease or illness, although if they do I shall certainly note this fact. My question is whether we must modify conclusions arrived at on the empirical evidence about the status of homosexuality. This leaves open the possibility that the causal speculations tell us nothing new about disease and illness.

14. Engelhardt (1976) similarly points out how balanced heterozygote fitness causes problems for Boorse.
15. Remember however that as far as kin selection is concerned, it could come into play causing homosexuality despite the people involved being superhealthy, if they had qualities that made them particularly fitted to aid relatives (like high intelligence?) But although this would rule out Boorsian disease/illness, such people would not necessarily be happy. Evolution does not maximize happiness, but reproductive ability.
16. This idea comes in a letter written by Richard Alexander (University of Michigan) to Fred Suppe (University of Maryland), February 13, 1978. In a letter to me, Suppe tells me that he thinks the idea has considerable merit.
17. I do emphasize that I cannot claim to have shown the failure of any value-free approach to the concept of disease.

REFERENCES

Alexander, R. D. 1974. The evolution of social behavior. *Ann. Rev. Ecology and Systematics* 5:325–84.

Bell, A. P., and Weinberg, M. S. 1978. *Homosexualities: A Study of Diversity Among Men and Women.* New York: Simon and Schuster.

Bieber, I. et al. 1962. *Homosexuality.* New York: Basic Books.

Bieber, I. 1965. Clinical aspects of male homosexuality. In *Sexual Inversion: The Multiple Roots of Homosexuality*, ed. J. Marmor, pp. 248–267. New York: Basic Books.

______. 1973. Homosexuality—An adaptive consequence of disorder in psychosexual development. A symposium: Should homosexuality be in the APA nomenclature? *Am. J. Psychiatry* 130:1209–11.

Boorse, C. 1975. On the distinction between disease and illness. *Philosophy and Public Affairs* 5:49–68.

______. 1976. What a theory of mental health should be. *Journal for the Theory of Social Behaviour* 6:61–84.

______. 1977. Health as a theoretical concept. *Phil. Sci.* 44:542–73.

Brown, R. 1977. Physical illness and mental health. *Philosophy and Public Affairs* 7:17–38.

Caplan, A., ed. 1978. *The Sociobiology Debate.* New York: Harper and Row.

Dörner, G. 1976. *Hormones and Brain Differentiation.* Amsterdam: Elsevier.

Engelhardt, H. T., Jr. 1975. The concepts of health and disease. In *Evaluation and Explanation in the Biomedical Sciences*, ed. H. T. Engelhardt, Jr., and S. Spicker Dordrecht: Reidel.

Engelhardt, H. T. 1976. Ideology and etiology. *J. Med. and Phil.* 1:256–68.

Fisher, S. and Greenberg, R. P. 1977. *The Scientific Credibility of Freud's Theories and Therapy.* New York: Basic Books.

Flew, A. 1973. *Crime or Disease?* London: Macmillan and Co.

Freud, S. 1905. *Three Essays on The Theory of Sexuality.* In *Collected Works of Freud.* vol. 7 ed. J. Strachey, London: Hogarth, 1953.

______. 1913. *Totem and Taboo.* In *Collected Works of Freud.* vol. 13 ed. J. Strachey, London: Hogarth, 1953.

Gold, R. 1973. Stop it, you're making me sick! A symposium: Should homosexuality be in the APA nomenclature? *Am. J. Psychiatry* 130:1211–12.

Green, R. 1973. Should heterosexuality be in the APA nomenclature? A symposium: Should homosexuality be in the APA nomenclature. *Am. J. Psychiatry* 130:1213–14.

Hutchinson, G. E. 1959. A speculative consideration of certain possible forms of sexual selection in man. *Am. Nat.* 93:81–91.

Jones, E. 1958. *Sigmund Freud: Life and Work.* London: Hogarth Press.

Kardiner, A., Karush, A., and Ovesey, L. 1959*a*. A methodological study of Freudian theory: I. Basic Concepts. *Journal of Nervous and Mental Disease* 129:11–19.

———. 1959*b*. A methodological study of Freudian Theory: II. The Libido Theory. *Journal of Nervous and Mental Disease* 129:133–143.

———. 1959*c*. A methodological study of Freudian theory: III. Narcissism, bisexuality and the dual instinct theory. *Journal of Nervous and Mental Disease* 129:207–221.

———. 1959*d*. A methodological study of Freudian theory: IV. The structural hypothesis, the problem of anxiety, and post-Freudian ego psychology. *J. Nerv. Ment. Dis.* 129:341–56.

Klerman, G. L. 1977. Mental illness, the medical model, and psychiatry. *J. Med. and Phil.* 2:220–43.

Levitan, M. and Montagu, A. 1977. *Textbook of Human Genetics*, 2d ed. New York: Oxford University Press.

Macklin, R. 1972. Mental health and mental illness: Some problems of definition and concept formation. *Phil. Sci.* 39 (1972): 341–65.

———. 1973. The medical model in psychotherapy and psychoanalysis. *Comprehensive Psychiatry* 14 (1973): 49–69.

Margolis, J. 1966. *Psychotherapy and Morality: A Study of Two Concepts.* New York: Random House.

———. 1976. The concept of disease. *J. Med. and Phil.* 1:238–55.

Marmor, J. 1973. Homosexuality and cultural value systems. A Symposium: Should homosexuality be in the APA nomenclature? *Am. J. Psychiatry* 130 (1973): 1208–9.

Marston, King, and Marston 1931. *Integrative Psychology.* New York: Harcourt, Brace, and World.

Meyer-Bahlburg, H. F. L. 1977. Sex hormones and male homosexuality in comparative perspective. *Arch. Sex. Beh.* 6:297–325.

Moore, M. 1975*a*. Some myths about mental illness. *Archives of General Psychiatry* 23:1483–97.

———. 1975*b*. Mental illness and responsibility. *Bulletin of the Menninger Clinic* 39: 308–28.

Ovesey, L. 1954. The homosexual conflict: an adaptational analysis. *Psychiat.*, pp. 243–50.

———. 1955*a*. The pseudohomosexual anxiety. *Psychiat.* 18:17–25.

———. 1955*b*. Pseudohomosexuality, the paranoid mechanism, and paranoia: an adaptational revision of a classical Freudian theory. *Psychiat.* 18:163–73.

Ovesey, L. 1956. Masculine aspirations in women: an adaptational analysis. *Psychiat.* 19:341–51.

———. 1965. Pseudohomosexuality and homosexuality in men: Psychodynamics as a guide to treatment. In *Sexual Inversion: The Multiple Roots of Homosexuality*, ed. J. Marmor New York: Basic Books, pp. 211–33.

Rado, S. 1940. A critical examination of the concept of bisexuality. *Psychosomatic Medicine* 2:459–67. Reprinted in *Sexual Inversion: The Multiple Roots of Homosexuality*, ed. J. Marmor New York: Basic Books.

———. 1949. An adaptational view of sexual behaviour. In *Psychosexual development in Health and Disease*, ed. P. Hock and J. Zubin New York: Grune and Stratton, pp. 186–213.

Ruse, M. 1973. *The Philosophy of Biology*. London: Hutchinson.

———. 1979. *Sociobiology: Sense or Nonsense.* Dordrecht: Reidel.

———. 1981. Are there gay genes? The sociobiology of homosexuality. *J. Homosexuality.*

———. (forthcoming). *Homosexuality: A Philosophical Perspective.* Calif.: University of California Press.

Salzman, L. 1965. "Latent" homosexuality. In *Sexual Inversion: The Multiple Roots of Homosexuality*, ed. J. Marmor New York: Basic Books, pp. 234–47.

Socarides, C. W. 1973. Homosexuality: Findings derived from 15 years of clinical research. A Symposium: Should homosexuality be in the APA nomenclature? *Am. J. Psychiatry* 130 (1973): 1212–13.

Spitzer, R. L. 1973. A proposal about homosexuality and the APA nomenclature. A symposium: Should homosexuality be in the APA nomenclature. *Am. J. Psychiatry* 130:1214–16.

Stoller, R. J. 1973. Criteria for psychiatric diagnosis. A symposium: Should homosexuality be in the APA nomenclature? *Am. J. Psychiatry* 130:1207–8.

Szasz, T. S. 1961. *The Myth of Mental Illness.* New York: Delta.

Trivers, R. L. 1974. Parent-offspring conflict. *Am. Zoo.* 14:249–64.

Wilson, E. O. 1975. *Sociobiology: The New Synthesis.* Cambridge, Mass.: Harvard University Press.

———. 1978. *On Human Nature.* Cambridge, Mass.: Harvard University Press.

Weinrich, J. D. 1976. *Human Reproductive Strategy.* Harvard Ph.D. thesis.

APPENDIX 1

Matrix comparing models of disease/illness against putative facts about homosexuality, empirical and causal.

	Naturalism		Normativism	
	Disease	*Illness*	*Disease*	*Illness*
Kinsey Study	All (homosexuals are diseased)	Few	Few	Few
Psychoanalytic				
Classical Freudian	All	Few	Few	Few
Phobic: Homosexuality	All	All	All	All
Pseudo-homosexuality	None	None	All	All
Endocrinal				
Hormonal Imbalance				
Male				
Survival	None	None	Few	Few
Reproduction	All	Few		
Female				
Survival	All	Few	Few	Few
Reproduction	All			
Sociobiological				
Balanced Heterozygote Fitness	None (All)*	None	Few	Few
Kin Selection	Some → All**	Few → Many	Few → Many	Few → Many
Parental Manipulation	None (All)	Some (Many?)	Some	some
Masturbation	All	Few	Few	Few

*I suspect that this is the result that the normativist really wants.

**But disease/illness is not the result of homosexuality, which is in fact a "cure"!

6.7

The "Unnaturalness" of Aging—A Sickness Unto Death?

Arthur L. Caplan

I. NORMALITY, NATURALNESS, AND DISEASE

It may seem somewhat odd to question the "naturalness" of a process as familiar and as universal as aging. After all, if aging is not a natural process, what is? While the prospect of aging may be greeted with mixed feelings, there would seem to be little reason to doubt the fact that aging is understood to be a normal and inevitable feature of human existence.

The belief that aging is a normal and natural part of human existence is reflected in the practice of medicine. For example, no mention is made in most textbooks in the areas of medicine and pathology of aging as abnormal, unnatural, or indicative of disease. It is true that such texts often contain a chapter or two on the related subject of diseases commonly associated with aging or found in the elderly. But it is the diseases of the elderly, such as pneumonia, cancer, or atherosclerosis, rather than the aging process itself, that serve as the focus of description and analysis.

Why should this situation exist? What is so different about the physiological changes and deteriorations concurrent with the aging process that these events are considered to be unremarkable natural processes, while other debilitative changes are deemed to be diseases constituting health crises of the first order? Surely it cannot simply be the life-threatening aspects of diseases, such as cancer or atherosclerosis, that distinguish these processes from aging. For while it may be true that hardly anyone manages to avoid contracting a terminal disease at some point in life, aging itself produces the same ultimate consequence as these diseases. Nor can it be the familiarity and universality of aging that inure medical science to its unnatural aspects. Malignant neoplasms, viral infections, and hypertension are all ubiquitous phenomena. Yet medicine maintains a radically different stance toward these physical processes from that which it holds toward the so-called "natural" changes that occur during aging.

It might be argued that the processes denoted by the term "aging" do not fit the standard conception of disease operative in clinical medicine. However, in medical dictionaries disease is almost always defined as any pathological change in the body. Pathological change is inevitably defined as constituting any morbid process in the body. And morbid processes are usually defined in terms of disease states of the body.[1] Regardless of the circularity surrounding this explication of the concept of somatic disease, aging would seem to have a prima facie claim to being counted as a disease. Pathological or morbid changes are often the sole criteria by which age is assessed in organic tissues.

What seems to differentiate aging from other processes or states traditionally classified as diseases is the fact that aging is perceived as a natural or normal process. Medicine has traditionally viewed its role as that of ameliorating or combating the abnormal, either through therapeutic interventions or preventive, prophylactic regimens. The natural and the normal, while not outside the sphere of medicine, are concepts that play key roles in licensing the intervention of the medical practitioner. For it is in response to or in anticipation of abnormality that physicians' activities are legimated. And as E. A. Murphy, among others, has noted, "the clinician has tended to regard disease as that state in which the limits of the normal have been transgressed."[2] Naturalness and normality have, historically, been used as base lines to determine the presence of disease and the necessity of medical activity.

In light of the powerful belief that the abnormal and unnatural are indicative of medicine's range of interest, it is easy to see why many biological processes are not thought to be the proper subject of medical intervention of therapy. Puberty, growth, and maturation *as processes in themselves* all appear to stand outside the sphere of medical concern since they are normal and natural occurrences among human beings. Similarly, it seems odd to think of sexuality or fertilization as possible disease states precisely because these states are commonly thought to be natural and normal components of the human condition.

Nonetheless, it is true that certain biological processes, such as contraception, pregnancy, and fertility, have been the subject in recent years of heated debates as to their standing as possible disease states. The notions that it is natural and normal for only men and women to have sexual intercourse or for women to undergo menopause have been challenged to many quarters. The question arises as to whether the process of aging in and of itself can be classified as abnormal and unnatural in a way that will open the door for the reclassification of aging as a disease process and, thus, a proper subject of medical attention, concern, and control.

II. AGING AND MEDICAL INTERVENTION

The past few years have seen the rise of a powerful movement for the "right to die." Some have even gone so far as to claim that physicians and health professionals have a moral obligation to play an active role in allowing patients to die under certain circumstances. To a great extent, the status of aging and dying as natural processes looms large in discussions about the "right to die" and "death with dignity." Often those who debate the degree to which the medical profession should intervene in the process of dying disagree about the nauralness of the phenomena of aging and dying. If the alleged right to die is to be built on a conception of the naturalness of aging and dying, then the conceptual status of these terms vis-à-vis "naturalness" must be thoroughly examined. The question of the naturalness of aging, senescence, and death must not be permitted to become lost in complex debates concerning the rights and obligations of patients and health professionals.

The perception of biological events or processes as natural or unnatural is frequently decisive in determining whether physicians treat states or processes as diseases.[3] One need only think of the controversies that swirl around allegations concerning the biological naturalness of homosexuality or schizophrenia to see that this is so. This claim is further borne out by an argument that is frequently made by older physicians to new medical students. Medical students often find it difficult to interact with or examine elderly patients. They may feel powerless when confronted with the seemingly irreversible debilities of old age. To overcome this reluctance, older physicians are likely to point out that aging and senescence are processes that happen to everyone, even young medical students. Aging is simply part of the human condition; it should hold no terror for a young doctor. Students are told that aging is natural and that, while there may be nothing they can do to alter the inevitable course of this process, they must learn to help patients cope with their aging as best they can. It is as if teaching physicians feel obligated to label the obviously debilitative and disease-like states of old age as natural in order to discourage the students' inclination to treat the elderly as sick or diseased.

III. WHAT IS AGING?

What are the grounds on which this label is applied? Why do we think of aging as a natural process? The reason that comes immediately to mind is that aging is a common and normal process. It occurs with a statistical frequency of one hundred percent. Inevitably and uniformly bones become brittle, vision dims, joints stiffen, and muscles lose their tone. The obvious question that arises is whether commonality, familiarity, and inevitability are sufficient conditions for referring to certain biological states as natural. To answer this question, it is necessary to first draw a distinction between aging and chronological age.

In a trivial sense, given the existence of a chronological device, all bodies that exist can be said to age relative to the measurements provided by that device. But since physicians have little practical interest in making philosophical statements about the time-bound nature of existence, or empirical claims about the relativity of space and time, it is evident that they do not have this chronological sense in mind in speaking about the familiarity and inevitability of aging. In speaking of aging, physicians are interested in a particular set of biological changes that occur with respect to time. In the aged individual, cells manifest a high frequency of visible chromosomal aberrations. The nuclei of nerve cells become distorted by clumps of chromatin and the surrounding cytoplasm contains fewer organelles, such as mitochondria. Collagen fibers become increasingly rigid and inflexible, as manifest in the familiar phenomenon of skin wrinkling. The aorta becomes wider and more tortuous. The immunological system weakens and the elderly person becomes more susceptible to infections. Melanin pigment formation decreases and, consequently, hair begins to whiten.[4]

IV. NATURALNESS, DESIGN, AND FUNCTION

Changes of this kind, in association with aging, are universal and inevitable. Universality and inevitability do not, however, seem to be sufficient conditions for referring to a process as natural. Coronary atherosclerosis, neoplasms, high blood pressure, sore throats, colds, tooth decay, and depression are all nearly universal in their distribution and seemingly inevitable phenomena and yet we would hardly agree to calling any of these things natural processes or states. The inevitability of infection by microorganisms among all humans does not cause the physician to dismiss these infections as natural occurrences of no particular medical interest. The physician may not intervene, nor even attempt to prevent such diseases, but such behavior is a result of a decision concerning an unnatural disease, not a natural process.

So, if universality and inevitability are not adequate conditions for naturalness, are any other criteria available by which naturalness can be assessed and used to drive a wedge between aging and disease? There is a further sense of "natural"[5] that may prove helpful in trying to understand why physicians are reluctant to label aging a disease; preferring to think of it as a natural process.

This sense of naturalness is rooted in the notions of design, purpose, and function. Axes are designed to serve as tools for cutting trees. Scalpels are meant to be used in cutting human tissue. It would seem most unnatural to use axes for surgery and scalpels for lumberjacking. In some sense, although a skillful surgeon might in fact be able to perform surgery with an axe, it would be unnatural to do so. Similarly, many bodily organs—the liver, spleen, blood vessels, kidneys, and many glands—can perform compensatory functions when certain other organic tissues are damaged or removed. But these are not the purposes or functions they were "designed" to perform. While the arteries of many organisms are capable of constricting to maintain blood pressure and reduce the flow of blood during hemorrhage-induced shock, the function of arteries is not to constrict in response to such circumstances. The presence of vasoconstriction in arteries is in fact an unnatural state that signals the physician that something has gone seriously awry in the body. It would seem that much of our willingness to accept aging as a natural process is parasitic upon this sense of natural function.

Two answers are commonly given to the question: What is the function of aging? The first is a theological explanation. God, as a punishment for the sins of our ancestors in the (proverbial) garden of Eden, caused humans to age and die. On this view, people age because the Creator saw fit to design them that way for retribution or punishment. Aging serves as a reminder of our moral fallibility and weakness.

The second view, which is particularly widespread in scientific circles, is that the purpose or function of aging is to clear away the old to make way for the new for evolutionary reasons. This theory was first advanced by the German cytologist and evolutionary biologist August Weisman at the turn of the century.[6] Weisman argued that aging and debilitation must be viewed as adaptational responses on the part of organisms to allow for new mutational and adaptive responses to fluctuating environments. Aging benefits the population by removing the superannuated to make room for the young. The function of aging is to ensure the death of organisms to allow evolutionary change and new adaptation to occur.

On both of these views aging has an intended purpose or function. And it is from this quasi-Aristotelian attribution of a design that the "naturalness" of aging is often thought to arise.

V. THE CONCEPT OF BIOLOGICAL FUNCTION

The claim that the naturalness of aging can be established by analyzing what is meant by serving a role or function is likely to bring a gleam to the philosopher's eye since it may be possible for the philosopher to contribute to the medical profession's understanding of the meaning of aging. If the naturalness of aging resides in a functional interpretation, the philosopher can tap a rich and abundant literature on the subjects of function and purpose. However, rooting the source of the naturalness of biological processes in ideas of function or purpose also has its drawbacks, the primary problem being that philosophers have by no means reached anything even vaguely resembling a consensus about the meaning of such terms as function or purpose.

Fortunately, it is possible to avoid becoming bogged down in an analysis of functional or purposive statements in analyzing the function of aging. The only distinction required for understanding the function of aging is that between the aim of explaining the existence of a particular state, organ, or process, and that of explaining how a state, organ, or process works in a particular system or organism. Functional or purposive statements are sometimes used to explain the existence of a trait or process, historically. At other times such statements are used mechanistically to explain how something works or operates. If we ask what is the function, or role, or purpose of the spleen in the human body, the question can be interpreted in two ways: How does the spleen work—what does it do in the body? Or, why does the spleen exist in its present state in the human body—what is the historical story that explains why persons have spleens?[7]

It is this latter sense of function, the historical sense, that is relevant to the determination of the naturalness or unnaturalness of aging as a biological process. For while there is no shortage of theories purporting to explain how aging works or functions, these theories are not relevant to the historically motivated question about the function of aging. The determination of the naturalness of aging, if it is to be rooted in biology, will depend not on how the process of aging actually operates, but rather on the explanation one gives for the existence or presence of aging humans.[8]

VI. DOES AGING HAVE A FUNCTION?

Two purported explanations—one theological, one scientific—of the function or purpose of aging have been given. Both are flawed. While the theological explanation of aging may carry great weight for numerous individuals, it will simply not do as a scientific explanation of why aging occurs in humans. Medical professionals may have to cope with their patients' advocacy of this explanation and their own religious feelings on the subject. But, from a scientific perspective, it will hardly do to claim that aging, as a result of God's vindictiveness, is a natural biological process, and hence not a disease worthy of treatment.

More surprisingly, the scientific explanation of aging as serving an evolutionary role or purpose is also inadequate. It is simply not true that aging exists to serve any sort of evolutionary purpose or function. The claim that aging exists or occurs in individuals because it has a wider role or function in the evolutionary scheme of things rests on a faulty evolutionary analysis. The analysis incorrectly assumes that is possible for biological processes to exist that directly benefit or advance the evolutionary success of a species or population. In other words, it supposes that processes such as aging exist because they serve a function or purpose in the life history of a species—in this case, that of removing the old to make way for the new. However, evolutionary selection rarely acts to advance the prospects of an entire species or population. Selection acts on individual organisms and their phenotypic traits and properties. Some traits or properties confer advantages in certain environments on the organisms that possess them and this fact increases the likelihood that the genes responsible for producing these traits will be passed on to future organisms.

Given that selective forces act on individuals and their genotypes and not species, it makes no sense to speak of aging as serving an evolutionary function or purpose to benefit the species. How then do evolutionary biologists explain the existence of aging?[9] Briefly, the explanation is that features, traits, or properties in individual organisms will be selected for if they confer a relative reproductive advantage on the individual, or, his or her close kin. Any variation that increases inclusive reproductive fitness has a very high probability of being selected and maintained in the gene pool of a species. Selection, however, cannot look ahead to foresee the possible consequences of favoring certain traits at a given time; the environment selects for those traits and features that give an immediate return. An increased metabolic rate, for example, may prove advantageous early in life, in that it may provide more energy for seeking mates and avoiding predators; it may also result in early deterioration of the organism due to an increased accumulation of toxic wastes in the body of an individual thus endowed. Natural selection cannot foresee such delayed debilitating consequences.

Aging exists, then, as a consequence of lack of evolutionary foresight; it is simply a by-product of selective forces working to increase the chances of reproductive success in the life of an organism. Senescence has no function; it is simply the inadvertent subversion of organic function, later in life, in favor of maximizing reproductive advantage, early in life.

The common belief that aging serves a function or purpose, if this belief is based on a misapprehension of evolutionary theory, is mistaken. And, if this is so, it would seem that the common belief that aging is a natural process, as a consequence of the function or purpose it serves in the life of the species, is also mistaken. Consequently, unless it is possible to motivate the description on other grounds, it would seem that aging cannot be understood as a natural process. And if that is true, and if it is actually the case that what goes on during the aging process closely parallels the changes that occur during paradigmatic examples of disease,[10] then it would be unreasonable not to consider aging a disease.

VII. THEORIES OF AGING AND THE CONCEPT OF DISEASE

A consideration of the changes that constitute aging in human beings reinforces the similarities existing between aging and other clear-cut examples of somatic diseases. There is a set of external manifestations or symptoms: greying hair, increased susceptibility to infection, wrinkling skin, loss of muscular tone, and frequently, loss of mental ability. These manifestations seem to be causally linked to a series of internal cellular and subcellular changes. The presence of symptoms and an underlying etiology closely parallels the standard paradigmatic examples of disease. If the analogy is pushed a bit further, the cause for considering aging a disease appears to become even stronger.

There are many theories as to what causes changes at the cellular and subcellular level that produce the signs and symptoms associated with aging.[11] One view argues that aging is caused by an increase in the number of cross-linkages that exist in protein and nucleic acid molecules. Cross-linkages lower the biochemical efficiency and dependability of certain macromolecules involved in metabolism and other chemical reactions. Free radical by-products of metabolism are thought to accumulate in cells, thus allowing for an increase in available linkage sites for replicating nucleic acid strands and activating histone elements. This sort of cross-linkage is thought to be particularly important in the aging of collagen, the substance responsible for most of the overt symptoms we commonly associate with aging, such as wrinkled skin and loss of muscular flexibility.

Another view holds that aging results from an accumulation of genetic mutations in the chromosomes of cells in the body. The idea underlying this theory is that chromosomes are exposed over time to a steady stream of radiation and other mutagenic agents. The accumlation of mutational hits on the genes lying on the chromosomes results in the progressive inactivation of these genes. The evidence of a higher incidence of chromosomal breaks and aberrations in the aged is consistent with this mutational theory of aging.

Along with the cross-linkage and mutational theories, there is one other important hypothesis concerning the cause of aging. The autoimmune theory holds that, as time passes and the chromosomes of cells in the human body accumulate more mutations, certain key tissues begin to synthesize antibodies that can no longer distinguish between self and foreign material. Thus, a number of autoimmune reactions occur in the body as the immunological system begins to turn against the individual it was "designed" to protect. Arthritis and pernicious anemia are symptomatic of the sorts of debilities resulting from the malfunction of the immunological system. While this theory is closely allied to the mutation theory, the autoimmune view of aging holds that accumulated mutations do not simply result in deterioration of cellular activity, but, rather, produce lethal cellular end products that consume and destroy healthy tissue.

It would be rash to hold that any of the three hypotheses cited—the cross-linkage, mutational, or autoimmune hypotheses—will, in the end, turn out to be *the* correct explanation of aging. All three views are, in fact, closely related in that cross-linkages can result from periodic exposure to mutagenic agents and can, in turn, produce genetic aberrations that eventuate in cellular dysfunction or even autoimmunological reactions. What is important, however, is not whether *one* of these theories or *any* of them is in fact *the* correct theory of aging, but that all of them postulate mechanisms that are closely analogous to those mechanisms cited by clinicians in describing disease processes in the body.

The concept of disease is, without doubt, a slippery and evasive notion in medicine.[12] Once one moves away from what can be termed "paradigmatic" examples of disease, such as tuberculosis or diptheria, toward more nebulous examples, such as acne or jittery nerves, it becomes difficult to say exactly what are the criteria requisite for labeling a condition a somatic disease. However, even though it is notoriously difficult to concoct a set of necessary and sufficient conditions for employing the term "organic disease," it is possible to cite a list of general criteria that seem relevant in attempting to decide whether a bodily state or process is appropriately labeled a disease.

One criterion is that the state or process produces discomfort or suffering. A second is that the process or state can be traced back to a specific cause, event, or circumstance. A third is that there is a set of clear-cut structural changes, both macroscopic and microscopic, that follow in a uniform, sequential manner subsequent to the initial precipitating or causal event. A fourth is that there is a set of clinical symptoms or manifestations (headache, pain in the chest, rapid pulse, shortness of breath) commonly associated with the observed physiological alterations in structure. Finally,[13] there is usually some sort of functional impairment in the functions, behavior, or activity of a person thought to be diseased. Not all diseases will satisfy all or any of the criteria I have suggested. One need only consider the arguments surrounding the classification of astigmatism, alcoholism, drug-addiction, gambling, and hyperactivity to realize the inadequacy of these criteria as necessary and sufficient conditions for the determination of disease. But that the suggested criteria are relevant to such determination is shown by the fact that advocates of all persuasions regarding controversial states and processes commonly resort to considerations of causation, clinical manifestations, etiology, functional impairment, and suffering in arguing the merits of their various views concerning the status of controversial cases.

With respect to the conceptual ambiguity surrounding the notion of disease, it is important to remember that medicine is by no means unique in being saddled with what might be termed "fuzzy-edged" concepts. One need only consider the status of terms such as "species," "adaptation," and "mutation" in biology, or "stimulus," "behavior," and "instinct" in psychology, to realize that medicine is not alone in the ambiguity of its key terms. It is also true that, just as the biologist is able to use biological theory to aid in the determination of relevant criteria for a concept, the physician is able to use his or her knowledge of the structure and function of the body to decide on relevant criteria for the determination of disease.

If one accepts the relevance of the five suggested criteria, aging, as a biological process, is seen to possess all the key properties of a disease. Unlike astigmatism or nervousness, aging possesses a definitive group of clinical manifestations or symptoms; a clear-cut etiology of structural changes at both the macroscopic and microscopic levels; a significant measure of impairment, discomfort, and suffering; and, if we are willing to grant the same tolerance to current theories of aging as we grant to theories in other domains of medicine, an explicit set of precipitating factors. Aging has all the relevant markings of a disease process. And if my earlier argument is sound, even if an additional criterion of unnaturalness were appended, aging would still meet all the requirements thought relevant to the classfication of a process or state as indicative of disease.

VIII. SOME ETHICAL ARGUMENTS AGAINST TREATING AGING AS A DISEASE

What hinges on the decision to refer to a process or state such as aging by the word disease rather than by some other term? Obviously, a great deal. Medical attention, medical support, medical treatment, and medical research are devoted to the treatment, care, amelioration, and prevention of disease. While it is possible to view the activation of this vast professional machine either as a positive good or as a serious evil, an array of connotations and implications surrounds the medical profession's decision to consider a phenomenon worthy of its attention. Some groups have actively proselytized for the acceptance of certain conditions, such as alcoholism or gambling, as diseases. Other groups have worked to remove the label of disease from behavior such as homosexuality, masturbation, and schizophrenia. A number of motives and concerns underlie these arguments. The question is, what kinds of considerations should be considered relevant to the determination of whether a particular state, process, or condition is a disease?

I do not propose to try to answer the difficult question of what are the relevant nonorganic criteria affecting the choice of the disease label. Rather, I want to consider three specific arguments that might be raised against calling aging a disease—a classification that, of necessity, keeps the aged in touch with the medical profession.

The first counter-argument is that the decision to call aging a disease would be pointless, since doctors cannot at present intervene to treat or cure aging. This argument does not stand up to critical scrutiny. There are many diseases in existence today for which no cure is known, but no one proposes that these disorders are any less diseases as a consequence. Furthermore, the emphasis on treatment and cure implicit in this argument ignores the equally vital components of medical care involving understanding, education, and support. The profession's and the patient's interest in the healing function of medicine might make it difficult for physicians to accept aging as a disease, but the difficulty in achieving such acceptance does not provide a reason for rejecting the view.

The second argument is that to call aging a disease would involve the stigmatization of a large segment of the population; to view the aged as sick or diseased would only increase the burdens already borne by this much abused segment of society. The problem with this argument is that it tends to blend public perceptions of disease in general with the particular problem of whether seeing aging as a disease ought to carry negative and undesirable connotations. To deny that aging is a disease may be simply an easy way to avoid the more difficult problem of educating the medical profession and the lay public toward a better understanding of the threatening and nonthreatening aspects of disease. Contagiousness, death, disability, and neglect may be the real objects of concern in speaking of disease, not disease in itself.

Finally, it might be claimed that there would be a tremendous social and economic cost to calling aging a disease. The claim is perhaps the most unconvincing of the three that I have offered. One factor especially relevant to the determination or diagnosis of disease would seem to be that the physician confine his or her concerns to the physical and mental state of the individual patient; social and economic considerations would appear to be quite out of place. Genetic and psychological diseases place a large burden on society: dialysis machines and tomography units are enormously expensive. But these facts do not in any way change the disease status of mongolism, schizophrenia, kidney failure or cancer. It may be the case that the government may decide not to spend one cent on research into aging or the treatment of aging. But such a decision should be consequent on, not prior to, a diagnosis of disease. This argument simply blurs the value questions relevant to a decision as to whether something is a disease, with value questions relevant to deciding what to do about something after it has been decided that it is a disease.

I have suggested a number of possible value issues and social problems that may enter into the decision of the medical profession to label a state or process a disease.[14] I have also suggested that none of these issues and problems would seem to rule out a consideration of aging as a disease. The determination of disease status and the question of how physicians and society should react to disease are distinct issues. Considerations of the latter variety ought not to be allowed to color our decisions about what does and what does not constitute a disease.

Most persons in our society would be loath to see aging classified and treated as a disease. Much of the resistance to such a classification derives from the view that aging is a natural process and that, like other natural processes, it ought not, in itself, be the subject of medical intervention and therapeutic control. I have tried to show that much of the reasoning that tacitly underlies the categorization of aging as a natural or normal process rests on faulty biological analysis. Aging is not the goal or aim of the evolutionary process.

Rather it is an accidental by-product of that process. Accordingly, it is incorrect to root a belief in the naturalness of aging in some sort of perceived biological design or purpose since aging serves no such end. It may be that good arguments can be adduced for excluding aging from the purvue of medicine. However, if such arguments can be made, they must draw on considerations other than that of the naturalness of aging.[15]

NOTES

1. See, for example, *Dorland's Illustrated Medical Dictionary*, 25th ed. (Philadelphia: W. B. Sanders, 1974).
2. E. A. Murphy, *The Logic of Medicine* (Baltimore: Johns Hopkins, 1976), p. 122. See also E. A. Murphy, "A Scientific Viewpoint on Normalcy," *Perspectives in Biology and Medicine*; and G. B. Risse, "Health and Disease: History of the Concepts," in *Encyclopedia of Bioethics*, ed. W. T. Reich (New York: The Free Press, 1978), pp. 579–585.
3. S. Goldberg, "What is 'Normal'?: Logical Aspects of the Question of Homosexual Behavior," *Psychiatry* 38 (1975): 227–242; Charles Socarides, "Homosexuality and Medicine," *Journal of the American Medical Association* 212 (1970):1199–1202; and I. Illich, "The Political Uses of Natural Death," *Hastings Center Studies* 2 (1974):3–20.
4. Leonard Hayflick, "The Strategy of Senescence," *Gerontologist* 14 (1974):37–45.
5. Cf. D. B. Hausman, "What is Natural?," *Perspectives in Biology and Medicine* 19 (1975):92–101, for an illuminating discussion of the concept.
6. August Weisman, *Essays Upon Heredity and Kindred Biological Problems*, 2d ed. (Oxford: Clarendon Press, 1891).
7. For a sample of the extant explications of the concept of function see L. Wright, "Functions," *Philosophical Review* 82 (1973): 139–168; R. Cummins, "Functional Analysis," *Journal of Philosophy* 72 (1975): 741–765; and M. A. Boden, *Purposive Explanation in Psychology* (Cambridge, Mass.: Harvard, 1972). See also E. Nagel, *Teleology Revisited* (New York: Columbia, 1979).
8. Further discussion of the distinction between explaining the operation of a trait or feature and explaining the origin and presence of a trait or feature can be found in A. L. Caplan, "Evolution, Ethics and the Milk of Human Kindness," *Hastings CenterReport* 6, 2 (1976): 20–26.
9. G. C. Williams, *Adaptation and Natural Selection* (Princeton: Princeton University Press, 1966); and M. T. Ghiselin, *The Economy of Nature and the Evolution of Sex* (Berkeley: University of California Press, 1974).
10. For an interesting attempt to analyze the concepts of illness and disease, see C. Boorse, "On the Distinction Between Illness and Disease," *Philosophy and Public Affairs* 5, 1 (1975):49–68.
11. A. Comfort, "Biological Theories of Aging," *Human Development* 13 (1970):127–39; L. Hayflick, "The Biology of Human Aging," *American Journal of Medical Sciences* 265, 6 (1973): 433–45; A. Comfort, *Aging: The Biology of Senescence* (New York: Holt, Rinehart and Winston, 1964).
12. R. M. Veatch, "The Medical Model: Its Nature and Problems," *Hastings Center Studies* 1, 3 (1973):59–76.

13. See Boorse, "On the Distinction Between Illness and Disease."
14. The role played by values in explicating the concepts of health and disease is notoriously controversial. See for example J. Margolis, "The Concept of Disease," *Journal of Medicine and Philosophy* 1 (1976):238–255. I do not wish to enter this debate here. Rather, I simply am making the point that if aging is to avoid the label of disease, it must be on valuational grounds alone.
15. I would like to thank the members of the Project in Ethics and Values at the College of Physicians and Surgeons, Columbia University, for their helpful comments on an earlier draft of this paper.

PUBLICATION DETAILS

These papers are in the public domain.

Paper

2.1 T. Sydenham, "Preface to the Third Edition" of *Observationes Medicae from R.G. Latham, Trans., The Works of Thomas Sydenham, Vol. 1* (London: Printed for Sydenham Society, 1848).

2.2 G.B. Morgagni, "The Author's Preface," in Morgagni *The Seats and Causes of Disease* (Boston: Wells and Lilly, 1824).

2.3 Xavier Bichat, "Preliminary Discourse" in Bichat, *Pathological Anatomy* (Philadelphia: John Grigg, 1827), pp. 6–22.

2.5 Rudolf Virchow, "Natural Scientific Methods and Standpoints in Therapy," *Archiv für Pathologische Anatomie und Physiolgie und für Klinische Medicin* 2 (1849): 36–37; "Concerning Standpoints in Scientific Medicine," *Archiv für Pathologische Anatomie und Physiologie und für Klinische Medicin* 1 (1847): 3–7; *One Hundred Years of General Pathology*, (Berlin: Hirschwald, 1895), pp. 35–41. All translated by Susan G. M. Engelhardt.

3.3 S.A. Cartwright, "Report on the Diseases and Physical Peculiarities of the Negro Race," *The New Orleans Medical and Surgical Journal* (May, 1851): pp. 691–715.

3.4 J.M. Fort, "Should the Morphine Habit Be Classed as a Disease?", *The Texas Courier Record of Medicine* 12 (11) (July, 1895): 293–297.

4.1 F.J.V. Broussais, *On Irritation and Insanity*, trans. by Thomas Cooper (Columbia, S.C.: S.J. McMorris, 1831). pp. ix–xxi.

These papers are original contributions to this volume.

Paper

6.1 Caroline Whitbeck, "A Theory of Health."

6.2 Mark Siegler, "The Doctor–Patient Encounter and Its Relationship to Theories of Health and Disease."

6.3 Jonathan D. Moreno, "The Continuity of Madness: Pragmatic Naturalism and Mental Health Care in America."

6.5 Elsie L. Bandman and Bertram Bandman, "Health and Disease: Nursing Perspective."

6.6 Michael Ruse, "Are Homosexuals Sick?"

6.7 Arthur L. Caplan, "The 'Unnaturalness' of Aging—A Sickness Unto Death?"

Paper

1.3 Abraham Maslow and Bela Mittelmann, "The Meaning of 'Health' ('normal') and of 'Sick' ('abnormal')," in Maslow and Mittelmann, *Principles of Abnormal Psychology: The Dynamics of Psychic Illness*, revised edition (New York: Harper, 1951), pp. 12–21.

1.5 World Health Organization, "Constitution," in *The First Ten Years of The World Health Organization* (Geneva, WHO, 1958), p. 449.

1.6 Victor R. Fuchs, "Concepts of Health—An Economist's Perspective," *The Journal of Medicine and Philosophy* 1 (3) (September, 1976): 229–236.

1.8 Lester King, "What is Disease?", *Philosophy of Science* 21 (3) (July, 1954): 193–203.

1.9 Peter Sedgwick, "Illness—Mental and Otherwise," in P. Sedgwick, *Psycho-Politics* (New York, Harper and Row), forthcoming.

1.10 Horatio Fabrega, Jr., "The Scientific Usefulness of the Idea of Illness," *Perspectives in Biology and Medicine* 22(1979): 545–558.

2.4 Claude Bernard, *Introduction to the Study of Experimental Medicine*, trans. by Henry Copley Greene (New York: Dover Publications, 1957), pp. 87–95; 190–195.

2.7 H. Cohen, "The Evolution of the Concept of Disease," in Brandon Lush, ed., *Concepts of Medicine* (Oxford: Pergamon Press, 1961), pp. 159–169.

2.8 Ilza Veith, "Historical Reflections on the Changing Concepts of Disease," *California Medicine* 110 (1969): 501–506.

3.2 Smith-Rosenberg and Rosenberg, "The Female Animal: Medical and Biological Views of Woman and Her Role in Nineteenth-Century America," *The Journal of American History* 60 (September, 1973): 332–356.

3.5 R. Green, "Homosexuality as a Mental Illness," *The International Journal of Psychiatry* 10 (March, 1972): 77–98.

4.2 Heinz Hartmann, "Psycho-Analysis and the Concept of Health," *The International Journal of Psychoanalysis* 20 (1939): 308–321.

4.3 F.C. Redlich, "The Concept of Health in Psychiatry," in A.H. Leighton, J.A. Clausen and R.N. Wilson, eds., *Explorations in Social Psychiatry* (New York: Basic Books, 1957), pp. 138–164.

4.4 Ruth Macklin, "Mental Health and Mental Illness: Some Problems of Definition and Concept Formation," *Philosophy of Science* 39 (3) (1972): 341–365.

4.6 Antony Flew, "Disease and Mental Illness," in *Crime or Disease?* (New York): Oxford, 1973), pp. 38–48

4.7 R.E. Kendell, "The Concept of Disease and Its Implications for Psychiatry," *British Journal of Psychiatry* 127 (1975): 305–315.

5.1 David Mechanic, "The Concept of Illness Behavior," *Journal of Chronic Diseases* 15 (2) (1962): 189–194.

5.2 Horacio Fabrega, Jr., "Concepts of Disease: Logical Features and Social Implications," in *Perspectives in Biology and Medicine* 15 (4) (1972), pp. 538–617.

5.3 Robert Veatch, "The Medical Model: Its Nature and Problems," *The Hastings Center Studies* 1 (3) (1973): 59–76.

5.4 Christopher Boorse, "On the Distinction Between Disease and Illness," *Philosophy and Public Affairs* 5 (Fall, 1975): 49–68.

5.5 Joseph Margolis, "The Concept of Disease," *The Journal of Medicine and Philosophy*, 1 (3) (1976): 238–255.

5.6 F.K. Taylor, "The Medical Model of the Disease Concept," *British Journal of Psychiatry* 128 (1976): 588–594.

5.7 G.L. Engel, "The Need for a New Medical Model: A Challenge for Bio-Medicine," *Science* 196 (April 8, 1979): 129–136.

6.4 Michael D. Bayles, "Physicians as Body Mechanics," in *Contemporary Issues in Biomedical Ethics*, ed. by J.W. Davis, B. Hoffmaster and S. Shorten, (Clifton, N.J.: Humana Press, 1978), 167–178.

These papers are reprinted with special permission from the original copyright owners as indicated.

Paper

1.1 Leon Kass, "Regarding the End of Medicine and the Pursuit of Health." Reprinted with permission of the author from *The Public*

Interest, No. 40 (Summer 1975), pp. 11–42. ©1975 by National Affairs, Inc.

1.2 H.T. Engelhardt, Jr., "The Concepts of Health and Disease," in H.T. Engelhardt, Jr., and S. F. Spicker, eds., *Evaluation and Explanation in the Biomedical Sciences,* pp. 125–141. Copyright 1975. Reprinted by permission of D. Reidel Publishing Company, Dordrecht, Holland.

1.4 Talcott Parsons, "Definitions of Health and Illness in the Light of American Values and Social Structures." Reprinted with permission of Macmillan Publishing Company, Inc. from *Patients, Physicians, and Illness* by E. G. Jaco, pp. 165–187. (New York: Free Press, 1958).

1.7 Mervyn Susser, "Ethical Components in the Definition of Health," *International Journal of Health Services* 4 (3) (1974): 539–548. Copyright 1974, Baywood Publishing Company.

2.6 Walter B. Cannon, "Relations of Biological and Social Homeostasis," in Cannon, *The Wisdom of the Body* (New York: Norton, 1932), pp. 305–324. Reprinted with permission of Norton Publishing Company, and acknowledgement to Routledge and Kegan Paul, Ltd., Publishers.

2.9 Lester King, "Some Basic Explanations of Disease: An Historian's Viewpoint," in H.T. Engelhardt, and S.F. Spicker, eds., *Evaluation and Explanation in the Biomedical Sciences*, pp. 11–27. Copyright 1975. Reprinted by permission of D. Reidel Publishing Company, Dordrecht, Holland.

2.10 Owsei Temkin, "The Scientific Approach to Disease: Specific Entity and Individual Sickness," in A.C. Crombie, ed., *Scientific Change: Historical Studies in the Intellectual, Social and Technical Conditions for Scientific Discovery and Technical Invention from Antiquity to the Present*, pp. 629–647. ©Heinemann Educational Books, Ltd., 1963, Basic Books, Inc., Publishers Inc., N.Y.

3.1 H.T. Engelhardt, Jr., "The Disease of Masturbation: Values and the Concept of Disease," *Bulletin of the History of Medicine* 48 (1974): 234–248. Copyright 1974.

4.5 Aaron Lazare, "Hidden Conceptual Models in Clinical Psychiatry." Printed by permission from the New England Journal of Medicine, volume 238, pages 345–351, February 15, 1973.

4.8 Thomas S. Szasz, "The Concept of Mental Illness: Explanation or Justification" in H.T. Engelhardt, Jr., and S.F. Spicker, eds., *Mental Health: Philosophical Perspectives*, pp. 235–250. Copyright 1978. Reprinted with permission of D. Reidel Publishing Company, Dordrecht, Holland.

4.9 Baruch Brody, "Szasz on Mental Illness," in H.T. Engelhardt, Jr., and S.F. Spicker, eds., *Mental Health: Philosophical Perspectives*, pp. 251–257. Copyright 1978. Reprinted with permission of D. Reidel Publishing Company, Dordrecht, Holland.

Author Index

Author Index

. Numbers in parentheses refer to footnotes/notes.

Subject Index

Subject Index